Dear Parent:
Your child's love of reading starts here!

I Can Read Books have introduced children to the joy of reading since 1957. Featuring award-winning authors and illustrators and a fabulous cast of beloved characters, I Can Read Books set the standard for beginning readers. From books your child reads with you to the first books they read alone, there are I Can Read Books for every stage of reading:

SHARED READING
Basic language, word repetition, and whimsical illustrations, ideal for sharing with your emergent reader

BEGINNING READING
Short sentences, familiar words, and simple concepts for children eager to read on their own

READING WITH HELP
Engaging stories, longer sentences, and language play for developing readers

READING ALONE
Complex plots, challenging vocabulary, and high-interest topics for the independent reader

ADVANCED READING
Short paragraphs, chapters, and exciting themes for the perfect bridge to chapter books

Every child learns in a different way and at their own speed. Some read through each level in order. Others go back and forth between levels and read favorite books again and again. You can help your young reader improve and become more confident by encouraging their own interests and abilities.

A lifetime of discovery begins with the magical words, **"I Can Read!"**

Preface

Mapping the essentials of chemical biology

Chemical biology is a new, rapidly emerging branch of chemistry that represents all aspects of chemical endeavour, devoted to understanding the way biology works at the molecular level. Chemical biology is unashamedly inter-disciplinary, and chemical biology research is essentially problem driven and not discipline driven. Organic, physical, inorganic and analytical chemistry all contribute towards the chemical biology whole. Some might say that chemical biology is just another way to rebadge biochemistry. However, such a comment misses the point. Biochemistry may have started as a discipline devoted to the study of individual biological macromolecules, but this discipline has been steadily evolving into increasingly descriptive, empirical studies of larger and larger macromolecular assemblies, structures and interacting molecular networks. The molecular increasingly gives ground to the cellular. In contrast, chemical biology is about chemistry-trained graduates and researchers taking a fundamental interest in the way biology works. Consequently, the focus is on the molecular and the quantitative, where molecular properties are investigated, studied and then gradually linked to macromolecular and cellular behaviour where possible. This is a fundamentally 'bottom-up' approach to understanding biology in keeping with the chemist's natural enthusiasm and appreciation for molecular structure and behaviour first and foremost.

This textbook has been produced with the third/fourth year graduate student and young researcher in mind, namely those who have a solid background in chemical principles and are ready to apply and grow their chemical knowledge to suit a future degree or career interest in chemical biology. In preparing this textbook our objective has not been to try and cover everything currently seen as chemical biology, but instead to ask ourselves what topics and themes should be described as the essentials of chemical biology and how should these be presented in a way most appropriate and appealing for those of a chemical rather than a biological orientation. In doing this, we concluded that the true essentials of chemical biology are represented by the structure, characterisation and measurable behaviour of the main biological macromolecules and macromolecular lipid assemblies found in all cells of all organisms. We have also concluded that the activities of small molecules in biology for respiration and primary and secondary metabolism should not be included in the essentials of chemical biology except where they feature as protein prosthetic groups or otherwise modify macromolecule behaviour. In our view, simple metabolism and metabolite interconversions are the stuff of biochemistry, whilst fascination with secondary metabolism, secondary metabolites and their interconversions has been the traditional preserve of bio-organic chemistry (a subset of organic chemistry).

Hence, in our textbook we begin with structure (Chapter 1) and synthesis (Chapters 2 and 3), then consider how structure is determined (Chapters 4–6), followed by a consideration of dynamic behaviour and molecular interactions (Chapters 7–9), concluding with molecular evolution and thoughts on the origins of life, quintessentially from the chemistry point of view (Chapter 10). Armed with such essentials, we hope that readers will then be ready to think about and then tackle any problem of their chosen interest at the chemistry–biology and/or chemistry–medicine interfaces, after a little more detailed and specific reading of course. Foremost, we hope that our textbook will provide a valuable tool for chemical biology students and researchers to open the door and step through into the extraordinary world of biology without feeling that they must leave their chemical principles behind them!

Andrew Miller
Julian Tanner

Glossary of physical terms

Chapter 1

Potential energy	V	J	[kg m^2 s^{-2}]
Electrical point charge	q_n	C	
Vacuum permittivity	ε_0	F m^{-1}or C^2 m^{-1} J^{-1}	[C^2 kg^{-1}m^{-3} s^2]
Permittivity of medium	ε	F m^{-1}or C^2 m^{-1} J^{-1}	[C^2 kg^{-1}m^{-3} s^2]
Distance between (charge/nuclear) centres	r	m	
(Electric) dipole moment	μ_n	C m	
Polarisability volume	α'_n	m^3(Å^3, cm^3)	
Ionisation energies	I_n	J	[kg m^2 s^{-2}]
J is Joule; F is Farad; C is Coulomb	μ_{ind} or μ_{ind}	C m	

Chapter 4

(Time dependent) induced dipole moment			
(Time dependent) electronic polarisability	$\alpha(\nu_v)$	C m^2 V^{-1}	
(Oscillating) electric field (of light)	$?(\nu_v)$	V m^{-1}	
Absorbance	A or $A(\lambda)$	arbitrary units	
Optical density	$OD(\lambda)$	arbitrary units	
Pathlength (optical)	l	cm	
Extinction coefficient	$\varepsilon_{???}$ or g$\varepsilon(\lambda)$	l mol^{-1} cm^{-1}	
Biological macromolecular concentration	c_M	mol l^{-1}	
Wavelength	λ	nm	
Molecular weight (of protein)	M_p	D or kD	[g mol^{-1}]
Molecular weight (of nucleotide)	M_{nt}	D or kD	[g mol^{-1}]
Concentration (of nucleotide)	c_{nt}	mol l^{-1}	
Differential absorbance	$\Delta A(\lambda)$,	arbitrary units	

Essentials of Chemical Biology   Andrew Miller and Julian Tanner
© 2008 John Wiley & Sons, Ltd

Differential molar extinction coefficient	$\Delta\varepsilon(\lambda)$,	$l\ mol^{-1}\ cm^{-1}$	
Ellipticity	$\theta(\lambda)$	deg	
Molar ellipticity	$[\theta(\lambda)]$	$deg\ l\ mol^{-1}\ cm^{-1}$	
Vibrational frequency of light	ν_v	s^{-1}	
(Equilibrium) electric field (of light)	$?_0$	$V\ m^{-1}$	
Equilibrium polarisability component	$\alpha_0(\nu_v)$	$C\ m^2\ V^{-1}$	
Nuclear oscillation component	$\alpha_R(\nu_R)$	$C\ m^2\ V^{-1}$	
Frequency of vibrational modes (molecular)	ν_R	s^{-1}	
Frequency of emitted light	ν_{em}	s^{-1}	
Planck's constant	h	$J\ s\ or\ N\ m\ s$	$[kg\ m^2\ s^{-1}]$
Speed of light	c	$m\ s^{-1}$	
Radiative lifetime (fluorescence)	$\tau_R\ s$		
Radiative lifetime (phosphorescence)	$\tau_{R,Phor}s$		
Rate of spontaneous emission (fluorescence)	$k_F s^{-1}$		
Rate of internal conversion (fluorescence)	$k_{IC}s^{-1}$		
Rate of intersystem crossing (fluorescence)	$k_{IS}s^{-1}$		
Rate of quenching (fluorescence)	$k_q s^{-1}$		
Fluorescence intensity (no $\mathbf{Q}$)	$I_{em}\ or\ F_0$	arbitrary units	
Fluorescence intensity (in presence of $\mathbf{Q}$)	F	arbitrary units	
FÖrster length	$R_0 m$		
Interfluorophore distance	$R_F m$		
Fluorescence quantum yield	ϕ_F		
Fluorescence quantum yield (of donor, $\mathbf{D}$)	ϕ_D		
Refractive index	$?_R$		
X-ray absorption coefficient	$\mu_{ab}\ m^{-1}$		
Incident intensity (of X-ray)	I_{x0}	arbitrary units	
Transmitted intensity (of X-rays)	I_x	arbitrary units	
V is Volt ($J\ C^{-1}$); D is Daltons and kD kiloDaltons	J	$J\ s\ rad^{-1}$	$[kg\ rad\ s^{-1}]$

Chapter 5

(Nuclear) angular momentum		
Gyromagnetic ratio	γ	$rad\ s^{-1}\ T^{-1}$
Magnetic moment (z-axis)	μ_z	$J\ T^{-1}\ or\ A\ m^2$
Nuclear magneton	$\mu_N J\ T^{-1}$	

Nuclear g-factor	g_I		
Charge (of an electron)	e C		
Mass (of proton)	m_p kg		
Applied magnetic field	B_z T or N m^{-1}A^{-1}		
Lamor (precession) frequency	ν_L s^{-1}		
Planck's constant	h J s	[kg m^2 s^{-1}]	
	$h/2\pi$	J s rad^{-1}	[kg rad s^{-1}]
Coupling constant	J	s^{-1}(Hz)	
Boltzmann constant	k	J K^{-1}	[kg m^2 s^{-2} K^{-1}]
(Absolute) temperature	T	K	
(Scalar) longitudinal relaxation time constant	T_1	s	
Transverse relaxation time constant	T_2	s	
Longitudinal magnetisation – polarisation	$?_z(?)$		
Transverse magnetisation – coherence	$?_y(?)$		
Spectral line width (half peak intensity)	$\Delta\nu_{L,1/2}$	s^{-1}(Hz)	
(Electron) angular momentum	J_e	J s rad^{-1}	[kg rad s^{-1}]
Electron gyromagnetic ratio	γ_e	rad s^{-1} T^{-1}	
Electron magnetic moment	μ_z^e 7	J T^{-1}	
Bohr magneton	μ_B	J T^{-1}	
g-factor	g_e		
Mass (of an electron)	m_e	kg	
rad is radians (2π); T is Tesla; A is ampere (C s^{-1})	d_{hkl}	Å	

Chapter 6

Distance between lattice planes			
Scattering length	b_{X-ray}	cm	
Distance of resolvable separation - resolution	d_R	Å	
Planck's constant	h	J s	[kg m^2 s^{-1}]
Charge (of an electron)	e C		
Electrical potential difference (in Field Emission gun)	Φ	V or ?g?^{tx}	[kg m^2 s^{-2}C^{-1}]
Mass (of an electron)	m_e	kg	
Maximum particle size	D	m	
Büttiker-Landauer tunnelling time	τ^{BL}	s	
Variable (z-axis) barrier dimension	s_z	m	
Barrier crossing constant	Φ	m^{-1}	
Piezo electric bar changes in length	Δl_p	m	
(Piezo electric biomorph) displacement	Δx_p	m	

(Piezo electric) potential difference	U_p	V or ?g?^{tx}	$[kg\ m^2\ s^{-2} C^{-1}]$
(Piezo electric) coefficient	d_{31}	$m\ V^{-1}$ or $C\ N^{-1}$	$[C\ s^2\ m^{-1}\ kg^{-1}]$
Tunnelling current	$I_T A$		
Van-der-Waals interactions (tip to surface)	$F_{VDW}(d_z)$	N	$[kg\ m\ s^{-2}]$
Hamaker constant	H	N m or J	$[kg\ m^2\ s^{-2}]$
Distance (z-axis)	d_z	m	
Radius of tip above surface	R_z	m	
Surface-to-tip interaction forces	F_{ST}	N	$[kg\ m\ s^{-2}]$
Spring constant	c_{ST}	$N\ m^{-1}$	$[kg\ s^{-2}]$
Youngs Modulus	E_M	Pa or $N\ m^{-2}$	$[kg\ m^{-1}\ s^{-2}]$
Pa is Pascal $(N\ m^{-2})$	V_h	cm^3 or m^3	

Chapter 7

Hydrated volume			
Macromolecular molecular weight	M_{MM}	D or kD	$[g\ mol^{-1}]$
Avogadro's number	N_0	mol^{-1}	
Macromolecular partial specific volume	V_{MM}	$cm^3\ g^{-1}$	
Hydration level	Δ		
Coefficient of translational frictional force	$f_{trans,sph}$	$kg\ s^{-1}$ or $g\ s^{-1}$	
Spherical macromolecular radius	r_{sph}	cm or m	
Viscosity	η	Pa s or $N\ m^{-2}$ s	$[kg\ m^{-1}\ s^{-1},\ g\ cm^{-1}\ s^{-1}]$
Coefficient of rotational frictional force	$f_{rot,sph}$	$kg\ m^2\ s^{-1}$ or $g\ cm^2\ s^{-1}$	
Spherical macromolecular volume	V_{sph}	m^3 or cm^3	
General coefficient of translational frictional force	f_{trans}	$kg\ s^{-1}$ or $g\ s^{-1}$	
General coefficient of rotational frictional force	f_{rot}	$kg\ m^2\ s^{-1}$ or $g\ cm^2\ s^{-1}$	
Macromolecular flux	J_{MM}	$kg\ m^{-2}\ s^{-1}$ or $g\ cm^{-2}\ s^{-1}$ $mol\ m^{-2}\ s^{-1}$	
Macromolecular concentration	C_{MM}	$kg\ m^{-3}$ or $g\ cm^{-3}$ $mol\ m^{-3}$	
Average macromolecular velocity	$\langle v_{MM} \rangle$	$m\ s^{-1}$ or $cm\ s^{-1}$	
Macromolecular diffusion coefficient	D_{MM}	$m^2\ s^{-1}$ or $cm^2\ s^{-1}$	
Boltzmann constant	k	$J\ K^{-1}$	$[kg\ m^2\ s^{-2}\ K^{-1}]$
Debye length	r_D	m	
Ionic strength	?	$mol\ m^{-3}$ or $mol\ kg^{-1}$ $M\ (mol\ l^{-1})$	
Permittivity of medium	ε	$F\ m^{-1}$ or $C^2\ m^{-1}\ J^{-1}$	$[C^2\ kg^{-1} m^{-3}\ s^2]$
Association constant	K_a	M^{-1}	

Dissociation constant	K_d	M	
Moles (of ligand) bound per mole (of receptor)	B	(Mol fraction)	
Total molar quantity (of ligand) bound (to receptor)	m_{RL}	mol	
Total molar quantity (of ligand) added	m_{L0}	mol	
Total system volume	V_{tot}	m^3, dm^3 (l), cm^3	
Chemical potential of species i μ_i		$Jmol^{-1}$	$[kg\ m^2\ s^{-2}\ mol^{-1}]$
Concentration of species i	c_i	M (mol l^{-1})	
Molar gas constant	R	$J\ K^{-1}\ mol^{-1}$	$[kg\ m^2\ s^{-2}\ K^{-1}\ mol^{-1}]$
Standard free energy change	ΔG^0	$J\ mol^{-1}$, $kJ\ mol^{-1}$	$[kg\ m^2\ s^{-2}\ mol^{-1}]$
Standard enthalpy change	ΔH^0	$J\ mol^{-1}$, $kJ\ mol^{-1}$	$[kg\ m^2\ s^{-2}\ mol^{-1}]$
Standard entropy change	ΔS^0	$J\ mol^{-1}K^{-1}$	$[kg\ m^2\ s^{-2}\ mol^{-1}K^{-1}]$
(Exchangeable) heat energy	?	J	$[kg\ m^2\ s^{-2}]$
(Fractional) change in enthalpy	dH	J	
Electric field	E_e	$V\ m^{-1}$ or $J\ C^{-1}\ m^{-1}$	$[kg\ m\ s^{-2}\ C^{-1}]$
Electrophoretic velocity	v_e	$m\ s^{-1}$	
Electrophoretic mobility	μ_e	$m^2\ V^{-1}\ s^{-1}$	$[C\ s\ kg^{-1}]$
Apparent electophoretic mobility	μ_a	$m^2\ V^{-1}\ s^{-1}$	$[C\ s\ kg^{-1}]$
EOFelectophoretic mobility	μ_{EOF}	$m^2\ V^{-1}\ s^{-1}$	$[C\ s\ kg^{-1}]$
Time to detector	t_e	s	
Effective length (of capillary)	l_e	m	
Total length (of apparatus)	L_e	m	
Applied potential difference	$?_e$	V or $J\ C^{-1}$	$[kg\ m^2\ s^{-2}\ C^{-1}]$
Rate of association (complex formation) (**on**-rate)	k_{ass}	$M^{-1}s^{-1}$	
Rate of dissociation (complex) (**off**-rate)	k_{diss}	s^{-1}	
Resonant angle	Y_t	arc s	
Concentration dependent **on**-rate (complex formation)	k_{on}	s^{-1}	
Chapter 8	ν	$M\ s^{-1}$	$[mol\ l^{-1}\ s^{-1}]$
Initial rate of (biocatalysis)			
Initial substrate concentration	[S]	M	$[mol\ l^{-1}]$
Unimolecular rate constant for mechanism step **n**	k_n	s^{-1}	
Bimolecular rate constant for mechanism step **n**	k_n	$M^{-1}\ s^{-1}$	$[l\ mol^{-1}\ s^{-1}]$
Michaelis constant	K_m	M	$[mol\ l^{-1}]$
Equilibrium dissociation constant for **ES** complex	K_s	M	$[mol\ l^{-1}]$

Term	Symbol	Units	SI units
Catalytic rate constant (when $[S] \gg K_m$)	k_{cat}	s^{-1}	
Maximum initial rate (when $[S] \gg K_m$)	V_{max}	$M\,s^{-1}$	$[mol\,l^{-1}\,s^{-1}]$
Catalytic rate constant (when $K_m \gg [S]$)	k_{cat}/K_m	$M^{-1}\,s^{-1}$	$[l\,mol^{-1}\,s^{-1}]$
Inhibitor equilibrium dissociation constant	K_I	M	$[mol\,l^{-1}]$
Base equilibrium ionization constant	$K_d{}^B$	M	$[mol\,l^{-1}]$
Acid equilibrium ionization constant	$K_d{}^A$	M	$[mol\,l^{-1}]$
Saddle-point vibration frequency	$\nu_{??}$	s^{-1}	
Transition state forward decomposition rate constant	$k_c{}^{\ddagger}$	s^{-1}	
Quasi-equilibrium association constant	$K_c{}^{\ddagger\cdot}$	M^{-1}	
Forward rate constant	k_p	$M^{-1}s^{-1}$	
Partition function for molecular population	$z\,q^z$		
Boltzmann constant	k	$J\,K^{-1}$	$[kg\,m^2\,s^{-2}\,K^{-1}]$
Transition state-ground state energy difference	E_0	J	$[kg\,m^2\,s^{-2}]$
Planck's constant	h	$J\,s$	$[kg\,m^2\,s^{-1}]$
Standard free energy (of activation)	$\Delta G_0{}^{\ddagger}$	$kJmol^{-1}$	$[kg\,m^2\,s^{-2}mol^{-1}]$
Free energy (of activation) (from E and S)	$\Delta G_{ES}{}^{\ddagger}$	$kJmol^{-1}$	$[kg\,m^2\,s^{-2}mol^{-1}]$
Free energy (of activation) (from ES complex)	$\Delta G_T{}^{\ddagger}$	$kJmol^{-1}$	$[kg\,m^2\,s^{-2}mol^{-1}]$
Free energy (of association) of (E and S)	ΔG_S	$kJmol^{-1}$	$[kg\,m^2\,s^{-2}mol^{-1}]$
Molar gas constant	R	$J\,K^{-1}mol^{-1}$	$[kg\,m^2\,s^{-2}\,K^{-1}mol^{-1}]$
Rate constant for electron transfer	k_{ET}	s^{-1}	
Equilibrium association constant (for D and A)	$K_{a,DA}$	M^{-1}	$[l\,mol^{-1}]$
Edge to edge distance (between D and A)	R_{ET}	m	
Beta value	β_{ET}	m^{-1}	
Chapter 9			
Unitary charge of an ion	z		
Accelerating electrostatic potential	$?_z$	V or $J\,C^{-1}$	$[kg\,m^2\,s^{-2}\,C^{-1}]$
Velocity of ion travel	$\nu_? s^{-1}$		
Ion mass	m	D, kD (or a.m.u.)	
Time to detector	t_z	s	
Length (of field-free flight tube)	L_z	m	

1

The Structures of Biological Macromolecules and Lipid Assemblies

1.1 General introduction

All living organisms are comprised of cells that may vary considerably in terms of size, shape and appearance; in complex multicellular organisms, many cells are organised into diverse, functional organs to perform a collective function (Figure 1.1). In spite of their wide morphological diversity, all cells of all living organisms, wherever they are located, are comprised of **proteins**, **carbohydrates**, **nucleic acids** and **lipid assemblies**. These together give a cell form and function. To know and understand the chemistry of these biological macromolecules is to comprehend the basic infrastructure not only of a cell but also of living organisms. In functional terms, macromolecular lipid assemblies provide for compartmentalisation in the form of membrane barriers, which not only define the 'outer limits' of each cell but also divide up the intracellular environment into different organelles or functional zones (Figure 1.2). Membrane barriers are fluidic and lack rigidity, so proteins provide a supporting and scaffolding function not only in the main fluid bulk of the cell, known as the **cytosol**, but also within organelles. Within the **nucleus**, proteins also provide a nucleic acid packaging function in order to restrain and constrain spectacular quantities of nucleic acids within the nuclear volume. Everywhere in any cell, proteins also perform other individualised functions in outer membranes (as pores or receptors for example), in organelle membranes (as selective transporters, redox acceptors or energy transducers), in the cytosol or organelle volumes (as enzyme catalysts, molecular chaperones or 'communication and control' centres) and in the nucleus (as regulators and transcribers of the genetic code). The extraordinary variety

Essentials of Chemical Biology   Andrew Miller and Julian Tanner
© 2008 John Wiley & Sons, Ltd

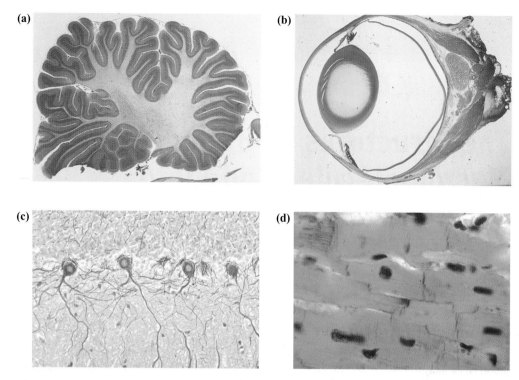

Figure 1.1   Organs and Cells. (a) cross section of mammalian brain showing the complex surface folds. There are an incalculable number of cells that make up the mammalian brain; **(b) cross section of mammalian eye ball** in which the lens is made of proteins controlled in function by peripheral muscles. There is an enormous morphological and functional diversity between cells required for muscle control, light reception, and signal transduction along the optic nerve; **(c) cross section of mammalian neurological tissue** illustrating the neuron cell bodies with complex axonal/dendritic processes surrounded by support cells all of a wide range of size, shape, structure and function; **(d) cross section of mammalian heart tissue** showing clusters of muscle fibres (single cell myocytes) that make up the heart wall. Myocytes are multinucleate with a very different shape, composition and function to neurological cells (all illustrations from Philip Harris Ltd, Weston Super Mare, UK).

of protein functions and the 'workhorse'-like nature of proteins in biology has made them endlessly fascinating to biochemists and now to chemical biologists alike.

Nucleic acids are found in two main classes, namely **deoxyribonucleic acid (DNA)** and **ribonucleic acid (RNA)**. DNA is largely restricted to the nucleus and harbours genetic information that defines the composition and structure of cells and even the multicellular organisation of complex organisms, reaching even beyond this to influence organism behaviour as well. DNA molecules are partly segmented into **genes** that contain coding information for protein structures, but also into many other delineations associated with control over gene use. In fact, the level and sophistication of this control may well be the primary determinant of complexity in multicellular organisms: the more extensive and sophisticated the level of control, the more sophisticated and complex the multicellular organism. By contrast, RNA's most important role is in shuttling information from the nucleus to the cytosol. The primary function of RNA equates to the processing of genetic information from the DNA storage

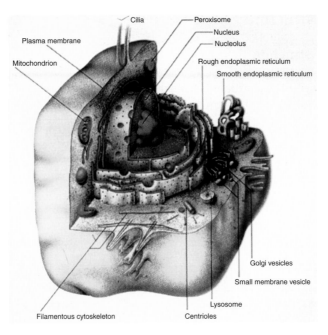

Cilia
Peroxisome
Nucleus
Nucleolus
Plasma membrane
Mitochondrion
Rough endoplasmic reticulum
Smooth endoplasmic reticulum
Golgi vesicles
Small membrane vesicle
Lysosome
Filamentous cytoskeleton
Centrioles

Figure 1.2 General structure of a cell showing the main compartments (organelles) into which the interior is partitioned. All cells of all organisms are constructed from the main biological macromolecules **proteins**, **carbohydrates**, and **nucleic acids**; together with macromolecular **lipid** structures that comprise the membranes. (illustration from Philip Harris Ltd, Weston Super Mare, UK).

form into actual protein structures. RNA makes possible the central dogma of biology, that *genes code for proteins*. Finally, carbohydrates, if not stored in complex forms for primary metabolism, are known to decorate some intracellular proteins and attach to outer membrane proteins, forming a **glycocalyx** covering the surface of many cells, essential for communication between cells. In the plant and insect kingdoms, gigantic carbohydrate assemblies also provide the exoskeleton framework to which cells are attached, giving form as well as function to plants and insects alike.

In all cases, proteins, carbohydrates and nucleic acids are polymers built from standard basis sets of molecular building blocks. In a similar way, lipid assemblies are built from a standard basis set of lipid building blocks associated through non-covalent bonds. What all biological macromolecules and macromolecular assemblies have in common is that they then adopt defined three dimensional structures that are the key to their functions (dynamics, binding and reactivity). Remarkably, these three dimensional structures are not only central to function but they are the result of weak, non-covalent forces of association acting together with stereoelectronic properties inherent within each class of polymer or macromolecular assembly. Without structure, function is hard to understand, although structure does not necessarily predict function. Therefore, the chemical biology reader needs to have a feel for the structures of proteins, carbohydrates, nucleic acids and lipid assemblies before embarking on any other part of this fascinating subject. Accordingly, the principles of structure are our main topic for Chapter 1, concluding with some explanation about those critical weak non-covalent forces of association that are all so important in shaping and maintaining these structures.

1.2 Protein structure

1.2.1 Primary structure

Proteins are polymers formed primarily from the linear combination of 20 naturally occurring L-α-amino acids, which are illustrated (Table 1.1) (Figure 1.3). Almost all known protein

Table 1.1   Structures of all **naturally occuring** L-α-amino acids that are found in all proteins of all organisms. Included are the full name, the **three letter code** name and the **one letter code** name. Amino acids are grouped into those with **hydrophobic** side chains (**left panel**) and those with **hydrophilic** side chains (**right panel**). Where appropriate, measured functional group pK_a values are given Note that in Chapter 8, the term pK_a is replaced by pK_d^A or pK_d^B depending upon whether an acid or base dissociation is under consideration respectively.

pK$_a$ 7.8   pK$_a$ 3.6

R	Name	Abbrev.	R	Name	Abbrev.	pK_a
	Glycine	Gly (G)		Tyrosine	Tyr (Y)	9.7
	Alanine	Ala (A)		Serine	Ser (S)	15
	Valine	Val (V)		Threonine	Thr (T)	15
	Leucine	Leu (L)		Cysteine	Cys (C)	9.1
	Isoleucine	Ile (I)		Aspartic Acid	Asp (D)	4.0
	Phenylalanine	Phe (F)		Asparagine	Asn (N)	
	Tryptophan	Trp (W)		Glutamic Acid	Glu (E)	4.5
				Glutamine	Gln (Q)	
	Methionine	Met (M)		Lysine	Lys (K)	10.4
	Proline	Pro (P)		Arginine	Arg (R)	12
				Histidine	His (H)	6.0

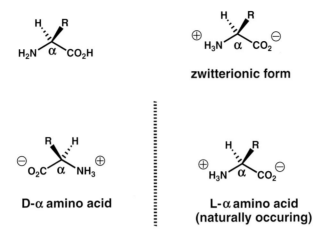

Figure 1.3 **Structures of α-amino acids** the monomeric building blocks of proteins.

structures are constructed from this fundamental set of 20 α-amino-acid building blocks. These building blocks fall into two main classes, **hydrophobic** and **hydrophilic**, according to the nature of their **side-chains** (Table 1.1). Protein architecture is intimately dependent upon having two such opposite sets of α-amino-acid building blocks to call upon. Individual α-amino-acid building blocks are joined together by a **peptide link** (Figure 1.4). When a small number (2–20) of amino acids are joined together by peptide links to form an unbranched chain, then the result is known as an **oligopeptide** (Figure 1.5). However, peptide links can join together anything from 20 to 2000 amino-acid residues in length to form substantial unbranched polymeric chains of L-α-amino acids. These are known as **polypeptides**. Within

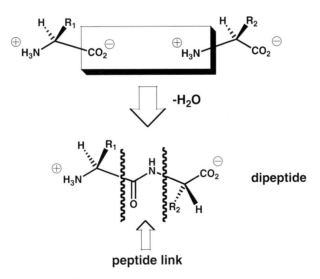

Figure 1.4 **Schematic of peptide link formation**, central virtual bond of polypeptide and protein backbones.

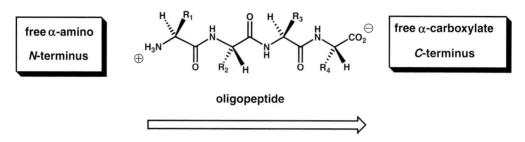

free α-amino

N-terminus

free α-carboxylate

C-terminus

oligopeptide

Figure 1.5   General structure of tetrapeptide; by convention the highest priority end is the free *N*-terminus and the lowest priority the free *C*-terminus giving the backbone a directionality illustrated by the arrow. This convention applies for all peptides, polypeptides and proteins.

each polypeptide chain, the repeat unit $(-N-C_\alpha-C(O)-)n$, neglecting the α-amino-acid side-chains, is known as the **main chain** or **backbone**, whilst each constituent, linked α-amino-acid building block is known as an **amino-acid residue**. The order of amino-acid residues, going from the free, uncombined α-amino-terminal end (*N*-terminus) to the free, uncombined α-carboxyl terminus (*C*-terminus), is known as the **amino-acid sequence**.

Quite clearly, each peptide link is in fact a simple secondary amide functional group but with some unusual properties. In fact, the N, H, C and O atoms of a peptide link, together with each pair of flanking α-carbon atoms, actually form a rigid, coplanar unit that behaves almost like a single bond, owing to restricted rotation about the N–C(O) bond caused by nitrogen atom lone pair resonance and the build-up of N–C(O) double bond character (Figure 1.6). For this reason, the peptide link and flanking C_α atoms together are sometimes referred to as a **virtual bond**. We might say that the C_α atom of each amino-acid residue in a polypeptide chain belongs simultaneously to two such virtual bonds (Figure 1.7). The spatial relationship between each C_α-linked pair of virtual bonds is then defined using the conformational angles ϕ and ψ, which are the main chain dihedral angles subtended about the N(H)–C_α and C_α–C(O) σ bonds respectively of each amino-acid residue (Figures 1.7 and 1.8). Only certain combinations of ϕ and ψ are now allowed, owing to steric congestion between the side-chains of adjacent amino-acid residues (Figure 1.8). Consequently, the overall conformation of a given polypeptide chain is also very restricted, with direct consequences for the three dimensional structures of proteins. In effect, conformational restrictions imposed by lack of

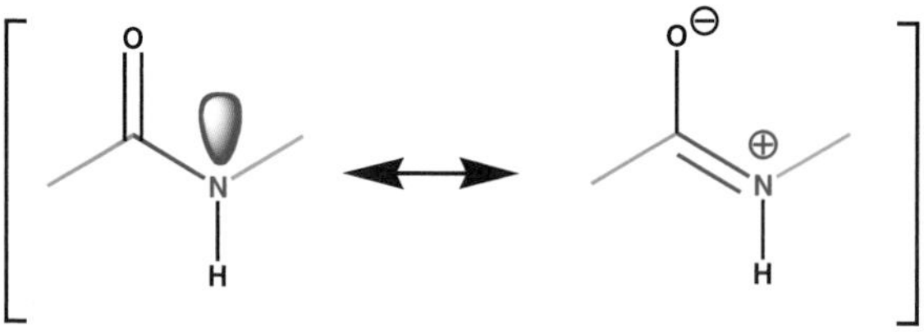

Figure 1.6   **Peptide link** resonance structures illustrating partial double character in the C(O)—N bond (blue) sufficient to prevent free rotation thereby restricting conformational freedom of peptide or polypeptide backbones.

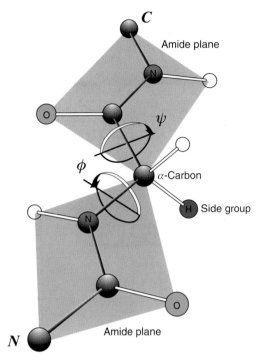

Figure 1.7 **Peptide link** C, O, N and H atoms act as a rigid coplanar units equivalent to a single bond (**virtual bond**) so that consecutive peptide links act as rigid coplanar units that pivot around individual C α-atoms (from Voet, Voet & Pratt, 1999 [Wiley], Fig. 6-4).

free rotation in the peptide link and the natures of each peptide-linked amino-acid residue place substantial restrictions upon the conformational freedom of a given polypeptide and hence the range of possible three dimensional structures that may be formed by any given polypeptide polymer. In fact, the primary structure amino-acid sequence of a protein not only influences the three dimensional structure but also actually determines this structure. In other words, all the necessary 'information' for the three dimensional structure of a protein is 'stored' and available within the primary structure. This is the basis for self-assembly in biology and explains why proteins can be such excellent platforms or 'workbenches' for the development of defined functions and the evolution of living organisms.

1.2.2 Repetitive secondary structure

If primary structure is amino-acid residue sequence, then **secondary structure** represents the first major steps towards a functional three dimensional structure. Secondary structures are essentially transient three dimensional structural elements that polypeptides may form in solution and that can interlock or dock together for stability. Polypeptides are capable of forming remarkably beautiful helical structures that are known as the right-handed α **helix** (α_R)

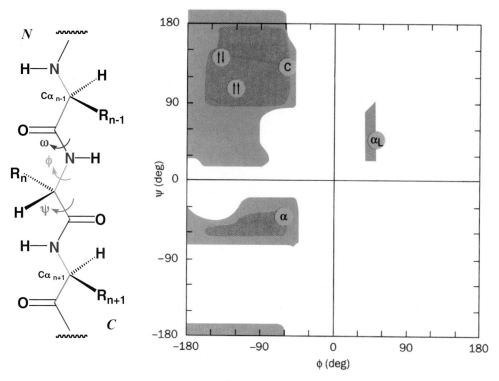

Figure 1.8   Amino acid residue side-chain interactions further restrict free rotation in peptide or polypeptide backbone. Rotational possibilities are defined by allowed values of dihedral angle ϕ subtended about N–C$_\alpha$ bond and ψ subtended about C$_\alpha$–C(O) bond (left). Theoretically allowed angles are shown in **Ramachandran plot** (right) together with positions of actual angles found in real protein secondary structures; α: right-handed α-helix; α_L: left-handed α-helix; ↑↑: parallel β-sheet; ↑↓: anti-parallel β-sheet; **C**: collagen, P$_{II}$ helix (see later). (Ramachandran plot from Voet, Voet & Pratt, 1999 [Wiley], Fig. 6-6).

and the right-handed **3$_{10}$ helix**. The term 'right handed' refers to the way in which the polypeptide main chain traces out the path of a right-handed corkscrew (incidentally, the left-handed α helix, α_L, is possible but is unknown in natural proteins so far). The α_R helix can be a surprisingly sturdy, robust and regular structural feature (Figures 1.9 and 1.10). Typically, α_R helices are comprised of up to 35 amino-acid residues in length and are very stereo-regular; the ϕ and ψ conformational angles of each amino-acid residue in the α_R helix are both about $-60°$ in all cases (Figure 1.11). Helices are held together by a regular network of non-covalent hydrogen bonds (see Section 1.6) formed between the peptide bond C=O and N–H groups of neighbouring amino-acid residues (Figure 1.12). There are 3.6 amino-acid residues per turn, with the result that the hydrogen bonds are formed between the C=O group lone pairs (hydrogen bond acceptors) of the nth residues and the N–H groups (hydrogen bond donors) of the $(n + 4)$th residues. The closed loop formed by one of these hydrogen bonds and the intervening stretch of polypeptide main chain contains 13 atoms (Figure 1.12). Hence, the α_R helix has also been christened a **3.6$_{13}$ helix**. By contrast, the 3$_{10}$ helix (or α_{II} **helix**) is effectively

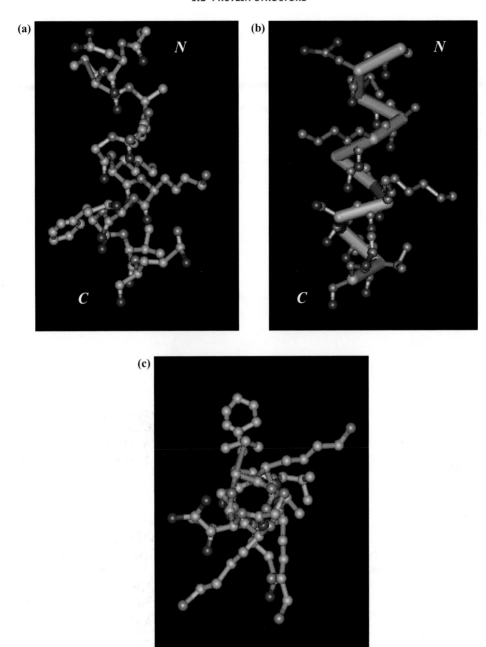

Figure 1.9 Various depictions of an α-helix from triose phosphate isomerase (chicken muscle) (pdb: **1tim**). (a) **ball and stick representation** (side view) of atoms and bonds shown with carbon (**yellow**), nitrogen (**blue**) and oxygen (**red**); (b) **CA stick display** of α-carbon backbone, atoms and bonds of amino acid side-chains are rendered in **ball and stick representations** with carbon (**grey**), nitrogen (**blue**) and oxygen (**red**); (c) **ball and stick representation** (top view) of atoms and bonds with labels as per (a).

N

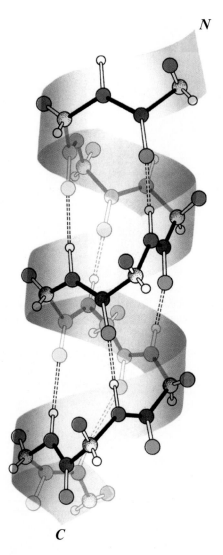

C

Figure 1.10 Cartoon rendition of α-helix in which right-hand helix path is illustrated as a ribbon over which a **ball and stick representation** of the α-**carbon backbone** is drawn using the code hydrogen (**white**), carbon (**grey**), nitrogen (**blue**) oxygen (**red**) and side chain atom (**purple**), in order to illustrate general **hydrogen bonding patterns** in the helix. (illustration from Voet, Voet & Pratt, 1999 [Wiley], Fig. 6-8).

a smaller and slightly distorted version of the α_R helix but with only three amino-acid residues per turn and 10 atoms involved in the intervening stretch of polypeptide main chain (Figures 1.13 and 1.14). Hydrogen bonds are therefore formed between the C=O group lone pairs of nth residues and the N–H groups (hydrogen bond donors) of $(n + 3)$th residues; ϕ and ψ conformational angles are approximately -60 and $-30°$ respectively (Figure 1.15).

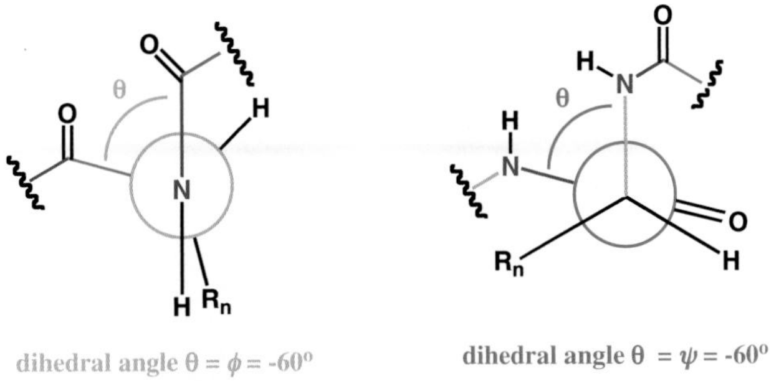

dihedral angle θ = φ = -60°   dihedral angle θ = ψ = -60°

Figure 1.11 Newman projections involving the N–C$_\alpha$ bond and C$_\alpha$–C(O) bond of the α-helix to demonstrate the consequences of highly regular dihedral angles ϕ and ψ respectively. Peptide backbone bonds are colour coded in the same way as in **Figs. 1.6** and **1.8**.

Sheetlike structures are the main alternative to helices. The origin of these structures can be found in the behaviour of polypeptide chains when they are fully extended into their β-**strand** conformations. A β strand has a 'pleated' appearance, with the peptide bonds orientated perpendicular to the main chain and with amino-acid residue side-chains alternating above and below (Figure 1.16). Both ϕ and ψ conformational angles are near 180° but are typically between −120 and −150° and +120 and +150° respectively (Figure 1.17). All β-**strand** conformations are unstable alone, but may be stabilised by the formation of non-covalent hydrogen bonds between strands, thereby resulting in a β **sheet** (Figures 1.16 and 1.18). Such β sheets may either be **antiparallel** (β) or **parallel** (β'), depending upon whether the β strands are orientated in opposite directions or the same direction with respect to each other (Figures 1.19 and 1.20). The hydrogen bonds that link β strands together are formed between

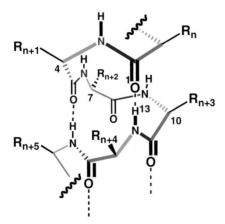

Figure 1.12 **Stereo-defined structure** of first turn of an α-helix to demonstrate the atom separation between N–H hydrogen bond donors and C=O hydrogen bond acceptors. The C=O acceptor of each n-th residue forms a hydrogen bond link with the N–H bond donor of the $(n + 4)$-th residue defining an atom separation of 13 between acceptor O-atom and donor H-atom. Peptide backbone bonds are colour coded in the same way as in **Figs. 1.6** and **1.8**.

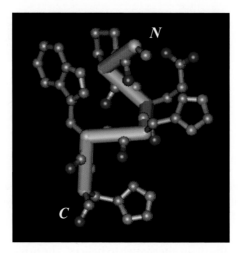

Figure 1.13   Depiction of **3_{10}-helix** (turn) from triose phosphate isomerase (chicken muscle) (pdb: **1tim**). **CA stick display** of α-carbon backbone, atoms and bonds of amino acid side chains are rendered in ball and stick representations with carbon (**grey**), nitrogen (**blue**) and oxygen (**red**).

the same functional groups as in helices. In antiparallel (β) β sheets, hydrogen bonds are alternately spaced close together then wide apart; in parallel (β') β sheets they are evenly spaced throughout (Figure 1.20).

1.2.3 Non-repetitive secondary structure

Helices and sheetlike structures are linked and/or held together by turns and loops in a given polypeptide main chain. **Tight turns** in the main chain (also known as β **bends** or β **turns**) are

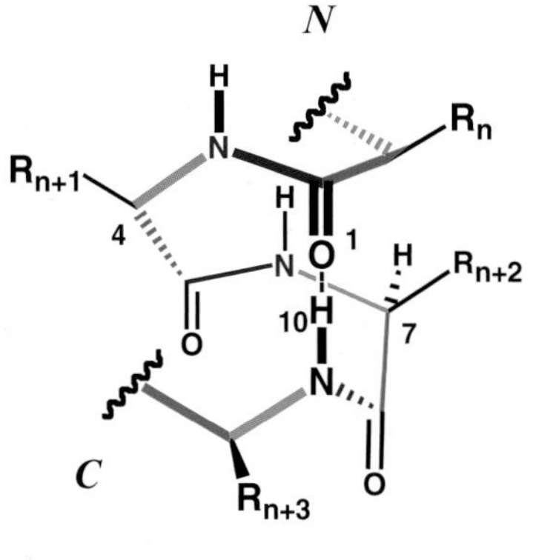

Figure 1.14   **Stereo-defined structure** of first turn of a 3_{10}-helix to demonstrate the atom separation between N—H hydrogen bond donors and C=O hydrogen bond acceptors. The C=O acceptor of each n-th residue forms a hydrogen bond link with the N—H bond donor of the $(n + 3)$-th residue defining an atom separation of 10 between acceptor O-atom and donor H-atom. Peptide backbone bonds are colour coded in the same way as in **Figs. 1.6** and **1.8**.

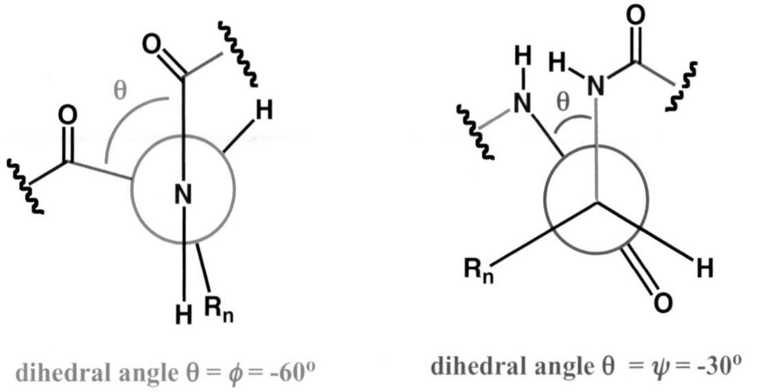

dihedral angle $\theta = \phi = -60°$ dihedral angle $\theta = \psi = -30°$

Figure 1.15 Newman projections involving the N–C_α bond and C_α–C(O) bond of the 3_{10}-helix to demonstrate the consequences of highly regular dihedral angles ϕ and ψ respectively. Peptide backbone bonds are colour coded in the same way as in **Figs. 1.6 & 1.8**. Tighter turn relates to smaller value of ψ.

very common. These typically involve four amino-acid residue units held together by a non-covalent hydrogen bond between C=O group lone pairs of the nth residue and the N–H group of the $(n + 3)$th residue. Given variations in the possible ϕ and ψ angles of the amino-acid residues involved, there are at least six possible variants; however, these are usually divisible into just two main classes, **type I** and **type II**, that differ primarily in the conformation of the

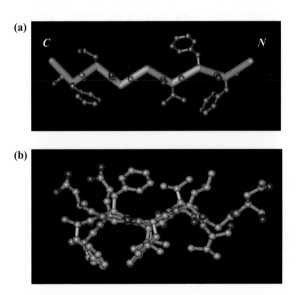

Figure 1.16 Depiction of β-**strand** and β-**sheet** from triose phosphate isomerase (chicken muscle) (pdb: **1tim**). **(a) CA stick Display** of α-carbon backbone (side view), atoms and bonds of amino acid side-chains are rendered in **ball and stick representation** with carbon (**grey**), nitrogen (**blue**) and oxygen (**red**). β-**strand** is shown to illustrate "zig-zag" extended conformation; **(b) Ball and stick representation** of β-**sheet** (side view) is shown with carbon (**grey**), nitrogen (**blue**) and oxygen (**red**) to illustrate "zig-zag" pleating and to show regular arrangement of amino acid residue side chains in close juxtaposition.

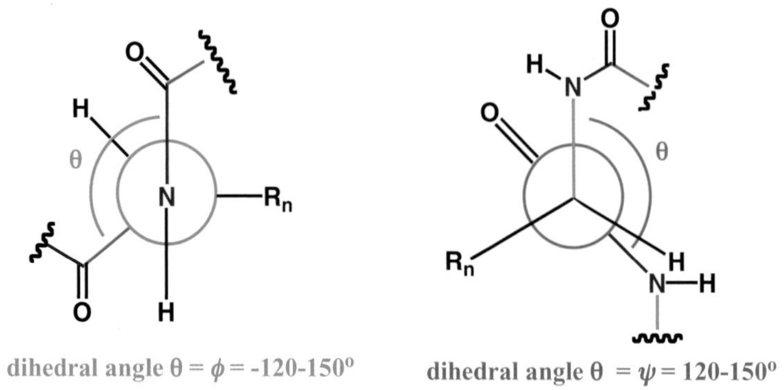

dihedral angle $\theta = \phi = -120\text{-}150°$ dihedral angle $\theta = \psi = 120\text{-}150°$

Figure 1.17   Newman projections involving the N—C_α bond and C_α—C(O) bond of a β-strand to demonstrate the consequences of highly regular dihedral angles ϕ and ψ respectively and extending the conformation. Peptide backbone bonds are colour coded in the same way as in **Figs. 1.6 & 1.8.**

peptide link between the second and third residues of the turn (Figures 1.21 and 1.22). **Loops** in the main chain are also very common, but interactions between amino-acid residue side-chains provide stability rather than peptide-link-associated hydrogen bonding. Consequently, the path mapped out by the main chain in forming a loop is a good deal less regular than that found in a tight turn (Figure 1.23). Occasionally, **disulphide bridges** in polypeptides replace and/or supplement peptide links. These bridges are formed between the thiol-functional groups of two different cysteine (cys, C) residues separated by at least two other amino-acid residues from each other in the amino-acid sequence of a polypeptide. These may be thought of as the polypeptide equivalent of a 'tie bar' or some other such reinforcing device. Both right-handed and left-handed spiral forms are known and a series of conformational angles $(\chi_1, \chi_2, \chi_3, \chi_{2'}, \chi_{1'})$ define the state of each given disulphide bridge (Figures 1.24 and 1.25).

1.2.4 Alternative secondary structures

In certain cases, a polypeptide main chain can map out helical structures that are rather more extended and elongated than the α_R helix. These structures are known either as the left-handed P_{II} **helix** or **collagen helix** (**C**), for reasons that will become apparent. This is unusual in being a left-handed structure when most biological macromolecule structures or substructures are right handed. The polypeptide main chain is extended so that in appearance it is some where in between the topography of an α_R helix and a β strand (Figures 1.26 and 1.27). There are about three amino-acid residues per turn of helix, with a rise per residue of about 3 Å between each residue as compared to 1.5 Å in the α_R helix. The required ϕ and ψ angles needed to form a P_{II} helix are unusual (Figure 1.8). Accordingly, most polypeptides are unable to adopt an extended P_{II}-helical conformation successfully, with the exception of polypeptides comprising a high proportion of glycine and proline residues (Table 1.1).

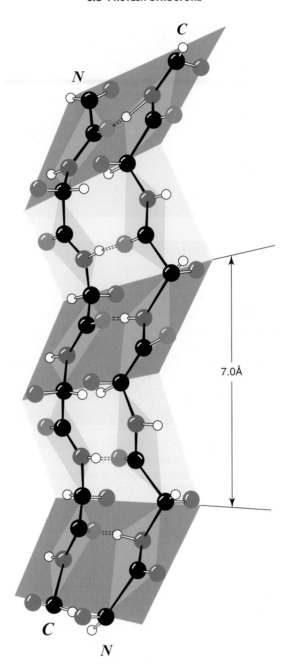

Figure 1.18 **Cartoon rendition of a** β-**sheet** in which pleating is illustrated as a sequence of intersecting planes over which a **ball and stick representation** of the α-carbon backbone is drawn using the code hydrogen (**white**), carbon (**black**), nitrogen (**blue**) oxygen (**red**) and side chain atom (**purple**), in order to illustrate general positioning of side chains above and below the sheet. (illustration from Voet, Voet & Pratt, 1999 [Wiley], Fig. 6-10).

(a)

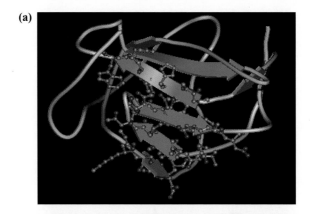

(b)

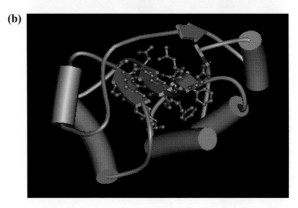

Figure 1.19   Depiction of β-**sheet** structures from indicated proteins. (**a**) **Schematic Display Structure** (see Section 1.2.5; each flat arrow is a β-strand with arrow head equal to C-terminus of each strand: cylinders are α-helices: remainder represent loops and turns) of **anti-parallel β-sheet segment** of carbonic anhydrase I (human erythrocyte) (pdb: **2cab**), atoms and bonds of amino acid side-chains are rendered in **ball and stick representation** with carbon (**grey**), nitrogen (**blue**) and oxygen (**red**); (**b**) **Schematic Display Structure** of **parallel β-sheet segment** of triose phosphate isomerase (chicken muscle) (pdb: **1tim**), atoms and bonds of side-chains are rendered as in (a).

1.2.5 Tertiary structure

The docking together and mutual stabilisation of three dimensional secondary structural elements results in an overall three dimensional fold known as the **tertiary structure** of a polypeptide. Many proteins are comprised of a single polypeptide chain, hence this fold becomes in effect the tertiary structure of the protein too. The overall shape of this fold is frequently globular and therefore proteins with such a fold are known as **globular proteins**. **Protein folding** is known as the process by which proteins acquire their tertiary structure. This field of study is enormously controversial, and where globular proteins/polypeptides are concerned debate still rages about whether secondary structures form first and dock together

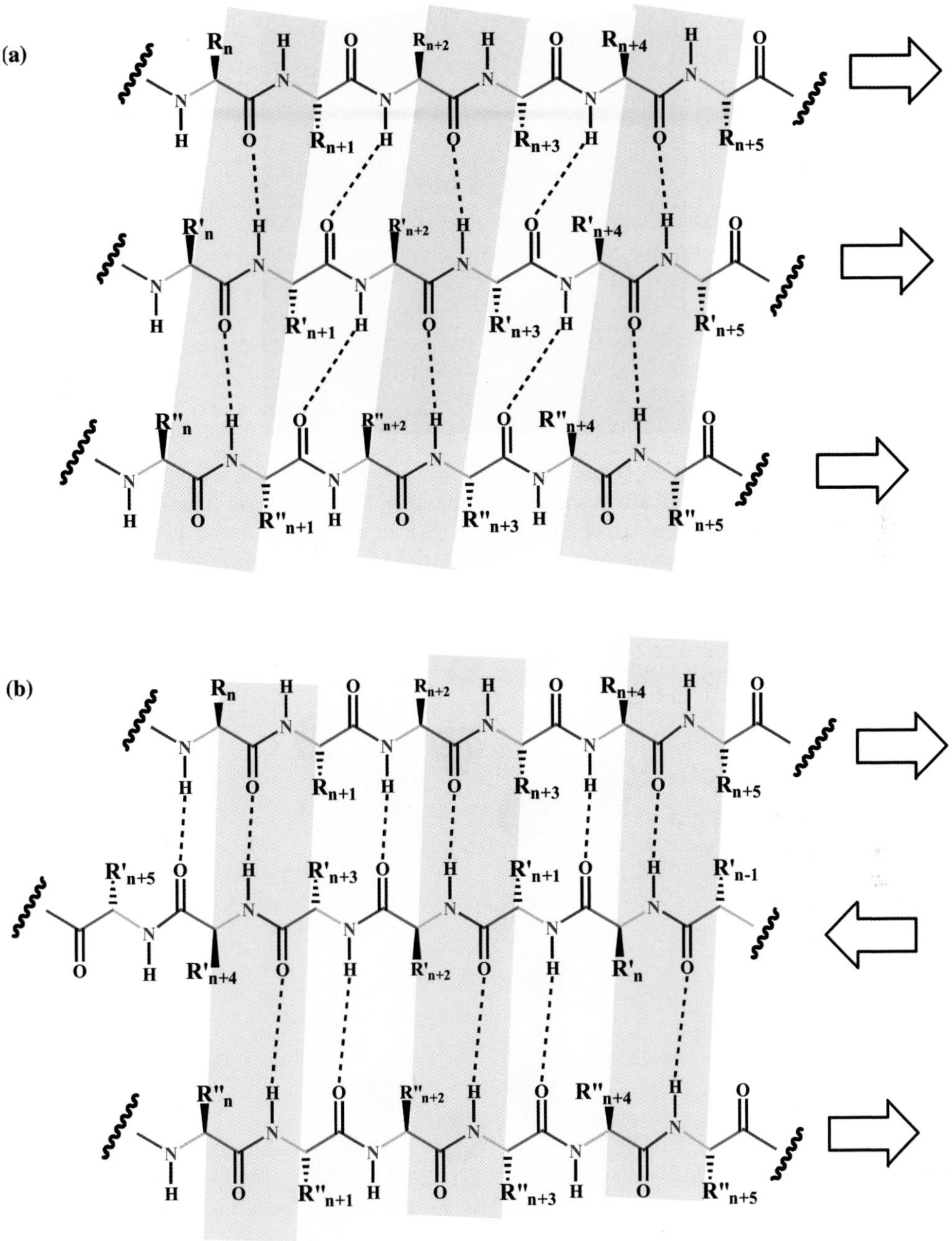

Figure 1.20 Stereo-defined structures of β-sheets. (a) Three stranded **parallel β-sheet** structure showing hydrogen bonding relationship between parallel β-strands. The N—H donor of each peptide link is able to form a hydrogen bond with the C=O acceptor of a peptide link in a parallel β-strand. Shading is used to demonstrate pleating and emphasise amino acid residue side-chain orientations with respect to the sheet and with respect to each other. Peptide backbone bonds are colour coded in the same way as **Figs. 1.6** & **1.8**. Arrows define N to C chain directions; (**b**) three stranded **antiparallel β-sheet** structure as for (**a**) except that hydrogen bonding occurs between peptide links in neighbouring antiparallel β-strands.

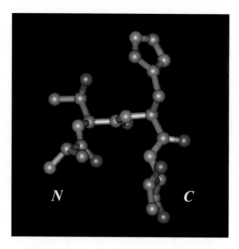

Figure 1.21 Depiction of β-**turn** (**Type I**) from carbonic anhydrase I (human erythrocyte) (pdb: **2cab**). **Ball and stick representation** of atoms and bonds with carbon (**grey**), nitrogen (**blue**) and oxygen (**red**).

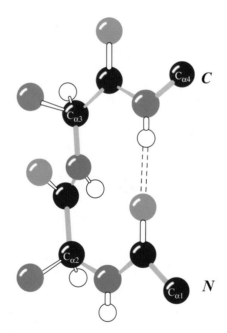

Figure 1.22   Cartoon of β-turn (Type II). Ball and stick representation of atoms and bonds with carbon (**black**), nitrogen (**blue**), oxygen (**red**), and side chain atom (**purple**), in order to illustrate how the C=O acceptor of the first n-th residue forms a hydrogen bond with the N—H bond donor of the $(n + 3)$-th residue defining an atom separation of 10 between acceptor O-atom and donor H-atom. This is the same of the Type I turn (**Fig. 1.21**). The main difference between Type I and Type II is the orientation of the peptide link joining the $(n + 1)$-th to the $(n + 2)$-th residue (illustration from Voet, Voet & Pratt, 1999 [Wiley], Fig. 6-20b).

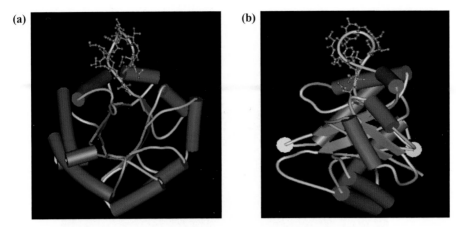

Figure 1.23 Depiction of **loop** structure from triose phosphate isomerase (chicken muscle) (pdb: **1tim**). (a) **Schematic display structure** (see Section 1.2.5; each flat arrow is a β-strand with arrow head equal to C-terminus of each strand: cylinders are α-helices: remainder is loops and turns) of triose phosphate isomerase (top view), atoms and bonds of amino acid side chains of key loop are rendered in **ball and stick representation** with carbon (**grey**), nitrogen (**blue**) and oxygen (**red**); (b) schematic display structure of triose phosphate isomerase (side view), atoms and bonds of amino acid side chains rendered as in (a).

to form tertiary structure (**framework model**) or whether a crude tertiary structure forms first, followed by a process of 'side-chain' negotiation to create stabilised secondary structures (**molten-globule model**). The latter model appears the more popular today, consistent with the realisation that there are multitudinous 'pathways' of protein folding, which are themselves highly dependent upon the primary structure of the particular protein/polypeptide of interest. Yet, we still do not know how exactly the primary structure drives the formation of the tertiary structure, so given a certain primary structure we remain far from sure what the globular tertiary structure will be in many many cases.

Given the general atomic complexity of protein architecture, several shorthand representations of globular protein/polypeptide three dimensional structures have been devised, of which the easiest to understand are the **ribbon display structures** (Figure 1.28). There are other representations too including **surface display**, **CPK** and **schematic display structures**, all designed to highlight different aspects of protein structure during analysis (Figure 1.29). The illustrated structures show all the main classes of **globular proteins**, namely **small metal rich proteins**, **small SS rich proteins**, **anti-parallel α proteins**, **anti-parallel β proteins** and **parallel α/β proteins** according to the **Richardson classification**, based upon the topographical behaviour of repetitive secondary structure elements in the tertiary structure (Figures 1.28 and 1.29). Almost without exception, the interior of a globular protein will contain hydrophobic amino-acid residues (e.g. leucine (leu, L), valine (val, V), phenylalanine (phe, F) etc.), whilst the exterior is made up of hydrophobic and hydrophilic amino-acid residues, though hydrophilic amino-acid residues predominate. The importance of this will become clear later, but for now let us say that globular proteins have a 'waxy' interior and a 'soapy' exterior. This 'waxy' interior is amazingly crystalline. In fact, the interior packing

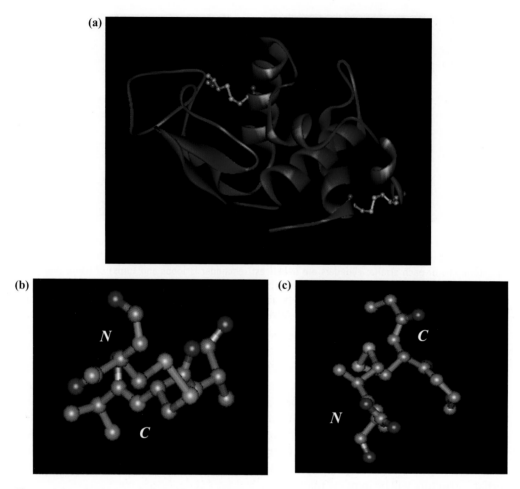

Figure 1.24 Depiction of **disulphide bridges** from lysozyme (hen egg-white) (pdb:**6lyz**). (a) **Ribbon Display Structure** (see Section 1.2.5; each flat helical ribbon is an α-helix; each flat strand is β-strand: thin strands are loops and turns) of lysozyme (side view), atoms and bonds of amino acid side chains of cysteine residues involved in disulphide bridges are rendered in **ball and stick representation** with sulphur (**yellow**) carbon (**grey**), nitrogen (**blue**) and oxygen (**red**); (b) **ball and stick representation** of cysteine residues forming a **right-handed disulphide bridge**, atoms and bonds labelled as for (a); (c) **ball and stick representation** of cysteine residues from a **left-handed disulphide bridge**, atoms and bonds labelled as for (a).

of hydrophobic amino-acid residues is remarkably similar to the crystalline state of organic solids. This amino-acid residue distribution indicates that close range non-covalent van der Waals forces and hydrophobic interactions (see Section 1.6) are critical to the stability of the globular protein/polypeptide chain, whereas the non-covalent hydrogen bond is largely responsible for the formation of repetitive and much non-repetitive secondary structure (except for the disulphide bridge). Of late, there is a realisation that other forces, defined as **weak**

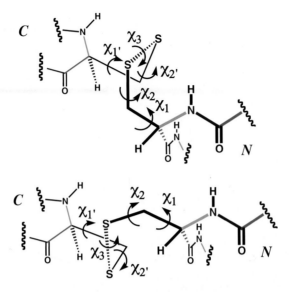

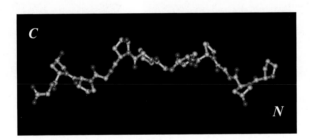

Figure 1.25 Detailed **structural description of disulphide bridges. (a) Right-handed disulphide bridge** showing all the main conformational angles; **(b) Left-handed disulphide bridge** similarly indicating all the main conformational angles. In both cases, **N** refers to a cysteine residue closest to the *N*-terminus of the polypeptide and **C** refers to a residue closest to the *C*-terminus.

Figure 1.26 Depiction of left-handed P_{II}-**helix** from collagen (pdb: **1bkv**). **Ball and stick representation** of atoms and bonds with carbon (**grey**), nitrogen (**blue**) and oxygen (**red**).

Figure 1.27 **Cartoon depiction of the extended P_{II}-helix.** Depiction emphasises the left handed character of this helix type (adapted from Voet, Voet & Pratt, 1999 [Wiley], Fig. 6-17).

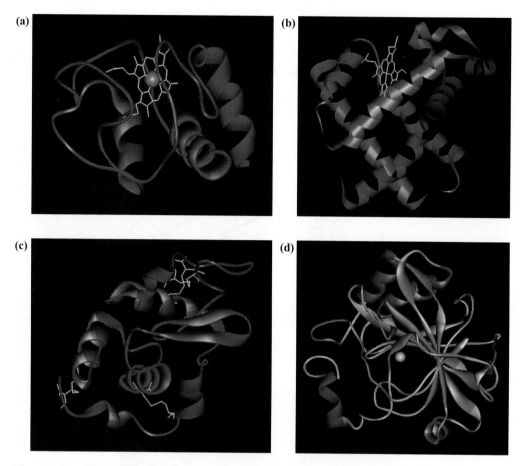

Figure 1.28   Ribbon display structure cartoon depictions. (**a**) *Small metal rich protein* **cytochrome c** (horse heart) (pdb: **1hrc**). Polypeptide backbone is shown as a ribbon (**red**). Stick bonds constituting porphyrin macrocycle (prosthetic group) are highlighted (**yellow**). Van der Waal's sphere (**blue**) represents central iron ion; (**b**) *Anti-parallel α-protein* **myoglobin** (sperm whale) (pdb: **1mbi**) with labelling system as for (a); (**c**) *Small SS rich protein* **lysozyme** (hen eggwhite) (pdb: **6lyz**). Polypeptide backbone is shown as a ribbon (**red**), stick bonds of cysteine amino acid residues linked by disulphide bridges are also shown (**yellow**); (**d**) *Anti-parallel β-protein* **carbonic anhydrase I** (human erythrocyte) (pdb: **2cab**). Polypeptide backbone is coloured according to secondary structure with α-helix (**red**), anti-parallel β-sheet (**light blue**), loop structures (random coil) (**light grey**). Van der Waals sphere (**yellow**) represents central zinc ion.

polar forces, may also have a significant role to play in stabilising protein/polypeptide tertiary structure as well (see Section 1.6). Indeed, there may yet be other forces to be discovered. Without doubt, globular protein/polypeptide structure remains a rich and fascinating if not controversial area of research.

Globular proteins/polypeptides are frequently employed in cells as functional proteins, responsible for respiration, metabolism and communication. However, the vast majority of proteins inside and indeed outside cells have structural, scaffolding functions. In these cases,

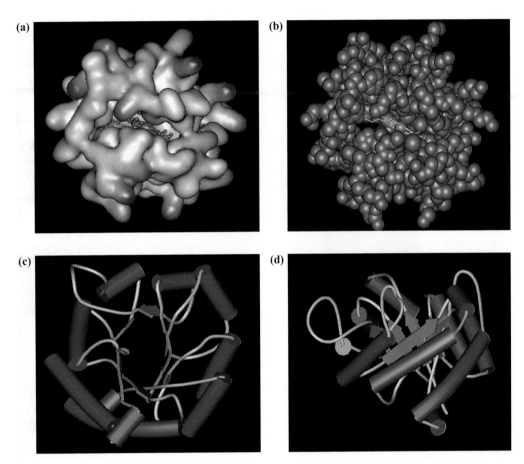

Figure 1.29 Alternative cartoon depictions of proteins. (a) **surface display structure** of *small metal rich protein* **cytochrome c** (horse heart) (pdb: **1hrc**) showing Van der Waal's surface coloured for positive charge (**blue**) and for negative charge (**red**). Ball and stick representations of **iron-porphyrin macrocycle** (**prosthetic group**) are shown (**red**) for each subunit with central iron ion rendered as Van der Waals sphere (**light blue**); (b) **CPK structure** of **cytochrome c** in which all polypeptide atoms are rendered as Van der Waals spheres (**purple**). Porphyrin and iron ion are shown as in **Fig. 1.28**; (c) **schematic display structure** (top view) of *parallel α/β-protein* **triose phosphate isomerase** (chicken muscle) (pdb: **1tim**) with α-helix shown as cylinders (**red**), β-strands as arrowed ribbons (**light blue**), loop structures (random coil) as rods (**light grey**); (d) **schematic display structure** (side view) of **triose phosphate isomerase**, otherwise as for (c).

protein polypeptides generally exhibit an extended rather than globular overall fold and hence proteins are known as **fibrous proteins**. First and foremost amongst these should be considered collagen, the main structural component of bone. The collagen molecular fold is created essentially through the association of three extended left-handed P_{II} **helices** to give a right-handed P_{II} **triple helix** or **collagen triple helix** (Figures 1.30 and 1.31), wherein each constituent P_{II} helix is linked to neighbours by hydrogen bonds, resulting in high lateral as well as longitudinal stability. Other forces are also thought to be involved but remain to be

(a)   (b)

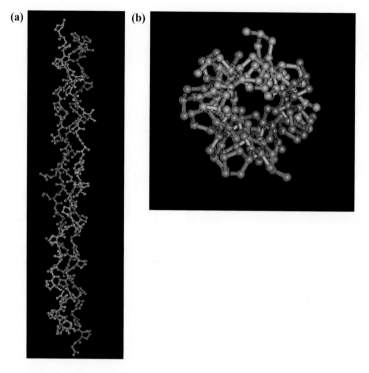

Figure 1.30 Depiction of right-handed **collagen triple helix**. (pdb: **1bkv**) (a) **Ball and stick represen-tation** of atoms and bonds of triple helix (side view) with complete, individual polypeptide chain single coloured (**yellow**, **brown** or **blue**) (side view); (**b**) **Ball and stick representation** of atoms and bonds of triple helix (top view), polypeptide chains rendered as in (a).

fully characterised. Since only polypeptides comprising glycine and proline residues are able to form extended P_{II} helices, owing to the unusual ϕ and ψ angles required, then collagen molecules too must contain a disproportionately high level of proline and glycine residues compared with other globular proteins/polypeptides. Strictly speaking, the term tertiary structure refers to the overall fold of a single polypeptide (as noted above). Yet while a collagen triple helix can be formed from a single polypeptide, the collagen triple helix that makes up the collagen fold is actually constructed from three different collagen polypeptides linked together initially by disulphide bridges. Therefore, the collagen triple helix that comprises the collagen molecular fold should perhaps be described not as the tertiary structure of collagen but as a form of quaternary structure (see Section 1.2.6). Nevertheless, when bone is formed, collagen molecules associate through their collagen triple helices forming extended bundles that mineralise to form the matrix of bone. Arguably, we should characterise these bundles as the collagen quaternary structure instead. In conclusion, we would like to point out that there is a small population of single polypeptide proteins whose tertiary structures are actually a combination of globular and fibrous protein folds including dominant but not exclusive P_{II} triple helical regions. These are regarded as hybrid proteins that are both globular and fibrous proteins simultaneously.

Figure 1.31 Cartoon depiction of the right-handed collagen triple helix. Depiction emphasises how three polypeptides in left-handed P_{II} helical conformations associate to form the triple helical structure wherein each polypeptide adopts a gentle right-handed rope-like twist in order to maximise stabilising inter-chain hydrogen bond interactions. Structure is also stabilised by a sheath of ordered water molecules of solvation (illustration from Voet, Voet & Pratt, 1999 [Wiley], Fig. 6-17).

1.2.6 Quaternary structure

Different polypeptide chains may interact to form more complex multi-polypeptide proteins, wherein each individual polypeptide is known as a **subunit**. Subunit interactions and interrelationships are illustrated for the tetrameric protein haemoglobin (Figure 1.32). In the case of globular proteins, polypeptide chain association allows functions of individual polypeptide elements to be coordinated or indeed supplemented to give the whole molecule the opportunity to perform multiple biological functions. In the case of fibrous proteins, quaternary structure formation enhances overall molecular strength.

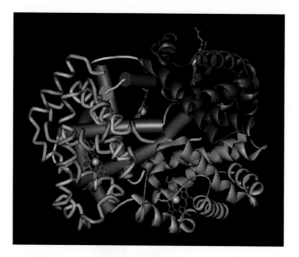

Figure 1.32   Quaternary structure of hemoglobin (human foetal) (pdb: **1a3n**). This protein is comprised of 4 distinct polypeptides (**subunits**), α_1, α_2, β_1, and β_2 which are rendered two as **ribbon display** structures (**red** and **yellow; right-side**), one as a **schematic display** structure (**left-side, rear**), and one as **CA stick display** (**left-side, front**). **Ball and stick representations** of **iron-porphyrin macrocycle (prosthetic group**) are shown (**green**) for each subunit with central iron ion rendered as Van der Waals sphere (**light grey**). Subunits are all associated non-covalently with each other which is usual for polypeptide subunits that comprise a multi-polypeptide protein.

1.2.7 Prosthetic groups

Many globular proteins/polypeptides, especially those involved in the catalysis of chemical reactions, also have non-peptidic structures that may be associated covalently or non-covalently with the polypeptide. These are known as **prosthetic groups**. All such prosthetic groups belong with proteins in order to confer particular functionalities that might otherwise not exist. A good example is the iron porphyrin ring in the proteins haemoglobin (Figure 1.32), myoglobin and cytochrome c (Figures 1.28 and 1.29) that enables the first two of these proteins to act in respiration as molecular oxygen carriers/scavengers and the last to act as a redox substrate. Other prosthetic groups will be described in Chapter 4.

1.3 Carbohydrate structure

1.3.1 Primary structure

Carbohydrate polymers are formed from the linear and branched combination of a wide variety of different naturally occurring simple sugars known as **monosaccharides**. Monosaccharides are a reasonably diverse set of molecular building blocks, each capable of linking to other monosaccharides in a variety of different ways, with the result that the exquisite

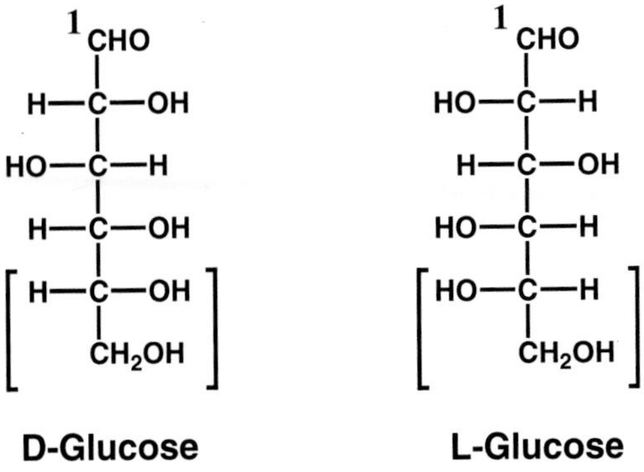

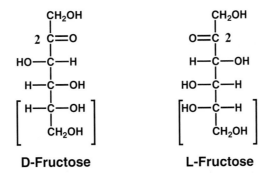

D-Glucose   L-Glucose

Figure 1.33 D- and L-glucose

hierarchy of structural elements found in protein structures is not so readily duplicated with carbohydrate polymers. Having said this, those carbohydrate homopolymers that are constructed from only one or two monosaccharide building blocks can possess really impressive three dimensional structures. Therefore, read on!

Monosaccharides may be classified into families according to the number of carbon atoms they contain, usually between three and seven. The **triose** family has the empircal formula $C_3H_6O_3$, the **tetrose** family $C_4H_8O_4$, the **pentose** family $C_5H_{10}O_5$, the **hexose** family $C_6H_{12}O_6$ and the **heptoses** $C_7H_{14}O_7$. An alternative classification has been to name monosaccharides as either **aldehydo-aldose** or **ketose** sugars depending upon whether they possess an aldehyde or ketone functional group respectively. By way of illustration, the well known sugar **glucose** is both a hexose, with six carbon atoms, and an aldehydo-aldose monosaccharide owing to the aldehyde functional group at carbon atom 1 (C-1) (Figure 1.33). **Fructose** is also a hexose but is otherwise known as a ketose sugar because of the ketone functional group positioned at carbon atom 2 (C-2) (Figure 1.34). Each exists in two enantiomeric forms (either D or L), as defined by the absolute stereochemistry of the penultimate carbon atom in the chain (in both cases carbon atom 5, C-5) with reference by convention to the C-2 stereochemistry of D- or

D-Fructose   L-Fructose

Figure 1.34 D- and L-fructose

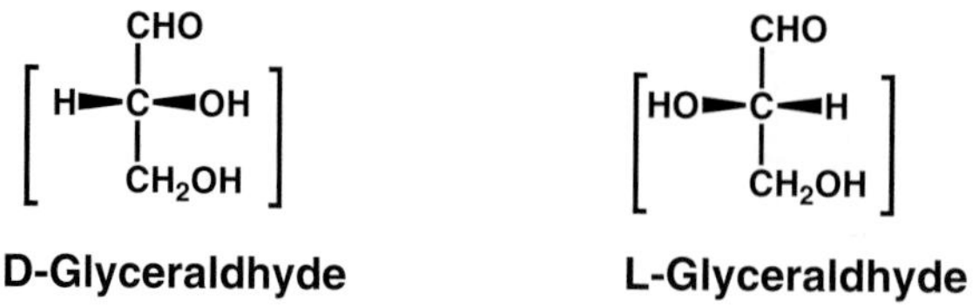

D-Glyceraldhyde   **L-Glyceraldhyde**

Figure 1.35 D- and L-glyceraldehyde to illustrate principles of the **Fischer Projection**. The D and L absolute configuration convention for all sugars refers to the stereochemistry of the bracketed terminal carbons whose configuration is compared with the two enantiomers of glyceraldehyde.

L-glyceraldehyde (Figure 1.35). The D-enantiomers of glucose and fructose tend to predominate in natural carbohydrate polymers. This is also true of most other monosaccharides found in natural carbohydrate polymers as well.

The conformational behaviour of monosaccharides in solution is complicated. In solution, acyclic D-glucose readily converts into cyclic **five-member** (*f*, **furanose**) and/or **six-member** (*p*, **pyranose**) rings (Figure 1.36). Furanose (*f*) and pyranose (*p*) rings always exist as pairs of **anomers** (α or β). These α and β anomers differ from each other only in their hydroxyl group

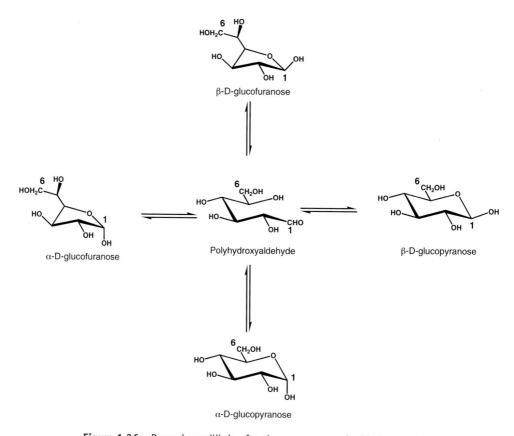

Figure 1.36 Dynamic equilibria of D-glucose monosaccharide in solution.

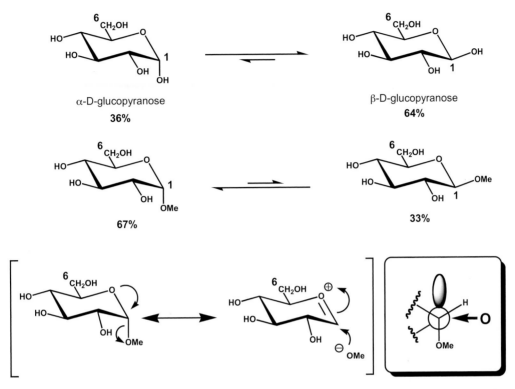

Figure 1.37 Illustration of the **anomeric effect** in monosaccharides. The anomeric effect is defined as the preference of electronegative functional groups attached to anomeric Carbon C-1 to adopt an unexpected axial configuration. In D-glucopyranose, the equatorial β-anomer is favoured but the trend is reversed with alkylation. The origin of the effect is the transdiequatorial interaction between Oxygen long pair and the σ* orbital of the bond linking C-1 with the electronegative function group.

configuration at the **anomeric carbon**. In D-glucose this is the hemi-acetal carbon C-1 (Figure 1.36). Since pyranose rings are largely stable, D-glucose actually prefers to exist in solution as **α-D-glucopyranose** or **β-D-glucopyranose** (Figure 1.36). The relative proportions of either the α **anomer** or the β **anomer** in solution depend upon the **anomeric effect**. The anomeric effect may be defined as the thermodynamic preference for one anomer over another resulting from a combination of internal stereo-electronic effects and solution conditions. Typically, the opportunity for hyperconjugation involving oxygen lone pairs favours the anomer with axial substituents attached to the anomeric carbon (Figure 1.37), although under aqueous solution conditions the equatorial β anomer β-D-glucopyranose is actually favoured over the axial α anomer α-D-glucopyranose. Conformationally speaking, either anomer may adopt one of two main chair (**C**) conformations. For example, the two main chair conformations of β-D-**glucopyranose** are $^4C_1$, where C-4 is above and C-1 is below the plane mapped out by oxygen and carbon atoms 2, 3 and 5, or $^1C_4$, where the reverse is true (Figure 1.38). Unsurprisingly perhaps, the all-equatorial $^4C_1$ is the more stable of the two and hence is the dominant conformation in solution. By contrast, α-D-glucofuranose or β-D-glucofuranose

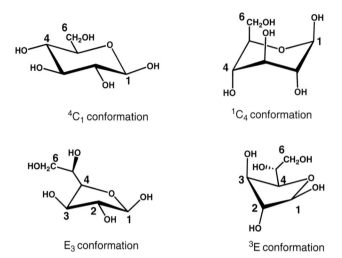

$^4C_1$ conformation $^1C_4$ conformation

E_3 conformation ^3E conformation

Figure 1.38 Conformational extremes of β-D-glucopyranose (top) and β-D-glucofuranose (bottom). Anomeric Carbon C1 is on right-hand side by convention.

anomers exist in one of two main envelope (**E**) conformations. For example, the two main envelope conformations of β-D-glucofuranose are ^{3}**E**, where C-3 is above the plane mapped out by oxygen and carbon atoms 1, 2 and 4, or **E**$_3$, where the reverse is true (Figure 1.38).

D-fructose shows similar equilibrium behaviour to D-glucose in that cyclic forms are preferred in solution where the anomeric carbon is the hemi-ketal carbon C-2. In the case of D-fructose though, both pyranose and furanose rings are relatively stable and so there is a preference for D-fructose to exist primarily in solution in the cyclic forms α-D-**fructopyranose** or β-D-**fructofuranose** (Figure 1.39). Generally speaking, only the most stable cyclic conformation of either D-glucose or D-fructose will appear in natural carbohydrate polymers. The same is true of the other main monosaccharide building blocks found in natural carbohydrate polymers as well (Figure 1.40). The preferred, stable cyclic conformations are shown together with the appropriate three letter monosaccharide code and the short code for preferred conformation (Figure 1.41).

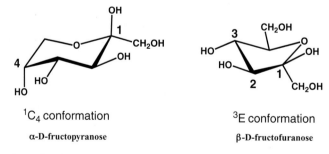

$^1C_4$ conformation ^3E conformation

α-D-fructopyranose   β-D-fructofuranose

Figure 1.39 Conformational extremes of α-D-fructopyranose (left) and β-D-fructofuranose (right). Anomeric Carbon C1 is on right-hand side by convention.

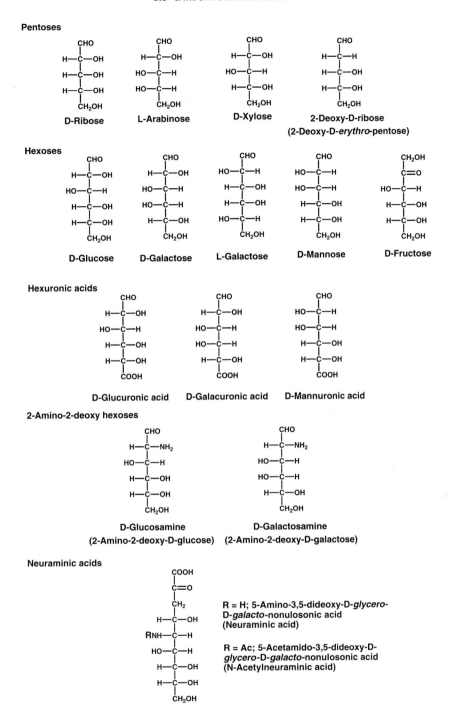

Figure 1.40 Structural summary of all main monosaccharides found in natural carbohydrates. All monosaccharides are displayed as their Fischer Projections to shown differences in absolute configuration.

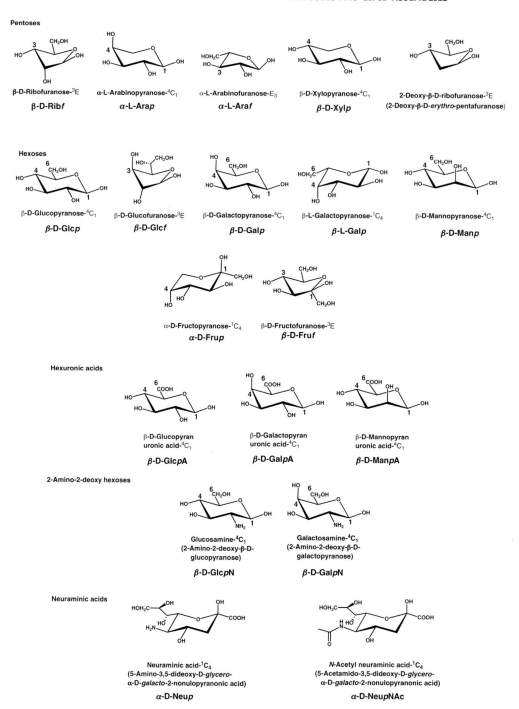

Figure 1.41 Structural summary of the preferred cyclic conformations of all main monosaccharides found in natural carbohydrates.

1.3.2 O-glycosidic link

In natural carbohydrate polymers, monosaccharide building blocks are joined together by means of the **O-glycosidic link**. The O-glycosidic link is an ether functional group that originates by convention from the anomeric carbon atom of one monosaccharide residue and terminates at the appropriate carbon atom of a neighbouring residue (Figure 1.42). Each linked monosaccharide building block is known as a **monosaccharide residue**. If an O-glycosidic link is defined as $(1 \rightarrow 4)$ then this implies that the link originates from the anomeric carbon C-1 of one monosaccharide residue and terminates at carbon atom C-4 of the next. In common with the peptide bond, the O-glycosidic link has some associated rigidity due to steric congestion between neighbouring monosaccharide residues. The resulting spatial relationships between neighbouring residues can then be defined in terms of two conformational angles ϕ and ψ, which are respectively the main dihedral angles subtended about the anomeric carbon to oxygen bond (C_{an}–O) and the following oxygen to carbon bond (O–C) (Figure 1.43). In contrast with proteins, allowed values of ϕ and ψ vary substantially, depending upon the identities of the linked monosaccharide residues (Figure 1.44); therefore, carbohydrate polymers comprised of a number of different monosaccharide residues cannot easily form stereo-regular three dimensional structures.

By definition, when two monosaccharide building blocks are linked together by an O-glycosidic link, the result is known as a **disaccharide**. Two well known disaccharides have been shown to illustrate how their structures are defined in terms of the three letter monosaccharide code and their O-glycosidic links (Figure 1.45). Typically, when two to 20 monosaccharide residues are linked together, in a linear or branched fashion, the resulting carbohydrate polymers are described as **oligosaccharides** (Figure 1.46). When 20–100 monosaccharide residues (usually 80–100) are linked together then resulting polymers are described as **polysaccharides**. Unbranched oligo- or polysaccharides are said to consist of one carbohydrate main

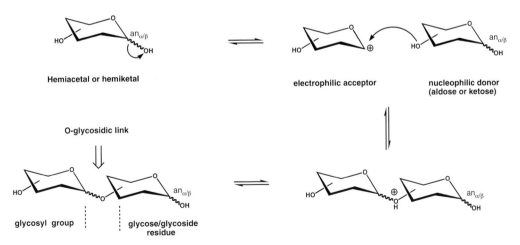

Figure 1.42 Schematic illustration of the **O-glycosidic link** formed by dehydration of an anomeric carbon centre.

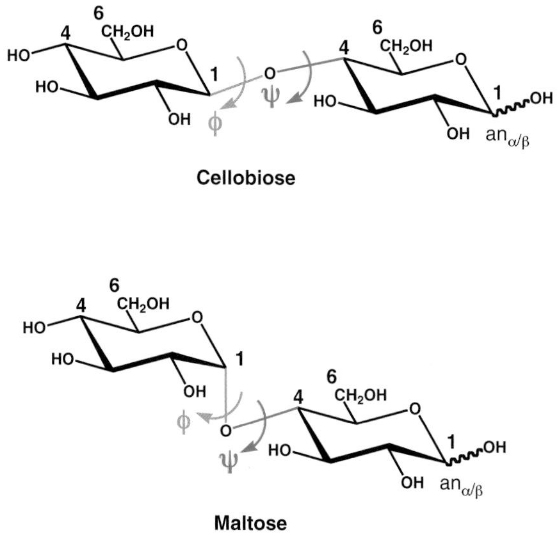

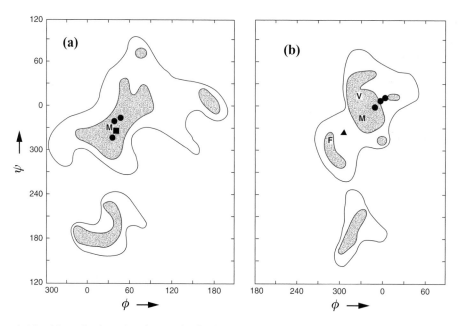

Figure 1.43   Main O-glycosidic link conformational angles; ϕ is dihedral angle subtended about the C_{an}—O bond and ψ is dihedral angle subtended about subsequent O—C bond.

**Figure 1.44   Allowed values ϕ and ψ angles for O-glycosidic link of cellobiose (a) or maltose (b). In (a) black squares or circles indicate positions of observed conformational angles in cellobiose or cellobiose units found in larger polysaccharide systems. In (b) black triangle or circles indicate position of observed conformational angles in maltose or maltose units found in a larger polysaccharide systems (adapted from Rees & Smith, 1995, Figs. 7 & 5).

Typical Aldehydo-aldose or Glycosyl-glycose

Typical Ketose or Glycosyl-glycoside

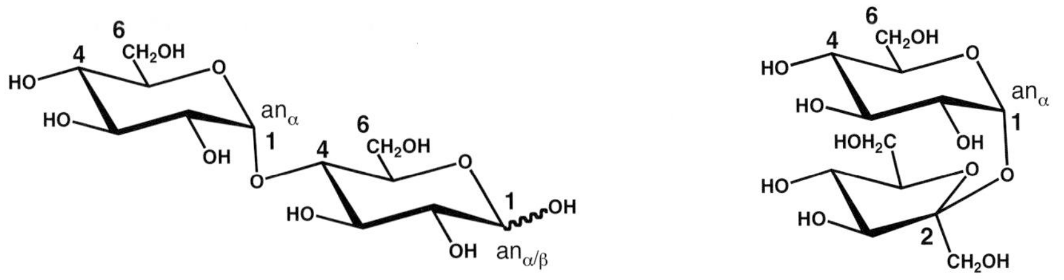

Maltose

(4-O-α-D-glucopyranosyl-D-glucopyranose)

α-D-Glc*p*-(1→4)-D-Glc

Sucrose

(2-O-α-D-glucopyranosyl-β-D-fructofuranoside)

α-D-Glc*p*-(1→2)-β-D-Fru*f*

Figure 1.45 Structures of two main **disaccharides** with a single O-glycosidic link. Maltose is a representative **glycosylglycose** and Sucrose a representative **glycosylglycoside**. Full trivial names are given as well as **3-letter code**-based nomenclature that is used for more complex systems. By convention, the highest priority end is the glycosyl group and the lowest priority the glycose/glycoside residue. This convention applies for all oligosaccharides, polysaccharides and carbohydrates.

chain. Branched oligo- or polysaccharides are said to consist of a main chain to which are attached any number of branch chains. By convention, oligosaccharide and polysaccharide main chains end at the monosaccharide residue that retains a free anomeric carbon not involved in an O-glycosidic link. This terminal residue is known either as a **glycose residue**, if derived from an aldehydo-aldose monosaccharide, or as a **glycoside residue**, if derived from a ketose monosaccharide. The residue at the start of a given oligo- or polysaccharide chain, main or branched, is then known as a **glycosyl group** (Figure 1.46). All monosaccharide residues in between may be called **glycosyl residues**. The complete list of linked monosaccharide residues in travelling from the highest priority glycosyl group(s) to the lowest priority terminal glycose/glycoside residue is known as the **carbohydrate sequence**, or **carbohydrate primary structure**. Where branched polymers are concerned, the longest continuous chain provides the parent sequence to which are attached branch chains with their own daughter sequences. For each branch chain, daughter sequences begin with glycosyl groups and end where the branch chain meets the main chain.

1.3.3 Polysaccharides: secondary, tertiary and quaternary structures

The sequences of many oligosaccharides are often too diverse and too short to encourage the formation of stable three dimensional structures. Therefore, for the most part oligosaccharides and shorter polysaccharides exist only as **random coil**. The same is not true of a significant number of the much longer chain polysaccharides. Polysaccharides can also be known as **glycans**, hence polysaccharides containing only one type of monosaccharide residue are known as **homoglycans**, and those with between two and six different types of

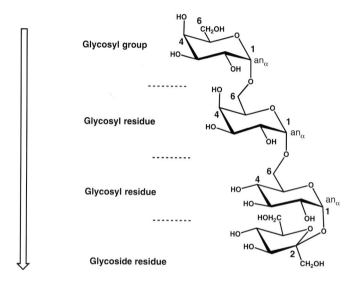

Figure 1.46 Structures of two main **tetrasaccharides** with a three O-glycosidic links. **Cellotetraose** is representative of a glycose tetrasaccharide and **Stachyose** of glycoside tetrasaccharide. The **3-letter code**-based nomenclature is used. Arrows show chain directions as determined by the convention described in the legend to **Fig. 1.45**.

residue are known as **heteroglycans**. Homoglycans and a few heteroglycan polysaccharides can form extensive periodic secondary structures, and these regular structures are usually related geometrically to a helix even if they may not necessarily conform to the conventional idea of a helix. Regular structures are defined in terms of two parameters that are known as n, the number of glycosyl residues per turn, and h, the projected length of each glycosyl residue on the 'helix' axis (Figure 1.47). Parameter n is either positive or negative, depending

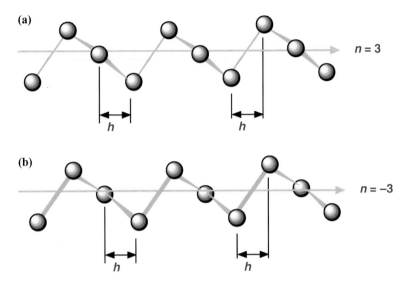

Figure 1.47 Simplified description of **right-hand (a)** and **left-hand (b) polysaccharide helices** where h is the length of each monosaccharide residue projected on the helix axis, and n is the number of residues per turn. A negative value implies left-hand and a positive value implies right hand. Spheres represent O-glycosidic links between monosaccharide residues.

upon whether the helix is perceived to be right handed or left handed respectively. In the event, almost all homoglycan and heteroglycan polysaccharides that are able to form periodic secondary structures exist only in four main families. These are the **ribbon family** ($n = 2 \pm 4$; $h =$ approx. 5 Å (approximate length of glycosyl residue)), the **hollow helix family** ($n = 2 \pm 10$; $h = 2.5 \pm 2.5$ Å), the **crumpled family** and the **loosely jointed family**. The latter two are rare in biological systems and will not be described further.

The most common homoglycans are the plant cell wall polysaccharide components **cellulose** (($1 \rightarrow 4$)-β-D-glucan) (approximately 5000 residues) and **mannan** (($1 \rightarrow 4$)-β-D-mannan), the starch component **amylose** (($1 \rightarrow 4$)-α-D-glucan) (1000–2000 residues) and the insect skeletal polysaccharide **chitin** (($1 \rightarrow 4$)-β-D-2-N-acetylamido-2-deoxyglucan). In the case of natural cellulose (**cellulose I**), flat ribbons will align parallel with respect to each other and form sheets stabilised through extensive inter-ribbon hydrogen bond networks that are somewhat analogous to the β-sheet structures of proteins. These sheets can further pack in a parallel, staggered fashion giving the appearance of a periodic polysaccharide tertiary/quaternary structure (Figure 1.48). In the main natural form of chitin (β-**chitin**), flat ribbons similarly organise into parallel, hydrogen bonded sheets that further pack in a parallel, staggered fashion resulting in a similar periodic tertiary/quaternary structure to that observed with natural cellulose (Figure 1.48). Sheets can also pack antiparallel, giving rise to α-**chitin**, or in a mixed parallel/antiparallel fashion, giving rise to what is known as γ-**chitin**. All three forms of chitin are known in biological systems. Mannan too prefers to form flat ribbons that assemble into sheets. By contrast, amylose forms into a variety of hollow helix

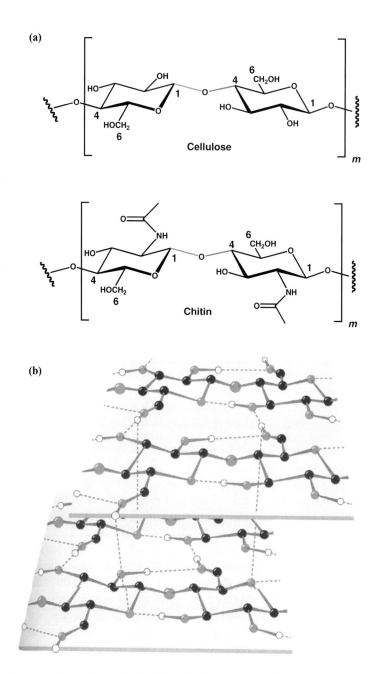

Figure 1.48 Repeat unit structures (**a**) of **cellulose** (primary structural component of plant cell walls) and **chitin** (principal structural component of exoskeletons of invertebrates; crustaceans, insects and spiders: major component of fungal and algal cell walls); (**b**) cartoon showing how cellulose chains in **ribbon conformations** interact to form hydrogen bonded **sheets**. These sheets (secondary structure) are then packed in a staggered arrangement (**Cellulose I**) to maximise stabilising hydrogen bond contacts between sheets (tertiary structure). Colour code, carbon (**black**), oxygen (**red**) and hydrogen (**white**). In Cellulose, sheets are always in parallel alignment. Chitin adopts very similar layered sheet structures but sheets may be in parallel alignment (similar to **b** above) (β-chitin), or antiparallel (α-chitin) (illustration from Voet, Voet & Pratt, 1999 [Wiley], Fig. 8-9).

a)

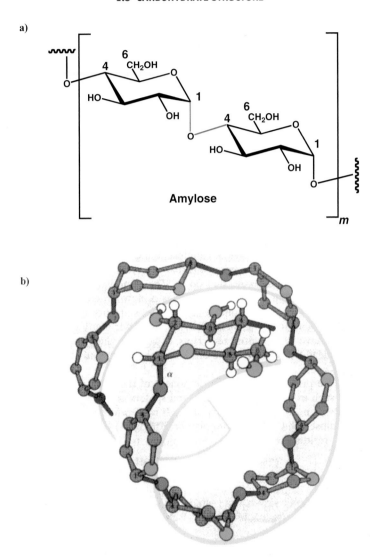

Amylose

b)

Figure 1.49 Repeat unit structure (**a**) of **amylose** (primary storage form of glucose in cells); (**b**) cartoon showing how amylose chains exist in a **hollow helix** (**V-form**) (secondary structure) conformation in the presence and inclusion of a guest molecule such as polyiodide. Such helices become destabilised in the absence of a guest molecule and combine to form double hollow helix structures (**A-form**) as illustrated (see **Fig. 1.50**). Colour code, carbon (**black**), oxygen (**red**) and hydrogen (**white**) (illustration from Voet, Voet & Pratt, 1999 [Wiley], Fig. 8-10).

secondary structures, of which the best known is the **V form**, which is a highly compressed form of left-handed hollow helix stabilised by enclosure of small molecules with amphiphilic characteristics such as phenols or polyiodide (Figure 1.49). Otherwise, in the absence of such guest molecules or complexation agents, natural amylose apparently prefers to reside in the form of a left-handed double hollow helix structure known as the **A form**.

Heteroglycans are usually complex sequences of pentoses, hexoses, 6-deoxyhexoses, hexuronic acids and hexosamines (2-amino-2-deoxy hexoses), which may also be derivatised as sulphates, acetates or methyl ethers at appropriate hydroxyl groups, as well as cyclised. Regular heteroglycans like the homoglycans mentioned above can be notably effective at secondary and even tertiary/quaternary structure formation. Two important examples of such heteroglycans are **carrageenan** and **agarose**, which both coat the outer surfaces of marine red algae for protection and for the facilitation of metabolite transfer between cells. Both are able to generate A-form helices stabilised by inter-residue hydrogen bonds involving the hydroxyl groups of neighbouring monosaccharide glycosyl residues (Figure 1.50). The ability

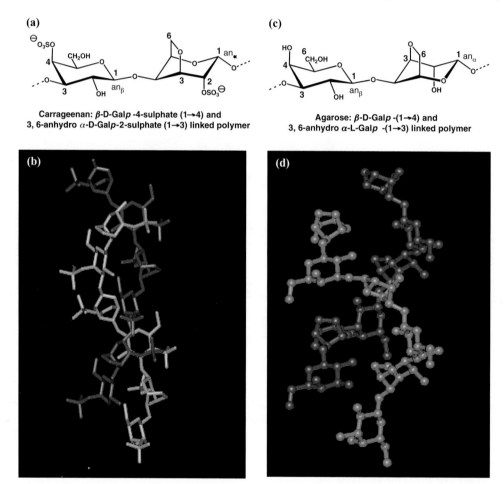

Figure 1.50 Structures of two main **polysaccharides** with ordered secondary structures (**hollow helices, A-form**). **Carrageenan** has the repeat unit structure shown (**a**) and double extended hollow helical secondary structure (**b**) with both separate strands rendered in the **stick bond representation** (**yellow** and **red**) (pdb: **1car**). **Agarose** has the alternative repeat structure shown (**c**) and double extended hollow helical secondary structure (**d**) with both separate strands rendered in the **ball and stick representation** (**green** and **red**) (pdb: **1aga**).

to form such double helical secondary structures is the reason that carrageenan and agarose polysaccharides are then able to form gels. Left-handed double hollow helix structures generated from different polysaccharide chains link different polysaccharide chains together, creating three dimensional non-periodic networks of interlinked polysaccharide chains that are resistant to fluid flow and hence have gel behaviour. In effect, both carrageenan and agarose exhibit not only secondary structure forming characteristics but also non-periodic tertiary/quaternary structure forming characteristics as well!

1.4 Nucleic acid structure

As noted in Section 1.1, there are two basic types of nucleic acid found in cells, namely deoxyribonucleic acid (DNA) and ribonucleic acid (RNA). DNA represents the ultimate long term storage form of genetic information because of its greater apparent chemical stability compared with RNA. RNA, in the guise of **messenger RNA (mRNA)**, **transfer RNA (tRNA)** and **ribosomal RNA (rRNA)**, plays an intermediary role in processing the genetic information locked away in DNA structures into physical reality in the form of the polypeptides/proteins that give individual cells both form and function. The precise interrelationships between DNA, rRNA, tRNA and mRNA will be looked at briefly later on in this section, but for now let us press on with structure!

1.4.1 Primary structures of DNA and RNA

DNA is a mixed polymer made up respectively of **2′-deoxyribonucleotide** (or **deoxynucleotide**) building blocks. Only a single set of four monomeric deoxynucleotide building blocks go to make up all DNA in every cell of every organism. This amazingly small set of building blocks is all that it takes to store the genetic information of all organisms! These deoxynucleotides are composed of **2′-deoxy-β-D-ribofuranose**, linked via an **N-β-D-glycosidic linkage** (originating at anomeric carbon atom C-1′) to a nitrogen heterocyclic **base**, and phosphorylated on carbon atom C-5′ (Figure 1.51). The base may be either a bicyclic purine **adenine** or **guanine**, or a monocyclic pyrimidine **cytosine** or **thymine** (Figure 1.52). The combination of 2′-deoxy-β-D-ribofuranose and N-linked base alone is known as a **2′-deoxyribonucleoside** (or **deoxynucleoside**) (**dN**); the four DNA deoxynucleosides are

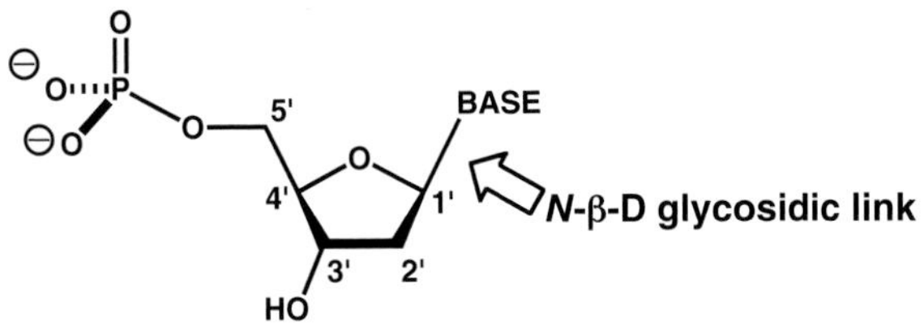

Figure 1.51 Basic structure of **2′-deoxyribonucleotide** (or **deoxynucleotide**)

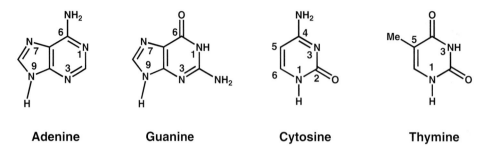

Adenine   **Guanine**   **Cytosine**   **Thymine**

Figure 1.52   Structures of bicyclic **purine** and **pyrimidine** bases found in DNA

known as **2′-deoxyadenosine (dA), 2′-deoxyguanosine (dG), 2′-deoxycytidine (dC)** and **2′-deoxythymidine (dT)** (Figure 1.53). Hence, the principal deoxynucleotide building blocks from which DNA is constructed are known as **2′-deoxyadenosine 5′-monophosphate (dpA)**, **2′-deoxyguanosine 5′-monophosphate (dpG), 2′-deoxycytidine 5′-monophosphate (dpC)** and **2′-deoxythymidine 5′-monophosphate (dpT)** (Figure 1.54).

   RNA is similarly a mixed polymer constructed substantially from **ribonucleotide (or nucleotide)** building blocks that are very similar to the four monomeric deoxynucleotide building blocks of DNA, the major difference being that β-D-ribofuranose is used in place of 2′-deoxy-β-D-ribofuranose (Figure 1.55). In addition, RNA molecules are frequently

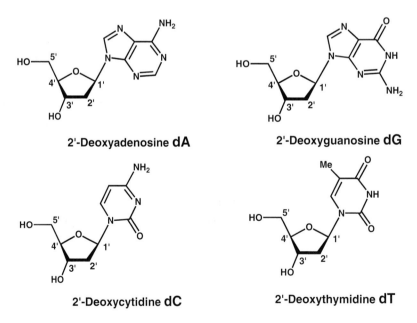

Figure 1.53   Structure of four **DNA 2′-deoxyribonucleosides** (or **deoxynucleosides**)

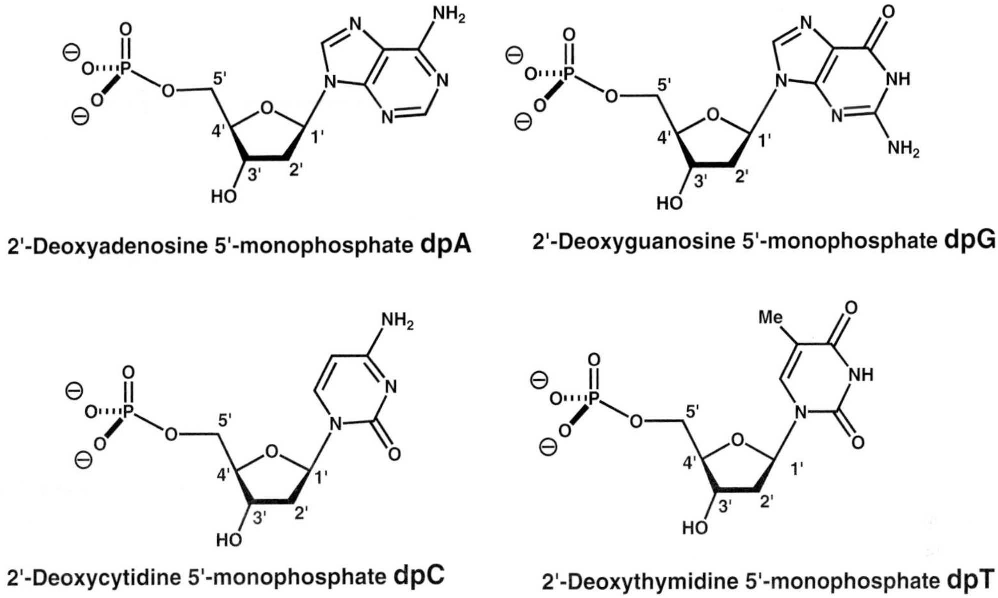

Figure 1.54 Structure of four **DNA 2′-deoxyribonucleoside 5′-monophosphates** (2′-deoxyribonucleotide or **deoxynucleotides**).

constructed from an expanded set of nucleotide building blocks. By analogy to DNA, RNA is constructed from four central nucleotide building blocks, namely **adenosine 5′-monophosphate (pA)**, **guanosine 5′-monophosphate (pG)**, **cytidine 5′-monophosphate (pC)** and **uridine 5′-monophosphate (pU)** (Figure 1.56), but this set is also often supplemented by alternative nucleotide building blocks such as **thymidine 5′-monophosphate (pT)**, **1-methyladenosine 5′-monophosphate (pm^{1}A)**, **7-methyl-guanosine 5′-monophosphate (pm^{7}G)**, **N^2-dimethyl guanosine 5′-monophosphate (pdm^{2}G)**, **5-methylcytidine 5′-monophosphate (pm^{5}C)** and even **pseudouridine 5′-monophosphate (pΨ)** (Figure 1.57). The expanded set of nucleotide building blocks used to construct RNA has a significant impact upon the structural diversity of RNA molecules in comparison to DNA.

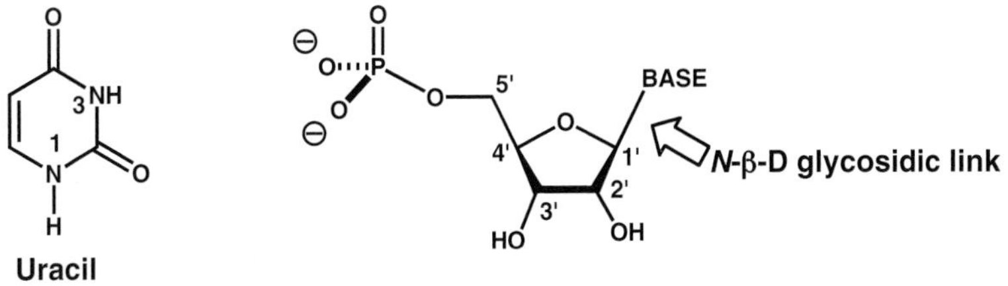

Figure 1.55 Basic structure of **ribonucleotide** (or **nucleotide**) and RNA specific pyrimidine base **uracil**.

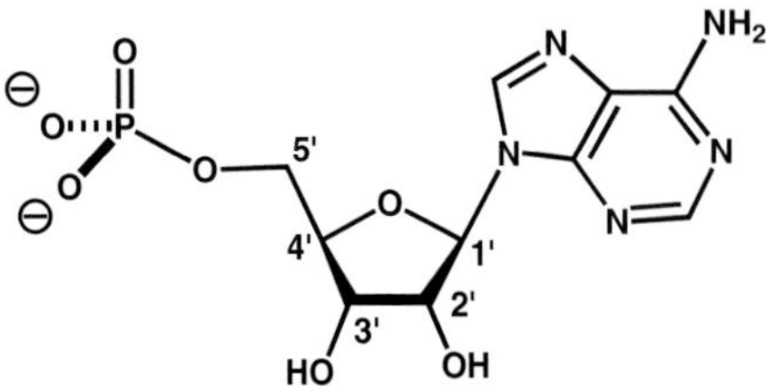

Adenosine 5'-monophosphate pA

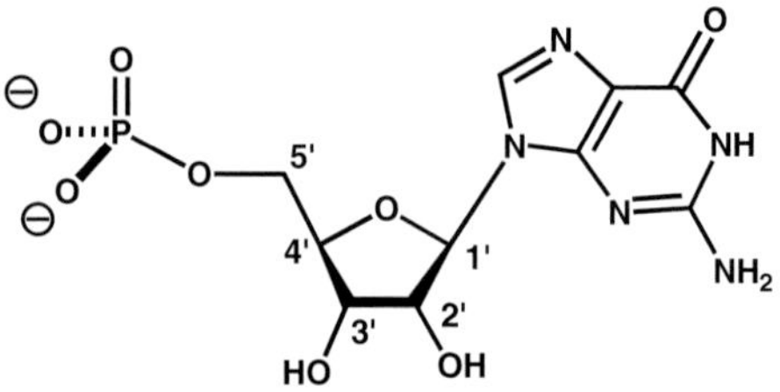

Guanosine 5'-monophosphate pG

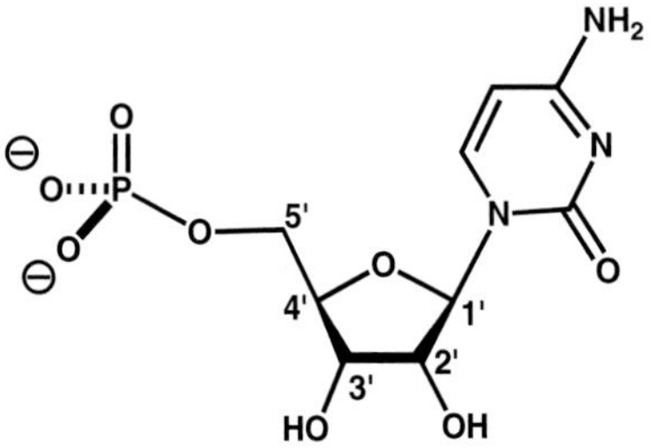

Cytidine 5'-monophosphate pC

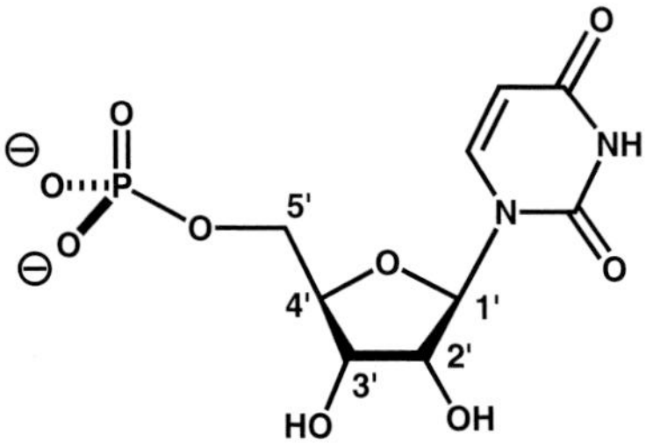

Uridine 5'-monophosphate pU

Figure 1.56 Structure of four main **RNA ribonucleoside 5′-monophosphates (ribonucleotides** or **nucleotides**).

1.4.2 Phosphodiester link

The deoxynucleotide building blocks of DNA are joined together by **phosphodiester links** (Figure 1.58). Unbranched chains of deoxynucleotide units are formed with ease. A short chain (2–20 units) is known as an **oligodeoxynucleotide** whilst a long chain (upwards of 20 units) is called a **polydeoxynucleotide.** Each constituent deoxynucleotide unit of DNA is usually called a **deoxynucleotide residue.** The same phosphodiester link also appears in RNA to generate equivalent unbranched chains of nucleotide units, known individually as **nucleotide residues.** By analogy to DNA, a short chain of RNA (2–20 units) is known as an **oligonucleotide** whilst a long chain of RNA (upwards of 20 units) is called a **polynucleotide.**

In DNA and RNA, the chain of phosphodiester links and sugar rings is known as the **phosphodiester backbone**; the bases may be regarded in both cases almost as 'side-chains'. By convention, DNA or RNA chains begin at the 5′-end (i.e., where carbon atom C-5′ of the terminal residue is not involved in a phosphodiester link) and terminate at the 3′-end (where carbon atom C-3′ is not involved in a phosphodiester link). Each chain is therefore said to run by convention from 5′ to 3′ (5′→3′). Several shorthand conventions are used to describe the sequences of deoxynucleotide or nucleotide residues in DNA and RNA respectively. These include the Fischer, linear alphabetic and condensed alphabetic conventions that draw upon the letter codes for bases and deoxynucleosides or nucleosides as described previously (Figure 1.59).

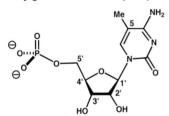

Thymidine 5'-monophosphate pT

1-Methyladenosine 5'-monophosphate pm^{1}A

7-Methylguanosine 5'-monophosphate pm^{7}G

2-*N,N*-Dimethylguanosine 5'-monophosphate pm$^2_2$G

5-Methylcytidine 5'-monophosphate pm^{5}C

Pseudouridine 5'-monophosphate pΨ

Figure 1.57 Structure of unusual **ribonucleoside 5'-monophosphates (ribonucleotides** or **nucleotides)** found in RNA.

The phosphodiester link in DNA and RNA has some characteristics in common with the peptide link. Like the peptide link, the phosphodiester link shows considerable conformational rigidity. The link may be thought of as consisting of two atomic segments C$^{4'}$—C$^{3'}$—O$^{3'}$—P (blue) and P—O$^{5'}$—C$^{5'}$—C$^{4'}$ (red) (Figure 1.60). Each segment acts as a rigid, coplanar unit that behaves as a single bond. The phosphodiester link therefore consists in effect of two virtual bonds that pivot about phosphorus. The spatial relationship between the virtual bonds that make up each phosphodiester link are defined by conformational angles ζ and α, which are the main dihedral angles about the O$^{3'}$—P and P—O$^{5'}$ bonds respectively. Both angles ζ and α are approximately $+300°$ ($-60°$) under most circumstances, causing the phosphodiester link to occupy a **gauche conformation** (Figures 1.61 and 1.62). Favourable anti-periplanar interactions of oxygen atom O-3' lone pairs with the P—O$^{5'}$ bond matched by a similar interaction of oxygen atom O-5' lone pairs with the P—O$^{3'}$ bond are thought to promote this conformation. In addition, the conformational preference for all deoxynucleotide (and nucleotide) residues to adopt the synclinal (**+sc**) conformation in preference to the main anti-periplanar (**ap**) alternative helps to 'fix' conformational properties further in DNA and RNA (Figure 1.63).

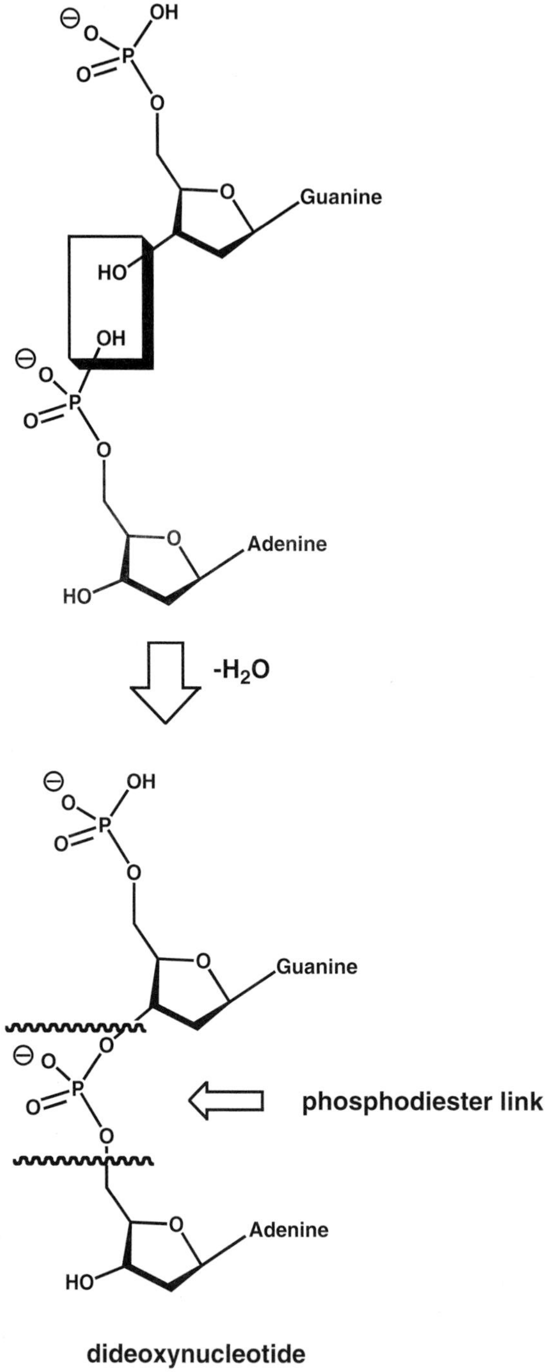

Figure 1.58 Schematic illustration of formation of **phosphodiester** link from deoxynucleotides for generation of DNA. Identical link can be formed from nucleotides for the generation of RNA.

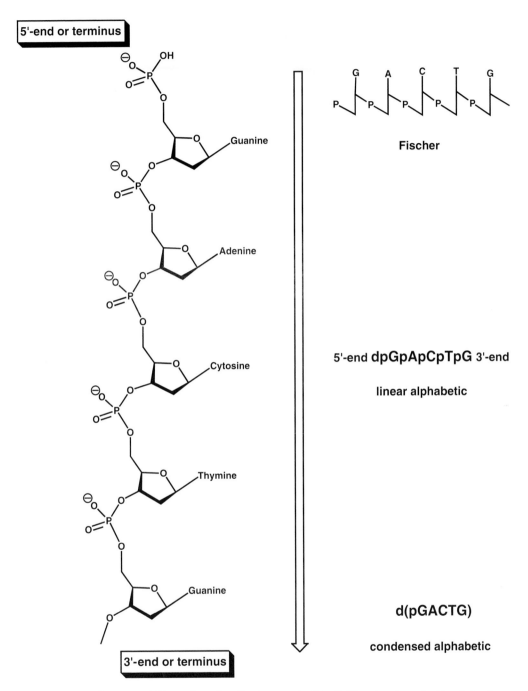

Figure 1.59 Full structural illustration of a oligodeoxynucleotide (left) and various shorthand structures (right) commonly used to define oligo-polydeoxynucleotide structures simply. Similar short hand structures exist for oligo-polynucleotide structures except that "**d**" for "deoxy" is dispensed with.

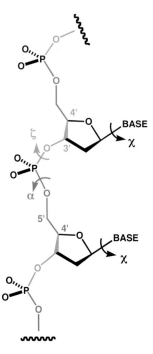

Figure 1.60 Illustration of **oligo-polydeoxynucleotide** chain section highlighting the two atomic segments $C^{4'}$—$C^{3'}$—$O^{3'}$—P (light blue) and P—$O^{5'}$—$C^{5'}$—$C^{4'}$ (red). Each segment acts as a rigid, coplanar unit, hence behaves as a **virtual bond** pivoting at phosphate. Key dihedral angles involved that characterise conformation are ζ a, the angle subtended about the $O^{3'}$—P bond and α, the angle subtended about the P—$O^{5'}$ bond. The same arguments apply in oligo-polynucleotide chains too.

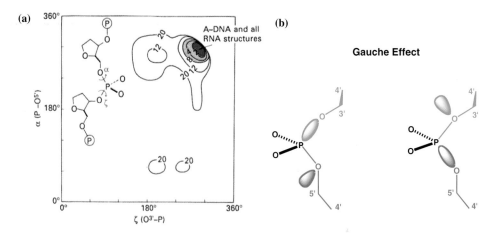

Figure 1.61 Conformational freedom is heavily restricted in nucleic acids owing to lack of free rotation about $O^{3'}$—P and P—$O^{5'}$ bonds. (**a**) **Nucleic acid equivalent of the Ramachandran plot** illustrating the theoretically allowed angles of ζ and α. (**b**) Free rotation is primarily damped owing to the gauche effect in which lone-pair-σ^* orbital overlaps in phosphodiester links generate double bond character in O—P bonds that restrict free rotation (adapted from Govil, 1976 [Wiley]).

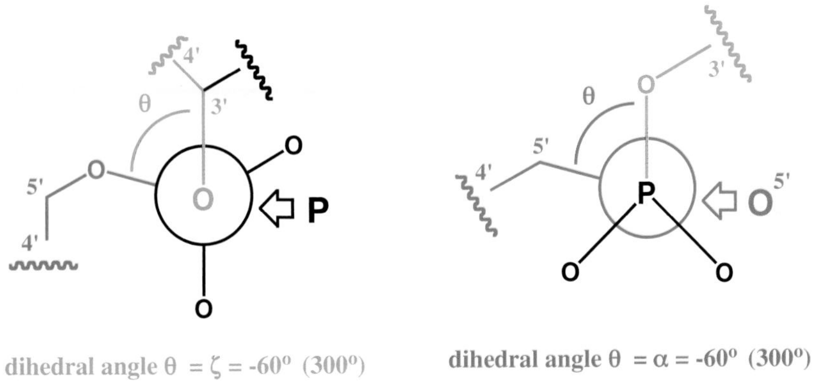

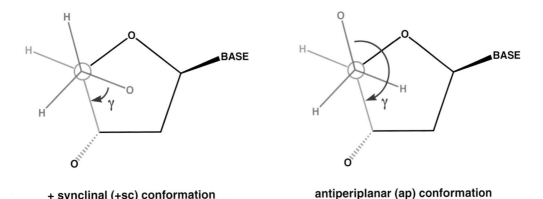

dihedral angle θ = ζ = -60° (300°)   dihedral angle θ = α = -60° (300°)

Figure 1.62 Newman projections of to show the dihedral angles subtended about the $O^{3'}$—P and P—$O^{5'}$ bonds (ζ and α respectively) in order to demonstrate how highly regular dihedral angles set up a highly extended phosphodiester backbone conformation. Bonds are colour coded in the same way as **Figs. 1.60** & **1.61**.

1.4.3 Secondary structure of DNA

This is where we meet the famous double helix immortalised by many books, articles, television programmes and of course films. The DNA **double helix** is the key element of DNA three dimensional structure. In the 1950s, when James Watson and Francis Crick first proposed the double helix as the key piece of DNA three dimensional structure, they generated enormous scientific and popular excitement, since for the first time the inheritance of genetic information could be understood explicitly in terms of a real chemical structure! In order to appreciate this structure, there is a requirement to understand more about the heterocyclic bases (see Section 1.4.1) and their unrivalled capacity for specific hydrogen bonding. All these bases are aromatic but paradoxically prefer keto/amine to enol/imine tautomeric forms

+ synclinal (+sc) conformation   antiperiplanar (ap) conformation

Figure 1.63 Illustration of conformational preferences of the conformational angle γ subtended about the $C^{4'}$—$C^{5'}$ bond. Each deoxynucleotide (or nucleotide) residue adopts either a +**sc** or **ap** conformation. The former is usually preferred but for exceptional circumstances.

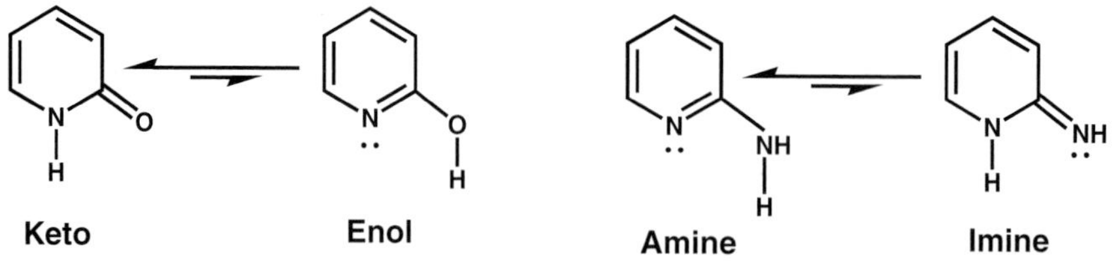

Figure 1.64   Illustration of the **keto-enol** and **amine-imine** tautomeric equilibria

(Figure 1.64). The four bases found in DNA show a remarkable pairwise complementarity with respect to each other. Guanine is able to supply two hydrogen bond donor groups and one acceptor group to complement the two hydrogen bond acceptor groups and one donor group of cytosine, while adenine is able to supply one hydrogen bond donor and one acceptor group to complement the single hydrogen bond acceptor and one donor group of thymine (Figure 1.65). Complementary hydrogen bonding gives rise to the specific **Watson–Crick base pairings, dG.dC** and **dA.dT**, which also show a remarkable **isomorphous geometry** (Figure 1.66). These pairings are not unique and there can be an impressive number of alternatives (Figures 1.67 and 1.68), but they dominate owing to preferable interactions and relative geometries.

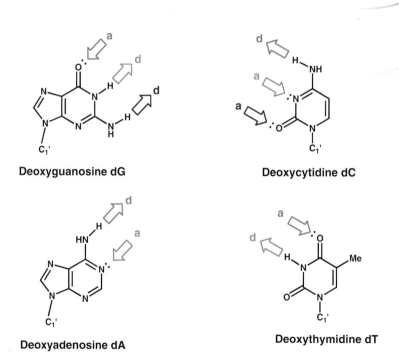

Figure 1.65   Illustration of the matched hydrogen-bond **accept**or (**a**) and **donor** (**d**) relationships that exist between the bases of deoxyadenosine & deoxythymidine, and the bases of deoxyguanosine & deoxycytidine.

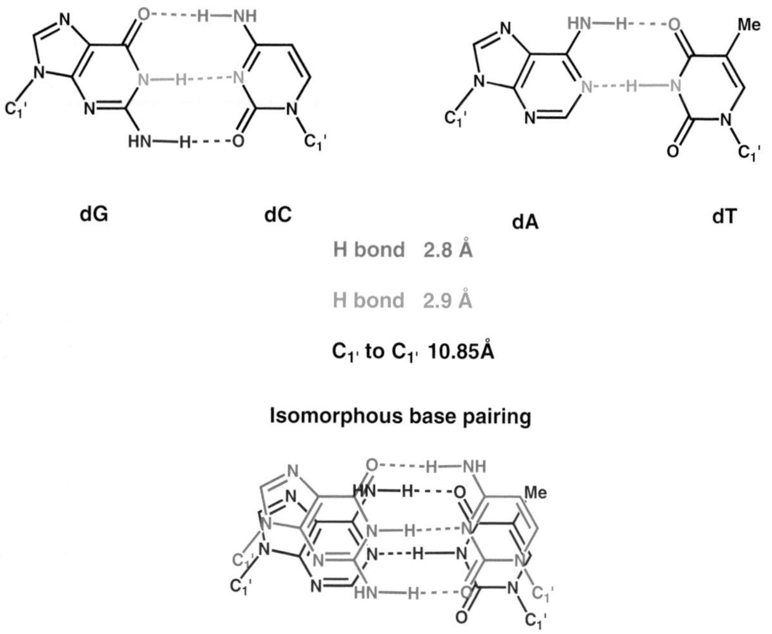

dG   dC   dA   dT

H bond   2.8 Å

H bond   2.9 Å

C$_{1'}$ to C$_{1'}$ 10.85Å

Isomorphous base pairing

Figure 1.66 Illustrations of the **specific Watson-Crick base pairings, dG.dC** and **dA.dT** involving complementary deoxynucleoside residues. Overlay structure provides visual demonstration of the **dG.dC/dA.dT isomorphous geometry**.

The chemical biology reader should also be aware that the natural conformational preference of a given polydeoxynucleotide chain (see Section 1.4.2) is to exist in an extended conformation with heterocyclic bases presented in an **anti** conformation projecting away from the attached 2'-deoxy-β-D-ribofuranose ring (Figure 1.54), in preference to the **syn** conformation. In the anti conformation specific Watson–Crick base pairings between bases in two independent polydeoxynucleotide chains can be achieved with ease. The optimal arrangement for hydrogen bonding between two independent polydeoxynucleotide chains is for each chain to align antiparallel with respect to the other (i.e., one chain is orientated in the 5'→3' direction and the other in the 3'→5' direction) and for the two chains to coil around each other in such a way that the backbone of each chain forms a right-handed helix. However, this arrangement is inherently unstable, given the high charge of the phosphodiester backbone, unless every deoxynucleotide residue in one polydeoxynucleotide chain is able to enter into a specific Watson–Crick base pairing arrangement with a deoxynucleotide residue in the other polydeoxynucleotide chain, thereby 'cementing' the chains together by a series of specific inter-chain **base pair** (**bp**) hydrogen bond interactions. In other words, both polydeoxynucleotide chains must be completely **complementary** to each other in terms of their capacity to form complete Watson–Crick base pairings, otherwise the structure will not be stable. The need for such complete base pairing also ensures that both polydeoxynucleotide chains are completely complementary to each other in terms of their deoxynucleotide residue sequence and base composition as well. In these specific Watson–Crick base pairings lie the

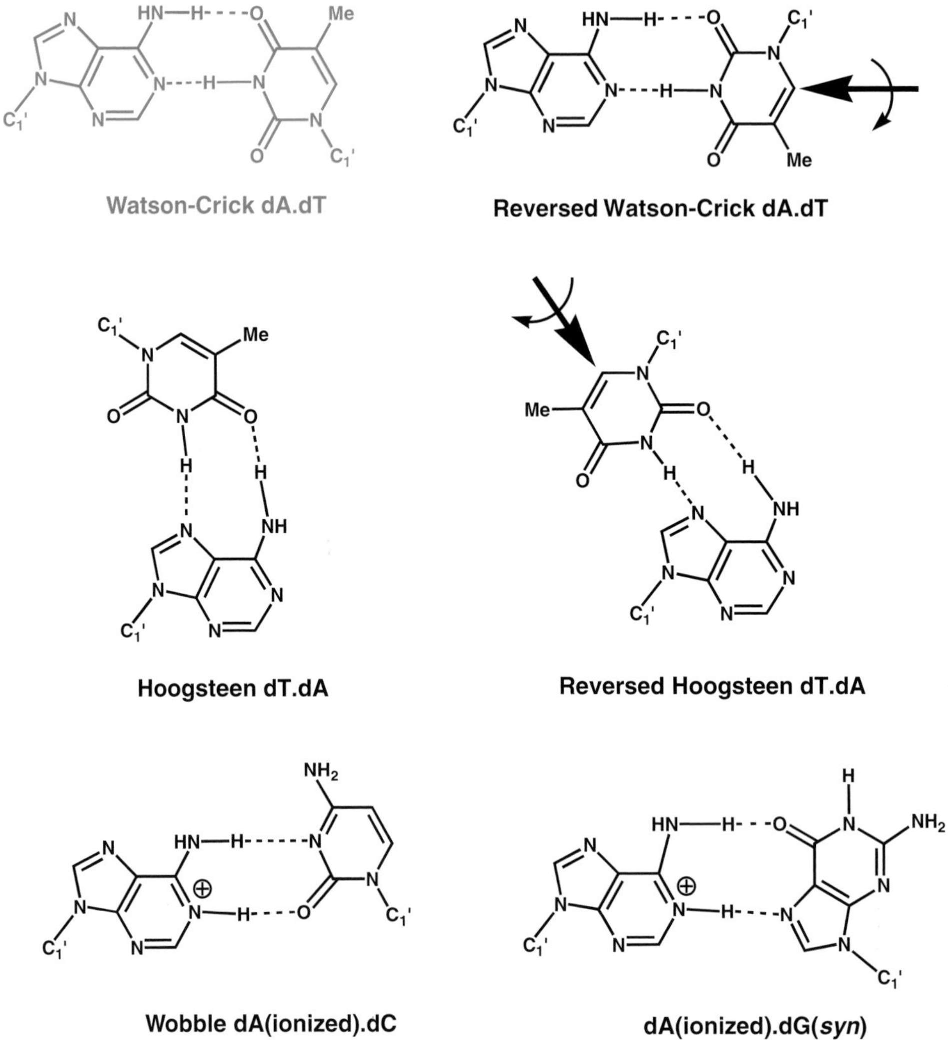

Figure 1.67 Structures of **non-Watson-Crick base pairings** involving deoxyadenosine. Original **dA.dT** Watson-Crick base pairing is shown (**red, top left**) for comparison.

foundations of the genetic code and the inheritance of genetic information (see Section 1.4.6). Nevertheless, even given these strict requirements, there is a significant amount of plasticity in the DNA double helix structure that may be essential for a variety of important biological reasons. This means that there can be a number of DNA double helical subtypes. Note that complete Watson–Crick base pairing also creates the possibility for extended $\pi-\pi$ **stacking interactions** between sequential base pairs. Such weak covalent interactions doubtless contribute significantly towards DNA double helix stability in addition to Watson–Crick base pair hydrogen bonds.

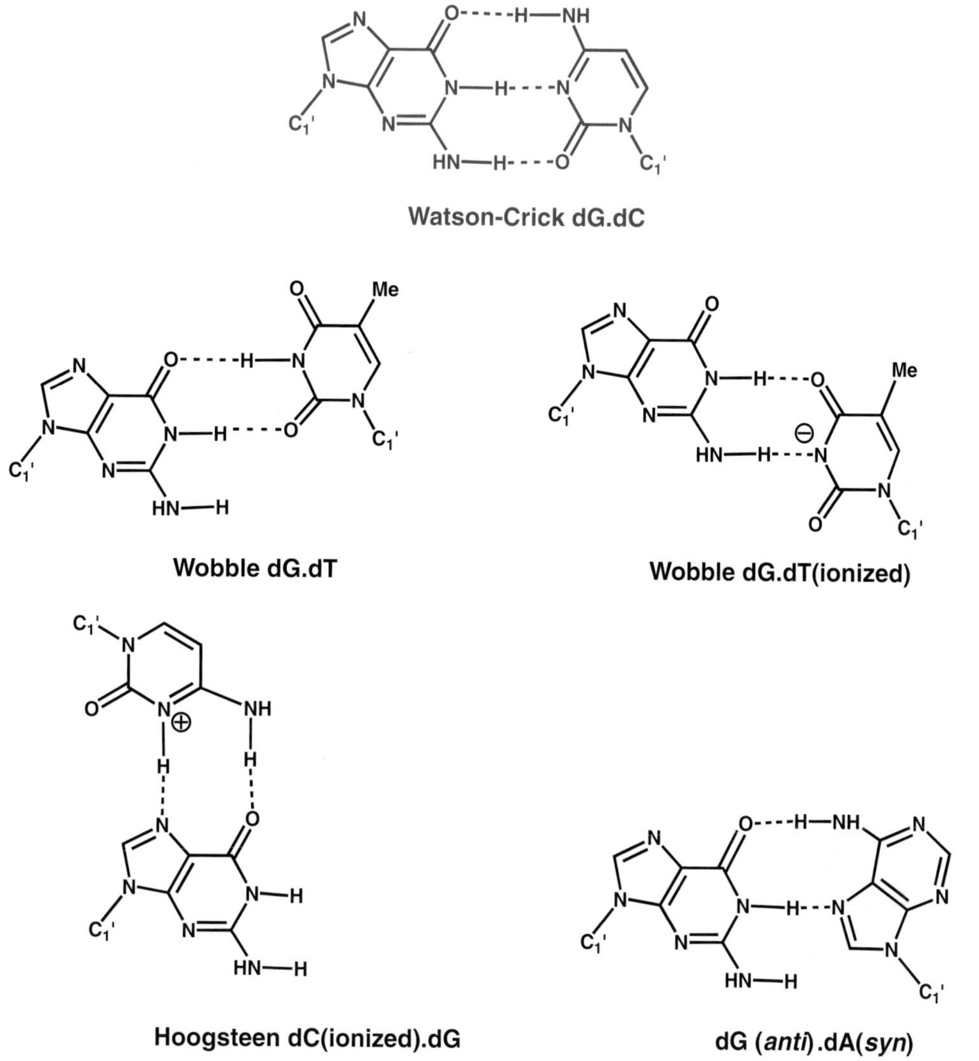

Watson-Crick dG.dC

Wobble dG.dT

Wobble dG.dT(ionized)

Hoogsteen dC(ionized).dG

dG (*anti*).dA(*syn*)

Figure 1.68 Structures of **non-Watson-Crick base pairings** involving the guanine base of deoxyguanosine. Original **dG.dC** Watson-Crick base pairing is shown (**blue, top**) for comparison.

1.4.3.1   B-form DNA

B-form DNA is the most common form of DNA in solution and is much the most important biologically speaking. The double helical conformation of B-form DNA also conforms most closely with the original model structure for DNA devised by Watson and Crick. The main architectural features of the B-form DNA double helix are illustrated using **ribbon display**, **ring display** and **ladder display structures** (Figure 1.69 and 1.70). Backbones are shown as

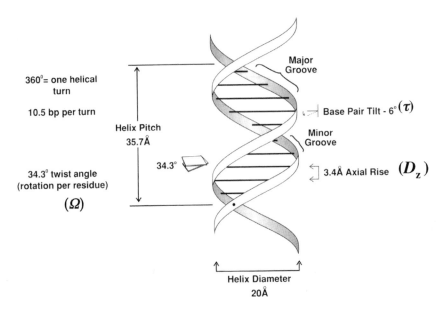

Figure 1.69   Ribbon Display to show the main structural features of **B-form DNA** with ideal dimensions and angles (illustration from Sinden, 1994, Fig. 1.12).

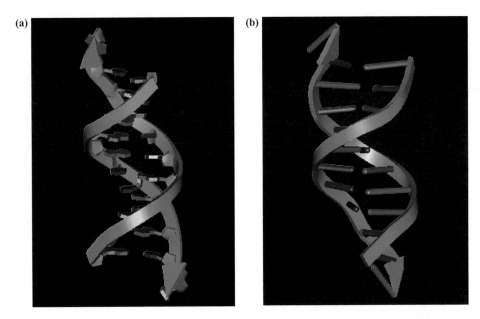

Figure 1.70   Two depictions of **B-form DNA**. (pdb: **1bna**) (**a**) **Rings Display** in which the anti-parallel phosphodiester backbones are shown as arrowed ribbons (**green**); ribose rings (**green**), purine bases (**red**) and pyrimidine (**blue**) bases are shown in structural outline. (**b**) **Ladder Display** in which the anti-parallel phosphodiester backbones are shown as arrowed ribbons (**green**); ribose rings are omitted; purine (**red**) and pyrimidine (**blue**) bases are shown as rods.

Table 1.2 Summary of all the main differences between B-, A- and Z-form DNA in terms of dimensions, angles and conformations.

Parameter	A-DNA	B-DNA	Z-DNA
Helix Sense	Right	Right	Left
Residue per turn	11	10 (10.5)	12
Axial Rise (Å)	2.55	3.4	3.7
Helix Pitch (Å)	28	34	45
Base Pair Tilt (Å)	20	−6	7
Rotation per residue (Å)	33	36 (34.3)	−30
Diameter of Helix (Å)	23	20	18
Glycosidic bond			
dA, dT, dC	*anti*	*anti*	*anti*
dG	*anti*	*anti*	*syn*
Sugar Pucker			
dA, dT, dC	C3′ endo	C2′ endo	C2′ endo
dG	C3′ endo	C2′ endo	C3′ endo
Phosphate-Phosphate (Å)			
dA, dT, dC	5.9	7.0	7.0
dG	5.9	7.0	5.9

ribbons and inter-chain interacting base pairs as either rings or rods perpendicular to the helical axis. There are two structural grooves that corkscrew along the length of the double helix, the wider of which is called the **major groove** and the narrower the **minor groove** (Figure 1.69). The helix and base pair parameters of B-form DNA are also summarised (Table 1.2). The helix sense of B-form DNA is right handed, there are 11.5 base pair residues per turn, and the 2′-deoxy-β-D-ribofuranose rings do not adopt the characteristic envelope conformation of furanose rings, but instead exist in a **C$^{2'}$-endo** twist conformation (Figure 1.71).

In the original model structure for DNA devised by Watson and Crick, base pairs are coplanar and base pair planes stack perpendicular to the main helix axis. In reality, whilst this is essentially true, there are always distortions away from such ideality. A number of parameters are frequently used as a guide to define these distortions. These parameters include a description of **helix sense**—whether right handed or left handed, **helix diameter** (in Å), **helix pitch** (**P**)—the length of one complete helical turn (in Å), the number of **residues per turn**, **axial** or **average rise** (D_z)—the distance between adjacent base pair planes (in Å), **base pair twist** or **helix rotation** (Ω)—the angle of rotation between adjacent base pair planes—and **base pair tilt** (τ)—the angle which a base pair plane makes relative to a line drawn perpendicular to the main helix axis (Figure 1.72). In addition, there are other base pair parameters that are used to describe more heavily distorted DNA. These are **base pair roll** (ρ)—the average angle that adjacent base pairs make relative to the main helical axis—and **base pair propeller twist** (ω)—the angle between the planes of the two paired bases of a base pair when the base pair is no longer coplanar (Figure 1.72).

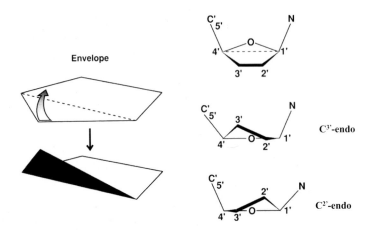

Figure 1.71   Main conformational preferences of 2′-deoxy-β-D-ribofuranose rings in polydeoxynucleotides (right). Cartoon illustration of these main envelope conformations (left) (illustrations from Sinden, 1994, Fig. 1.4).

1.4.3.2   A-form and Z-form DNA

Other than B-form DNA, there are other forms of DNA that are more distorted from Watson and Crick ideality. These include **A-form**, **C-form**, **D-form** and **T-form DNA**. Of these, **A-form DNA** is the most similar to B-form DNA (Figure 1.73). The only major difference is that the 2′-deoxy-β-D-ribofuranose rings of A-form DNA exist in an alternative **C³′-endo** twist conformation (Figures 1.71 and 1.73). Consequently, the helix diameter is wider and there are 11 base pair residues per turn (Table 1.2). A-form DNA also possesses shallow major and minor grooves. **Z-form DNA**, by contrast, is radically different from B-form

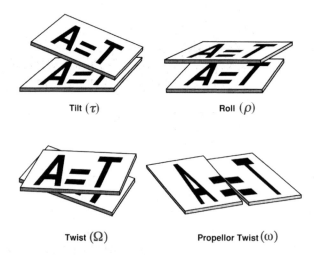

Figure 1.72   Cartoon illustrations of the main forms of base-pair (**bp**) flexibility that allows DNA structures to deviate from ideal dimensions and angles (illustrations from Sinden, 1994, Fig. 1.13).

(a)

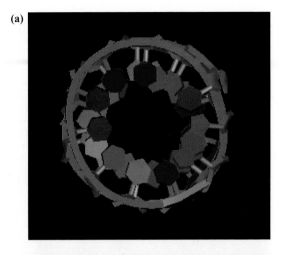

(b)

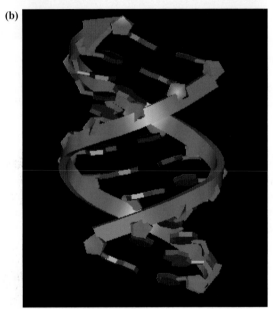

Figure 1.73 Depiction of **A-form DNA**. (pdb: **2d47**) (a) **Rings Display** (top view) in which the anti-parallel phosphodiester backbones are shown as arrowed ribbons (**green**); ribose rings (**green**), purine bases (**red**) and pyrimidine (**blue**);(b) **Rings** Display (side view).

DNA (Table 1.2) (Figure 1.74). The helix sense of Z-form DNA is now left handed and the backbones of the two poly deoxynucleotide chains map out a zigzag spiral path. This results from the tendency of deoxyguanosine nucleotide residues to distort so that their 2′-deoxy-β-D-ribofuranose rings adopt a C$^{3'}$-endo instead of C$^{2'}$-endo twist conformation (Figure 1.71). However, in addition, the guanine bases move to a *syn* conformation (positioned over the top of their attached furanose rings), instead of the more usual *anti* conformation

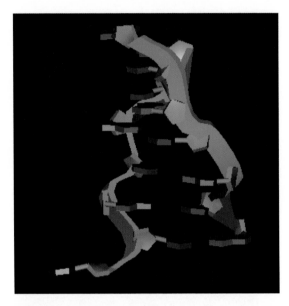

Figure 1.74 Depiction of **Z-form DNA**. (pdb: **331d**) using **Rings Display** (side view) in which the anti-parallel phosphodiester backbones are shown as arrowed ribbons (**green**); ribose rings (**green**), purine bases (**red**) and pyrimidine (**blue**). This side view demonstrates how the phosphodiester backbone now takes on a "zig-zag" appearance, hence the name of this DNA conformation. This double helix is now left-handed.

(Figure 1.75), and deoxyguanosine nucleotide residues also adjust to adopt an anti-periplanar (**ap**) conformation in preference to the more usual synclinal (**+sc**) conformation (Figure 1.63). A-form and Z-form DNA are not thought to be biologically important except as minor components of otherwise B-form DNA. However, both A-form and Z-form may help assist the formation of DNA supercoiling structures such as those illustrated (Figure 1.76).

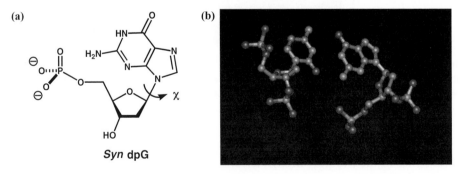

Figure 1.75 Z-form DNA results from wholesale conformational changes in deoxyguanosine nucleotide (**dpG**) residues. The more usual *anti*, **+sc**, **C2′ endo** nucleotide conformation gives way to a *syn*, **ap**, **C3′ endo** conformation. (**a**) Illustration of *syn* **dpG** conformation. (**b**) **Ball and stick** depiction of **pdG(***syn***, ap, C3′ endo).pdC** base pair as found in Z-form DNA.

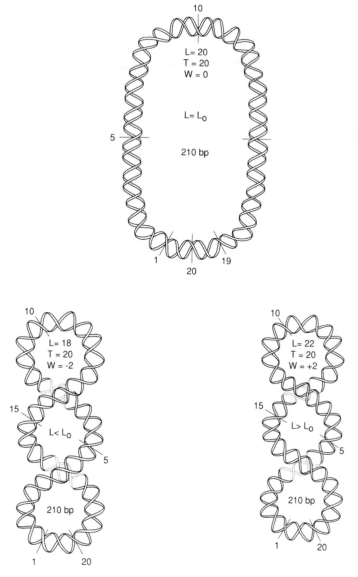

Figure 1.76 Schematic illustration of closed circular DNA in open conformation (**top**) and then in a **negative supercoiled** conformation (**bottom left**) and **positive supercoiled** conformation (**bottom right**). (illustration adapted from Sinden, 1994, Fig. 3.4).

1.4.4 Supercoiling and tertiary structures of DNA

DNA supercoiling provides conformational potential energy for DNA tertiary structure formation such as the development of **DNA cruciform structures** (Figure 1.77). Supercoiling also leads to the creation of **DNA triple helix** (**DNA triplex**) structures, which form when an oligodeoxynucleotide chain, with an appropriately complementary deoxynucleotide residue

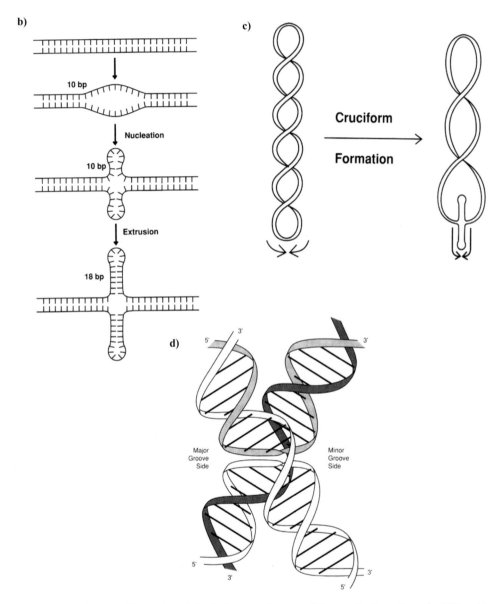

a)

Inverted Repeat

5' GGAATCGATCTTAAGATCGATTCC 3'
3' CCTTAGCTAGAATTCTAGCTAAGG 5'

b)

10 bp

Nucleation

10 bp

Extrusion

18 bp

c)

Cruciform

Formation

d)

5'   3'   3'

Major
Groove
Side

Minor
Groove
Side

5'
3'   3'
5'

Figure 1.77 Schematic illustration of the **influence of supercoiling** on the formation of additional tertiary structure elements in closed circular DNA. **(a)** Double helical deoxynucleotide **palindrome sequence** (**inverted repeat**) that is a necessary prerequisite for **cruciform** formation; **(b)** schematic diagram to show cruciform formation under conformational pressure of supercoiling as shown in **(c)**; **(d)** more detailed **ribbon cartoon** to illustrate how phosphodiester backbones are "shared" at the cruciform junction (illustrations adapted from Sinden, 1994, Figs. 4.1, 4.3, 4.5 and 4.17 respectively).

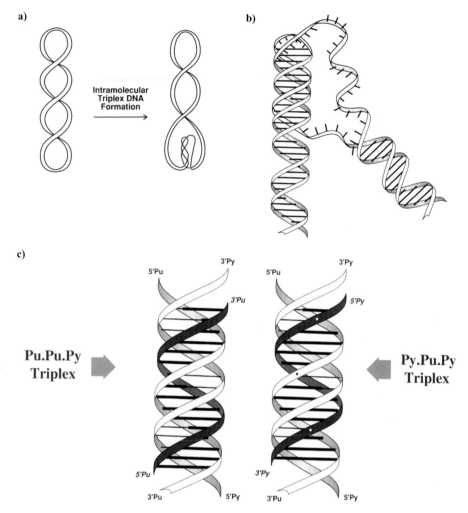

Figure 1.78 Schematic illustration of the **influence of supercoiling** on the formation of **triplex DNA** tertiary structure elements in closed circular DNA. **(a)** Schematic diagram to show triplex formation under conformational pressure of supercoiling; **(b)** **ribbon cartoon** to show how triplex DNA forms after local DNA strand separation occurs ; **(c)** more **detailed ribbon cartoon** to illustrate DNA phosphodiester backbone arrangements in two main types of triplex DNA. In both cases triplex is formed when a short, liberated oligodeoxynucleotide chain with the appropriate complementary deoxynucleotide sequence inserts into the major groove of B-form DNA. These triplex types are named after the triplex base pairs involved in their formation and stabilisation (**Fig. 1.79**) (illustrations adapted from Sinden, 1994, Figs. 6.6, 6.4 and 6.1 respectively).

sequence, becomes associated with the major groove of a B-form DNA double helix. This is shown using a ribbon display structure (Figure 1.78). Since Watson–Crick base pairings are already involved within the double helix, some alternative base pairings are needed to bind the oligodeoxynucleotide chain. These are known as **tertiary base pairings** or **Hoogsteen structures**. There are four basic stable Hoogsteen structures involved, which by convention

(a)

Py.Pu.Py triplex base pairs

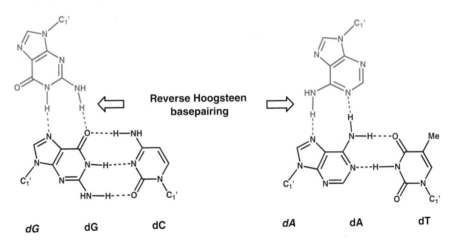

Hoogsteen/Watson-Crick triplex base pairs

(b)

Pu.Pu.Py triplex base pairs

Reverse Hoogsteen/Watson-Crick triplex base pairs

Figure 1.79   Illustration of triplex base pairs that enable triplex DNA to form. **(a) Pyrimidine: Purine:Pyrimidine (Py:Pu:Py) Hoogsteen/Watson-Crick triplex base pairs** that form between the indicated deoxynucleoside residues (see **Figs. 1.68 & 1.67**); **(b) Purine:Purine:Pyrimidine (Pu:Pu:Py) Reverse Hoogsteen/Watson-Crick triplex base pairs** that form between indicated deoxynucleoside residues.

are described as **dT.dA.dT**, **dC⁺.dG.dC**, **dA.dA.dT** and **dG.dG.dC** (Figure 1.79). The single letter codes in normal type correspond to normal Watson–Crick base pairings, the italic letter to the tertiary oligodeoxynucleotide base in each case. The formation of a moderately stable DNA triplex requires that all the bases of the oligodeoxynucleotide chain form correct tertiary base pairings with all the base pairs of the double helix where association is being made. In other words, the oligodeoxynucleotide chain must be complementary with the double helix base pairs with respect to the optimal tertiary base pairings. The existence of these DNA tertiary structures is now well established, but their biological utilities remain mysterious even today. Such tertiary structures may have important functions in the control of gene expression either in positive or negative ways, linking back to comments made in Section 1.1. Evidence remains to be gathered, but this subject is certain to remain of significant interest to chemical biology researchers for a significant time to come.

1.4.5 Secondary and tertiary structures of RNA

Within RNA, the Watson–Crick base pairing equivalents are **G.C** and **A.U** (Figure 1.80), isomorphous with the standard DNA Watson–Crick base pairings (Figure 1.66). The natural

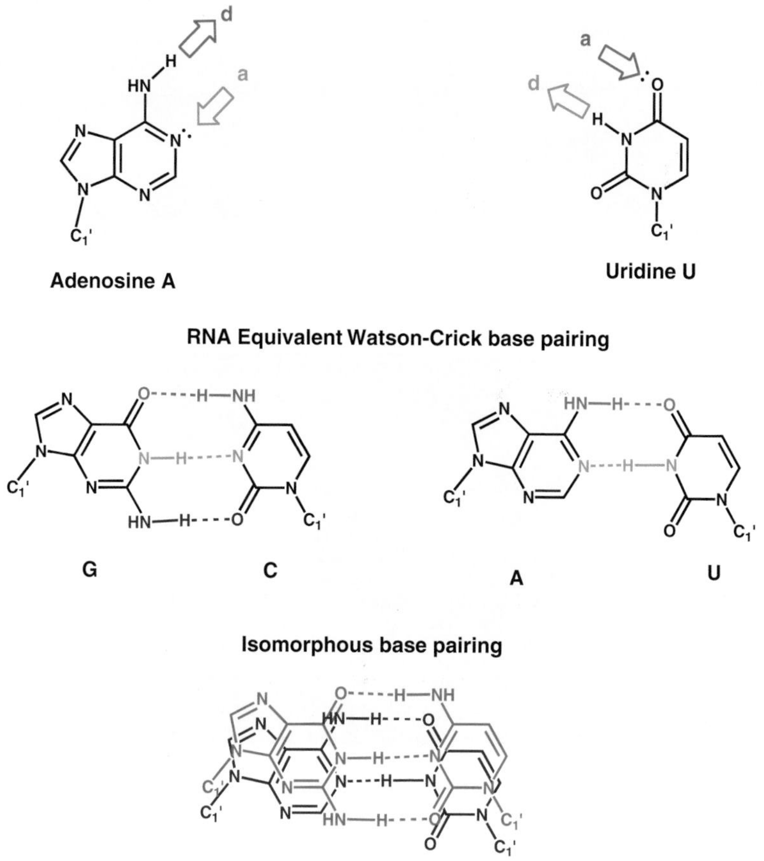

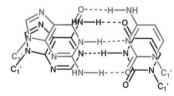

Adenosine A   **Uridine U**

RNA Equivalent Watson-Crick base pairing

G   C   A   U

Isomorphous base pairing

Figure 1.80   Illustrations of the **specific RNA equivalent Watson-Crick base pairings, G.C** and **A.U** involving complementary nucleoside residues. Overlay structure provides visual demonstration of the **G.C/A.U isomorphous geometry.**

conformational preferences of polynucleotide chains are also equivalent to those of poly-deoxynucleotide chains. Therefore, RNA may form double helical structures in the same way as DNA. However, owing to the presence of the $C^{2'}$-hydroxyl functional group in each β-D-ribofuranose ring, polynucleotide chains appear unable to generate sustained double helical structures, and appear able to form only fragmentary A-form or A′-form double helices comprising a few short turns (Table 1.2) (Figure 1.81). The RNA equivalent B-form double helix

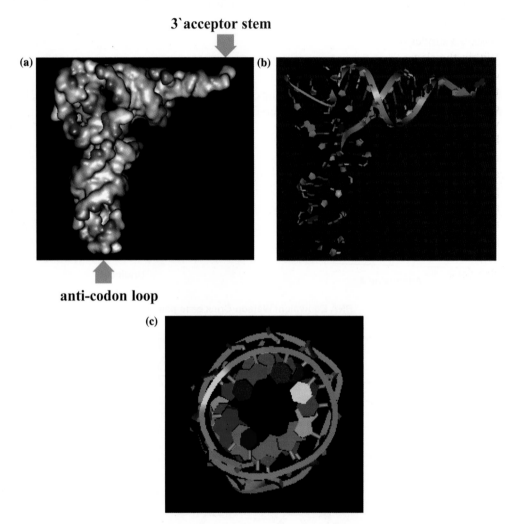

Figure 1.81   Two depictions of **transfer RNA (tRNA)** (pdb: **1tn2**). **(a) Surface Display** in which the Van der Waals surface of all atoms is shown and negative charge (**red areas**). This display clearly demonstrates the bent shape of the molecule; **(b) Rings Display** in which phosphodiester backbone is shown as an arrowed ribbon (**green/black**); ribose rings (**green**), purine bases (**red**) and pyrimidine (**blue**) bases are shown in structural outline; **(c) Rings Display** of distorted **A-form RNA helix** that forms part of the acceptor stem of tRNA. Both **anti-codon loop** and **3′-acceptor stem** are illustrated given their functional importance in **translation** (see Section 1.4.6).

does not exist mainly because β-D-ribofuranose rings of oligo- and polynucleotides are constrained to adopt a $C^{3'}$-endo conformation that automatically favours A-form type double helices (Table 1.2). As a result, individual mRNA molecules comprised of pG, pC, pA and pU nucleotide residues frequently generate complex, unique tertiary structures consisting of A- or A'-form helical regions separated by loops and extensions lacking Watson–Crick base pairing. These mRNA structures could almost be said to rival proteins in their three dimensional complexity!

The structure of tRNA molecules is a peak of RNA structural variation. All tRNA molecules possess a similar overall tertiary structure known as the **clover-leaf structure** (Figure 1.81). Within the clover leaf, there are secondary structure elements comprised of A- or A'-form double helical regions involving RNA equivalent Watson–Crick base pairings (Figure 1.80), that are separated by loops and bulges comprised substantially of representatives from the expanded set of RNA nucleotide building blocks such as pm^1A, pm^7G, pdm^2G, pm^5C and $p\Psi$, which were described previously (Figure 1.57). Furthermore, RNA equivalent Watson–Crick base pairings are also supplemented by base pairings involving the less common nucleotide residues such as pm^1A, pm^7G, pdm^2G, pm^5C and $p\Psi$ (Figure 1.57), together with occasional tertiary base pairings (Figure 1.79). Even RNA equivalent non-Watson–Crick base pairings such as the **G.U wobble base pairing** may be found (Figure 1.82)! Perhaps the main reason that RNA is capable of such structural diversity in comparison with DNA is that numerous stabilising hydrogen bonding interactions can take place between C2'-hydroxyl groups of the polynucleotide phosphodiester backbone and bases. These interactions presumably act to stabilise tertiary structures at the expense of secondary structural double helical elements.

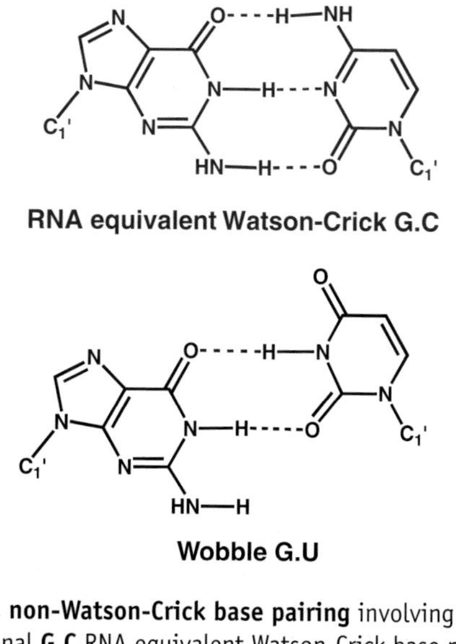

RNA equivalent Watson-Crick G.C

Wobble G.U

Figure 1.82 Structure of **G.U, non-Watson-Crick base pairing** involving the guanine base of guanosine and uracil base of uridine. Original **G.C** RNA equivalent Watson-Crick base pairing is shown (**blue, top**) for comparison.

1.4.6 The genetic code and structure

A general appreciation of the relationship between DNA structure and protein structure, not to mention the functional interplay between the different types of DNA and RNA polymer, is a critical component of biology and essential background knowledge here. In spite of their apparent structural equivalence, the two antiparallel poly deoxynucleotide chains or **strands** of DNA are not functionally equivalent in biology. By convention, one strand is called the **sense** or (+) **strand**, the other is called the **complementary** or (−) **strand**. Therefore, genes must consist of a sense and complementary strand too. Within each gene, the specific sequence of deoxynucleoside bases in the sense strand (read sequentially in the $5' \rightarrow 3'$ direction) is known as the **gene sequence**, and it is this sequence that codes for a corresponding polypeptide sequence, after decoding with the assistance of the **genetic code** (Table 1.3). According to the principles that underlie the genetic code, all gene sequences are divisible into sequential, non-overlapping groups of three deoxynucleoside bases known as **triplet codons** and each triplet codon codes for one amino-acid residue in almost all cases. When the entire set of triplet codons that make up a specific gene sequence are read sequentially ($5' \rightarrow 3'$ direction) with the assistance of the genetic code from one end of a given gene to the other, then the primary structure (complete amino-acid residue sequence) of a corresponding polypeptide/protein is revealed ($N \rightarrow C$-terminus direction). In other words, specific linear gene sequences decode to reveal linear amino-acid residue sequences. Crucially, mention was made earlier (Section 1.2.1) of the fact that the three dimensional structure of a polypeptide is determined by the amino-acid residue sequence itself. Therefore, any given gene sequence by default specifies not only the primary structure of a polypeptide/protein but also the secondary and tertiary structure as well!

Needless to say, the actual overall process of decoding with the genetic code and subsequent conversion of gene sequences into polypeptide/proteins in cells is enormously complex and dynamic, involving as it does many many biological macromolecular 'actors' such as enzymes (protein catalysts) and various binding proteins. However, the chemical biology reader needs to be aware of the overall process in order to appreciate properly the relationships between DNA and the various forms of RNA described here as mRNA, rRNA and tRNA. The whole process of decoding a sequence of deoxynucleoside bases requires initially that each specific gene sequence of interest should be 'copied' from DNA into an mRNA form (Figure 1.83). This copying process is known as **transcription** and takes place in the nucleus. Transcription literally involves the faithful rendering of the specific gene sequence in DNA into a portable mRNA copy that migrates to the cytosol for **translation** into a corresponding polypeptide sequence. Faithful rendering in transcription is made possible by using the complementary gene sequence, located on the complementary strand of DNA, as a molecular template upon which mRNA is assembled according to Watson–Crick base pairing rules (Figure 1.83). Translation takes place in the cytosol at ribosomes, gigantic biological macromolecular assemblies that are substantially comprised of rRNA. Ribosomes are workbenches for translation. Amino acids are transported to ribosomes by means of specific tRNA molecules. Each type of specific tRNA molecule covalently binds only one specific amino acid out of the 20, and also possesses an **anti-codon** nucleoside base sequence that may only bind with an mRNA codon (by Watson–Crick base pairing) that specifically codes for the attached amino acid (as defined

Table 1.3 The Genetic Code; sense strand DNA (a) and mRNA versions (b)

Sense strand DNA ⇨ mRNA ⇨ Protein

a)

First 2'-Deoxynucleotide (5'-end)	Second 2'-Deoxynucleotide				Third 2'-Deoxynucleotide (3'-end)
	T	C	A	G	
T	TTT Phe	TCT Ser	TAT Tyr	TGT Cys	T
	TTC Phe	TCC Ser	TAC Tyr	TGC Cys	C
	TTA Leu	TCA Ser	TAA Stop	TGA Stop	A
	TTG Leu	TCG Ser	TAG Stop	TGG Trp	G
C	CTT Leu	CCT Pro	CAT His	CGT Arg	T
	CTC Leu	CCC Pro	CAC His	CGC Arg	C
	CTA Leu	CCA Pro	CAA Gin	CGA Arg	A
	CTG Leu	CCG Pro	CAG Gin	CGG Arg	G
A	ATT lle	ACT Thr	AAT Asn	AGT Ser	T
	ATC lle	ACC Thr	AAC Asn	AGC Ser	C
	ATA lle	ACA Thr	AAA Lys	AGA Arg	A
	ATG Met	ACG Thr	AAG Lys	AGG Arg	G
G	GTT Val	GCT Ala	GAT Asp	GGT Gly	T
	GTC Val	GCC Ala	GAC Asp	GGC Gly	C
	GTA Val	GCA Ala	GAA Glu	GGA Gly	A
	GTG Val	GCG Ala	GAG Glu	GGG Gly	G

b)

First Nucleotide (5'-end)	Second Nucleotide				Third Nucleotide (3'-end)
	U	C	A	G	
U	UUU Phe	UCU Ser	UAU Tyr	UGU Cys	U
	UUC Phe	UCC Ser	UAC Tyr	UGC Cys	C
	UUA Leu	UCA Ser	UAA Stop	UGA Stop	A
	UUG Leu	UCG Ser	UAG Stop	UGG Trp	G
C	CUU Leu	CCU Pro	CAU His	CGU Arg	U
	CUC Leu	CCC Pro	CAC His	CGC Arg	C
	CUA Leu	CCA Pro	CAA Gin	CGA Arg	A
	CUG Leu	CCG Pro	CAG Gin	CGG Arg	G
A	AUU Ile	ACU Thr	AAU Asn	AGU Ser	U
	AUC Ile	ACC Thr	AAC Asn	AGC Ser	C
	AUA Ile	ACA Thr	AAA Lys	AGA Arg	A
	AUG Met	ACG Thr	AAG Lys	AGG Arg	G
G	GUU Val	GCU Ala	GAU Asp	GGU Gly	U
	GUC Val	GCC Ala	GAC Asp	GGC Gly	C
	GUA Val	GCA Ala	GAA Glu	GGA Gly	A
	GUG Val	GCG Ala	GAG Glu	GGG Gly	G

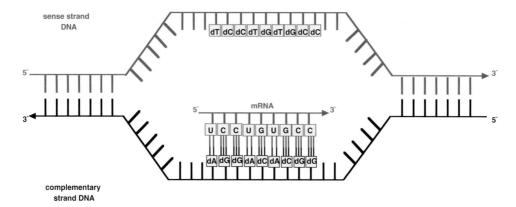

Figure 1.83   Schematic of **Transcription Bubble**. The complementary strand of DNA in the region of a gene acts as a template upon which to synthesize mRNA with the assistance of Watson-Crick base pairing. Watson-Crick base pairing ensures that the mRNA nucleoside sequence is the RNA equivalent of the deoxynucleoside sequence found in the sense strand of DNA. Hence coding information in sense strand DNA is smoothly transcribed into an mRNA form for translation into polypeptide sequences (See **Fig. 1.84**).

by the genetic code). Such dual functionality allows each type of specific tRNA to simultaneously bind non-covalently by Watson–Crick base pair hydrogen bonds to a specific mRNA codon, and covalently with the very amino acid coded for by that mRNA codon. The translation process now begins at the 5′-end of mRNA beginning with the first and second triplet codons. Specific tRNA molecules with their amino acids attached bind to mRNA at these codons (Figure 1.84). Thereafter, the amino acid associated with the second triplet codon is close enough to attack the α-carboxyl functional group of the amino acid associated with the first triplet codon, creating a dipeptide. The amino-acid-free tRNA attached to the first triplet codon may now dissociate, after which a new specific tRNA molecule with its amino acid attached binds to the third triplet codon in line. This new amino acid associated with the third triplet codon is close enough once again to attack the C-terminal α-carboxyl functional group of the dipeptide associated with the second triplet codon, thereby creating a tripeptide. Now, the amino acid-free tRNA attached to the second triplet codon can dissociate and the process continues in a similar way until specific tRNA molecules with their amino acids attached have bound to all the mRNA codons in turn (as far as the 3′-end of mRNA). The overall effect is to realise the synthesis ($N \rightarrow C$-terminus direction) of a polypeptide chain through the sequential association (5′ $\rightarrow$ 3′ direction) of specific tRNA molecules to mRNA codons. Clearly, the dual functionality of each type of specific tRNA molecule ensures that the sequence of the new polypeptide is precisely that determined by the original DNA gene sequence decoded according to the genetic code. The critical importance of tRNA should now be very clear, indeed so much so that the question as to how exactly each type of specific tRNA molecule meets with the correct amino-acid residue and the correct mRNA codon coding for the attached amino acid is absolutely central to the fidelity of the link between DNA and protein structure and remains a subject of enormous current interest in chemical biology circles.

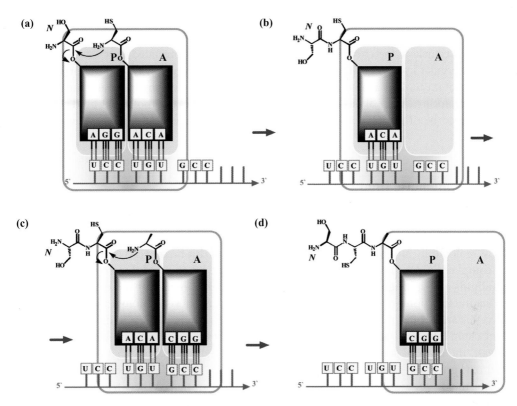

Figure 1.84 Schematic of **translation**. The mRNA codons are read and converted from nucleoside sequences to protein primary structure by means of **cognate aminoacyl-tRNAs**. All mRNA codons are translated at a **ribosome** (prepared from rRNA) that has two cognate aminoacyl-tRNA binding sites; **P (peptidyl)** and **A (aminoacyl)**. All tRNAs are "adaptors" that can bind a particular mRNA codon through their **anticodon loop**, using Watson-Crick base pairing, and also associate covalently with the appropriate amino acid residue coded for by the corresponding mRNA codon! When two cognate aminoacyl-tRNA molecules bind mRNA in **P** and **A** sites (**a**), then both are close enough for peptide link formation to take place with the emergence of a peptide chain (**b**). As amino acyl tRNA molecules continue to dock sequentially onto mRNA codons (in the direction 5′ →3′) (**c**), and amino acid residues continue to be added ($N \rightarrow C$) (**d**), then the peptide chain will elongate progressively from oligo- to polypeptide until a stop signal is reached.

1.5 Macromolecular lipid assemblies

Curiously, there is a perception in some quarters that lipids are just 'dull', merely forming retentive membranes that mark the boundaries of cells and the territories of the various organelles or functional zones within them. However, although lipids are central to compartmentalisation, lipids and the macromolecular lipid assemblies that they form, including membranes, have a vast and complex dynamic behaviour, which underpins cellular metabolism as well as promoting the systems of communication and synergism between living cells in complex, multicellular organisms. There appears to be much yet to learn and much yet to study, since research into lipids and their macromolecular lipid assemblies has been relatively neglected in comparison with other fields in chemical biology. Nevertheless, the chemical biology reader should appreciated that the influence of macromolecular lipid assemblies on biological function is equally vast and important as the influence of the biological macromolecules such as proteins, carbohydrates and nucleic acids. Therefore, future chemical biology research into lipids and macromolecular lipid assemblies is certain to be of great significance in developing our understanding of the way biology works.

1.5.1 Monomeric lipid structures

Monomeric lipids may be broadly defined as molecules of intermediate molecular weight (MW 100–5000 Da) that contain a substantial portion of aliphatic or aromatic hydrocarbon. Most biologically important lipids belong to a subset of this broad class of molecules known as **complex lipids**. The major members of this subset are the **acylglycerols**, **glycerophospholipids** and **sphingolipids**. Other complex lipids are known, but these either have little structural function or else are of unknown or poorly characterised biological function. Acylglycerols are a combination of the triose glycerol and long chain fatty acids. Typical natural long chain fatty acids are shown in Figure 1.85. Whilst the number of possible acylglycerols is vast, the most biologically significant are the triacylglycerols, in which all three reactive hydroxyl groups of glycerol have been esterified by fatty acids (Figure 1.86). Triacylglycerols are the major storage form of lipids in plants and higher animals. Where triacylglycerols contain identical fatty acid acyl chains they are called **triglycerides** or **simple triacylglycerols**. Where different fatty acid acyl chains are involved, the term **mixed triacyl glycerols** is used (Figure 1.86).

Glycerophospholipids may be thought of as derivatives of triacylglycerols in which the carbon atom C-3 carboxylate ester has been replaced by a phosphate ester. The number of possible glycerophospholipids is also vast, so only the most widely studied and arguably most biologically important are illustrated (Figure 1.87). These glycerophospholipids are important predominantly as constituents of biological membranes. Sphingolipids are a combination of the base sphingosine and long chain fatty acids. Acylation of the carbon atom C-2 amine group by a fatty acid gives rise to the **ceramides**, from which **phosphoceramides** are derived by phosphate ester derivatisation of the C-1 hydroxyl group. Biologically significant members of both types are illustrated (Figure 1.88). Ceramides and phosphoceramides are important constituents of human skin lipids and neural membranes. The phosphoceramides, together with the glycerophospholipids, are collectively known as **phospholipids**.

1.5.2 Lyotropic mesophases of phospholipids

Macromolecular lipid assemblies arise from the amphiphilic character of phospholipids (Figure 1.89). Broadly speaking, all phospholipids contain a compact **polar region**, which is

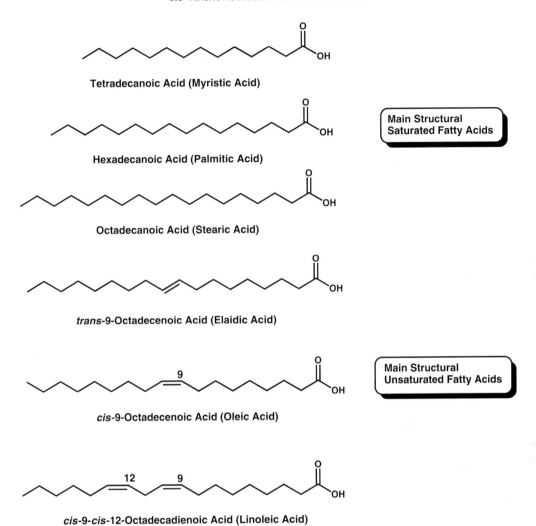

Figure 1.85 Structures of main **saturated and unsaturated fatty acids** in structural lipids that form lipid assemblies.

hydrophilic in character, and an extended **chain region**, which is hydrophobic in character. In the presence of water, the tendency of the hydrophobic chain regions to self-associate and simultaneously exclude water leads to macromolecular lipid assemblies that may be described as vast, extended non-covalent structures held together by van der Waals interactions and the hydrophobic effect, which adopt different phase states depending upon the character of the phospholipid involved and the local conditions. These phospholipid structures in their various phase states are also known as **lyotropic mesophases**. Some of the most well established

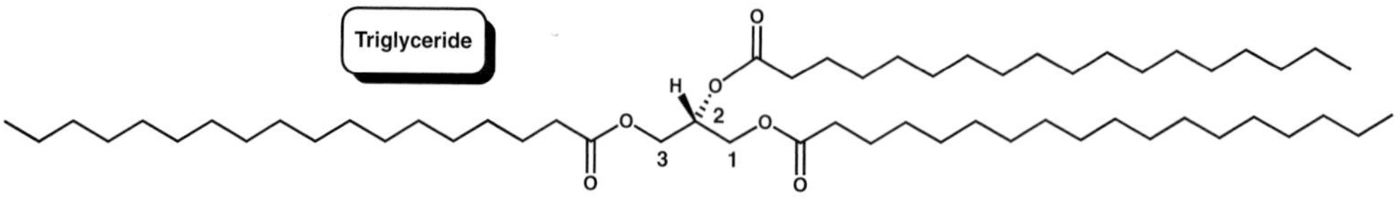

1,2,3-Trioctadecanoyl-*sn*-glycerol

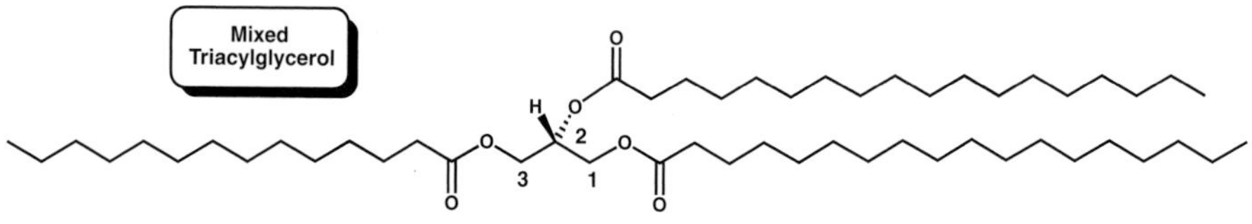

1,2-Dioctadecanoyl-3-tetradecanoyl-*sn*-glycerol

Figure 1.86 Illustrative structures of main storage lipids, the **triglycerides** and the mixed **triacylglycerols.**

lyotropic mesophases have been summarised (Table 1.4) using the **Luzzati nomenclature.** Structures and transitions between mesophases are very relevant to the biological behaviour of lipids and so these will be discussed. However, given the current state of knowledge on lipids and their macromolecular assemblies, there can be no absolute certainty concerning precisely which of the lyotropic mesophases are actually relevant in biology and which are not.

1.5.3 Solid-like mesophases

One or more **crystalline lamellar** (L_c) phases may be formed by all phospholipids at low temperature and/or low levels of hydration. When long and short range order is found in three dimensions then the result is a **3D lamellar crystal**, which is a true crystal. The three dimensional crystalline order results from the close packing of two dimensional phospholipid crystalline sheets (Figure 1.90). In all crystalline and ordered states, phospholipid close packing and molecular configuration is defined in terms of a number of parameters. These parameters are σ—the **mean cross sectional area** of a fatty acid alkyl chain perpendicular to the chain axis, ϕ—the **tilt angle of the chain** with respect to bilayer plane, d_p—the **thickness of the head group region**—and S—the **surface area at the bilayer plane** occupied by the individual phospholipid. When the two dimensional phospholipid crystalline sheets cease to maintain regular stacking arrangements with respect to each other, then three dimensional crystalline order breaks down, leading to series of two dimensional crystalline sheets, each irregularly stacked with respect to the next. Such mesophases are known as **2D lamellar crystals**, since they still maintain a good deal of crystalline order.

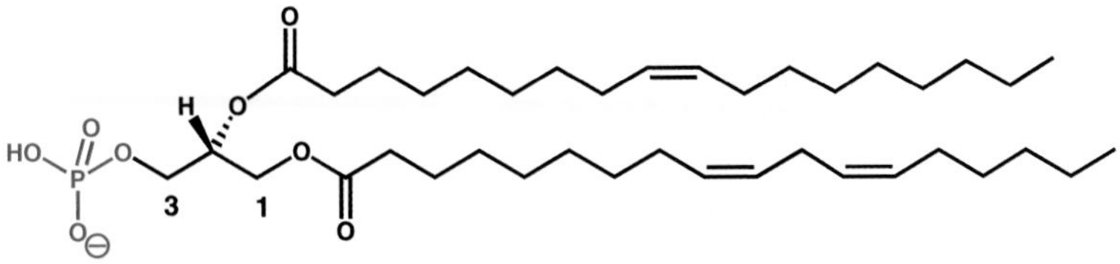

1-Linoleoyl-2-oleoyl-*sn*-glycero-3-phosphatidic Acid (LOPA)

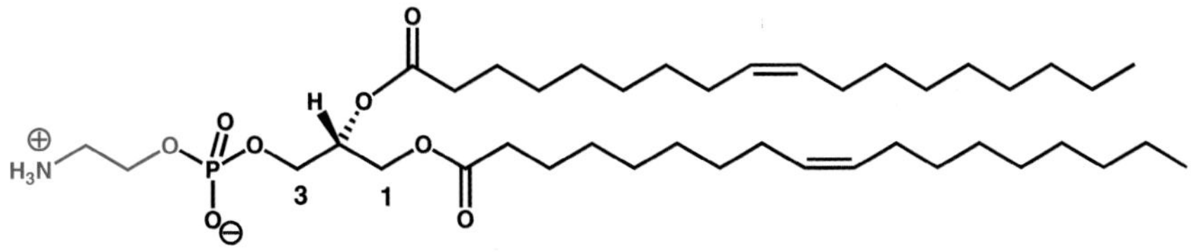

1,2-Dioleoyl-*sn*-glycero-3-phosphatidylethanolamine (DOPE)

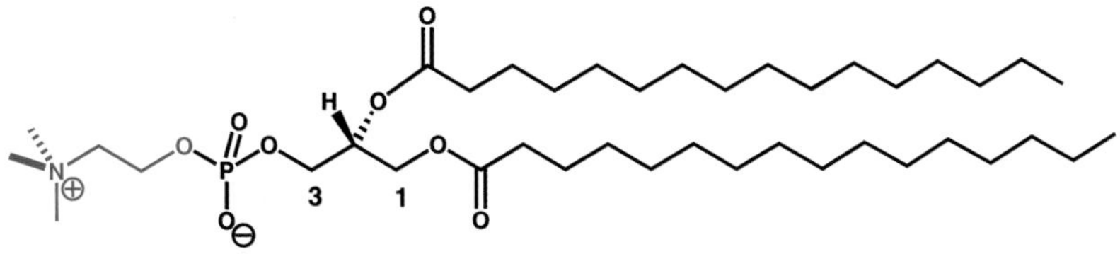

1,2-Dipalmitoyl-*sn*-glycero-3-phosphatidylcholine (DPPC)

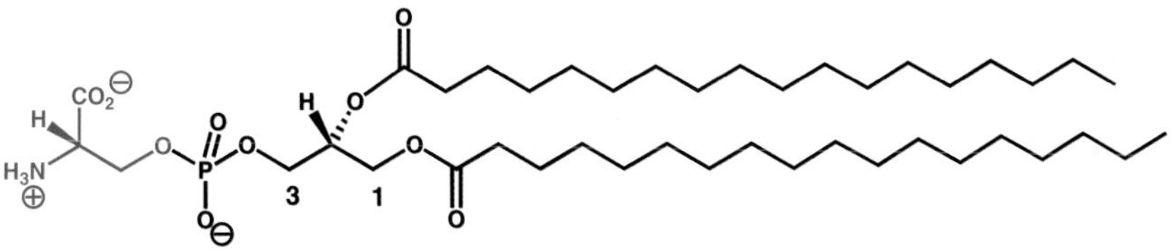

1,2-Distearoyl-*sn*-glycero-3-phosphatidylserine (DSPS)

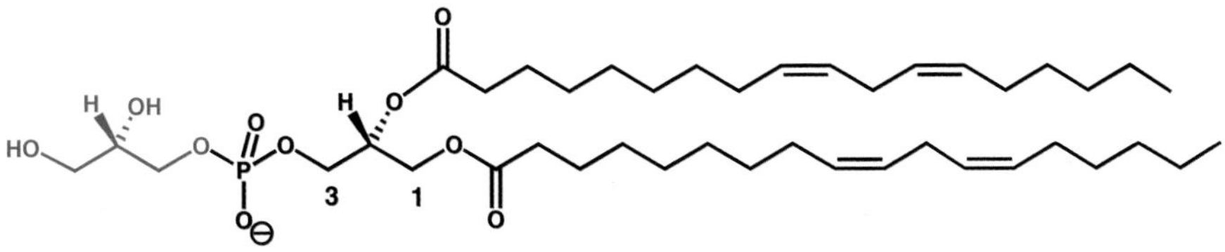

1,2-Dilinoleoyl-*sn*-glycero-3-phosphatidylglycerol (DLPG)

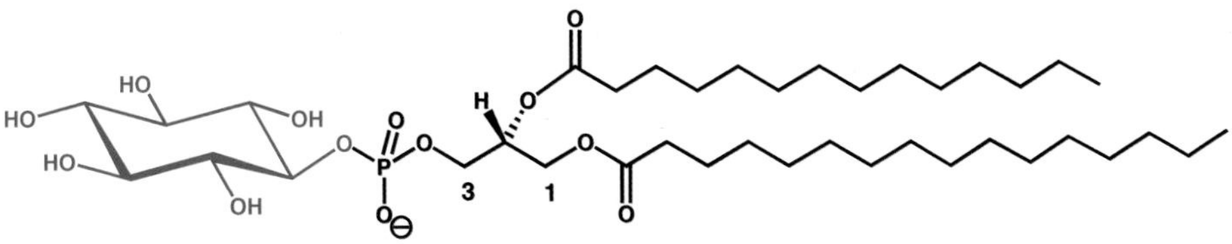

1-Palmitoyl-2-myristoyl-*sn*-glycero-3-phosphatidylinositol (PMPI)

Figure 1.87 Representative structures of first rank structural lipids, the **glycerophospholipids** or **phospholipids**, that are major and integral components of lipid assemblies.

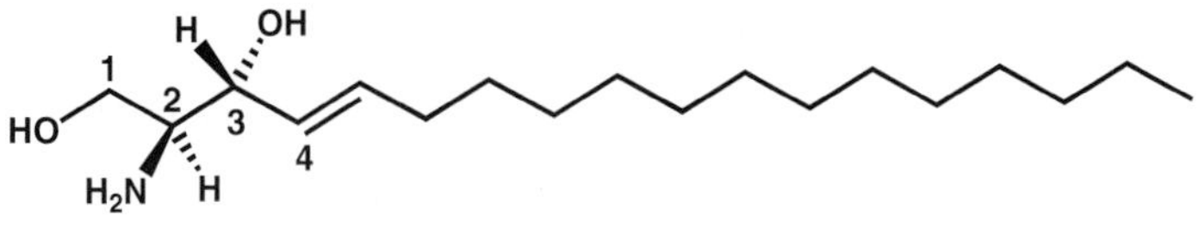

***D-erythro*-2-amino-4-octadecene-1,3-diol (Sphingosine)**

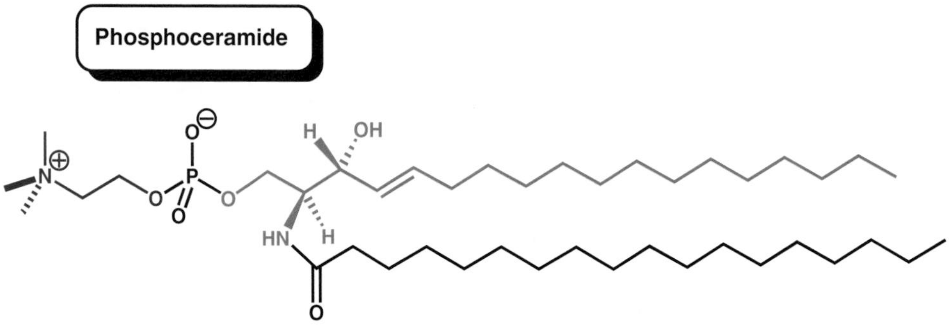

2-Stearoyl-1-phosphatidylcholine sphingosine (Stearoyl sphingomyelin)

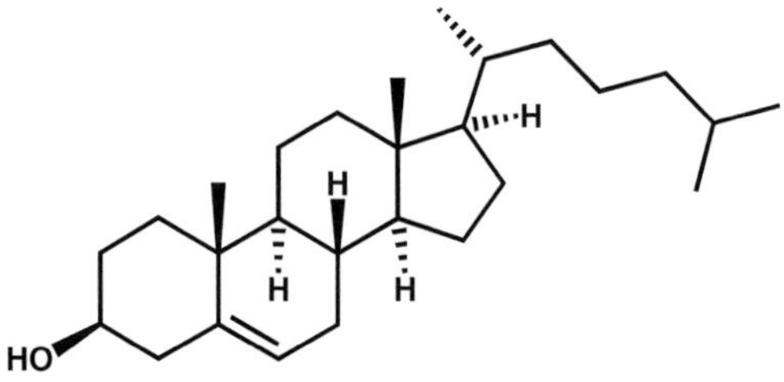

Cholest-5-en-3β-ol (Cholesterol)

Figure 1.88   Representative structure of second rank **structural lipids**, the **phosphoceramides**, that are formed from the amine diol **sphingosine**. These can be components of some lipid assemblies but in most cases are not dominant. The structure of **cholesterol**, another critical structural lipid is also shown.

1D ordered lamellar phases are known as gel states, and occur when phospholipids are arranged into bilayers that then stack into a multilayer with each bilayer separated by water. The fatty acid alkyl side-chains are stiff and extended, as in the 3D and 2D lamellar crystal phases, but may undergo hindered rotations about their chain axes. There are a number of types of 1D ordered lamellar phases depending upon the tilt angle ϕ; these are $\mathbf{L}_\beta$ ($\phi = 0$), $\mathbf{L}'_\beta$ ($\phi > 0$) and an interdigitated phase $\mathbf{L}_{\beta I}$ ($\phi = 0$) where fatty acid alkyl side-chains from different monolayers overlap with each other (Figure 1.91). One other 1D ordered lamellar phase, $\mathbf{L}_\delta$, is known, in which the fatty acid alkyl side-chains cease to be linear but adopt a helical conformation.

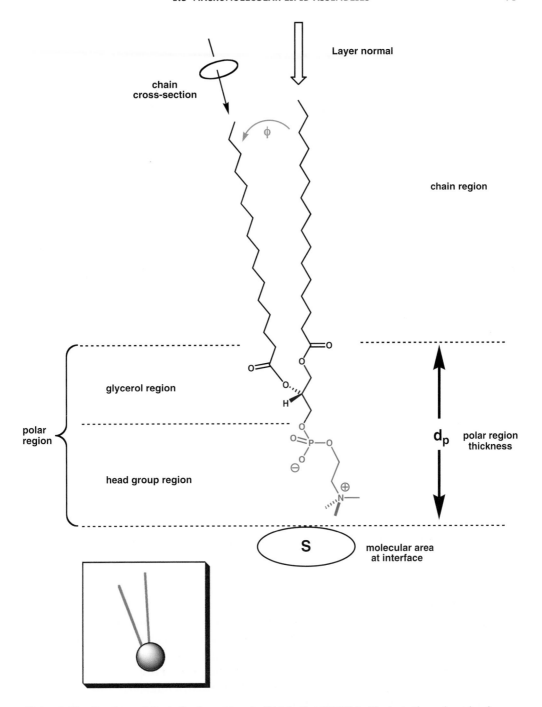

Figure 1.89 Structure of dipalmitoyl L-α-phosphatidylcholine (**DPPC**) to illustrate the main molecular parameters and structural features that dictate the formation of crystalline lamellar phases of macromolecular lipid assemblies. Schematic representation of a phospholipid molecule is also show (**inset**).

Table 1.4 Summary of the main lyotropic mesophases giving phase type with symmetry name and the nature of the mesophase structure in each case

Phase Type	Name	Phase Structure
Solid-like lamellar		
3D	L_c	3D crystal
2D	L_c^{2D}	2D crystal
	$P_{\beta'}$	rippled gel
1D	L_β	untilted gel
	$L_{\beta'}$	tilted gel
	$L_{\beta I}$	interdigitated gel
	$L_{\alpha\beta}$	partial gel
Fluid mesophases		
1D	L_α	fluid lammellar
2D	H	hexagonal
	H^C	complex hexagonal
	R	rectangular
	M	oblique
3D	Q	cubic
	T	tetragonal
	R	rhombohedral
	O	orthorhombic

1.5.4 Fluid mesophases

Under certain conditions of temperature and hydration, solid-like mesophases will undergo a transition into fluid mesophases. The physical conditions under which transitions of this type occur are very important in biological terms. The vast majority of **3D fluid phases** so far identified have **cubic (Q)** symmetry (Table 1.4). Six cubic phases have been characterised so far, and these appear to fall into two distinct families, one family based upon periodic minimal surfaces (bicontinuous) and the other on discrete lipid aggregates (micellar). 3D fluid phases may exist as either **type I (normal topology,** oil-in-water) or **type II (inverse topology,** water-in-oil) structures. Frequently, cubic phases of both type I and type II exist. For instance, the main bicontinuous phases (**Q230, Q224** and **Q229**) all form type I and type II structures consisting of two separate interwoven but unconnected networks of channels or rods, which are formed from either fatty acid side-chains or water respectively (Figure 1.92). **Type II rhombohedral (R)** or **tetragonal (T)** three dimensional fluid phases are also known. For example, the R_{II} phase consists of planar two dimensional hexagonal arrays, formed from aqueous channels, which are then regularly stacked to form a three dimensional lattice. In

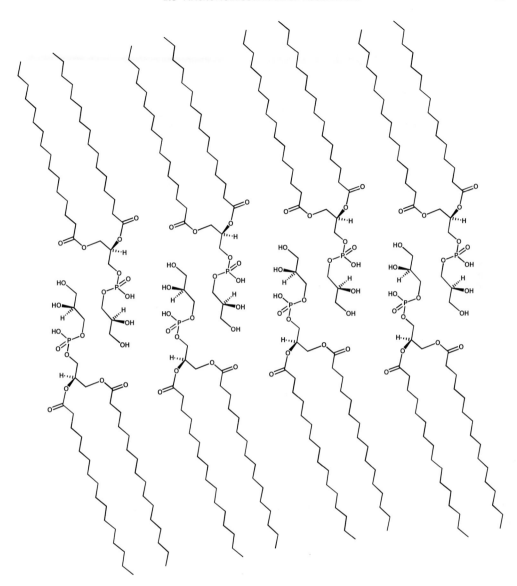

Figure 1.90 Dipalmitoyl L-α-phosphatidylglycerol (**DPPG**) layer to illustrate crystal packing in **2D-lamellar layers**. In lipid assembly terms this can be considered secondary/tertiary structure formation.

a similar way, the T_{II} phase is comprised of planar two dimensional square arrays that are once again stacked to form the three dimensional lattice. A debate is now raging amongst some chemical biology researchers concerning the potential existence of cubic phases in cells; indeed, there is a proposition that the membranes of cellular organelles may in fact adopt the normal cubic phase, Q_I.

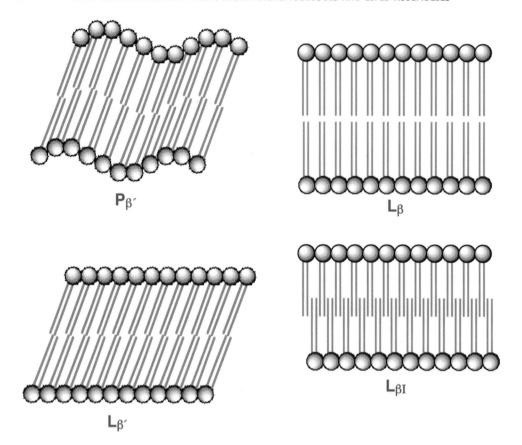

Figure 1.91 Selection of **2D modulated ordered lamellar phases** that are partially disordered, but exhibit translational ordering in two dimensions. These gel phases exist half way between crystalline L_c states and completely fluid phases such as the $L_{\alpha I}$ and H_{II} phases (**Figs. 1.93** and **1.94**). In lipid assembly terms, these represent the equivalent of secondary/tertiary structure formation.

Having said the above, membranes in cells are usually considered to adopt **1D fluid phases**, in particular the **fluid lamellar phases**, L_α (Figure 1.93), such as the normal topology type I structure, $L_{\alpha I}$. This $L_{\alpha I}$ phase is widely considered to represent the default phase state of all biological membranes under normal physiological conditions. Cellular membranes are also thought to be able to adopt certain **2D fluid phases** under certain circumstances, in particular **hexagonal phases**, H (Figure 1.94), such as the inverse topology type II structure, H_{II}. Both normal and inverse topology hexagonal phases, H_I and H_{II}, have the appearance of stacked cylinders. In the H_I phase, long alkyl acid side-chains are contained within the cylinders whilst polar head groups make up cylinder surfaces; in the H_{II} phase, cylinders of water are bordered by polar head groups and the spaces between cylinders are occupied by long alkyl side-chains (Figure 1.94). The interconversion within biological membranes between the $L_{\alpha I}$ fluid phase and inverse hexagonal phase H_{II} is currently

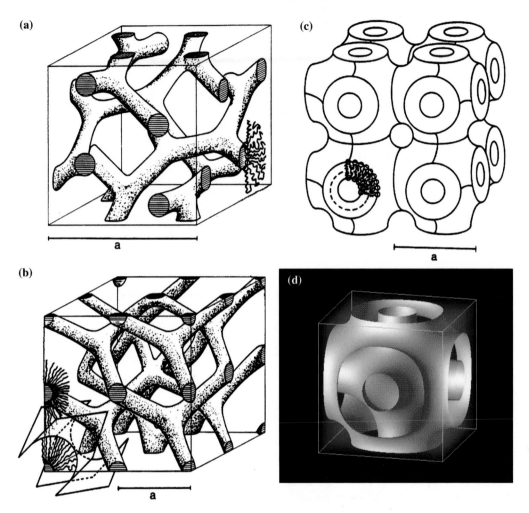

Figure 1.92 Structural representations of the main **cubic mesophases** formed by lipid assemblies. The mesophases shown are (**a**) **Ia3d** (Q^{230}) and (**b**) **Pn3m** (Q^{224}), both of which are Q_{II} fluid cubic phases; together with (**c**) **Im3m** (Q^{229}) which is a Q_{I} fluid cubic phase. Cartoon (**d**) provides an alternative representation of the Im3m (Q^{229}) mesophase. Subscript **I** refers to normal phase (lipid "inside") and **II** to reverse phase (lipid "outside"). In lipid assembly terms, these represent the equivalent of tertiary structure formation (illustrations a) to c) from Seddon, 1990, Fig. 6).

considered to be central to the dynamic behaviour of all manner of biological membranes, in particular to allow biological membranes to become temporarily more porous in the H_{II} phase prior to returning to the much less porous $L_{\alpha I}$ phase. In addition, this interconversion appears to be important to facilitate fusion events involving biological membranes as well.

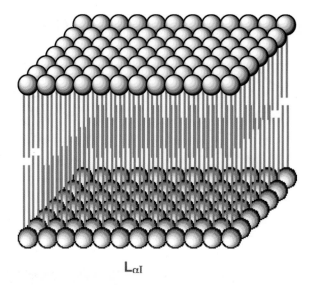

$L_{\alpha I}$

Figure 1.93   Structural representations of the $L_{\alpha I}$ phase, the main fluid lamellar mesophase formed by lipid assemblies and the primary mesophase adopted by biological membranes. Subscript **I** refers to normal phase (lipid "inside") and **II** to reverse phase (lipid "outside"). In lipid assembly terms, this represents the equivalent of secondary/tertiary structure formation.

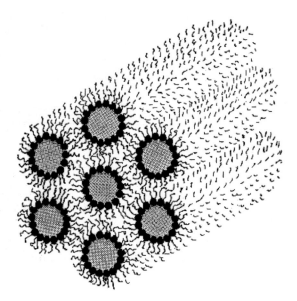

Figure 1.94   Structural representations of the H_{II} phase, the main fluid hexagonal mesophase formed by lipid assemblies. Subscript **I** refers to normal phase (lipid "inside") and **II** to reverse phase (lipid "outside"). In lipid assembly terms, this represents the equivalent of secondary/tertiary structure formation (illustration from Seddon, 1990, Fig. 3b).

1.6 Structural forces in biological macromolecules

Throughout this chapter, references have been made to the forces that give the structures of biological macromolecules and macromolecular lipid assemblies both form and function. The covalent bond should be well known to all chemical biology readers and need not be discussed further. However, the non-covalent forces are important, since these are central to the formation of three dimensional structure and therefore also to all functions of biological macromolecules and macromolecular lipid assemblies. There are four main types of non-covalent structural force that matter most in chemical biology, namely **electrostatic**, **van der Waals** and **dispersion**, **hydrogen bonding** and the **hydrophobic interactions**. These forces will be dealt with in order from first principles.

1.6.1 Electrostatic forces

1.6.1.1 Monopoles

Electrostatic forces are long range. This means that they have an influence through space between atoms that is longer than any other type of force that will be discussed here. Charges of opposite sign are attracted to each other and charges with the same sign repel each other. The simplest type of electrostatic force exists between two **point charges** (**monopoles**), q_1 and q_2, separated by a **distance** r in a vacuum (Figure 1.95). The strength of interaction between q_1 and q_2 may be described in terms of **potential energy**, V, which is defined by

$$V = \frac{q_1 q_2}{4\pi \varepsilon_0 r} \tag{1.1}$$

where ε_0 is a constant known as the **vacuum permittivity**. When q_1 and q_2 are opposite in sign (and are attracted), the value of V is negative and corresponds to the amount of energy required to separate the two point charges to a distance of infinity. If q_1 and q_2 are the same in sign (and repel each other), then the value of V becomes positive and represents the amount of energy required to maintain both charges in position after bringing them together from a distance of infinity. The concept of potential energy is a very useful way of defining the strength of weak forces and provides a useful link to thermodynamics as well, as we shall see. By definition, potential energy V is a measure of the ability of a system to 'do work' outside the system. Obviously, a system of charges in a state of repulsion is capable of doing work outside the system (hence the positive value of V), whilst a system of charges in a state of

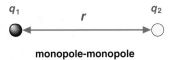

monopole-monopole

Figure 1.95 Illustration of **monopole/monopole interactions** where q_1 and q_2 are two monopoles; r is the distance of separation.

attraction is not (hence the negative value of V). The lower the value of V the less able is the system able to do work outside and the more stable is the arrangement of charges.

Biological macromolecules are usually found in a medium (aqueous buffer, for example), and the nature of the medium typically has a profound effect upon the magnitude of V. This is taken into account by exchanging ε_0 for another constant ε known as the **permittivity of the medium**, as shown:

$$V = \frac{q_1 q_2}{4\pi \varepsilon r} \tag{1.2}$$

which is a more general version of Equation (1.1). The ratio of ε to ε_0 is known as the **relative permittivity** or **dielectric constant** of the medium.

1.6.1.2 Dipoles

Equation (1.1) needs to be adapted differently if more complicated arrangements of charges are involved, for instance if a fixed dipole and a monopole are allowed to interact in a vacuum separated by a distance r. We usually define a dipole as two opposite point charges, for instance q_1 and $-q_1$, separated by a distance l (Figure 1.96). In this case the electrostatic influence of the dipole is described in terms of a **dipole moment**:

$$\mu_1 = q_1 l \tag{1.3}$$

The potential energy of interaction between dipole moment, μ_1, and point charge, q_2, can be expressed by modifying Equation (1.1) to give

$$V = \frac{-\mu_1 q_2}{4\pi \varepsilon_0} \frac{1}{r^2} \tag{1.4}$$

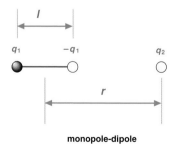

monopole-dipole

Figure 1.96   Illustration of **fixed dipole/monopole interactions** where charges $q_1/-q_1$ separated by a distance l represent the fixed dipole and and q_2 is a monopole; r is the distance of separation between dipole midpoint and monopole.

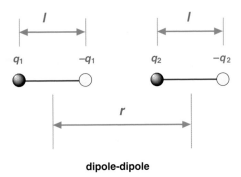

dipole-dipole

Figure 1.97   Illustration of **fixed dipole/ fixed dipole interactions** where charges $q_1/-q_1$ separated by a distance l represent one fixed dipole; $q_2/-q_2$ also separated by a distance l represent the other fixed dipole; r is the distance of separation between dipole midpoints.

Furthermore, the potential energy of interaction between two fixed dipoles (Figure 1.97) can be expressed by a simple expansion of Equation (1.4) to give

$$V = \frac{-\mu_1\mu_2}{4\pi\varepsilon_0}\frac{2}{r^3} \tag{1.5}$$

What happens if more complex charge systems are interacting, each involving clusters of four (**quadrupole** or 2^2-pole) or even eight (**octupole** or 2^3-pole) charges? Obviously the equations must become more complex. However, by comparing the forms of Equations (1.1), (1.4) and (1.5), a general proportionality may be deduced. If an **n-pole** charge cluster is able to interact with an adjacent **m-pole** charge cluster, then the potential energy of interaction may be defined by the multipole proportionality:

$$V \propto \frac{1}{r^{n+m-1}} \tag{1.6}$$

Thus far, the equations and proportionality discussed in this section were actually derived assuming the dipoles or higher multipoles to be fixed in space. In order to be more realistic, rotation must be allowed for. In this case, if two multipoles were able to rotate freely in the vicinity of each other, then the overall interaction would be characterised by an **average potential energy**, $\langle V \rangle$, of zero! However, mutual potential energy depends on relative orientation. Therefore, the rotation of one dipole is heavily dependent upon the position and rotational behaviour of the other (Figure 1.98). There is no free rotation, even in the gas phase. Consequently, the actual value of $\langle V \rangle$ will be given by

$$\langle V \rangle = -\frac{C}{r^6} \tag{1.7}$$

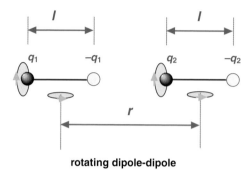

rotating dipole-dipole

Figure 1.98   Illustration of **rotating dipole/ rotating dipole interactions** where charges q_1/$-q_1$ separated by a distance l represent one rotating dipole; q_2/$-q_2$ also separated by a distance l represent the other rotating dipole; r is the distance of separation between dipole midpoints. Both dipoles rotate under mutual influence about dipole midpoints and axes.

where the **constant of proportionality**, C, is defined by

$$C = \frac{2\mu_1^2\mu_2^2}{3(4\pi\varepsilon_0)^2 kT} \tag{1.8}$$

in which k is known as the **Boltzmann constant**. The form of Equations (1.7) and (1.8) gives some insights into the effects of temperature T on $\langle V \rangle$. The higher is T, the smaller is C and hence the higher is the value of average potential energy $\langle V \rangle$. In other words, increasing T increases system average potential energy $\langle V \rangle$ by disorganising the given system, thereby minimising mutual dipole orientation and attractive interaction effects, which otherwise act to minimise $\langle V \rangle$ and stabilise the system.

Electrostatic interactions are involved in stabilising the structures of biological macromolecules. Globular protein surfaces are covered with charged amino-acid residues that interact with each other to form surface stabilising salt-links. Moreover, surface clusters of charges approximate to arrays of monopoles, dipoles and quadrupoles, hence all the electrostatic equations apply. These same surface clusters of monopoles, dipoles and quadrupoles also radiate electrostatic force-lines into solution, with consequences for protein–ligand interactions and molecular recognition phenomena (see Chapter 7). In the case of nucleic acids, charge–charge repulsions between the anti-parallel phosphodiester chains could be sufficient to cause chain separation. However, phosphate negative charges are usually counterbalanced by close neighbour counter-ions (cations or cationic proteins) that modulate the magnitude of the negative charges. In this case, the charges then provide sufficient charge–charge repulsion to maintain the positions of the anti-parallel phosphodiester chains, preventing hydrophobic collapse, without inappropriately perturbing the structure overall.

1.6.2 Van der Waals and dispersion forces

Van der Waals and dispersion forces are typically observed between 'closed shell' molecules and are short range in character. Such forces, together with hydrogen bonding (see Section 1.6.3), dominate the landscape of biological macromolecule interactions at short range and play a very dominant role in molecular recognition and binding/catalysis processes involving biological macromolecules and substrates/ligands. These forces are generated by interactions between partial charges in polar functional groups/molecules and induced partial charges in non-polar functional groups/molecules. There are three main contributions to van der Waals and dispersion forces and these are

    (a) weak dipole–weak dipole interactions

    (b) induced dipole–weak dipole interactions

    (c) induced dipole–induced dipole interactions.

1.6.2.1   Weak dipole–weak dipole interactions

Weak dipoles are associated with any bonds or functional groups involving carbon or hydrogen and an electronegative heteroatoms, such as peptide, phosphodiester or glycosidic links (see later). These weak dipoles interact in a manner described by expressions in the form of Equations (1.7) and (1.8).

1.6.2.2   Induced dipole–weak dipole interactions

When a weak dipole is in the presence of a polarisable functional group/molecule, then the electric field of that dipole will induce a temporary dipole in the polarisable functional group/molecule. The electrostatic influence of the weak dipole may be expressed in terms of a **permanent dipole moment** μ_1, and that of the induced dipole in terms of an **induced dipole moment** μ_2^*. The potential energy of interaction may then be defined by

$$V = -\frac{C'}{r^6} \tag{1.9}$$

where the constant of proportionality, C, is defined by

$$C' = \frac{\mu_1^2 \alpha_2'}{\pi \varepsilon_0} \tag{1.10}$$

The term α_2' is known as the **polarisability volume** of the functional group/molecule that harbours the induced dipole. Whilst the distance dependency of these induced dipole–weak dipole interactions is similar to that of dipole–dipole or weak dipole–weak dipole interactions, it is worth noting that there is actually no temperature dependency within the constant C'.

1.6.2.3   Induced dipole–induced dipole interactions

These interactions are also known as **dispersion** or **London interactions** and characterise non-polar functional group/molecule interactions with each other. Instantaneous transient dipoles are created in all functional groups or molecules due to electron movement. However, only in truly non-polar functional groups or molecules do such transient dipoles have a major impact, such as in the core of a globular protein (see later). In these cases, an instantaneous dipole in one non-polar functional group or molecule generates an electrostatic field that induces the formation of another instantaneous transient dipole in a non-polar functional group or molecule in the vicinity. The electrostatic influence of the first transient dipole may be defined in terms of **induced dipole moment** μ_1^*, and that of the second in terms of **induced dipole moment** μ_2^*. The potential energy between these moments may be expressed in terms of

$$V = -\frac{C''}{r^6} \tag{1.11}$$

where the constant of proportionality, C'', is given by

$$C'' = \frac{2}{3}\alpha_1'\alpha_2'\frac{I_1 I_2}{I_1 + I_2} \tag{1.12}$$

The terms α_1' and α_2' are polarisability volumes for each of the two functional groups/molecules involved respectively. I_1 and I_2 are the **ionisation energies** of the two functional groups/molecules involved respectively. The form of Equation (1.11) is exactly the same as for (1.9) and (1.7). Therefore, the distance dependencies of dipole–dipole, van der Waals and dispersion forces are exactly the same. Only the constant of proportionality has a bearing upon the contribution of each type of interaction force to the potential energy of a given system of charges and/or induced charges (see Table 1.5).

Van der Waals and dispersion forces are ubiquitous in stabilising the structures of biological macromolecules and macromolecular lipid assemblies. In the case of globular proteins, Van der Waals and dispersion forces are important stabilising forces within the interior of these proteins owing to the substantial presence of hydrophobic amino-acid residues located in the 'middle and centre' of globular proteins. These forces may also play a role in stabilising the 'interior' base pair axial middle of nucleic acids too. However, by far the greatest beneficiary of these forces is macromolecular lipid assemblies, given the vast numbers of interacting alkyl chains within membrane structures.

Table 1.5 Summary of the main forces involved in determining the three-dimensional structures of biological macromolecules and also their dynamics, binding behaviour and reactivity. The term *r* refers to distance between interacting entities. All interactions are attractive unless indicated

Interaction Type	Distance Dependency	V/kJ mol^{-1}	Remarks
Monopole-Monopole (ion-ion)	$1/r$	-250	Coulombic
Monopole-Dipole (ion-dipole)	$1/r^2$	-15	
Dipole-Dipole	$1/r^3$	-2	Static system
	$1/r^6$	-0.3	Rotating system
London	$1/r^6$	-2	All types of molecules
Hydrogen-bond		-20	
Repulsive	$1/r^{12}$		Very short range; all types of molecules

1.6.3 Hydrogen bonding

Hydrogen bond interactions are the shortest range non-covalent interactions and represent a special type of attractive interaction between closed shell functional groups arising from the atomic arrangement shown (Figure 1.99). A and B are very electronegative atoms (N, O or F);

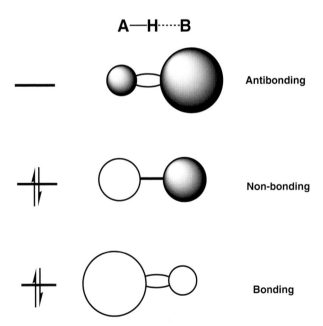

Figure 1.99 Illustration of **hydrogen bond interactions**. **A, B** = N or O. Contact of **AH** with **B** orbitals leads to the formation of three molecular orbitals according to theory of **linear combination of atomic orbitals** (**LCAO**). Relative sizes are as drawn. Orbital filling according to occupied energy ladder (left) just favours bonding interactions.

B possesses an available lone pair of electrons in a hybrid lone pair orbital that is then presented collinear to the A–H σ-bond axis as shown. An empirical molecular orbital description may then be used to describe the **hydrogen bond** in the form of a **three centre four electron bond**. According to the linear combination of atomic orbitals, mixing a hydrogen 1s orbital with a hybrid atomic orbital of A and a hybrid lone pair orbital of B results in three molecular orbitals as shown (Figure 1.99). Only bonding and non-bonding orbitals are occupied, with the result that a weak bonding interaction is established. This bonding interaction is purely a contact interaction 'turned on' when the A–H σ bond contacts with the hybrid lone pair orbital of B and 'turned off' immediately contact is broken.

Hydrogen bonding is clearly ubiquitous in stabilising protein secondary structures and nucleic acid double helices (by Watson–Crick base pairing between anti-parallel phosphodiester chains), and in the wide range of homoglycan secondary to quaternary structures.

1.6.4 Hydrophobic interactions

The subject of **hydrophobic interactions** is controversial but nevertheless appears to be a very important for biological macromolecular cohesion in aqueous media, including most especially the cohesion of macromolecular lipid assemblies. The structure of water is critical to the existence of hydrophobic interactions (Figure 1.100). Water molecules consist of

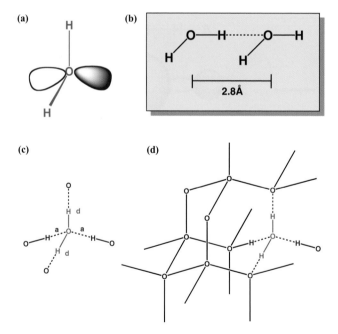

Figure 1.100 Illustration of **water structure in solid** (ice) and liquid state. (**a**) water has two **O—H** bonds and two lone pairs; each water molecule may form up to four short hydrogen bonds (**b**), two from **O—H** hydrogen bond donors d and two from **O** lone pair hydrogen bond acceptors a (**c**); together these water molecules create "adamantane-like" I_h hydrogen bonded structures (**d**).

a repulsive spherical core centred at oxygen ($d = 2.4$–2.8 Å). Directional hydrogen bonds ($V = 20$ kJ mol^{-1}) compete with the repulsive core to bring water molecules into close proximity with each other. In ice, hydrogen bonding creates an ordered lattice structure (I_h). In liquid water, large scale order is disrupted but significant local order is retained. This extends to the solvation of polar and hydrophobic (non-polar) molecules/functional groups in aqueous solution. The solvation of non-polar molecules/functional groups is particularly important for hydrophobic interactions (Figure 1.101). Immediately surrounding any given hydrophobic molecule/functional group, the first solvation shell consists of icelike hydrogen

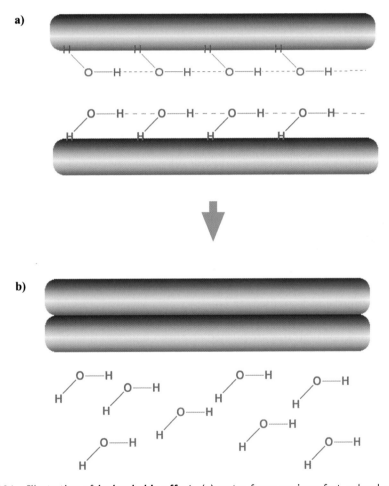

Figure 1.101 Illustration of **hydrophobic effect**. (a) water forms an imperfect ordered solvent cage around two hydrophobic entities (blue). Each water of solvation is prevented from forming four hydrogen bonds with neighbouring water molecules for steric reasons. Waters of solvation are excluded upon association of two hydrophobic entities (**b**). These increase system entropy by entering bulk solution and release enthalpy through enhanced hydrogen bond formation. Short range Van der Waals interactions between hydrophobic entities may also contribute to system enthalpy.

bonded arrays of water molecules. These 'close-packed' water molecules suffer a loss of hydrogen bonding potential as well as a loss of entropy as a result of being 'locked' in an ordered solvation shell covering the surface of the molecules/functional groups. Therefore, when two hydrophobic molecules/functional groups come into close proximity in aqueous medium, their association is driven by the opportunity to release ordered water molecules from these solvation cages. In effect, water drives the association of hydrophobic entities so as to minimise the hydrophobic exposed surface area that needs to be solvated, maximise entropy gain by releasing water molecules of solvation into the bulk medium and maximise enthalpy gain by allowing additional hydrogen bonds to be created in the bulk. The controversy about hydrophobic interactions is therefore justified. This has less to do with actual bonding interactions between hydrophobic entities and much more to do with the subtleties of water structure and the intermolecular bonding interactions involved. Nevertheless, hydrophobic interactions are obviously crucial for the structural integrity and functions of biological macromolecules (including macromolecular lipid assemblies) in aqueous solution.

The hydrophobic effect is believed to have a significant stabilising effect on globular proteins given the substantial presence of hydrophobic amino-acid residues located in the 'middle and centre' of globular proteins. Clearly the hydrophobic effect forces may also play a role in stabilising the 'interior' base-pair axial middle of nucleic acids too. However, the greatest beneficiary of the hydrophobic effect should be once again macromolecular lipid assemblies given the vast numbers of interacting alkyl chains within membrane structures.

1.6.5 Other forces

There are undoubtedly other forces involved in stabilising biological macromolecules and macromolecular lipid assemblies, such as weak polar interactions (Section 1.2.5), that are yet to be fully described and accounted for. However, although we have said a lot about forces of attraction in Section 1.6, next to nothing has been said about forces of repulsion. In fact, when molecules or functional groups are pushed or pulled together, then nuclear and electronic repulsions will eventually begin to dominate over forces of attraction at very short range. Forces of repulsion are very complicated to define and depend heavily upon the nature and electronic structure of the interacting species. Nevertheless, the Lennard-Jones potential has been found to be a good overall description of how potential energy varies between species with inter-atomic distance by taking into account the behaviour of forces of repulsion. This potential is

$$V = \frac{C_n}{r^n} - \frac{C_6}{r^6} \tag{1.13}$$

where C_6 and C_n are constants, and n is a large integer (often given as 12). When n is 12, then Equation (1.13) is said to describe a Lennard-Jones (12,6) potential. Forces of attraction are represented by the negative $1/r^6$ term, since weak forces of attraction typically obey a $1/r^6$ dependence with distance of separation (see Equations (1.7), (1.9) and (1.11)). Forces of repulsion are represented by the positive $1/r^n$ term (where n is usually 12), in line with the fact that such forces can only dominate at very short range. The complete list of the main structural forces in biological macromolecules and macromolecular lipid assemblies is given with distance dependence in Table 1.5, including forces of repulsion.

2
Chemical and Biological Synthesis

2.1 Introduction to synthesis in chemical biology

Chemical synthesis and biological synthesis are amongst the most powerful tools available to chemists interested in chemical biology. In synthesis begins the process of determining structure and dynamics. Without synthesis, there is insufficient material to study structure. Without synthesis, critical probes are not available to study dynamics. Chemical biology is perhaps unique in requiring both chemical and biological approaches to synthesis; herein rests a key fundamental of the chemical biology approach.

Traditional chemical synthesis has an incredibly rich heritage and record of success in the directed synthesis of a multiplicity of molecules, from unusual inorganic compounds to complicated and intricate organic molecules, built up from readily available, small molecule starting materials. By contrast, biological synthesis has a much shorter though no less distinguished record of success in the directed synthesis of biological macromolecules by means of 'factory organisms' such as the bacterium *Escherichia coli*, which employ complex anabolic intracellular pathways for the assembly of biological macromolecules. The directed biological syntheses of many biological macromolecules are heavily dependent on recombinant technologies and gene cloning techniques (Chapter 3).

Although the overall philosophy and objectives of both chemical and biological synthesis are the same – directed synthesis and isolation of a target molecule – the two approaches are obviously radically different. Accordingly general courses in chemistry may incorporate certain aspects of biological synthesis, but for the most part biological synthesis is not covered. In Chapter 1, the chemical biology reader was introduced to the structures of the main biological macromolecules and lipid macromolecular assemblies. In this chapter, we aim to provide a balanced introduction to both chemical and biological approaches for the syntheses of biological macromolecules and lipids. We hope that the reader will emerge with not only

Essentials of Chemical Biology   Andrew Miller and Julian Tanner
© 2008 John Wiley & Sons, Ltd

a proper appreciation of each approach, but also a proper appreciation of their respective limits as well.

2.2 Chemical synthesis of peptides and proteins

2.2.1 Basic principles – peptide synthesis

As a first step to understanding the challenges of peptide synthesis, consider the synthesis of a dipeptide from the constituent amino acids. The amino-acid residue sequence must be correct, side reaction products should be prevented from forming, and α-carbon racemisation should be avoided. In order to meet all these requirements, N- and C-terminal protecting groups are required to ensure chemoselective formation of only the single, desired peptide link in coupling. Overall the synthetic strategy may therefore be considered as a five-stage process (Figure 2.1):

    (a) protection of the α-amino group of the N-terminal residue

    (b) protection of the carboxyl group of the C-terminal residue

    (c) activation of the carboxy group of the α-N-protected amino acid

    (d) coupling (peptide link formation) to give fully protected dipeptide

    (e) deprotection (as appropriate).

For the synthesis of most dipeptides, protection of amino-acid residue side-chain functional groups will also be appropriate in order to avoid additional undesirable side reactions.

The construction of a tripeptide from a dipeptide requires that Step (e) should only involve selective deprotection of the N-terminal α-amino group of a dipeptide. A third amino-acid residue may then be added by coupling the free α-amino group of the dipeptide to the free carboxyl group of a selected α-N-protected amino acid. Further selective deprotection can then give rise to the coupling of a further selected α-N-protected amino acid, and so on. The whole process of di-, tri-, tetrapeptide etc synthesis relies on **selective deprotection** of the α-N-protecting group. Such selective deprotection requires that the conditions of deprotection need to be as different as possible (**orthogonal**) to the conditions required for the removal of other protecting groups involved in the synthesis. Therefore, provided that the α-N-protecting group can be removed under conditions that do not affect the remaining protecting groups, this protecting group can be said to be orthogonal with respect to the remaining protecting groups and can be said to be subject to selective deprotection. The use of selective deprotection and orthogonal protecting groups is central to successful solution phase peptide synthesis in order to avoid low yields and horrendous product mixtures.

Furthermore, coupling (peptide link formation) need to be performed under very carefully controlled conditions, otherwise α-carbon racemisation becomes a serious problem, especially during coupling. This is so because, each selected N-terminal protected amino acid

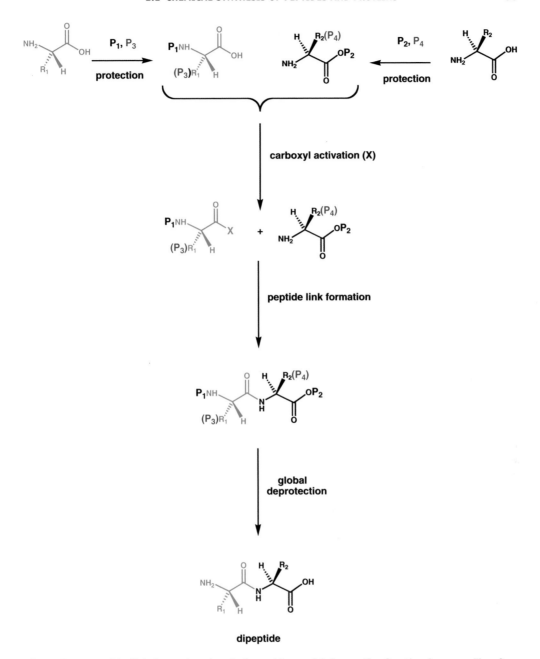

Figure 2.1 Peptide link formation. L-α-Amino acids are rich in reactive functional groups. Therefore, chemo-selective peptide link formation is not possible without protecting groups. A future *N*-terminal residue must be α-*N*-protected (**P$_1$**) (with optional **P$_3$** side chain protection) while future *C*-terminal residue must be α-*C* protected (**P$_2$**) (with optional **P$_4$** side chain protection). The protected *N*-terminal residue must then be activated to allow peptide link formation to take place. Global deprotection reveals a dipeptide product.

chosen to extend the peptide chain must be activated for peptide link formation (Figure 2.1). Activation renders the α-carbon position more acidic and hence more likely to undergo acid dissociation leading to racemisation. Clearly, solution phase synthesis requiring an approach such as this becomes a significant challenge for any peptide of greater than a few amino-acid residues in length. Indeed, the involved and painstaking solution phase synthesis of the nonapeptides oxytocin and vasopressin by **Vincent du Vigneaud** even resulted in the award of a Nobel Prize for Chemistry in 1955!

2.2.2 Solid phase peptide synthesis (SPPS)

Problems in solution phase peptide synthesis have been largely overcome by the development of **solid phase peptide synthesis (SPPS)**. The chemical principles of peptide link formation and peptide synthesis remain the same, but in SPPS the growing peptide chain is anchored to a solid phase resin, thereby easing the iterative process of peptide bond formation, removing the need for crystallisations and purifications after each step of the synthesis, and in some ways simplifying protection/deprotection problems. SPPS earned **Bruce Merrifield** a Nobel Prize in 1986, and has eased the technical challenges of peptide synthesis to the extent that the process can now be automated.

Solid phase synthesis can be simplified to the following steps (Figure 2.2).

(a) The first amino-acid residue (*C*-terminus) is coupled to reactive group X attached to an insoluble matrix (solid support) via its free carboxyl functional group. The amino-acid residue is otherwise α-*N*-protected (and at other functional groups as appropriate).

(b) The α-*N*-protecting group is selectively removed from the α-amino position then a second α-*N*-protected amino acid (also protected at other functional groups as appropriate) is introduced and activated for coupling with the first amino acid bound to the resin.

(c) Once the peptide link is formed, the process of α-*N*-deprotection and amino-acid coupling continues for as long as required.

(d) Finally, the desired length peptide is cleaved from the solid support by chemistry conditions suitable to cleave the linkage between solid support and peptide chain, and remove all the amino-acid side-chain protecting groups as well.

2.2.2.1   *Solid supports and linkers for SPPS*

The solid support should be well solvated to facilitate reactions to take place involving the two phases. The original supports were based on polystyrene but have generally been superseded by polyamide resins, which have an advantage in that they have a similar polarity to the peptide backbone. More recently, resins based on polyethylene glycol (PEG) grafted onto low

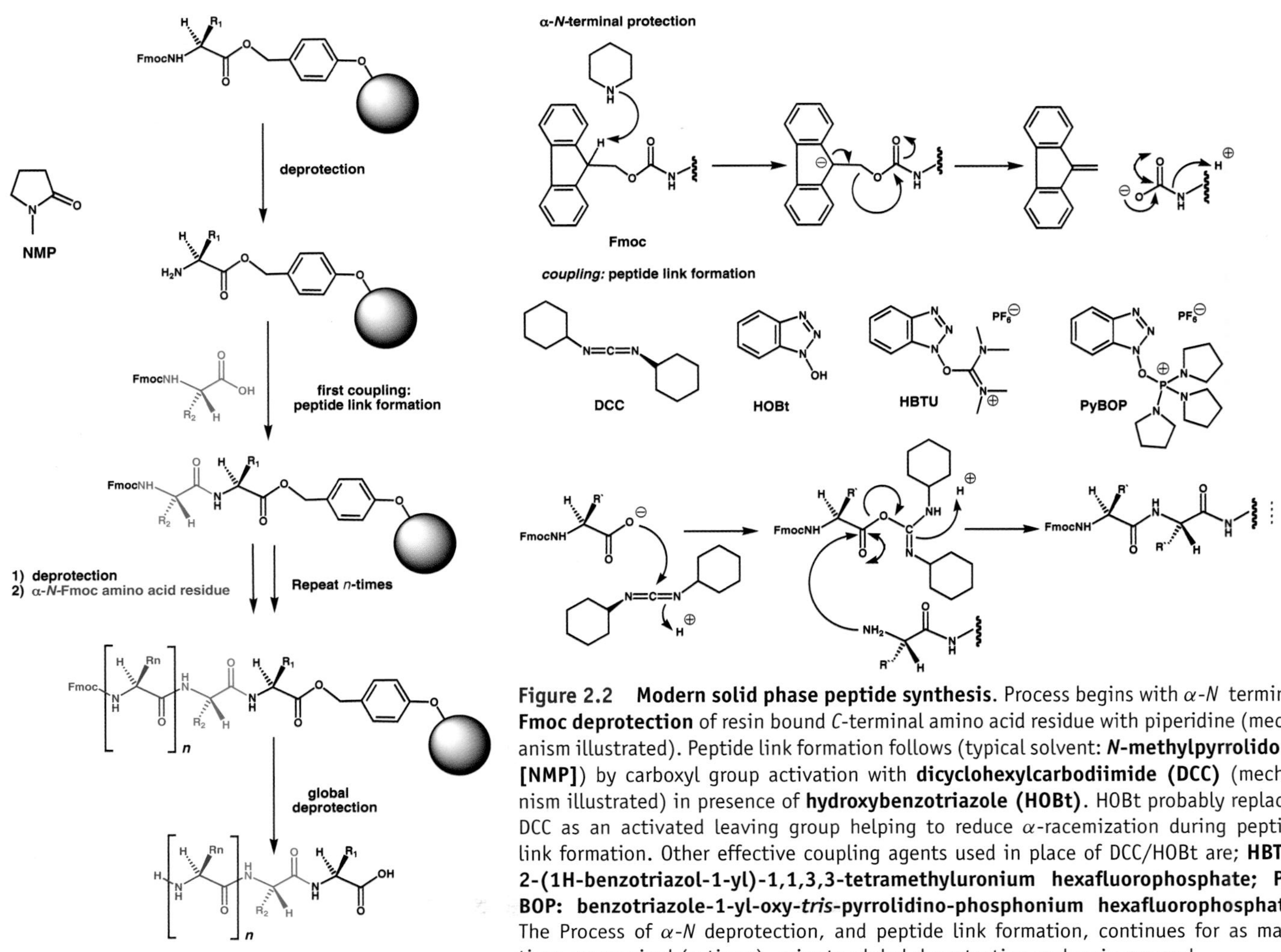

Figure 2.2   Modern solid phase peptide synthesis. Process begins with α-N terminal **Fmoc deprotection** of resin bound C-terminal amino acid residue with piperidine (mechanism illustrated). Peptide link formation follows (typical solvent: **N-methylpyrrolidone [NMP]**) by carboxyl group activation with **dicyclohexylcarbodiimide (DCC)** (mechanism illustrated) in presence of **hydroxybenzotriazole (HOBt)**. HOBt probably replaces DCC as an activated leaving group helping to reduce α-racemization during peptide link formation. Other effective coupling agents used in place of DCC/HOBt are; **HBTU: 2-(1H-benzotriazol-1-yl)-1,1,3,3-tetramethyluronium hexafluorophosphate; PyBOP: benzotriazole-1-yl-oxy-tris-pyrrolidino-phosphonium hexafluorophosphate.** The Process of α-N deprotection, and peptide link formation, continues for as many times as required (n-times), prior to global deprotection and resin removal.

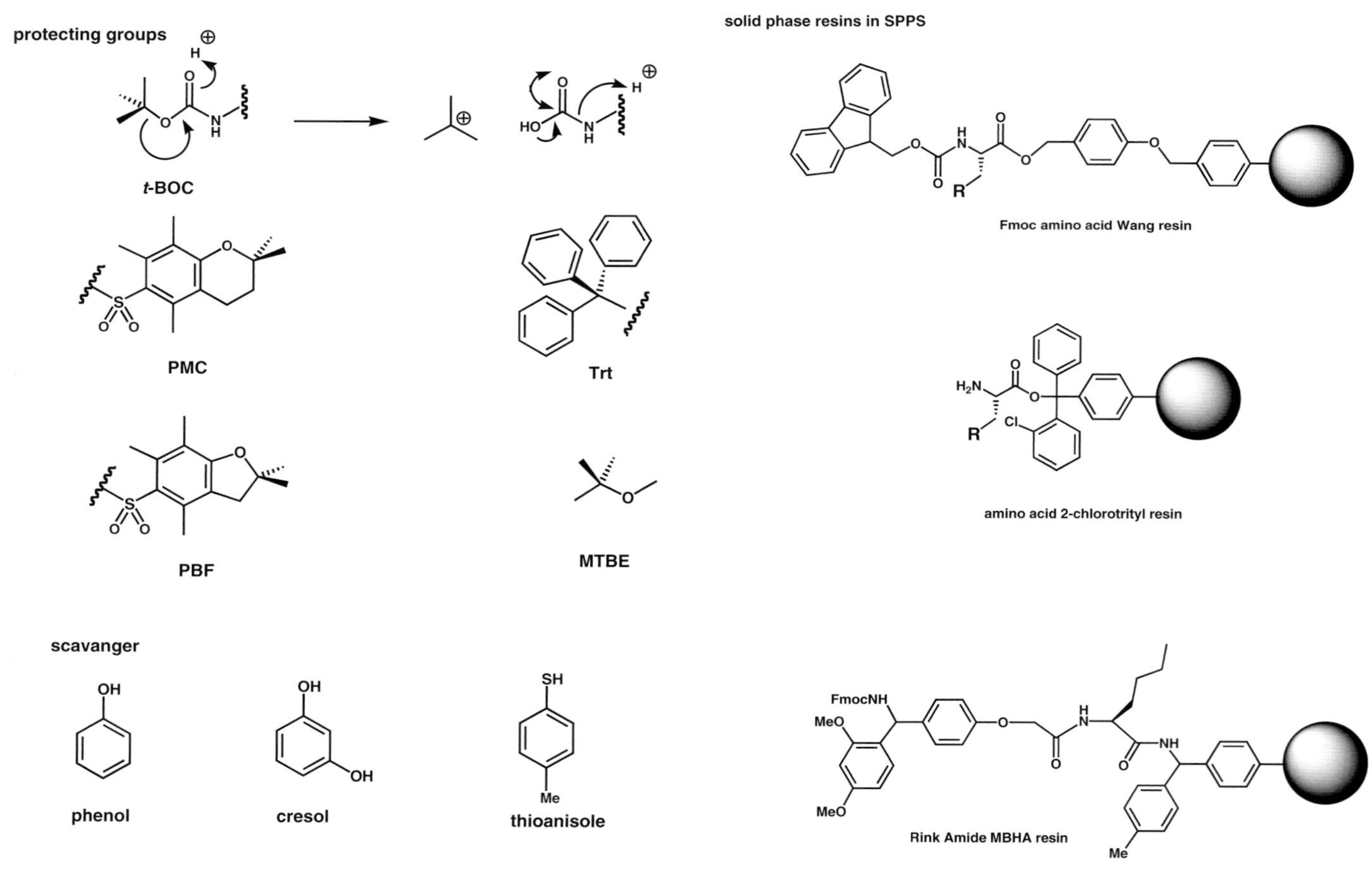

Figure 2.2   Modern solid phase peptide synthesis (Contd.). Most frequently used amino acid side chain protecting groups are shown: **t-BOC: tert-butyloxycarbonyl; Trt: trityl; PMC: 2,2,5,7,8-pentamethylchroman-6-sulphonyl; PBF: 2,2,4,6,7-pentamethyl-dihydrobenzofuran-5-sulphonyl.** These are all acid labile (see illustrated mechanism). Most common solid phase resins are also shown, all of which are labile to acidic release conditions too (the rink amide leaves a *C*-terminal amide in place). During global deprotection and resin removal, **scavengers** such as **phenol, cresol** or **thioanisole** are also included to capture reactive cationic species post deprotection. The desired product oligo-/polypeptide is then separated initially by precipitation by means of an agent such as **methoxy-*tert*-butyl ether (MTBE)** and purified finally by reversed phase liquid chromatography (see later in Chapter 2).

cross-linked polystyrene, or resins completely based on cross-linked PEG, have been used due to their superior swelling capacity, resulting in a larger solid/liquid interface. Each growing peptide chain is attached to the solid support by a **resin linker**. The resin linker must be sufficiently robust to be unaffected by all the α-N-deprotection and coupling steps involved that comprise a peptide synthesis. Thereafter, the resin linker must be cleaved quantitatively to release the full-length peptide at the end of the synthesis. In the present day, **Wang** (via *p*-benzyloxybenzyl), **Rink amide** (an even larger benzyl based linker) or **Super acid labile** (2-chlorotrityl) resins are most commonly used in place of the original polystyrene since these resins have been adapted to possess fundamentally acid sensitive resin linkers (Figure 2.2).

2.2.2.2 Coupling protected amino acids in SPPS

SPPS relies on very efficient amino-acid coupling. Each coupling step involves the linking of an α-N-protected amino acid with the α-N-deprotected amino terminus of a growing resin-linked peptide chain. Each such coupling step must take place at yields approaching 100 per cent in order that long peptide chains (>20 amino-acid residues) may be built up ($C \rightarrow N$) on resin prior to the cleavage of the resin linker. The extent of coupling can be monitored by means of the **ninhydrin test** (Figure 2.3). Ninhydrin reacts with primary α-amines to originate a

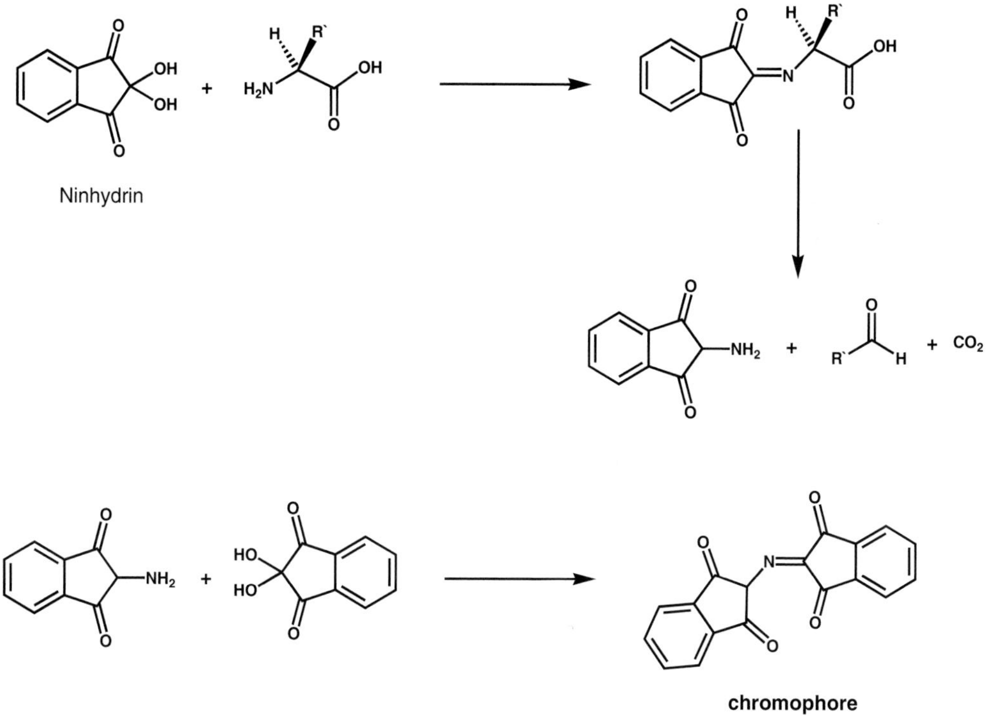

Figure 2.3 Ninhydrin Test. Ninhydrin combines with α-N-primary amine functional groups to form primary amine product that combines with a second molecule of ninhydrin to generate a **chromogenic chromophore**.

purple, blue or blue–green colour that may be monitored colorimetrically. Secondary amines such as proline are less reactive with ninhydrin and typically yield a reddish-brown colour. However, the ninhydrin test is a useful diagnostic for incomplete coupling, suggesting when a repeat coupling procedure should be performed.

Obviously coupling must also take place without reducing the optical purity of each α-N-protected amino acid added per cycle of chain extension. Hence the coupling agents chosen to activate free carboxyl groups during peptide link formation should be capable of suppressing racemisation completely. The carbodiimide **dicyclohexylcarbodiimide (DCC)** was the first main coupling agent to be introduced (Figure 2.2). This activates free carboxyl groups through the formation of highly reactive O-acylurea intermediates that are subject to facile nucleophilic attack by α-amino functional groups leading to peptide link formation. However, DCC is not sufficient in and of itself to reduce racemisation during coupling, hence **hydroxylbenzotriazole (HOBt)** was introduced to react with the O-acylurea in order to reduce the racemisation risk. The combined use of DCC and HOBt has now largely been superseded by the unitary use of **2-(1H-benzotriazol-1-yl)-1,1,3,3-tetramethyluronium hexafluorophosphate (HBTU)**, which is today much the most frequently used reagent to activate amino-acid coupling in peptide synthesis along with **benzotriazole-1-yl-oxy-tris-pyrrolidino-phosphonium hexafluor-phosphate (PyBOP)** (Figure 2.2).

2.2.2.3   Protection/deprotection strategies in SPPS

Merrifield's original protection strategy was to use the ***tert*-butyloxycarbonyl (*t*-BOC)** group for α-N-protection on every amino acid added to growing peptide chains, while amino-acid side-chain functional groups were given benzyl-protecting groups. The t-BOC group is acid labile (using a mixture of trifluoroacetic acid, TFA, in dichloromethane) (Figure 2.2). Accordingly, once peptide synthesis reached full length then separation of the full-length peptide from the resin and simultaneous side-chain deprotection was effected using liquid hydrogen fluoride, hardly mild resin cleavage conditions! Fortunately, a much milder orthogonal protecting group strategy has since been developed for peptide synthesis with the introduction of **9-*N*-fluorenylmethyloxycarbonyl (FMOC)** groups for α-N-protection. The FMOC group is sensitive to mild base piperidine (piperidine 20–50 per cent v/v in DMF for 20 min) but is otherwise stable to decomposition in neutral or acidic conditions (Figure 2.2). Consequently, not only may amino-acid side-chain functional groups be protected during peptide synthesis using protecting groups sensitive to only mild acid (or other sets of orthogonal) conditions, but so too separation of the full-length peptide from the resin can be adjusted or tuned to take place under similarly mild acid conditions.

Currently, amino-acid side-chain functional groups can be protected by a number of different groups such as the **N-benzyloxycarbonyl (Z)** amino protecting group that is typically cleaved by simple catalytic hydrogenolysis using a Pd/charcoal catalyst, or by strong acid. In contrast, hydroxy and carboxyl functional groups can be protected by ***tert*-butyl** masking while $\varepsilon$$-$amino groups in lysine and the N^l-position of tryptophan can be protected by t-BOC groups. In both cases, protecting groups are labile with respect to mild acid (HCl in organic solvents or TFA) treatment. Furthermore, the primary amide side-chains of asparagine and glutamine, the thiol of cysteine and the imidazole ring of histidine are commonly masked by

trityl group association. Trityl protection is also notably labile with respect to mild acid treatment in all the cases listed here. Finally the unusual guanidine functional group associated with the side-chain of arginine is frequently protected by **2,2,5,7,8-pentamethylchroman-6-sulfonyl chloride** (**PMC**) or **2,2,4,6,7-pentamethyl-dihydrobenzofuran-5-sulfonyl chloride** (**PBF**). Both PMC and PBF are mildly acidic labile protecting groups as well (Figure 2.2). Clearly the release of resin-bound, full-length peptide can result in the production of highly reactive species such as butyl cations (e.g., *t*Bu-cations and *t*Bu-fluoroacetate). Therefore, **scavengers** such as **phenol**, **cresol** or **thioanisole** are also included in the cleavage cocktail to capture these species and prevent side reactions. The appropriate cleavage mixture is then removed by evaporation and **diethyl ether** or **methyl-*tert*-butyl ether** (**MTBE**) added to precipitate the de-protected peptide product from solution, thereby eliminating many by-products. Finally, the crude deprotected peptide needs to be purified to homogeneity by reversed phase preparative high performance liquid chromatography (HPLC) (see later in Chapter 2).

2.2.3 Chemical synthesis of polypeptides

SPPS has allowed relatively facile peptide synthesis for peptides of up to 40 amino-acid residues, though it can be used to synthesise polypeptides in excess of 100 amino-acid residues in length. Clearly, the synthesis of long polypeptides and proteins should be best accomplished by biological synthesis (see below). However, there are instances when chemical synthesis presents a few significant advantages over biological synthesis, particularly where the incorporation of unusual amino-acid residues is required, such as **d-amino acids**, **fluorescent-labelled amino acids** (such as Aladan, see Chapter 4), linker moieties and other non-peptidic groups. However, the two approaches need not in fact be exclusive. For instance, it may be envisaged that a combination of chemical and biological synthesis (semi-synthesis) could become increasingly important in future chemical biology applications.

2.2.4 Chemical synthesis of peptide nucleic acids

Peptide nucleic acids (PNAs) are synthetic molecules where purine and pyrimidine bases are linked by a polypeptide backbone (Figure 2.4). PNA monomers are typically synthesised using modified protocols from standard peptide synthesis. The *N*-terminus is FMOC protected, whilst **benzhydryloxycarbonyl** (**BHOC**) is used to protect the exocyclic amino groups on adenine, cytosine and guanine. The backbone consists of repeating *N*-(2-aminoethyl)-glycine units resulting in a distance between the bases in PNA similar to natural DNA or RNA containing the usual phosphodiester backbone. Bases align perpendicular to the polypeptide backbone hence PNA may form antiparallel double helices like DNA and RNA wherein complementary strands are linked by Watson–Crick base pair hydrogen bonding. The uncharged backbone of PNA results in many useful and interesting properties. The lack of charge–charge repulsion in a **PNA/DNA duplex** results in far stronger binding than that observed in a DNA double helix (DNA/DNA duplex). Triple helical complexes can also be formed with DNA

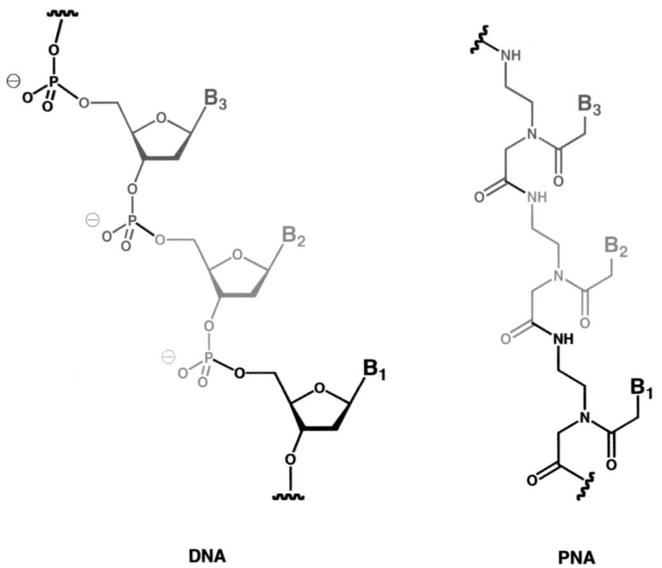

DNA   PNA

Figure 2.4   Comparison of PNA and DNA. PNA contains neither phosphodiester links nor the β-D-2′-deoxyribofuranose rings. Instead the backbone consists of **N-(2-aminoethyl)-glycine** repeat units conjoined by peptide links. The main purine and pyrimidine bases of DNA are linked to the the PNA backbone by methylene carbonyl bridge linkages. Watson-Crick base-complementary PNA strands are capable of Watson-Crick base pairing and hence anti-parallel double helix formation.

that are especially stable when the PNA involved is described as a homopyrimidine. Typically, **PNA/DNA triplex** has a PNA/DNA ration of 2:1. This structure requires a Watson–Crick PNA/DNA duplex annealed to a second PNA strand by Py.Pu.Py Hoogsteen base pairing (see Chapter 1). The stability of the PNA/DNA triplex has been crucial to many potential technological applications of PNA. PNA can invade double helical DNA, forming a PNA/DNA triplex with the complementary (antisense) strand of DNA. Although PNAs are most stable as homopyrimidines, low numbers of purines within the sequence can be tolerated. PNAs are also fairly resistant to both nucleases and proteases, and have significant lifetimes *in vitro* and *in vivo*, a useful advantage over standard nucleic acids. Furthermore, PNAs prepared by chemical synthesis can be modified easily by many of the techniques outlined later (Chapter 4) with fluorescent groups and other labels. The combination of strong binding to complementary nucleic acid sequences, excellent stability and easy derivatisation make these molecules potentially powerful tools in a variety of applications.

2.3 Chemical synthesis of nucleic acids

Merrifield's solid phase peptide synthesis presented a new approach to the chemical synthesis of biological macromolecules and the solid phase approach was quickly adapted to other fields. **Solid phase oligonucleotide synthesis** (**SPONS**) is another vital development in chemical synthesis that has had a major impact on the biological sciences. Whereas the main challenge in SPPS was precise formation of peptide links, the challenge for oligonucleotide synthesis has been precise formation of corresponding phosphodiester links.

Much of the development in SPONS arose from studies on polyphosphate and nucleotide coenzyme synthesis in the laboratory of **Alexander Todd** during the 1950s. Not long after, in the early 1960s, Khorana achieved the synthesis of the first sequence-defined oligonucleotides using DCC to activate phosphate–sugar coupling. However, in the late 1960s, **Letsinger** and co-workers developed the solid phase approach that eventually culminated in the triester chemical approach familiar today.

2.3.1 Chemical synthesis of oligodeoxynucleotides

Oligodeoxynucleotide synthesis today is virtually always carried out on a solid support. Initially, the polymeric solid supports were polystyrene cross-linked with divinylbenzene, but **controlled-pore glass beads** (**CPG beads**) with defined porosities are now used in preference. The 3'-hydroxyl of the first protected deoxynucleotide is precoupled to the solid support and then solid phase, multistage oligodeoxynucleotide synthesis may commence in the 3' → 5' direction, in direct analogy to SPPS (Figure 2.5).

(a) The first protected deoxynucleotide attached to the solid support is protected on the 5'-hydroxyl group with **dimethoxytrityl** (**DMT**). Deprotection with **trichloroacetic acid** (**TCA**) results in a free 5'-hydroxyl group and the release of the orange coloured DMT cation (detected as a measure of the efficiency of deprotection).

(b) A 5'-DMT-protected deoxynucleotide with attached 3'-phosphoramidite (Figure 2.6) or H-phosphonate group is then activated for coupling to the 5'-hydroxyl group of the 3'-solid-support-bound deoxynucleotide by means of a coupling reagent known as **tetrazole**.

(c) Iodine is introduced to oxidise the diester link formed from coupling to a complete phosphodiester link (with P(V) oxidation state). Diester links formed with phosphoramidites or H phosphonate are unstable (due to the P(III) oxidation state).

(d) Acetic anhydride is then added to block or cap any unreacted 5'-hydroxyl groups so that sequence truncations are not incorporated in later steps (Figure 2.7).

(e) With a phosphodiester link formed and 5'-hydroxyl capping performed, the sequential process of 5'-hydroxyl DMT deprotection and coupling of 5'-DMT-deoxynucleotide-3'-phosphoramidites, then iodine oxidation and capping again of unreacted 5'-hydroxyl groups, can take place in a repetitive, iterative manner until the desired full length oligo- or polydeoxynucleotide is prepared.

The entire oligo- or polydeoxynucleotide is then detached from the solid support and deprotected to complete the synthesis. After synthesis of the oligo- or polydeoxynucleotide

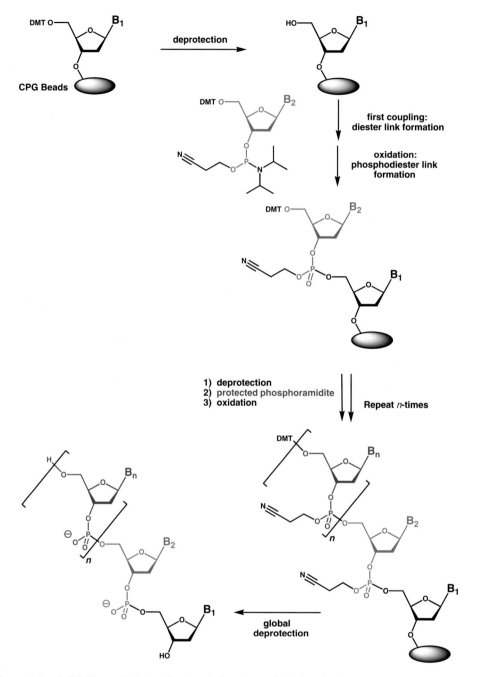

Figure 2.5   Solid Phase DNA Synthesis. 5′-dimethoxytrityl (DMT)-deprotection of resin bound 3′-terminal deoxynucleoside residue is effected with **trichloroacetic acid (TCA)** (mechanism shown) Thereafter the first coupling reaction is enabled by phosphoamidite activation with tetrazole (mechanism shown) followed by oxidation of the newly formed diester linkage to a phosphodiester link. The process of 5′-DMTr deprotection, phosphoramidite coupling and then diester oxidation, continues for as many times as required (*n*-times), prior to global deprotection and resin removal under basic conditions.

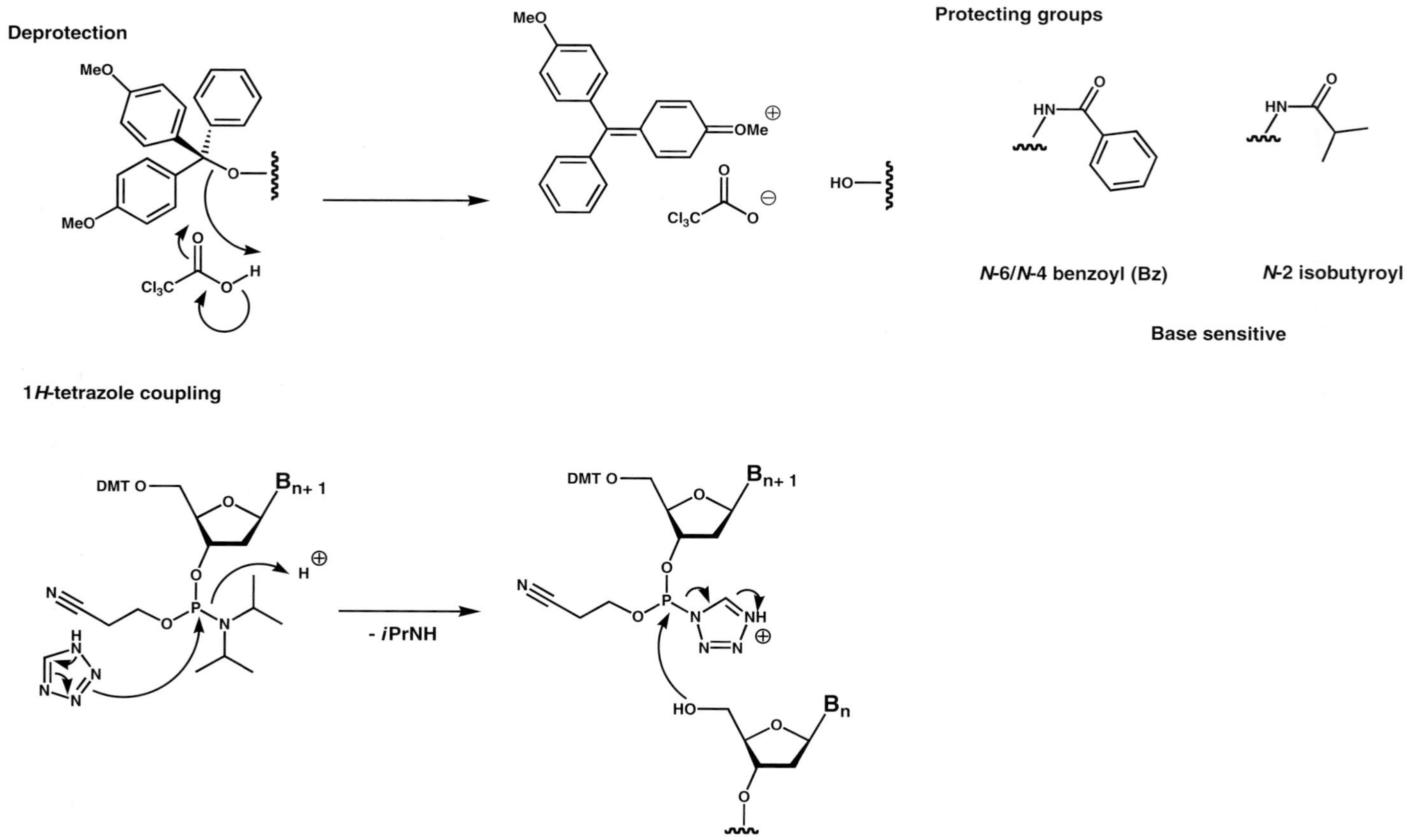

Protecting groups

Deprotection

1H-tetrazole coupling

N-6/N-4 benzoyl (Bz)

N-2 isobutyroyl

Base sensitive

- *iPrNH

Figure 2.5 Solid Phase DNA Synthesis Cycle (Contd.). Most frequently used base protecting groups are shown; **Bz:** *N-6* **benzoyl** (adenine), *N-4* **benzoyl** (cytosine); *N-2* **isobutyroyl** (guanine). All are base sensitive. DNA chain is built up from 3′ to 5′ on **controlled-pore glass (CPG)** bead solid support. Post global deprotection and resin removal, the desired product oligo–/polydeoxynucleotide is then separated initially by precipitation by means of an agent such as **ethanol** and purified finally by reversed phase liquid chromatography, or ion exchange chromatography as appropriate (see later in Chapter 2).

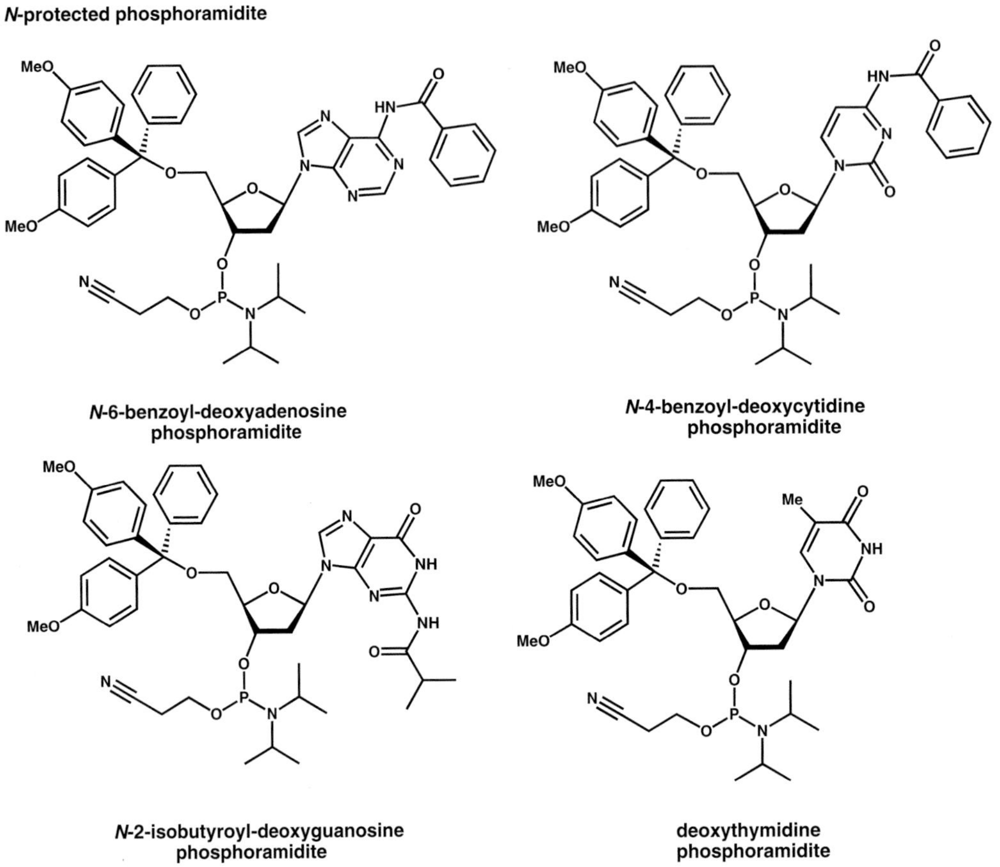

N-protected phosphoramidite

N-6-benzoyl-deoxyadenosine phosphoramidite

N-4-benzoyl-deoxycytidine phosphoramidite

N-2-isobutyroyl-deoxyguanosine phosphoramidite

deoxythymidine phosphoramidite

Figure 2.6   DNA Phosphoramidites. The four main phosphoramidite "building blocks" used in solid phase DNA synthesis are illustrated with base protecting groups where appropriate.

purification takes place. At its simplest this just involves desalting, but polyacrylamide gel electrophoresis (PAGE) (Chapter 3) is the most commonly used approach to purify a synthesised oligodeoxynucleotide with high levels of purity. For higher yields in purification, or for oligodeoxynucleotides with unusual fluorophores or other modifications, HPLC is the purification approach of choice after synthesis.

2.3.2 Chemical synthesis of oligonucleotides

Oligo- and polynucleotide synthesis is a more significant challenge than oligo- and poly-deoxynucleotide synthesis for two major reasons. First, RNA molecules are particularly sensitive to both chemical and enzymatic degradation. Second, the 2′-hydroxyl group in each β-D-ribofuranose ring is potentially reactive and must be protected during chain synthesis. However, the protecting group must also be labile enough to be removed at the end of the

capping

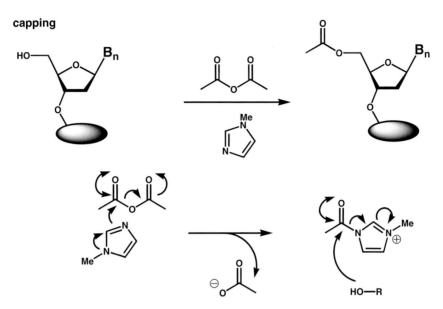

Figure 2.7 Capping. Capping is a critical step that can be included after oxidation to cover any 5′-terminal hydroxyl groups that failed to combine with phosphoramidites. Capping protects any unreacted 5′-hydroxyl groups and prevents "deletions" being incorporated into DNA during the synthesis. **Acetic anhydride** and **N-methylimidazole** are the capping reagents added for chemoselective combination with 5′-hydroxyl groups.

synthesis, but stable enough to allow differential protection of the 5′-hydroxyl group during oligo- or polynucleotide synthesis. In other words, 2′- and 5′-hydroxyl protecting groups should be properly orthogonal. This can now be achieved with 5′-DMT protection and **2′-tert-butyl dimethylsilyl** (**TBDMS**) group protection (Figure 2.8). All 5′-DMT deprotection steps that take place during oligo- or polynucleotide synthesis require TCA (as with DNA). TBDMS groups are relatively robust during oligo- or polynucleotide synthesis but are removed easily during final deprotection. At the end of oligo- and polynucleotide synthesis, a three-stage deprotection strategy is used. First, methyl groups are removed from the phosphodiester internucleotide links using **triethylammonium thiophenoxide**. Second, an ammonia/alcohol mixture is required to cleave the oligo- or polynucleotide from the solid support and also remove exocyclic amino-protecting groups. Third, **tetrabutylammonium fluoride** (**TBAF**) is used to remove the TBDMS groups in a highly chemoselective manner from 2′-hydroxyl positions. Automated oligo- and polynucleotide synthesis possible using the solid phase method but this procedure is not so routine as is DNA oligo- and polydeoxynucleotide synthesis.

2.3.3 Useful deoxynucleotide/nucleotide modifications

Starting with **backbone modifications**, we will consider first **phosphorothioate** links that result from the exchange of one non-bridging oxygen atom for a sulphur atom in a given

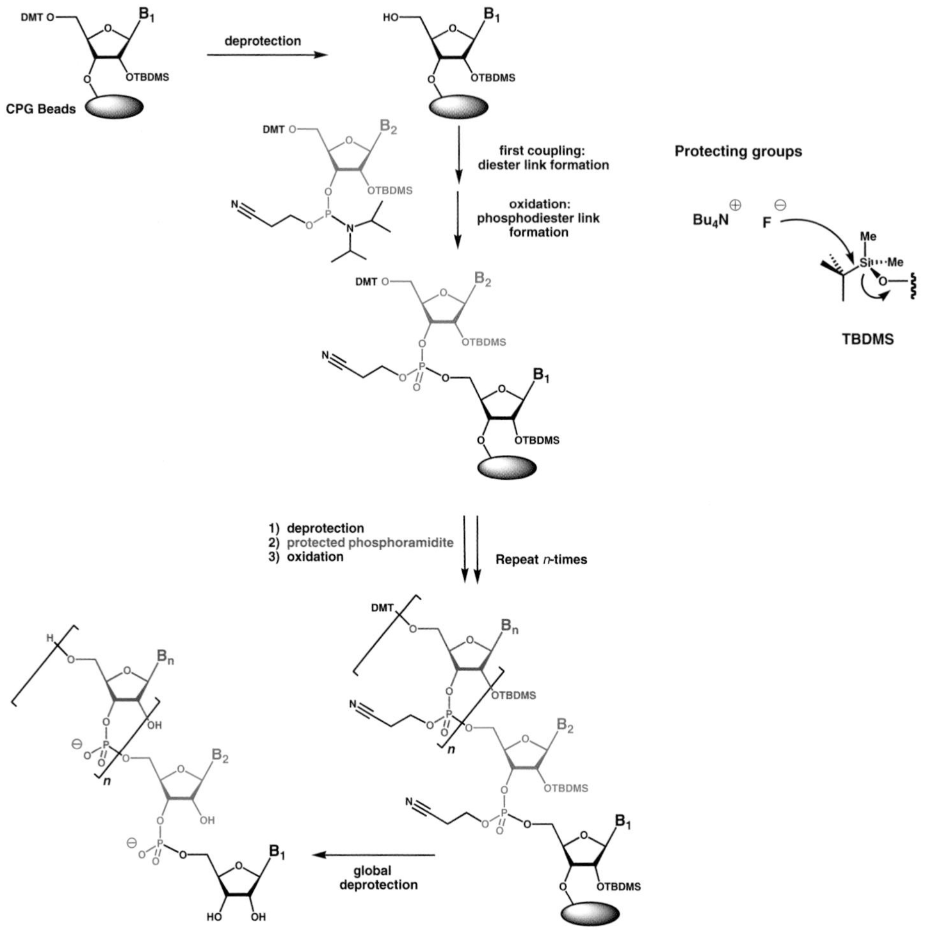

Figure 2.8 Solid Phase RNA Synthesis. 5′-**dimethoxytrityl (DMT)**-deprotection of resin bound 3′-terminal nucleoside residue is effected with **trichloroacetic acid (TCA)** (see **Fig. 2.5**). Thereafter the first coupling reaction is enabled by phosphoamidite activation with tetrazole (see **Fig. 2.5**) followed by oxidation of the newly formed diester linkage to a phosphodiester link. The process of 5′-DMT deprotection, phosphoramidite coupling and then diester oxidation, continues for as many times as required (n-times), prior to global deprotection and resin removal under basic conditions. RNA synthesis requires that 2′-hydroxyl groups are protected during the synthesis by **tert-butyl dimethyl silyl (TBDMS)** protecting groups labile only to fluoride treatment from **tetra butyl ammonium fluoride (TBAF)** (mechanism shown).

phosphodiester link. The new link becomes a **chiral phosphate** centre where two diastereomers are possible. Phosphorothioate links can be incorporated into either oligo-/polydeoxynucleotides or oligo-/polynucleotides for various reasons. First, the 'soft' sulphur can provide insight into metal ion function when compared to the 'hard' oxygen atom. Also, phosphorothioates are far more stable to nucleases compared to the normal phosphodiester links, so are useful in cell culture and even for functional studies in animals *in vivo*. Solid-state

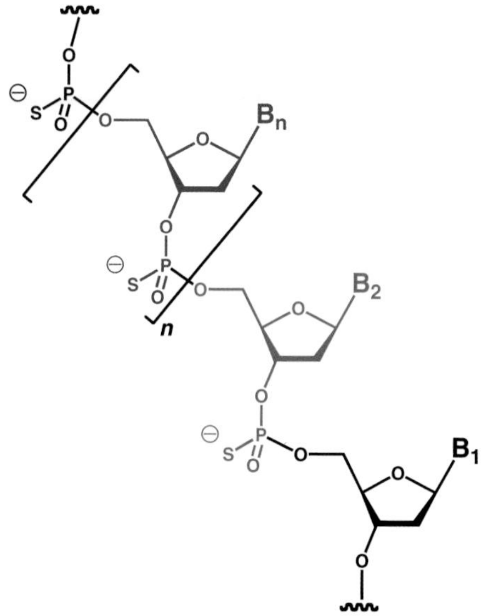

Figure 2.9 **Phosphorothioates**. Oligo-/polynucleotide or oligo-/polydeoxynucleotide phosphorothioates (as shown), have extra sources of chirality in that each phosphorothiodiester link can exist in either of two diasteromeric forms.

syntheses can be used to insert phosphorothioate links into oligo-/polydeoxynucleotides, but a sulphurising agent is needed to replace iodine in order to introduce the non-bridging sulphur atom at each link (Figure 2.9). Should sulphur atoms replace both non-bridging oxygen atoms then **achiral phosphorodithioate** links are the result. Such links are very stable to hydrolysis in general, but **phosphorodithioate** links can provoke significant deviations from standard oligo-/polynucleotide structures and so are little used in relative terms. In comparison, **methylphosphonate** linkages that result when a methyl group replaces a non-bridging oxygen atom are undeniably more interesting (Figure 2.10). Unlike the standard phosphodiester links, and the thioate links, methylphosphonates are non-ionic and can therefore help to provide insight into the importance of charge to the structure of oligo-/polynucleotides.

Sugar modifications are easily introduced into oligo-/polydeoxynucleotides or oligo-/polynucleotides by solid phase synthesis, and these can have many uses, particularly in introducing stability to oligo-/polynucleotide structures. Oligo-/polydeoxynucleotides are comprised of 2'-deoxy-β-D-ribofuranose rings that can adopt C2'-endo and C3'-endo conformations (Chapter 1). In contrast, oligo-/polynucleotide β-D-ribofuranose rings only exhibit the C3'-endo conformation. Accordingly, 2'-substituents such as fluoro, amino, methoxy, alloxy etc stabilise corresponding oligo-/polynucleotides with respect to conformation and also to hydrolytic attack. Most recently, this concept was extended into the development of **locked nucleic acids** (**LNAs**), which could be profoundly important in RNA therapeutics in future owing to their conformational and metabolic stability (Figure 2.10). Unsurprisingly, solid phase synthesis also lends itself to the incorporation of **non-natural base modifications** into

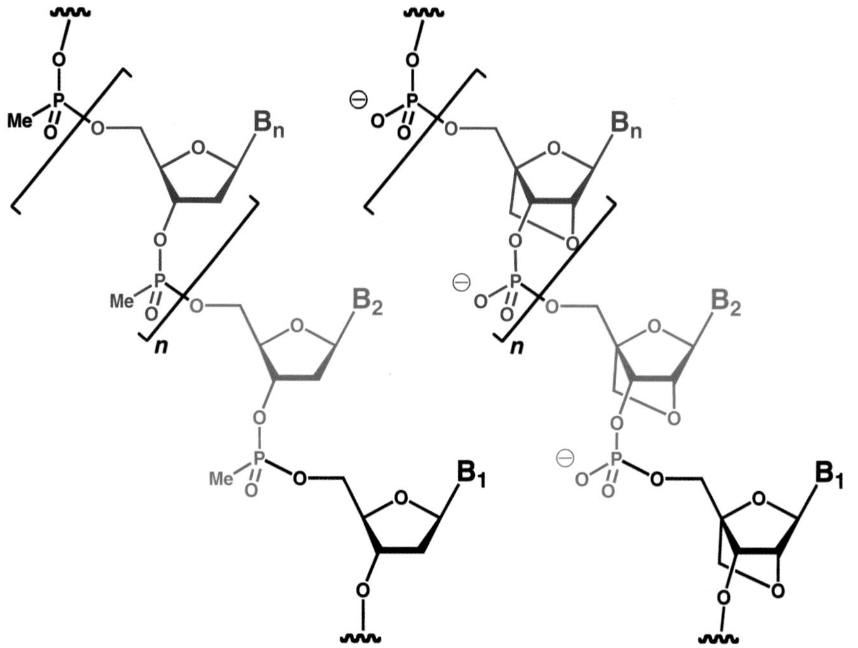

Figure 2.10   Methylphosphonate and Linked Nucleic Acids. Oligo-/polynucleotide or oligo-/polydeoxynucleotide (as shown) **methylphosphonates** (left) have chiral properties in common with phosphorothioates. However lack of charge on the phosphonodiester backbone results in quite significantly more hydrophobic biophysical characteristics. **Locked nucleic acids (LNAs)** (right) are now the subject of great interest since very stable RNA A-helices may be formed between wild-type RNA and base-complementary NAs.

an oligo-/polydeoxynucleotide or an oligo-/polynucleotide as well. Non-natural bases are useful probes for delineating structure and function. For example, **7-deazapurine nucleotides** that lack the N-7 nitrogen are useful probes for those situations where this nitrogen acts as a hydrogen bond acceptor (e.g. Hoogsteen base pairing; see Chapter 1). Base analogues may instead be fluorescent or dye labelled (see Chapter 4). For instance, **2-aminopurine (AP)** is a useful fluorescent probe that can directly substitute for adenine in dA/A nucleotides and can base pair with thymine in dT nucleotides without affecting the DNA double helical structure (Figure 2.11). Also, **3-methyl-8-isoxanthopterin** is another fluorescent probe that mimics the behaviour of guanine in dG/G nucleotides, and is introduced by chemical synthesis. The uses of such fluorescent probes are accounted for elsewhere (see Chapter 4). Furthermore, **chemical cross-linkers** and **photo-affinity cross-linkers** too can be introduced to bases in oligo-/polydeoxynucleotides or oligo-/polynucleotides during or post-synthesis. These can be used to attach oligo-/polydeoxynucleotides or oligo-/polynucleotides to surfaces or other associated molecules, if required. Alternatively some cross-linkers may even actually perturb nucleic acid functions by the introduction of significant covalent distortions, such as the 'nitrogen mustards' (dithiobis(alkylamines)) or *cis*-platin (a potent anticancer drug) (Figure 2.12).

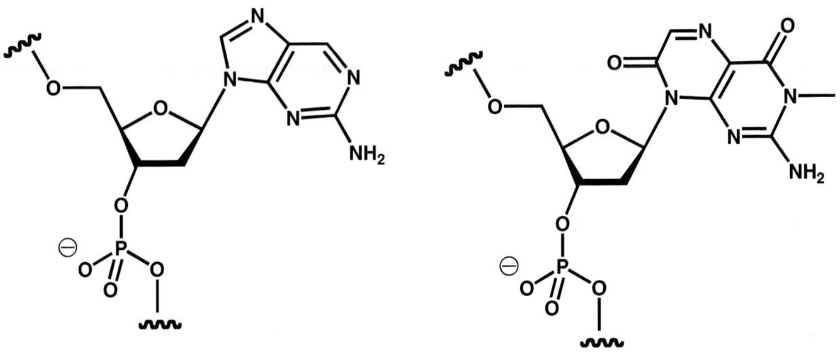

Figure 2.11 Fluorescent purines. Two very useful non-invasive DNA (base fluorophores that can be included by solid phase DNA synthesis are; **2-aminopurine** (*left*) and **3-methyl-isoxanthopterin** (*right*). The fluorescence quantum yield depends on the base stacking, and both bases are useful probes of conformational change/state in DNA.

2.4 Chemical synthesis of oligosaccharides

Whilst solid phase approaches dominate the chemical syntheses of the shorter nucleic acids and polypeptides, the same is not true for oligo-/polysaccharides. The problem is the complexity of oligo-/polysaccharide primary structures. Where homoglycans are concerned, this is not valid, but many oligo-/polysaccharides associated with proteins or lipids to form glycoproteins or glycolipids can be immensely complicated. The complexity comes from the fact that, while natural sugars all possess one anomeric carbon that acts as the 'electrophilic acceptor' for a glycosidic link, each monosaccharide can present at least two or more different 'nucleophilic donor' hydroxyl groups, leading to complex branching. Hence, primary structure branching and control of anomeric carbon stereochemistry are two of the great challenges for chemical synthesis of oligo-/polysaccharides. Consequently, oligo-/polysaccharide chemical syntheses demand a range of chemo-selective protecting groups capable of orthogonal, selective deprotections. Special reagents are also required to form glycosidic links with precise stereocontrol, possibly with the anchimeric assistance of neighbouring group protecting groups. Another challenging aspect of oligo-/polysaccharide chemical syntheses is that certain protecting groups and coupling reagents too may be useful for the protection and coupling involving only a small range of monosaccharide building blocks. Quite clearly, the chemical synthesis of oligo-/polysaccharides is very much 'work in progress', and still awaits the simplifying principles that underlie the chemical syntheses of peptides and nucleic acids. Nevertheless, there are some principles emerging that are worth reviewing with examples.

2.4.1 Protecting groups

Chemical synthesis of oligo-/polysaccharides demands the use of orthogonal protecting groups capable of selective removal. **Benzyl ether** protecting groups have seen widespread use

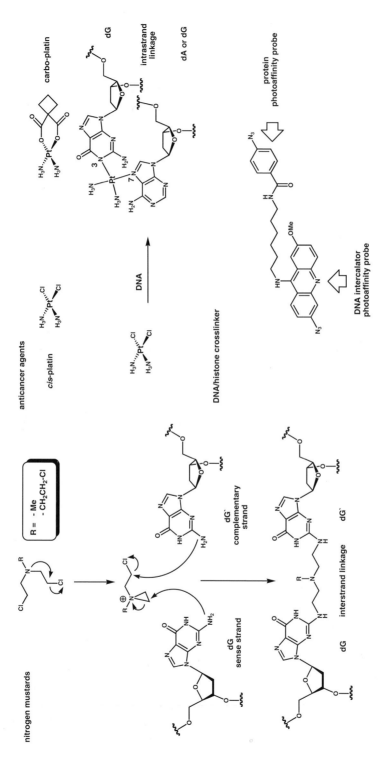

Figure 2.12 DNA crosslinking. The deleterious properties of **nitrogen mustards** are explained through the illustrated interstrand linkage mechanism that makes DNA impossible to duplicate or transcribe. Intrastrand crosslinking is the basis of action for anti-cancer drugs such as **cis-platin** and **carbo-platin**. This is intended to prevent DNA duplication and hence cancer cell division. DNA crosslinking to proteins (such as histones) uses a **non-covalent DNA intercalator** with two azide functional groups. Both azides are activated for covalent coupling under photo-chemical conditions so that DNA subsequently becomes covalently linked to protein.

in oligo-/polysaccharide chemistry. The benzyl ether acts as a 'permanent' protecting group introduced to protect hydroxyl functional groups not expected to be involved in glycosidic link formation. Hence, benzyl ether protected groups are robust enough to remain inert during oligo-/polysaccharide synthesis only to be removed by mild catalytic hydrogenolysis at the end. Otherwise, oligo-/polysaccharide synthesis makes use of **base-labile protecting groups** such as **acetyl**, **benzoyl** and **pivaloyl** that are frequent monosaccharide C-2 protecting groups. In this capacity, these protecting groups can offer **neighbouring group participation** during glycosidic link formation and so assist in the control of stereochemistry (Figure 2.13). Base-labile protecting groups are also intended to provide temporary protection during a synthesis to unmask a key hydroxyl group for reaction at just the right juncture. Other temporary protecting groups that may be used are **acid-labile protecting groups** such as the DMT group. There is also the TBDMS group, which may be removed by TBAF. Both DMT and TBDMS have also seen service in oligonucleotide synthesis.

2.4.2 Creating glycosidic links

Coupling of monosaccharides requires activation of the anomeric position in one monosaccharide (**electrophilic acceptor** or **glycosyl donor**) and protection of all functional hydroxyl group positions except for the selected hydroxyl group in the other monosaccharide (**nucleophilic donor** or **glycosyl acceptor**). The very simplest form of this is illustrated (Figure 2.13). Initially, protecting group manipulation is required, followed by coupling, which should be as stereocontrolled as possible. Protecting groups are chosen to assist in the current glycosidic link formation but also with an eye to subsequent glycosidic link formations. Making the right choices of protecting groups and coupling reagents is essentially an empirical exercise based upon a detailed knowledge of oligo-/polysaccharide chemistry. In other words, what will and will not work is still effectively the preserve of an initiated few who possess detailed experience. In recent times, the following synthetic methodologies have emerged as leading ways to effect glycosidic link formation:

(a) **glycosyl trichloroacetamidate** coupling

(b) **1,2 anhydrosugar-thioglycoside** coupling

(c) ***n*-pentenyl glycoside** coupling.

The first (a) has been extremely useful in many solution phase oligo-/polysaccharide syntheses. Glycosyl donors (electrophilic acceptors) are activated under very mild conditions by catalytic amounts of **trimethylsilyltriflate** (TMSOTf) and other triflates including **dibutyl boron triflate** (DBBOTf), not to mention **boron trifluoride** in **diethylether** (BF_3/Et_2O). This method of glycosidic link formation is striking for control of the stereochemistry (α or β) of the anomeric centre and hence of the glycosidic link (Figure 2.13). The second method (b) involves 1,2-anhydrosugars that are obtained easily from glycal precursors. Glycals are readily converted into corresponding anhydrosugars by epoxidation with **dimethyl**

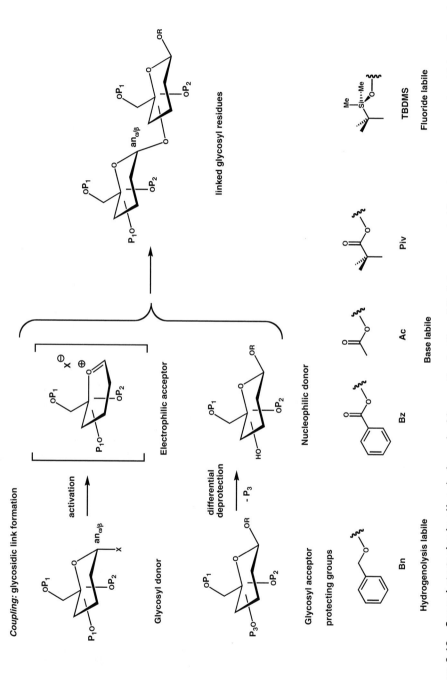

Figure 2.13 General strategies in oligo-/polysaccharides synthesis. Glycosidic links are created by a two step process in which a glycosyl donor (protected on alcoholic functional groups by protecting groups P_1 and P_2) becomes activated for coupling by the loss of leaving group **X**, thereby forming an electrophilic acceptor. In a separate process, a glycosyl acceptor (protected on alcoholic functional groups by protecting groups P_1, P_2 and P_3) is differentially deprotected on a selected alcohol functional group, thereby forming a nucleophilic donor. In combination, nucleophilic donor and electrophilic acceptor form a new glycosidic link with anomeric centre stereochemistry determined by conditions, reagents and neighbouring group participation from remaining protecting groups. Standard protecting groups are shown: **Bn: benzyl ether; Bz: benzoyl ester; Ac: acetoyl ester; Piv: pivaloyl ester; TBDMS: *tert*-butyl dimethylsilyl ether.**

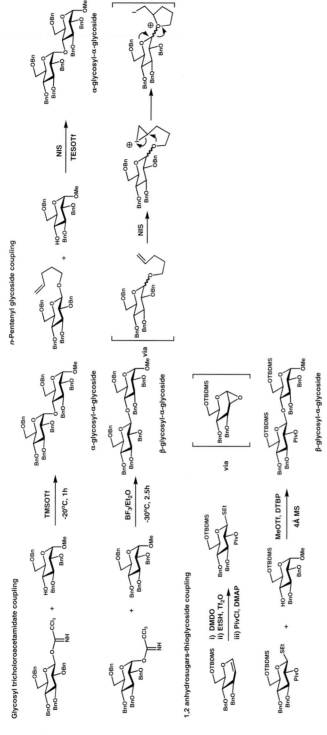

Figure 2.13 (Contd.) Glycosidic links are created by three main chemical strategies. In **trichloroacetamidate coupling**, the glycosyl donor can be activated by either **trimethylsilyl triflate (TMSOTf)** or **boron trifluoride (BF₃)** leading to glycosyl-glycoside products of opposite stereochemistry. In **anhydrosugar-thioglycoside coupling**, the glycosyl donor is activated in several stages, **dimethyldioxirane (DMDO)** epoxidation is followed by **thioethanol (EtSH)** ring opening aided by **triflic anhydride (Tf₂O)**, and the alcohol functional group so generated is capped by **pivaloyl chloride (PivCl)** activated by **dimethylaminopyridine (DMAP)**. Coupling then requires further **di-*tert*-butyl peroxide (DTBP)** activation of the glycosyl donor assisted by **methyl triflate (MeOTf)** and **molecule sieves (MS)** (4Å pore size). In **pentenyl glycoside coupling**, the glycosyl donor is activated by **N-hydroxy succinimide (NIS)** with **triethylsilyl triflate (TESOTf)**.

dioxirane (DMDO), only to react onwards with a thiolate to yield thioglycoside (Figure 2.13). These thioglycosides are robust glycosyl donors that are mobilised for coupling by treatment with thiophilic promoters such as **di-*tert*-butyl peroxide/methyl triflate (DTBP/MeOTf)**. Once again, high α or β selectivity can be achieved in glycosylation reactions. Finally, the third method (c) involves ***n*-pentenyl-glycoside- (NPG-)** derivatised glycosyl donors that are activated by strong electrophilic reagents such as ***N*-iodosuccinimide/triethylsilyltriflate (NIS/TESOTf)**. Coupling yields are typically excellent and so is control of stereoselectivity.

2.4.3 Solid phase oligosaccharide chemistry

Solid phase synthesis is developing surprisingly rapidly, given the ease with which much of the solution phase chemistry described above (see Sections 2.4.1 and 2.4.2) readily adapts for solid phase use. However, imperfect coupling yields and incomplete α/β stereocontrol with glycosidic link formation prevent this approach to oligo-/polysaccharide synthesis becoming routine. The solid support used in synthesis is typically a polymeric variation of the Merrifield resin. Two general approaches are used – either the glycosyl donor or the glycosyl acceptor can be initially immobilised on the solid support (Figure 2.14; one example of each). These two approaches can be sufficiently different to demand different coupling reagents, protecting groups and even linker to the solid support. The chemical nature of the linker determines all other protecting groups and coupling manipulations that may be carried out during the entire synthesis, especially since the linker chemistry must be inert (orthogonal) to all other deprotection and coupling steps that take place during the given synthesis. Hence when a **silyl ether** is used as a linker then obviously other silyl protecting groups cannot be employed elsewhere in the synthesis. Fortunately, silyl deprotection is undoubtedly orthogonal to other oligosaccharide-associated chemistries and these linkers are very resistant to the coupling conditions involving the three main methods of coupling described previously (see Section 2.4.2). In the event, the silyl ether appears to be most appropriate form of linker when an active glycosyl donor is initially immobilised on the solid support. Otherwise, **thioglycoside** and **ether** linkers appear to be more appropriate when an active glycosyl acceptor is initially bound to solid support instead. Thioglycoside linkers are robust to all but thiophilic reagents and so are cleaved by ***N*-bromosuccinimide/di-*tert*-butyl pyridine (NBS/DTBP)** in MeOH to leave a methylglycoside. Otherwise, the ether linkers can be subject to novel release conditions such as the use of **Grubb's catalyst** catalysed **metathesis** with **ethane** (Figure 2.15).

Depending upon whether an active glycosyl donor is solid phase attached or an active glycosyl acceptor as appropriate, a regular cycle of synthesis involves the cyclical introduction and coupling of a protected glycosyl acceptor or glycosyl donor respectively, usually preceded by a specific step of selective deprotection to make the coupling possible. In spite of progress in solid phase oligosaccharide synthesis, oligosaccharides of lengths over four to five monosaccharide units remain significant challenges for synthesis and there remains no universal protocol, unlike oligopeptide or oligonucleotide synthesis. However, the great impact of solid phase oligosaccharide synthesis over solution phase methods is that **libraries** of di- and trisaccharides can be synthesised. Such libraries can then be used in screening

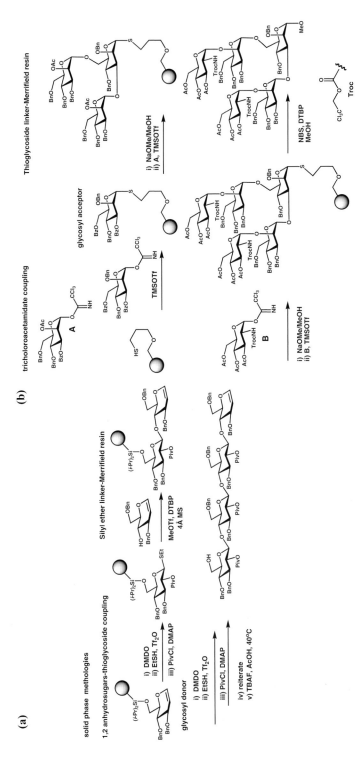

Figure 2.14 Alternative strategies for solid phase oligosaccharide synthesis. (a) Glycosyl donor immobilized by **silyl ether linker** to resin and activated for coupling by the anhydrosugar-thioglycoside coupling methodology (see **Fig. 2.13**). Final removal of the product is effected with fluoride ions delivered from **tetrabutyl ammmonium fluoride (TBAF)**. **(b)** Glycosyl acceptor immobilized by **thio-ether linker** to resin aided by **trimethylsilyl triflate (TMSOTf)**. Repetitive facile deprotection of **benzoyl (Bz)** protecting groups (sodium methoxide, NaOMe) and further TMSOTf assisted coupling of glycosyl donors to acceptors leads to the final product that is removed from the resin by **DTBP activation** assisted by **N-bromosuccinimide (NBS)**. Solid phase oligosaccharide synthesis is an excellent approach for the synthesis of combinatorial libraries of small oligosaccharides for use in screening in biological research. For most indicated protecting groups, see **Fig 2.13**, **Trichloroethyloxycarbonyl (Troc)** is another important protecting group in oligo-/polysaccharide synthesis.

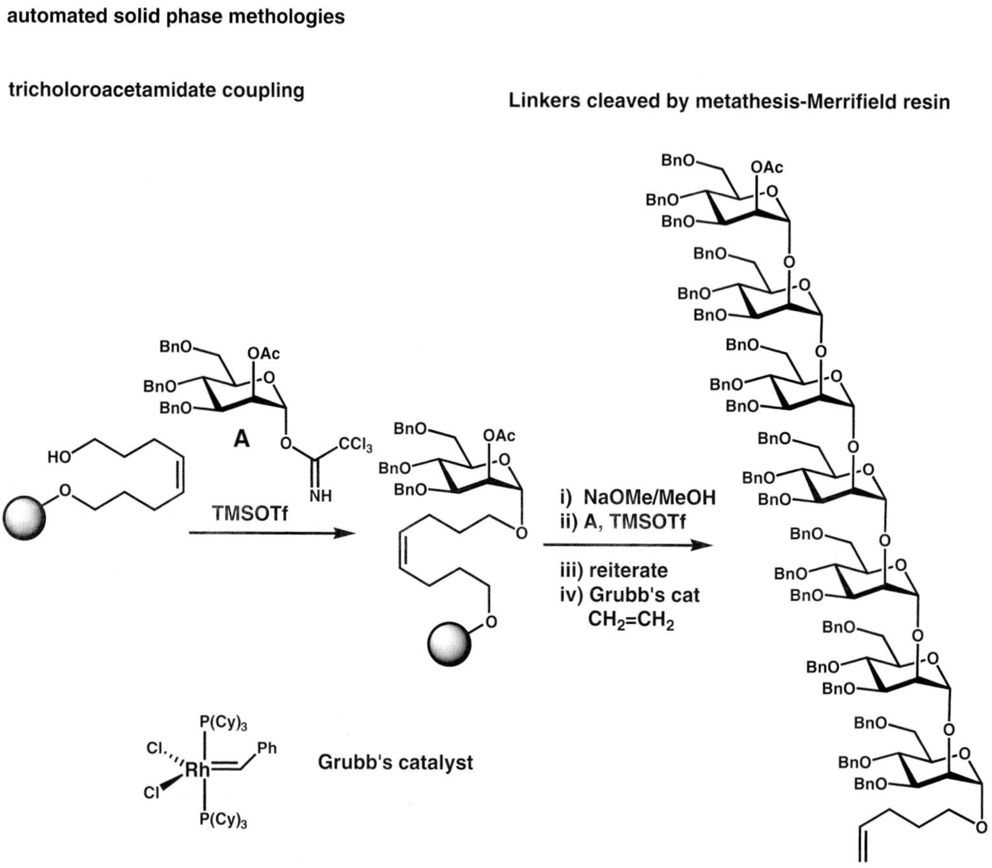

automated solid phase methologies

tricholoroacetamidate coupling

Linkers cleaved by metathesis-Merrifield resin

Figure 2.15 Automated solid phase oligo-/polysaccharide synthesis. Glycosyl donor (A) is coupled to a solid phase **Merrifield-like resin** through an **alkenyl alcohol linker**. The double bond allows for clean removal of product at the end of solid phase synthesis by metathesis using Grubb's catalyst in the presence of ethylene gas. For protecting groups, see **Fig 2.13. Trimethyl silyltriflate (TMSOTf)** activates the glycosyl donor through controlled removal of the trichloroacetamidate.

studies to probe a number of problems in chemical biology. Furthermore the final synthesis illustrated (Figure 2.15) was also actually performed with full automation as well. Hence the possibility for routine fully automated oligosaccharide synthesis should not be long to arrive.

2.5 Chemical synthesis of lipids

There is by and large no need for the chemical synthesis of many of the phospholipids that make up macromolecular lipid assemblies in cells, since these are readily available from natural sources and are purified from these by HPLC. In effect, biological syntheses of lipids dominate chemical syntheses. However, there is some value in illustrating the general method of synthesis of acylglycerols and phospholipids, since these synthetic approaches are important in lipid semi-synthesis should a fluorescent tag be required etc.

Acylglycerols derive from the controlled esterification of hydroxyl functional groups in the alkyltriol known as glycerol. One major problem with the synthesis of pure acylglycerols is that **mono- and diacylglycerols** easily migrate to adjacent free hydroxyl groups, typically catalysed by acid, base or heat. Therefore, a suitable protecting group strategy is absolutely essential for the chemical synthesis of defined acylglycerols. For instance, glycerol can react with acetone under acidic conditions to give a **1,2-isopropylidene** (**acetonide**), leaving one primary hydroxyl free for subsequent acylation. Alternatively, benzaldehyde can react to give **1,2-** or **1,3-O-benzylidenes** that can be separated by crystallisation and used for esterification. Typically, acylation can then be performed by **carbonyl diimidazole** (**CDI**) activation of the selected fatty acids (Figure 2.16). Thereafter, acetal deprotection can be followed by further esterification as appropriate. In the case of phospholipid synthesis, this can be reduced to the controlled esterification of L-α-**glycerophosphocholine.CdCl$_2$** (**GPC**) made possible by CDI activation of the selected fatty acids (Figure 2.17). Other phospholipids can then be prepared from this phosphatidylcholine by headgroup **transphosphatidylation** mediated by the enzyme known as **phospholipase D**. Lipid synthesis may appear trivial, but there is nothing trivial about the purification of lipids to homogeneity post synthesis. In this respect reversed phase HPLC becomes a powerful technique, but using a specially developed evaporative light scattering (ELS) detector to allow for the detection of eluting lipid analytes that do not possess any strong chromophore (see later in Chapter 2).

2.6 Biological synthesis of biological macromolecules

Biological synthesis is used here to describe harnessing the synthetic potential of living organisms for directed synthesis of biological macromolecules of interest. The study of biological macromolecule structure and function is highly dependent on the availability of material to study, hence there must be a huge emphasis on synthesis and purification before anything else is possible. Modern day biological syntheses, particularly of proteins and also nucleic acids, may frequently require recombinant techniques and the growth of recombinant organisms (in the cases of carbohydrates and lipids, this is not usually the situation) (see Section 2.7 and Chapter 3). Thereafter, the main challenge is purification of the biological macromolecule or lipid of interest to homogeneity in the face of all the other cellular components. In effect, since cells (whether recombinant or not) do the actual work of synthesis, then purification becomes our focus. Therefore, the chemical biology reader will be introduced first to those approaches frequently used in the purification of biological macromolecules and lipids from organisms.

2.6.1 Ion exchange chromatography

Ion exchange chromatography (IEC) separates molecules according to differences in their accessible surface charge. The method is very widely used, especially in protein purification,

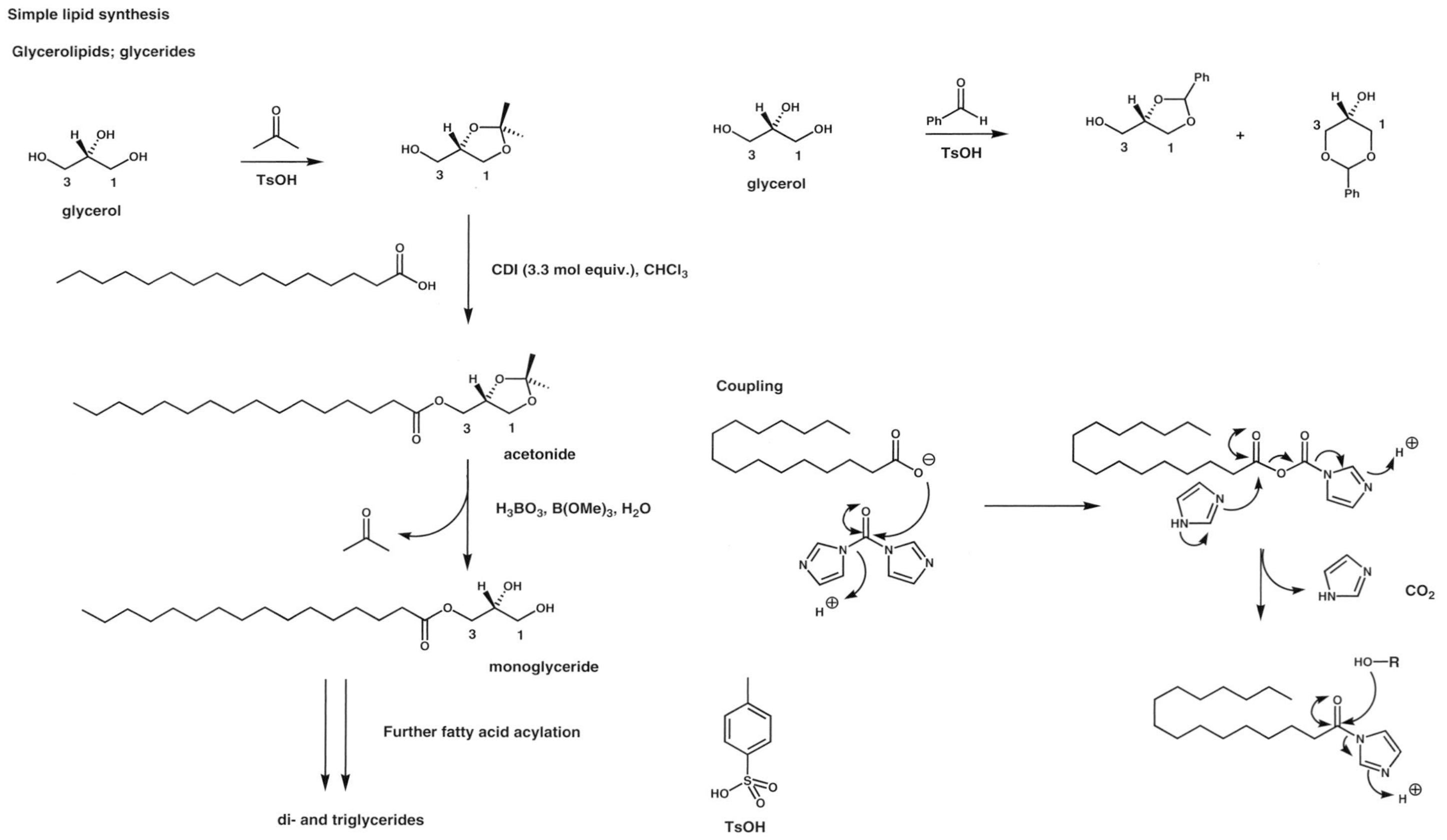

Simple lipid synthesis

Glycerolipids; glycerides

Figure 2.16 Glyceride synthesis. Protecting group strategies are typically used in the synthesis of **monoacylglyerols.** Differential protection is made possible with the assistance of **tosic acid (TsOH)** catalysis to give a variety of acetals. Unprotected alcohol functional groups can be esterified with free fatty acids with the assistance of **carbonyl diimidazole (CDI).** Deprotection is effected using mild lewis acids such as **methyl borate/boric acid.** **Mixed diacylglycerols** can be prepared in a similar way making use of protecting groups and esterification. **Triglycerides** can be prepared without the need for protecting groups.

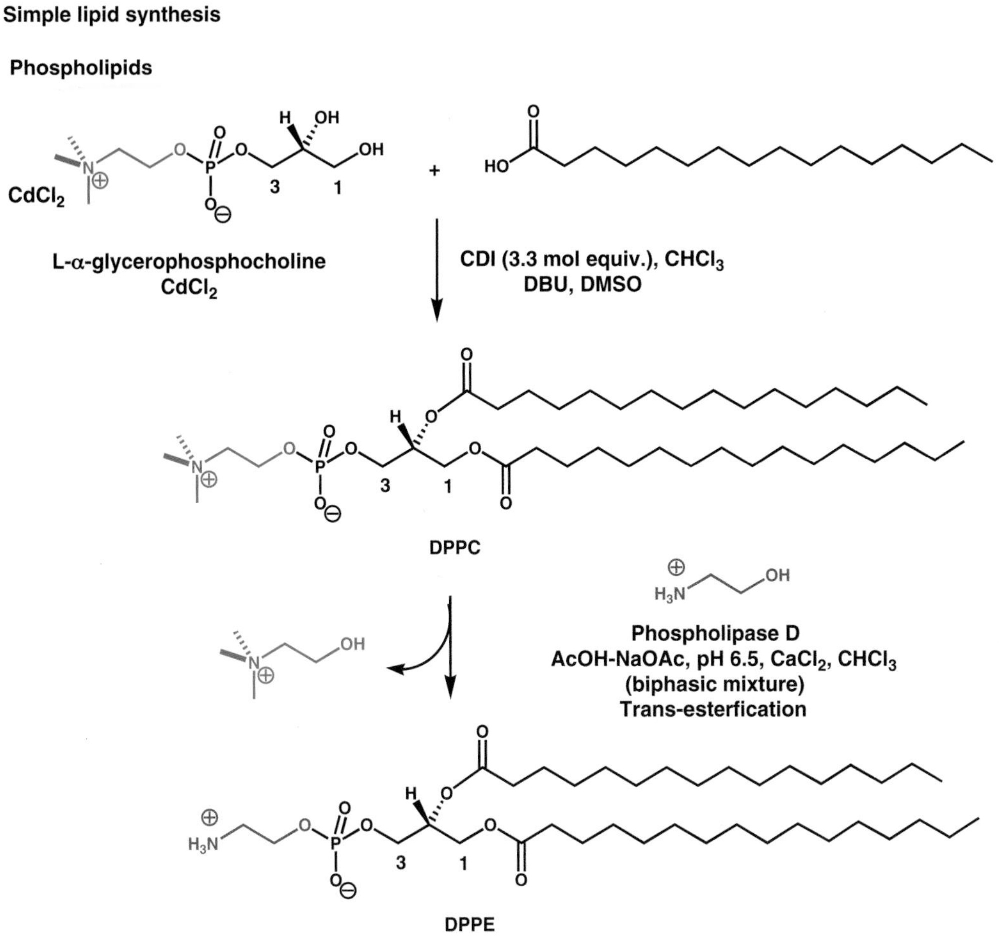

Simple lipid synthesis

Phospholipids

Figure 2.17 Phospholipid Synthesis. Starting from L-α-glycerophosphocholine CdCl$_2$, fatty acids are coupled to free alcohol functional groups by means of **carbonyl diimidazole (CDI)** yielding a **phosphocholine (PC)** product. Head group exchange is made possible with **Phospholipase D enzyme**.

as separation may be applied to any molecule that is charged and soluble in an aqueous system. The mild elution conditions also usually result in high recovery and high retention of biological activity in the eluting biological macromolecule (**analyte**). There are two classes of ion exchange (Figure 2.18). In **anion exchange**, the column carries functional groups bearing a positive charge, and hence separates molecules according to the negative (anionic) charges they carry. In **cation exchange**, the column carries functional groups bearing a negative charge, and hence molecules are separated according to the positive (cationic) charges that they carry. Binding is electrostatic in nature between analyte molecules of interest and the column. Since binding only takes place over a relatively short distance, the charges that are accessible on the surface are the most important factors. Both anion and cation exchange resins are classed as being either **weak** or **strong** – this does not refer to the strength of binding but to the effect

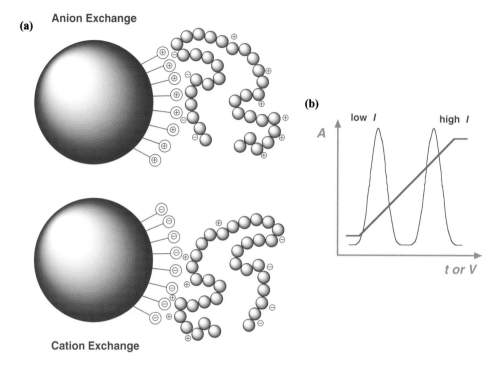

Figure 2.18 Cation and anion exchange chromatography. (**a**) Anion exchange columns carry a positive charge and bind negatively charged analyte molecules. Cation exchange columns carry a negative charge and bind positively charged analyte molecules; (**b**) Target analyte molecules are eluted by increasing the ionic strength, *I*, of the eluant from low *I* to high *I*. In order to monitor this process, **absorbance (*A*)** at a given wavelength is observed as a function of **elution volume (*V*)** or **time (*t*)**.

of pH on the charge of the functional groups. Weak ion exchange resins gain or lose electrical charge as the pH of the mobile phase changes. Strong ion exchange resins maintain their charge irrespective of pH changes in the mobile phase.

Functional groups associated with an ion exchange resin require a **counter-ion**: this can be either salt molecules, buffer molecules or the sample analyte itself. Binding to an ion exchange column occurs when the analyte acts directly as the counter-ion to the functional groups on the ion exchange resin. The usual method of running ion exchange chromatography is to bind the analyte onto the column under low salt conditions, then elute by increasing the salt so that salt molecules displace analyte back into the mobile phase, in so doing picking up a salt counter-ion from the mobile phase (Figure 2.19). Changing pH may also be used together with, or instead of, a salt gradient to elute the analyte, particularly when using weak ion exchange.

The pH of the mobile phase is vitally important in ion exchange chromatography, as most charged amino-acid residues on a protein surface for instance are themselves weak ion exchangers. In general this means that analyte molecules will be more positively charged at lower pH values, and more negatively charged at higher pH values. The **isoelectric point**

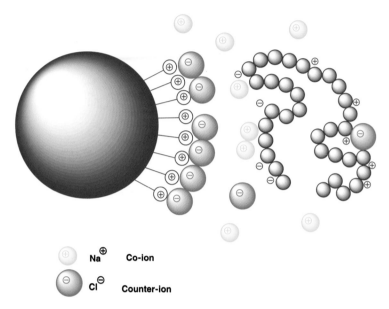

Na$^{\oplus}$ Co-ion

Cl$^{\ominus}$ Counter-ion

Figure 2.19 Elution from an **anion exchange column.** Negatively charged surfaces of analyte molecules interact with cationic gel beads at the given pH. As the salt concentration increases, chloride (Cl$^-$) **counter ions** help to displace analyte molecules from gel binding in order to encourage elution; sodium (Na$^+$) **co-ions** assist elution by associating closely with neutralizing the negative charges of newly exposed charged surfaces & analyte molecules.

(pI) is the pH at which the net charge on the molecule is zero – this is a useful starting point when considering which type of ion exchange medium to use for purification (Figure 2.20). An analyte with a high isoelectric point (basic) is positively charged at neutral pH, and therefore using a mobile phase at neutral pH would most likely result in surface positive charge. Therefore, the analyte would be best applied to a cation exchange column and *vice versa*. Isoelectric points should only be used as guidelines, since the isoelectric point is the pH at which the **net charge** is zero, a value that does not necessarily define **net surface charge**.

Besides choosing the type of exchange resin, a decision must also be made about whether to use strong or weak ion exchange resins. In most cases either may be used, but in extreme pH conditions (>10 for anion exchange or <4 for cation exchange) weak ion exchange resins lose their charge. Weak ion exchange media tend to take longer to equilibrate, due to the buffering capacity of the column, but are most useful in separations of analytes that bind extremely tightly to strong ion exchange columns and do not elute even with high salt concentrations. This is sometimes the case with large nucleic acids or phospholipids. An alternative elution in these cases is to use weak ion exchange resin followed by elution with acid (for cation exchange) or base (for anion exchange) to neutralise as much charge on the resin as possible. **Chromatofocusing** is essentially a variant of weak anion exchange, often using tertiary or quaternary amines as the stationary phase. Molecules will be separated roughly according to their pI. The analyte is initially bound at a pH above the pI of the target as for anion exchange. A focusing buffer of a lower pH is then applied to the column; no gradient is required as the

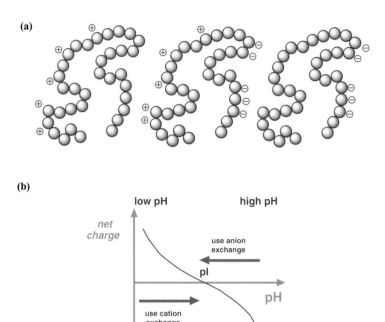

Figure 2.20 Isoelectric point and **ion exchange chromatography interactions.** (a) **pI** represents the pH at which the net charge of an analyte molecule in solution is zero (**middle**). At low pH, high protonation confers a positive charge (**left**): at high pH deprotonation confers a negative charge (**right**). (b) plotted variation of net charge as a function of pH. An analyte molecule of interest can be purified by ion exchange chromatography provided that the molecule possesses a net charge. If the pH is such that the analyte has a net positive charge then **cation exchange chromatography** should be used. If the analyte has a net negative charge then **anion exchange chromatography** should apply.

focusing buffer will titrate the buffering groups on the ion exchanger. Peak widths as small as 0.05 pH units may be resolved in this way, and very high concentrations of proteins may be eluted in a small volume. The method is a powerful analytical probe of surface charge, as well as being an important preparative technique. With regard to method development for ion exchange, it is best to start at a pH suitable for maximal binding, i.e. pH 8.5 for anion exchange, or pH 4.0 for cation exchange. Initially try a 0–1 M NaCl gradient over 50–100 column volumes. If solubility of the target analyte of interest is a problem in the separation (poor recovery or peak tailing) then addition of 20 per cent water-miscible solvent (methanol, glycerol, isopropanol or acetonitrile) should aid in both reducing hydrophobic interactions with the resin and solubilising the analyte molecules of interest.

2.6.2 Hydrophobic interaction chromatography

Hydrophobic interaction chromatography (HIC) separates biological macro molecules according to the hydrophobic groups on their surface. It shows many parallels to IEC; HIC is based on hydrophobicity whereas IEC is based on charge, and both have mild binding and elution conditions, and are therefore very useful particularly for protein purification. The HIC resin is similar to the IEC resin, except that the functional group on the surface is a hydrophobic group such as a phenyl. HIC can be thought of as a high-resolution method with parallels to ammonium sulphate precipitation. Most proteins will not bind to a HIC column using normal buffer conditions since these conditions are not sufficiently hydrophobic. The usual method is therefore to add a **lyotropic salt** such as ammonium sulphate to the solution, thereby reducing ionic interactions whilst increasing hydrophobic interactions. When hydrophobic surfaces bind to each other, water is released from the surfaces, thereby causing a favourable increase in overall entropy (Figure 2.21, see Chapter 1). Lyotropic salts increase the ordered structure of water, decreasing the entropy, therefore inducing analyte precipitation to

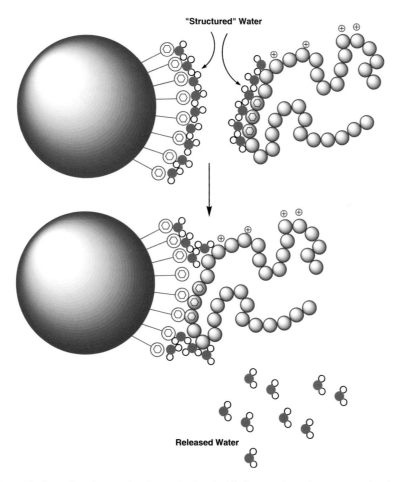

Figure 2.21 Binding of analyte molecules to **hydrophobic interaction chromatography (HIC)** media. Structured water covers the hydrophobic functional groups on the gel beads and hydrophobic surfaces of analyte molecules. This water is partially displaced when hydrophobic interactions take place between hydrophobic surfaces (see Hydrophobic effect, Chapter 1). Interactions are driven in part by entropy gains due to released water.

compensate for this decrease in entropy. As an entropy driven process, HIC is strongly affected by temperature; generally, the higher the temperature the stronger the binding to the column.

The key to HIC is to bind an analyte under an ammonium sulphate precipitation as high as possible that does not actually cause precipitation of the analyte; this can be easily determined in some pilot experiments. If the analyte is fairly hydrophobic relative to the other contaminants, then HIC should work well at a relatively low ammonium sulphate concentration. If the target is hydrophilic then it is best to use ammonium sulphate 'cuts' initially to remove the most hydrophobic contaminants in order to reach a salt concentration high enough to bind the target. Thereafter, a gradient of decreasing ammonium sulphate salt concentration is used to elute the analyte (Figure 2.22). If the analyte is extremely hydrophilic then **negative chromatography** should be considered as a purification method so that the target does not bind, but other molecules do. Some particularly hydrophobic proteins, such

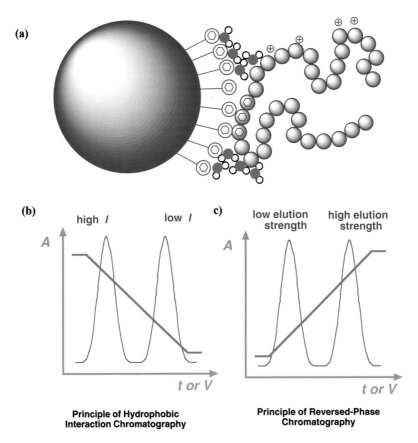

Figure 2.22 Comparison of the principles of **hydrophobic interaction chromatography** (**HIC**) and **reversed-phase chromatography.** (a) In HIC, analyte molecules are bound to the column under high ionic strength (high I) conditions (*i.e.*, typically high concentrations of ammonium sulphate). (b) Analyte molecules then are eluted (with respect to **time t** or **elution volume V**) by reducing the ionic strength (low I) of the eluant. (c) Reversed-phase chromatography works by the reverse principle where the eluant "strength" is increased with added organic solvent to encourage elution of more hydrophobic analyte molecules. In (b) and (c), elution is monitored by **absorbance** (**A**) at a given wavelength of detection.

as membrane proteins, will bind to the column even without ammonium sulphate. In this case, an increasing concentration of a **chaotropic salt** (such as guanidinium chloride, urea, or isothiocyanate salts) may be used to elute the analyte. Proteins are the optimal analytes for HIC.

2.6.3 Reversed phase chromatography

Reversed phase chromatography separates using an extremely hydrophobic stationary phase that can be varied, together with a polar mobile phase (usually an aqueous solution). In the form of **high performance liquid chromatography** (**HPLC**), this is the most common method for analysis of biological macromolecules and lipids, and for preparative separation of small molecules including lipids, oligo-/polypeptides, and oligo-/polynucleotides or oligo-/polydeoxynucleotides (Figure 2.22). HPLC is not often used for proteins as both the extremely hydrophobic stationary phase and the organic solvents used for elution tend to trigger irreversible denaturation of all but the most robust proteins. In contrast, HIC does not trigger denaturation because the high salt concentration and only weakly hydrophobic surface usually let the protein retain its correct conformation. Typically in HPLC, analytes are bound to the stationary phase under a solution of high polarity (e.g. water), after which the polarity of the mobile phase is reduced using a gradient with a water-miscible solvent (often acetonitrile, methanol or isopropanol). The pH of the mobile phase is an important consideration as some analyte functional groups when charged behave as hydrophilic groups, but when uncharged are essentially hydrophobic, and hence changes in pH can significantly effect retention on a reversed phase column. **Ion-pairing-agents** are often used to enhance the interaction of charged groups with the surface. Ion-pairing agents (typically trifluoroacetic acid, TFA, or formic acid) comprise both a hydrophobic region (to bind to the stationary phase) and a hydrophilic region (to ionically interact with any charges on the target) (Figure 2.23). Initially in attempting reversed phase chromatography for a separation, a relatively steep,

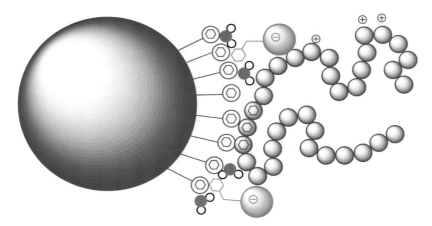

Figure 2.23   Ion-pairing agents used in reversed phase chromatography. Ion-pairing agents illustrated in pink enhance the interaction of charged groups with the hydrophobic surface. They also suppress the ionization of residual silanols on silica-based reversed-phase media.

broad gradient should be used to find the approximate retention of the target on the column. The start and end points can then be narrowed to the range of interest, and the resolution can often be increased in this way – it is often observed that as the gradient slope is decreased, molecules elute at a lower solvent strength. This is because elution is not strictly binary in nature; at a solvent strength slightly below the full elution from the column, the target can start to slowly move down the column; this effect is more pronounced with shallower gradients, leading to earlier elution.

2.6.4 Gel filtration chromatography

Gel filtration chromatography (GFC) separates molecules according to their size and shape (Figure 2.24). It is also known as **size exclusion chromatography** or **gel permeation chromatography**. The principle behind gel filtration chromatography is different from the other modes of column chromatography in that interactions among analyte, eluant and support should ideally all be equal, i.e. all efforts should be made to prevent any interaction between the analyte and the resin. Separation is enabled by particles in the stationary phase, each

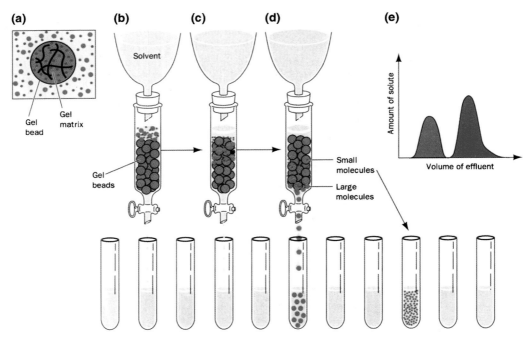

Figure 2.24 Gel filtration chromatography. (a) A **gel bead** consists of a **gel matrix** with pores from which larger molecule analytes (**blue**) are excluded. (**b-d**) Accordingly larger molecule analytes run faster through the gel than slower molecule analytes (**red**). (**e**) Therefore, larger analyte molecules elute first in advance of smaller analyte molecules (illustration from Voet & Voet, 1995 [Wiley] Fig.5-12).

containing a distribution of pore sizes. Larger molecules are excluded from the pores, and hence run through the column quickly, whereas smaller and smaller molecules have to navigate smaller and smaller pores, resulting in separation according to molecular weight. The range of separation depends on the pore size; certain pore sizes are best for separating in the small biomolecule range (>10 kDa), through to large analytes such as proteins (<200 kDa) and even up to the mass of small plasmids, organelles or viruses. This method is the 'softest' separation technique, since analytes are never actually changing their physical environment, nor actually binding to resin during the chromatography. GFC is often used as a final 'polishing step' in a purification procedure. One certain special class of gel filtration chromatography columns are known as **desalting columns** (or **buffer exchange columns**). A resin is used that completely excludes large analytes, but has no exclusion for salt, solvent or buffer molecules. The column is first equilibrated in the desired buffer that the analyte is to be transferred to, then a sample of analyte is applied, to elute well before the sample salts and buffers that otherwise get caught in the pores of the column. For small volumes, this technique tends to be quicker than **dialysis**, and is often useful for unstable molecules where dialysis would take too long. GFC even enables researchers to get a handle on the quaternary structure of proteins, as the columns may be calibrated with known proteins, and an approximate mass directly estimated from the time of elution.

2.6.5 Hydroxyapatite chromatography

Hydroxyapatite is a crystalline form of **calcium phosphate** $(Ca_5(PO_4)_3OH)_2$ that is sometimes used in analyte purification particularly of DNA and proteins. Unlike all the other resins, the stationary phase is actually crystalline, and binding of the analyte to the resin is both partially ionic and partially surface calcium ion specific. The technique is often used to separate proteins that co-purify by many other methods, and is often used as a final polishing step too. This has other advantages too in that stationary phase can be autoclaved and is useful therefore in strictly sterile work; however, flow rates are slow and the columns do not have long longevity (one problem is that carbon dioxide often binds to HA, causing a crust on the surface of the column). Proteins are usually adsorbed onto the column under low ionic strength phosphate buffer, then an increasing phosphate gradient is used to elute proteins, 0.5 M phosphate is usually sufficient to elute all adsorbed protein. Ceramic hydroxyapatite may now replace the original crystalline hydroxyapatite owing to much improved flow rates and operational column pressures.

2.7 Directed biological synthesis of proteins

The biological synthesis of proteins is central to so much chemical biology research today. Modern day biological synthesis of proteins requires that all proteins are purified from one organism or another. If particularly large quantities of proteins (mg–g levels) are required then recombinant techniques and the growth of recombinant 'factory organisms' are often essential (see Chapter 3). In this section, the chemical biology reader will be introduced to the most modern approaches to the biological syntheses of proteins and their purification. Critically, proteins vary widely in structure and physical properties therefore, though the biological syntheses of proteins are broadly similar, they can differ substantially in the details.

2.7.1 Wild-type or recombinant sources

There are two types of source for proteins prior to protein purification – either a natural source where the protein is found at its natural level, or a recombinant source. Natural sources were the only option before the advent of molecular biology and recombinant techniques, but remain commonly used when the primary structure of the protein of interest is unknown. Natural sources are also used when the protein is expressed at a naturally high level, or when factors such as correct **post-translational modification** are of particular importance. The alternative approach is to use a recombinant approach to protein synthesis that requires the creation of a recombinant or genetically engineered 'factory organism' (see Chapter 3) to over-produce the protein of interest. Typically, strains of the bacterium **Escherichia coli** (**E. coli**) are harnessed as factory organisms, though there are often problems with protein solubility and correct processing of the protein in *E. coli*. Alternative factory organism systems include **insect cell lines**, **yeast cells** and certain **mammalian cell lines**. Each system has certain advantages and disadvantages.

2.7.2 Expression in *E. coli*; early purification

Once a wild-type or recombinant organism becomes full grown, then the protein of interest may be purified from the other cell components in a multistep procedure. First, cell walls must be disrupted so as to efficiently release and, if possible, begin the process to fractionate out the protein of interest. For microbial extracts, **homogenisation** (by bead mill or through high pressure), **sonication** or the addition of **lysozyme** (protein bio-catalyst or enzyme, see Chapters 1 and 7) are often used to disrupt the cells. Lysozyme catalyses the weakening of the polysaccharide component to the cell wall coat of bacteria. Microbial extracts may then be centrifuged to separate soluble and insoluble fractions. **Non-ionic detergents** such as triton X-100 in buffer are frequently used at this stage to maximise the release of soluble protein of interest. Even at this stage, **protease inhibitors** are essential to prevent digestion of the protein of interest by endogenous biocatalysts (enzymes) suitable for proteolysis. These inhibitors are available as cocktails with broad specificity, or specific inhibitors are available that inhibit serine and acid proteases, metalloproteases and others (see Chapter 7). A suitable buffer must be chosen to maintain protein stability and activity – often a pH between 7.0 and 8.0 and a relatively high salt concentration (0.1– 0.5 M) as well as the possible addition of sucrose or glycerol (to around 10 per cent) can aid solubility of the protein. β-**mercaptoethanol** (β**ME**) or **dithiothreitol** (**DTT**) are used to maintain a reducing environment (under which cystine bridges do not form). Generally more thought needs to be put into the cell-free extract preparation from a eukaryotic system, as methods such as differential centrifugation may be used to partially fractionate intracellular organelles prior to release of the protein or interest.

At this stage, **precipitation** is often used as a convenient early step in protein purification to fractionate and concentrate the protein of interest. Three main methods of precipitation are used: **ammonium sulphate**, **organic sulphate** or **polyethyleneglycol** (**PEG**). At high sulphate concentrations, sulphate will bind to water molecules, reducing the amount of water available to shield hydrophobic patches on a protein surface. Sulphate concentrations are defined in terms of percentage 'cuts' (0–20 per cent w/v, 20–40 per cent w/v etc), with the percentage representing the degree of saturation. The wholesale aggregation of the protein of interest will usually be adjusted to occur in one percentage 'cut' (i.e., at one approximate level of sulphate saturation). Thereafter, the aggregate is collected by centrifugation and the pellet made ready for further purification. Organic solvents (commonly acetone or ethanol) may also be used to precipitate proteins. Progressively increasing the hydrophobic nature of the solvent by increasing solvent concentration will promote **intermolecular electrostatic interactions** leading to precipitation. PEG precipitation also works on a similar principle. In some cases, selective heat-induced denaturation is also occasionally used, where slowly increasing temperature may denature impurities leaving the protein of interest intact in solution.

Methods for the further purification of proteins may be split into two general areas – **classical chromatography** and **affinity chromatography**. Classical chromatography (Section 2.6) relies on differences in the chemical and physical nature of molecules, whereas affinity chromatography relies on the specific and reversible binding of the target to an affinity ligand immobilised on an insoluble matrix. Although recombinant techniques have increased significantly the relative use of affinity chromatography, classical chromatography may still be used *in toto* or else in combination with affinity chromatography purification steps. Protein purification is typically followed or monitored by **Sodium dodecyl sulphate (SDS)-polyacrylamide gel electrophoresis (PAGE)**. PAGE is discussed further in Chapter 3, SDS-PAGE in Chapter 9.

2.7.3 Affinity chromatography

Affinity chromatography uses specific biomolecular recognition between the protein of interest and a molecule bound to the matrix (Figure 2.25). There are a number of different types of affinity chromatography that are useful in purification (see below). Recombinant techniques have made affinity chromatography particularly useful, since **affinity purification tags** can be engineered into recombinant proteins to aid purification (see Chapter 3).

2.7.3.1 Immobilised metal affinity chromatography (IMAC)

Immobilised metal ions may be used to specifically coordinate with proteins so that they may be specifically isolated. The most common use of IMAC is that the protein is engineered to carry a sequence cluster of four to eight histidine residues, enabling simple purification,

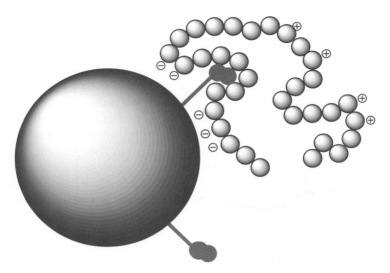

Figure 2.25   Affinity chromatography. Column associated ligands specifically recognize their target analyte molecule of interest, and the target is immobilized on the column by **selective binding**. The target analyte may be eluted by a variety of methods such as high salt concentrations, pH change or competitive elution with an alternate target for the ligand.

usually by interaction with immobilised Ni^{2+} localised on the matrix surface (Figure 2.26). Ni^{2+} binds less strongly than Cu^{2+} to polyhistidine sequences; however, using Ni^{2+} allows greater selectivity in the purification. Metals (often Cu^{2+}, Zn^{2+}, Ni^{2+}, Co^{2+} or Fe^{2+}) are usually immobilised via chelation to nitrilotriacetic acid on the solid matrix support, and elution is usually made possible with imidazole that competes with the histidine clusters in the protein of interest for co-ordination with the matrix-associated metals.

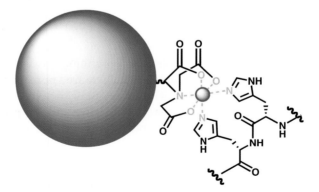

Figure 2.26   Immobilised Metal Affinity Chromatography (IMAC). Metal ions (for instance, Ni^{2+} ions) are gel-immobilized by chelation to groups covalently attached to the solid support. Histidine (His) residues in proteins (or part of a His-tag) have a high affinity for the immobilized ion. Elution is typically carried out by using a competitively high concentration of **imidazole**.

The engineering of proteins to carry **polyhistidine tails** (*N*-terminal or *C*-terminal **His tag**) in frame with their primary structure amino acid sequence is achieved by means of recombinant techniques (see Chapter 3) and confers a number of advantages. The His tag often provides a very simple means of purification of the protein by IMAC. Also, the use of such a small affinity sequence means that **antibodies** may be generated against the protein of interest without the need to remove the tag. Even insoluble proteins may be purified by pre-solubilising the protein in **guanidinium chloride** or **urea** and then applying the unfolded protein to metal affinity column purification under the same conditions as above. Refolding may then be attempted post affinity column purification. However, there are some drawbacks in using His-tag purification. For instance, the presence of the His tag may have a measurable distorting effect on the structure of the protein of interest and even on the function of the protein. Sometimes the protein of interest with the His tag is less soluble than the wild-type protein. Furthermore, the IMAC columns can leak heavy metal ions together with the protein of interest, which can lead to amino-acid side-chain damage from oxidation. This problem can be made worse by the general requirement to avoid using reducing agents such as DTT or high concentrations of βME during IMAC purification. Just occasionally, Co^{2+} has been immobilised in place of Ni^{2+}, via four chelating bonds, in order to increase the specificity of His-tag binding to metal ions and reduce leakage of heavy metal ions into the eluant. This system can even harness natural histidine clusters for example in the purification of chicken lactate dehydrogenase.

2.7.3.2   Glutathione-S-transferase tags

Glutathione-S-transferase (**GST**) was one of the original recombinant affinity tags. The usual role of GST is to catalyse the transfer of **glutathione** tripeptide onto endogenous or xenobiotic substrates that possess electrophilic side-chains or groups. GST (usually originally from *Schistosoma japonicum*) may be fused to the protein of interest to enable purification using immobilised reduced glutathione (Figure 2.27). Although the tag is relatively large, GST can confer solubility on some proteins that are insoluble when expressed alone. A further benefit of using GST is that the fusion protein has a simple activity assay. Active GST will transfer reduced glutathione onto **1-chloro-2,4-dinitrobenzene** (**CDNB**), a reaction easily monitored by UV–visible spectroscopy. GST is naturally dimeric and therefore the fusion protein will probably also be dimeric. Hence a GST tag may upset the natural quaternary structure of some proteins unless removed. Removal of the GST tag is effected by fusing the GST tag to the protein of interest via a short cleavable amino-acid residue spacer sequence.

2.7.3.3   Maltose binding protein tags

This tag is based on the natural maltose binding protein (MBP) from *E. coli*. The protein of interest may be fused to the maltose binding protein, a tag that enables purification by affinity to immobilised amylose. Maltose may then be used to elute the protein, Unlike GST, MBP is monomeric, but it is one of the largest tags (42 kDa). MBP is one of the best tags for encouraging **solubilisation** of an insoluble or sparingly soluble protein of interest.

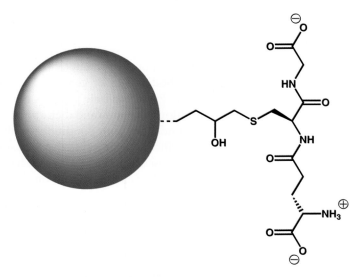

Figure 2.27 Immobilized glutathione for the purification of **Glutathione S-transferase (GST)**-tagged proteins. GST binds strongly to the immobilized glutathione, the target protein may be eluted by competitive elution with glutathione.

2.7.3.4 *Biotinylation of proteins*

The **biotin–avidin/streptavidin** interaction is one of the strongest non-covalent interactions known, and can be used to purify proteins. There are two approaches: the protein can be biotinylated *in vitro* using biotin-ester reagents, or a sequence may be used that is naturally biotinylated during synthesis. *In vitro* biotinylation is difficult to control as more than one lysine may be modified, and so this is not really an aid to protein purification. **Site-specific biotinylation** is made possible by creating a fusion protein containing a peptide tag that is biotinylated *in vivo* (for example the *C*-terminal residues of the **biotin carboxyl carrier protein, BCCP**). The target sequence is biotinylated at lysine 89 in *E. coli* (with the aid of the **biotin holoenzyme ligase** enzyme). The fusion protein of interest is then recovered by an avidin-affinity column. Biotin normally exhibits strength of binding to the natural tetrameric avidin/streptavidin that is almost irreversible (K_d appears to be approximately 10^{-13} M). However, avidin resins have now been developed using a resin-bound form or modified monomeric form of streptavidin that allows elution of the purified protein using biotin.

2.7.3.5 *Intein tags*

Inteins are peptide segments of proteins that naturally excise or **self-splice**, severing their covalent links with a parent polypeptide but leaving an intact daughter polypeptide chain behind them by assisting in the formation of a peptide link in place of the original intein segment. This remarkable process has been exploited to design proteins that can in principle self-splice to allow a protein of interest to separate from its attached protein affinity tag. Therefore, a protein of interest may be initially engineered with an intein protein affinity tag, but post affinity column purification the affinity tag may then be encouraged to dissociate, leaving the intact protein of interest behind in a highly purified state. A recent example of an intein protein affinity tag comprises a chitin-binding domain fused to an intein self-splicing element that derives from yeast (*Saccharomyces cerevisiae*). In the presence of thiols such as DTT, βME or cysteine, intein **self-cleavage** can occur without the need for biocatalysis (Figure 2.28).

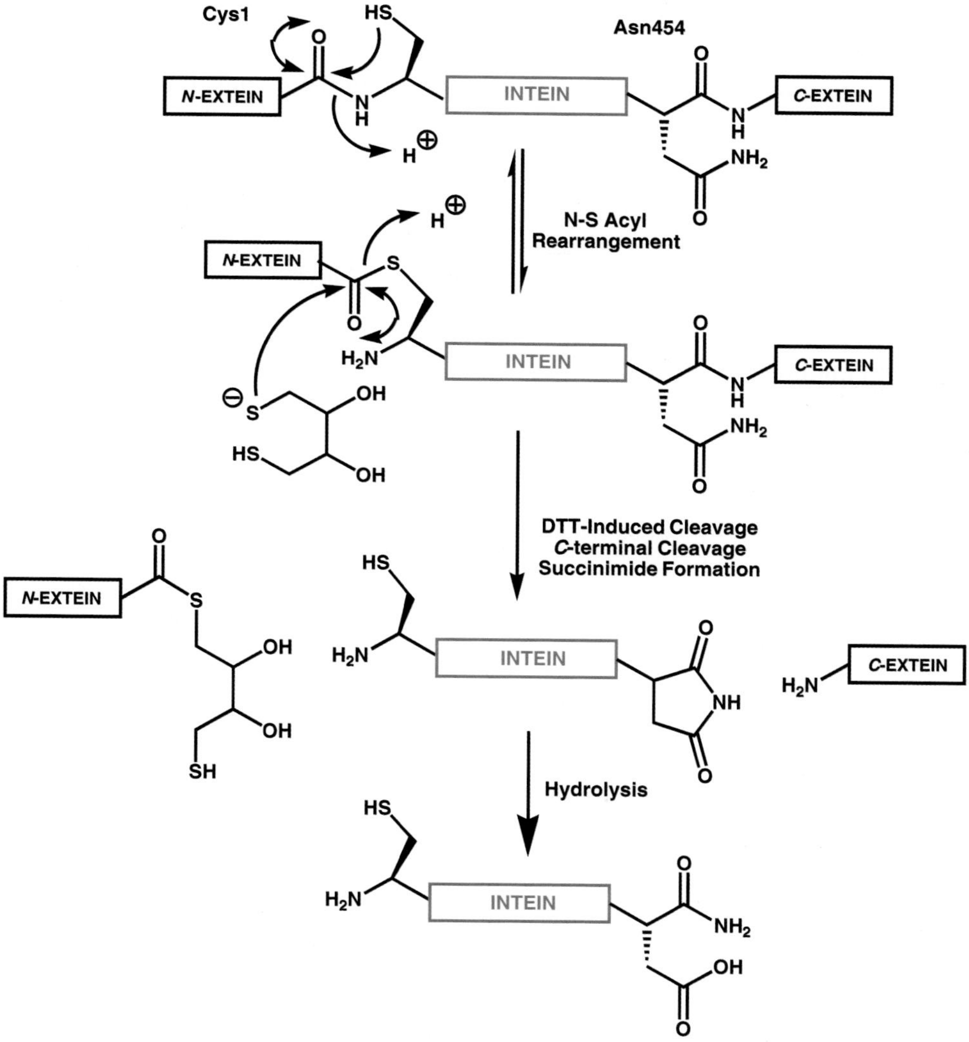

Figure 2.28 Chemical mechanism of **intein** cleavage that takes place in the presence of the dithiol reducing agent **dithiothreitol (DTT)**.

The real beauty of this system is that the self-cleavage reaction can be performed on an affinity column directly after purification on cellulose beads, so that the protein of interest can be eluted directly without any attached protein affinity tags. Naturally, fusion proteins may be engineered with an intein protein affinity tag fused at either the *N-* or *C*-terminus of the protein of interest, as appropriate.

2.7.3.6   *Other affinity tags and radio-labelling of proteins*

There are many other possible affinity tags that one could use in addition to those described above. Here is a simple survey of the possible diversity. First, there is **Protein A**, which binds strongly to **IgG immunoglobulins**. Conversely, mimics of the Z domains of an IgG can be used in fusion proteins in order to bind to protein A columns. Then there is the **S-peptide tag,** a 15-amino-acid residue peptide that binds strongly to a protein derived from pancreatic ribonuclease A. The **Strep-tag** is a 10-amino-acid residue peptide that binds strongly to streptavidin. **Strep-tag II** is the next generation, that is a nine amino-acid sequence which binds to a streptavidin derivative (**streptactin**). In both cases, fusion proteins are eluted from affinity columns using desthiobiotin, a biotin analogue. Moving on, the **flag tag** is a small hydrophilic peptide (*N*-AspTyrLysAspAspAspAspLys-*C*) that may be fused with a protein of interest such that the fusion protein can be purified using an anti-flag affinity resin. Next, the **calmodulin binding peptide** is a relatively small peptide (4 kDa) that binds to immobilised calmodulin protein and elutes from the affinity column under very mild conditions. In fact binding only requires the presence of Ca^{2+}, while elution is made possible in the same buffer in the presence of EGTA (a particularly effective Ca^{2+} chelator). By contrast, the **T7 tag** consists of an 11-amino-acid residue peptide from the T7 *10*-protein and purification is effected using an anti-T7 monoclonal antibody affinity column. However, elution from this column requires very acidic conditions – pH 2.2! Finally, the **cellulose binding domain tag (CBD tag)** ($\sim$12 kDa) binds strongly to homoglycan cellulose or chitin columns. The fusion protein may then be eluted with ethylene glycol, a very soft method of elution, after which the ethylene glycol may be easily removed by dialysis. A considerable advantage of this tag is that it is particularly cost effective since the resin is very inexpensive, robust and readily reusable.

The CBD tag approach is also well adapted to the labelling of proteins with radioactivity. However, an alternative radio-labelling procedure is to create fusion proteins with tag sequences that are recognised by **kinases** (proteins that act to introduce phosphates to other proteins) such as the *N*-ArgArgAlaSerVal-*C* tag sequence designed to trigger **cAMP-dependent-protein-kinase**-mediated [^{32}P]-phosphorylation of the tag serine residue. This labeling method requires that the protein of interest, post-purification, should be [^{32}P]-phosphorylated *in vitro* with the assistance of the appropriate kinase. This method is also very effective, but nowadays there is a considerable move to radio-label proteins using completely recombinant technology-driven approaches instead *in situ* in cells, rather than *in vitro*. *In situ* approaches aim to introduce [^{35}S]-labelling, which is much milder than [^{32}P]-labelling and more durable owing to a longer radioactive half-life.

2.8 Biological syntheses of nucleic acids, oligosaccharides and lipids

These are also just as important as the biological syntheses of proteins if a holistic view of biological macromolecule and lipid assembly structures and functions is to be obtained.

2.8.1 Biological synthesis of nucleic acids

If simple isolation of nucleic acids from cells is required then many of the chromatographic methods described in this chapter can be used to isolate and fractionate nucleic acids from natural sources. DNA is typically associated with cationic polyamines or proteins in cells and both can be removed with a phenol solution. Alternatively, proteins can be removed by denudation with **proteases** (proteins that degrade peptide links) or detached with the aid of detergents or chaotropes. Protein-free nucleic acids may then be precipitated with ethanol. Cellular RNA may be isolated distinct from DNA by using pancreatic DNAses (proteins that degrade phosphodiester links in DNA), or vice versa, wherein cellular DNA may be isolated from RNA by using RNAses (proteins that degrade phosphodiester links in RNA). Although electrophoresis is the usual approach to separating nucleic acids (see Chapter 3), HPLC is also particularly useful, as is HA chromatography. HA columns have a particular propensity to bind double-stranded DNA molecules very strongly, therefore HA chromatography is an effective approach for separating double helical DNA from cellular RNA and proteins. Some modifications of affinity chromatography can also be useful. For example, eukaryotic mRNA typically has a poly(A) sequence at its 3'-end. Therefore, immobilised-poly(U) on a solid support can represent a powerful tool for the isolation of mRNA from cellular extracts.

Obviously, there are times when there is a requirement to obtain and purify total cellular DNA or RNA (as described above). However, equally well there are times when one single DNA or mRNA molecule is required, in which case such a molecule must be identified, amplified and then purified clear of cellular debris. In this second instance, biological synthesis of such DNA or RNA molecules involves intensive use of cloning and other recombinant techniques (see Chapter 3) prior to purification protocols.

2.8.2 Biological synthesis of oligosaccharides

Oligo-/polysaccharides can also be purified by many of the methods described in Section 2.7, though they are often found linked to intracellular proteins (not in bacteria), membrane proteins and possibly to some extracellular proteins too. Some polysaccharides are also closely associated with lipids, forming **lipo-polysaccharides** (**LPSs**), which are extremely prevalent in some bacterial cell walls and can be very immunogenic. Oligo-/polysaccharides are co-precipitated together with nucleic acids and proteins using alcohol and protein linkages are cleaved by chemical means (where appropriate). Thereafter, charged proteins and nucleic acids can be removed from the uncharged/weakly charged oligo-/polysaccharides by ion exchange chromatography. Neutral and weakly charged oligo-/polysaccharides pass through columns whilst the nucleic acids and proteins bind and are removed from the sample. Oligo-/polysaccharides can then be further analysed and purified by some specialised types of anion exchange chromatography and by HPLC. Also, affinity chromatography is possible for instance using immobilised lectin (typically the jack bean protein **concanavilin A**), a protein that specifically binds glucopyranose and mannopyranose monosaccharide residues.

2.8.3 Biological synthesis of lipids

Typically, the biological synthesis of lipids relies on lipid synthesis in cells and their extraction from macromolecular lipid assemblies with organic solvents. Neutral lipids can be extracted using non-polar solvents such as diethyl ether or chloroform, whereas membrane-associated lipids require more polar solvents such as ethanol or methanol to disrupt intermolecular hydrogen bonding. Phospholipids used commercially in scientific research are typically purified from egg or bovine sources. Cholesterol is purified typically from egg or from wool grease (sheep derived). Sphingolipids are mostly purified from egg or mammalian tissue sources. Finally, phosphatidylinositols are extracted from soybean or bovine sources. Synthetic lipids are often prepared from a glycerol-3-phosphocholine precursor that is itself typically purified from soybean lecithin. After extraction from a natural source, individual lipids can be purified to homogeneity by HPLC.

3
Molecular Biology as a Toolset for Chemical Biology

3.1 Key concepts in molecular biology

Molecular biology is a powerful tool for the directed synthesis of biological macromolecules, in particular nucleic acids and proteins (see Chapter 2), and in its own right is a highly diverse forward-looking discipline. Too often, however, many chemists have drawn the line at the frontier between protein science and molecular biology. This is, in part, due to the change in language in moving towards a biological discipline. However, chemists have also seriously underestimated the potential of molecular biology to open up new opportunities for chemistry. The serious chemical biology reader cannot afford to make the same mistakes. Molecular biology, with its ever widening and improving range of recombinant techniques, is every bit as essential to the practise of chemical biology research as chemical synthesis in the quest to understand the way biology works at the molecular level. We hope in this chapter to provide a focused introduction to molecular biology, particularly aimed at the chemical biology reader most interested in harnessing molecular biology and recombinant techniques as a tool for biological synthesis.

3.1.1 The central dogma of molecular biology

The well known **central dogma** of molecular biology, as first discussed by Francis Crick, is that DNA is transcribed into RNA, which is translated into protein (see Chapter 1 and Figure 3.1). The first of these steps is occasionally reversible, as in the case of **reverse transcription** of RNA to DNA in the life cycle of some viruses, but there remains no instance of

Essentials of Chemical Biology   Andrew Miller and Julian Tanner
© 2008 John Wiley & Sons, Ltd

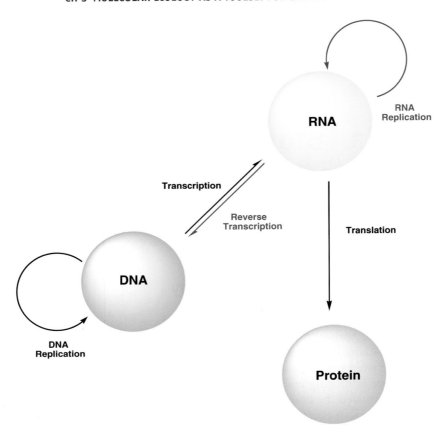

Figure 3.1   The Central Dogma of Molecular Biology. Black lines represent information transfers that occur frequently in cells. Blue indicates the exception of **reverse transcription** that occurs in some viruses, and **RNA-directed RNA polymerase** catalyzed **RNA replication** that also occurs in some plants and viruses only. Nucleic acids can be both stores and recipients of genetic information, whereas proteins are always recipients only of genetic information.

genetic code realised in proteins and polypeptides returning from polypeptide amino-acid residue sequences to deoxynucleotide base sequences in DNA. Hence DNA is central to all biological synthetic strategies since it is from DNA that RNA and polypeptides flow! Therefore, the initial goal should be to identify, isolate and clone those DNA segments of interest from a genome of interest. Typically, DNA segments of interest are **genes**, which are units of heredity that can contain at least one **open reading frame** (**ORF**), which harbours genetic coding information for a protein of interest, plus other non-coding control elements embedded in the DNA structure outside ORFs. The preliminary steps leading to isolation, cloning and identification of genomic DNA are the beginning of any number of activities including directed expression and purification of the protein coded for by a particular gene, or other more limited activities such as DNA sequencing.

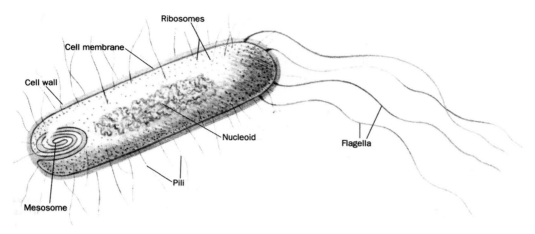

Figure 3.2 Summary illustration of **prokaryotic cell** such as *Escherichia coli.* Prokaryotic cells do not exhibit discrete compartmentalization so transcription and translation can take place concomitantly (Reproduced from Voet & Voet, 1995 [Wiley] Fig. 1-2).

3.1.2 The difference between prokaryotic and eukaryotic genes

Before proceeding to discuss methods of isolating DNA sequences, it is important to consider some fundamental differences between prokaryotic and eukaryotic DNA. **Prokaryotes** (**bacteria** and **cyanobacteria**) are defined as organisms that lack a distinct nucleus (Figure 3.2). They have a single circular DNA **chromosome**, and may possess smaller circular pieces of DNA called **plasmids** spread throughout the cell, which can also code for proteins. Prokaryotes are nearly always unicellular, and when grown on agar plates form groups of cells called **colonies**. In contrast, eukaryotic cells have a true nucleus, in which reside multiple DNA chromosomes (DNA bound to and condensed around nuclear proteins), plus numerous other intracellular compartments. These cells are also significantly larger than prokaryotic cells (Figure 3.3). **Eukaryotes** include both some unicellular organisms, such as yeast, and multicellular organisms, including all animals and plants. Whilst prokaryotes and eukaryotes share the same genetic code, there are significant differences between prokaryotes and eukaryotes at the molecular level in that eukaryotes use a vastly more complicated approach to processing mRNA after transcription (**post-transcriptional processing**), for very good reasons!

In **prokaryotes**, it is usual that the immediate products of mRNA transcription – the primary mRNA transcripts – are translated without any modification. It is even possible that translation can begin at the 5′ end of the mRNA molecule before transcription is completed at the 3′ end. In some cases, a single mRNA transcript may even harbour the contiguous genetic code for multiple proteins when this transcript has been transcribed from a DNA **operon** (i.e. a contiguous set of genes whose protein products usually have related functions, such as metabolism). Hence, genomic DNA sequences in prokaryotes can be directly translated into protein sequences. By contrast, the same cannot be said regarding prokaryotes. One of the major reasons for this is that most higher eukaryote genes comprise exons, which are

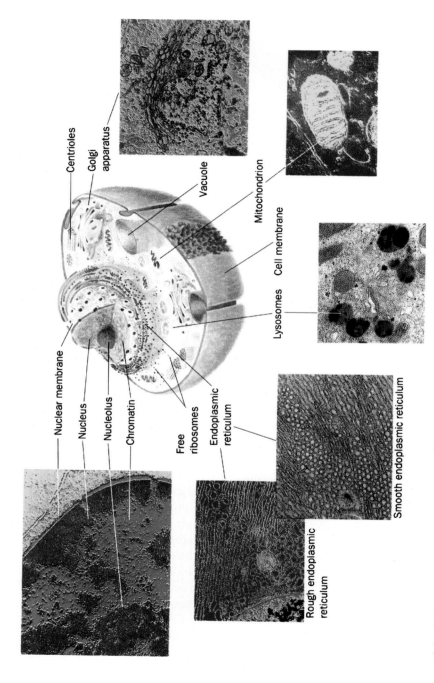

Figure 3.3 Depiction of a **eukaryotic** (animal) **cell.** All eukaryotic cells have evolved with significant compartmentalization resulting in spacio-temporal separation of transcription and translation. DNA is transcribed to mRNA in the nucleus before being shuttled out of the nucleus for translation in the cytosol where ribosomes are located (Reproduced from Voet & Voet, 1995 [Wiley] Fig. 1-5).

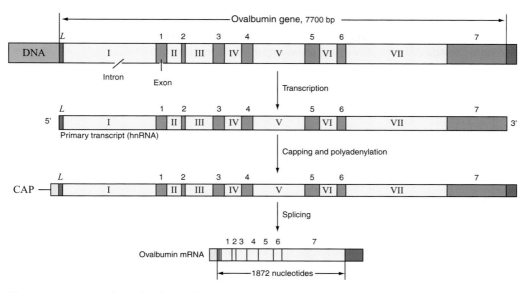

Figure 3.4   Processing of eukaryotic pre-mRNA to mature mRNA as demonstrated for the chicken ovalbumin gene. Most higher eukaryotic genes have both **introns** (which do not code for protein) and **exons** (which usually do code for the protein). There is significant posttranscriptional processing to form mature mRNA prior to translation (Reproduced from Voet & Voet, 1995 [Wiley] Fig. 29-35).

represented in the mature of the RNA, and **introns**, which are segments of DNA sequence that do not code for the protein of interest and are therefore not usually intended for direct translation with exons (Figure 3.4). In eukaryotes, transcription primarily takes place in the nucleus, and translation takes place in the cytoplasm, so it is impossible to have simultaneous transcription/translation as observed in prokaryotes. Initially, there are two essential post-transcriptional processing events:

(a) The primary eukaryotic mRNA transcript is capped with a $5'$–$5'$ triphosphate bridge linked to a 7-methylguanosine nucleoside, a process known as **$5'$ capping**.

(b) Post-capping, the $3'$ end is modified by the addition of a $3'$-poly(A) tail, a process known as **$3'$ polyadenylation**.

Thereafter, the process of intron **splicing** takes place. Introns must be excised and exons 'knitted back together' to create a mature mRNA transcript with a base sequence equivalent to the contiguous base sequences ($5' \rightarrow 3'$) of the original DNA exons in the eukaryotic gene. In simpler eukaryotes such as yeast, only a few genes contain introns. The situation in a higher eukaryote is quite different and genes contain typically around eight introns, whose total sequence length is four to 10 times the coding sequence found in the exons. It remains unclear why there is such extraordinary **redundancy** in higher eukaryotic genomes. To add to the complexity, higher eukaryotes exhibit **splicing variants** (i.e. where splicing events vary according to the cell type, time of expression or other environmental cues).

Hence, if eukaryotic gene structure is so complicated, how can we expect to obtain functionally useful genes for further molecular biology manipulation? The answer to this question lies with mature mRNA transcripts. Such mature transcripts from eukaryotes can be viewed as the functional equivalent of a primary mRNA transcript from a prokaryote. Mature mRNA transcripts contain processed intron-free nucleotide sequences, which harbour the complete genetic code for a protein of interest.

3.1.3 The creation of cDNA libraries

Mature mRNA transcripts (sense strand) from eukaryotic cells can be purified and then reverse transcribed, with the assistance of a **reverse transcriptase** enzyme (from **Moloney murine leukemia virus, MMLV**), into complementary DNAs (cDNAs) that will anneal with the mRNA transcripts by Watson–Crick base pairing to give anti-parallel **DNA/RNA duplexes** or double helices. The poly(A) tail in each mature mRNA transcript is actually a useful handle for each reverse transcriptase reaction. Thereafter, DNA/RNA duplexes must be broken down with the assistance of RNAse enzymes (specific for the hydrolysis of RNA phosphodiester links) and a sense strand of DNA constructed instead on each cDNA single strand so that equivalent, more stable antiparallel DNA/DNA duplexes are generated instead, with the assistance of a **DNA polymerase** enzyme. In this instance, the **poly(T) tail** in each cDNA molecule turns out to be important for the DNA polymerase reaction!

Overall, provided that this process of reverse transcription and DNA polymerisation is performed starting from a diverse enough population of different mature mRNA transcripts isolated from a given organism, then the resulting collection of DNA/DNA duplexes can represent relatively complete eukaryotic genomic information for that given organism, all in a functional form ideal for further molecular biology manipulation. This collection of DNA molecules is known as a **cDNA library**. In the final stage of preparation before use, **adapter** DNA sequences are ligated onto both ends of each DNA/DNA duplex, with the assistance of a **DNA ligase** enzyme. These adapters contain essential sequence elements for the conversion of every DNA/DNA duplex of the cDNA library into a genomic component that can be integrated with the paraphernalia of recombinant techniques into the complete tool-kit of genomic components associated with molecular biology (see Subsections 3.2.2 and 3.2.3).

3.2 Tools and techniques in molecular biology

The key to manipulation in molecular biology is the isolation, cloning and identification of genomic information in an appropriately useful DNA form. From this all else flows (see Section 3.1). What are the main tools and techniques available?

3.2.1 Plasmid DNA vectors

The **plasmid** is central to almost all molecular biology manipulations of genomic DNA or cDNA. The term plasmid refers to DNA that is able to replicate independently of chromosomal DNA. **Plasmid DNA (pDNA)** systems were first found in prokaryotes and were quickly realised to be ideal potential **vectors** (Figure 3.5). A vector is an autonomous DNA construct suitable for recombination with **heterologous DNA**, from genomic DNA or cDNA library sources, to form **recombinant pDNA constructs** for the purposes of cloning and/or heterologous gene expression. A vector based on pDNA should have an **origin of replication** together with one or more **selectable markers**. An origin of replication is a non-coding DNA sequence that defines the position from which pDNA replication commences when appropriate. Selectable markers are genes that code for a selectable trait such as antibiotic resistance. Vectors are divisible into two main types, **cloning vectors** and **expression vectors**, of which the latter can be used to direct expression *in vivo* of a desired protein or non-coding RNA (see Sections 3.3.1 and 3.3.3). Normal plasmids are only stable with heterologous DNA inserts of up to 10 kb. Other types of plasmids include so-called **phagemids**; these have both a plasmid origin of replication and a single-stranded **phage** origin for the preparation of single-stranded DNA. **Cosmids** are a type of plasmid that combine aspects of plasmid and λ-based vectors; in general cosmids are able to hold much larger sequences of DNA (35–45 kb) and are therefore useful for preparing genomic DNA libraries.

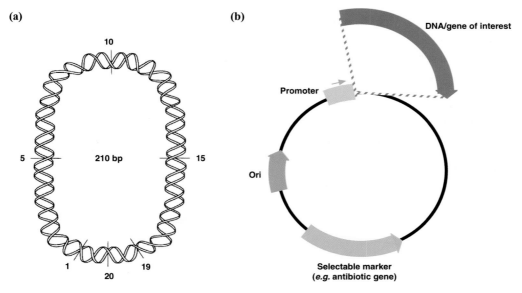

Figure 3.5 Schematic to show a cloning vector, the simplest form of pDNA. (**a**) diagram of **closed circular DNA (cccDNA)** (210 bp) to show how **double-stranded DNA (dsDNA)** links up to generate circular **plasmid DNA (pDNA)** molecules (adapted from Sinden, 1994, Fig. 3.4); (**b**) simplified diagram of pDNA cloning vector with **selectable marker**, non-coding **origin of replication (Ori)** and non-coding promoter **element** required for the control of expression of **heterologous (foreign) DNA** (DNA/gene of interest) eventually introduced downstream of the promoter (sense strand 3′-direction).

3.2.2 Restriction enzymes

Restriction enzymes are enzymes that cut double-stranded DNA (dsDNA) by hydrolysing two phosphodiester links (one per strand) without altering attached deoxynucleotides. The term restriction originates from the fact that these enzymes were originally discovered as a defence mechanism used by bacteria to restrict infection by certain **bacteriophages**, bacterium-specific viruses. Over 900 restriction enzymes have been discovered to date from various organisms, of which 30–40 are regularly used in a typical molecular biology laboratory. Since they hydrolyse phosphodiester links within a DNA sequence, then they are often referred to as **restriction endonucleases,** as opposed to **exonucleases,** which cut at the ends of DNA. Restriction enzymes act as 'molecular DNA scissors' for cutting dsDNA at sequence specific **restriction sites,** usually between 4 and 12 bp in length (Figure 3.6). Some restriction endonucleases cleave both DNA strands at the same position across the duplex (resulting in **blunt-ended** DNA fragments), while others perform offset cleavage thereby leaving 5′

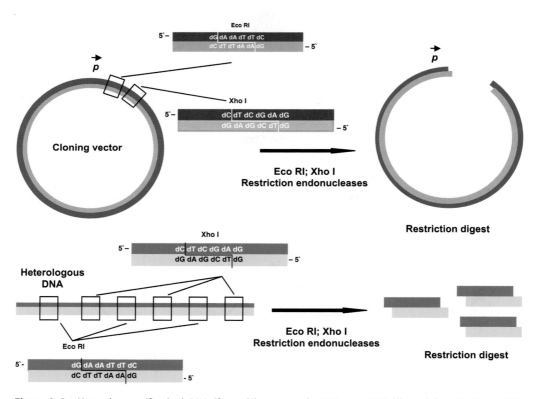

Figure 3.6 Heterologous (foreign) DNA (from either **genomic DNA** or a **cDNA library**) (see Section 3.2) is cut with two different **restriction endonuclease enzymes** (**Eco RI; Xho I**) producing a **restriction digest.** A cloning vector is also cut with the same pair of restriction endonucleases downstream of the promoter element (**p**) (see Figure 3.5). In cloning vector, pDNA sense strand is **dark grey**; complementary strand is in **light grey**. In heterologous DNA, sense strand is in **red**; complementary strand is in **yellow**.

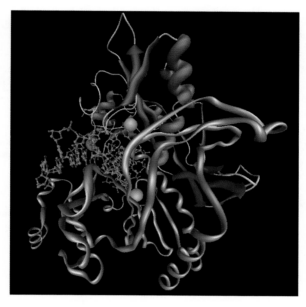

Figure 3.6   **(contd) EcoRV restriction endonuclease** rendered in **cartoon display** with α-carbon back-bone traced as a **solid ribbon** (pdb: **1az0**) DNA substrate double helix is shown with all atoms (minus hydrogen) in **ball and stick display**; carbon: green; oxygen: red; nitrogen: blue; phosphorus: purple. Magnesium ions are shown as **Van der Waals spheres** (light purple). The structure is shown to demonstrate the intimate association between DNA substrate phosphodiester links and restriction endonuclease enzymes that 'wrap around' the DNA sequences recognised for cleavage.

or 3′ deoxynucleotide overhangs of defined length at either ends of the cut (causing the formation of **cohesive** or **sticky-ended** DNA fragments). Typically, but not always, restriction endonucleases tend to recognise **palindromic** sequences (with a centre of rotational symmetry – see Chapter 1). For example, the famous Eco RI restriction enzyme recognises the sequence 5′-d(pGAATTC)-3′, which is rotationally symmetric between **dA** and **dT** in duplex DNA. The cleavage sites are offset between **dG** and **dA** in both sense and complementary DNA strands, resulting in sticky-ended DNA fragments with a 5′ overhang of four deoxynucleotides in length. Another similar such restriction enzyme is known as Xho I (Figure 3.6).

3.2.3 DNA ligases

DNA ligases are needed for the covalent **ligation** of heterologous duplex DNA fragments (Figure 3.7). DNA fragments that have been restricted (generated by restriction endonucleases) are rejoined with the aid of ligase enzymes. Both sticky-ended and blunt-ended ligation processes are possible with **T4 DNA ligase**, an ATP-dependent ligase enzyme, and the ***E. coli* ligase**, which requires a nicotinamide adenine dinucleotide (NAD) cofactor rather than ATP.

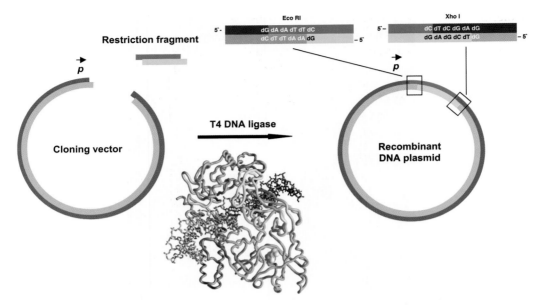

Figure 3.7   Heterologous DNA restriction digest fragments created from two restriction endonucleases (Eco RI; Xho I) are allowed to interact with restriction digest fragments from a cloning vector. Fragments **anneal** by Watson-Crick base pairing. Post annealing, phosphodiester links are regenerated by **T4 DNA ligase** catalysis. The result is a pool of **recombinant plasmid DNA constructs** with original heterologous DNA fragments under expression control from the promoter element in the cloning vector (See **Fig. 3.5**). Insert shows related **human DNA ligase** rendered in α-**carbon backbone display** (coloured by domain) and with bound DNA represented in **stick display** with atoms coloured according to atom type (pdb: **1x9n**).

In both cases, the enzymes reintroduce phosphate and regenerate the phosphodiester links removed by restriction. Ligation using sticky ends is a lot easier and simpler in general, so if there is the opportunity for choice then **sticky-end ligation** should be chosen (Figure 3.7). Should this not be possible for any reason due to lack of sequence complementarity then the following should apply. Where there are two non-complementary 5′ sticky ends to join then these overhangs should be filled in to form duplex DNA using **Klenow polymerase**, an enzyme derived from **DNA polymerase I** that has had its **5′→3′ exonuclease activity** removed. Where there are two 3′ sticky ends to join then overhangs should be filled in to form duplex DNA using **T4 DNA polymerase**. In either case, blunt-ended duplex DNA fragments are generated that may be conjoined when required by DNA-ligase-mediated **blunt-ended ligation**.

3.2.4 Hosts

A host is an organism that carries recombinant pDNA harbouring heterologous DNA. The chemical biology reader in approaching molecular biology should have already noticed that *E. coli* tends to be the most widely used workhorse organism for most experiments in molecular biology, even if the vector is eventually intended for use in other organisms such as yeast or in cell lines. The reasons for this are partly historical – *E. coli* has been extensively studied, is relatively well understood with regard to the mechanism of gene expression control and was one of the first organisms to be fully sequenced at the DNA level. Furthermore, many of the first plasmids to be used as vectors were initially found in *E. coli*, and there are a large number of bacterial strains readily available that can be used in a variety of circumstances. For molecular biology purposes, *E. coli* has also been attenuated to become a very low risk micro-organism. However, *E. coli* does have a few disadvantages. For instance, *E. coli* has no ability to effect gene splicing, and when used for protein biological synthesis many other problems can occur, which will be discussed later. Other host cells or host organisms include yeast, insect cells, mammalian cells and various other cells. However, most genetic manipulations are still performed out of preference in *E. coli*.

3.2.5 Cellular transformation

Exogenous pDNA is introduced into host cells by a process known as **transformation** (Figure 3.8) Cells are rendered **competent** to take up added exogenous pDNA by pre-treatment with calcium chloride solution on ice. After a short heat-shock at 42 °C for 2 min, the cellular transformation process is complete and host cells are now recombinant cells. An alternative technique to effect cellular transformation is **electroporation**. In electroporation, ice-cold cells are mixed with pDNA and are then placed in a cuvette across which a strong potential difference is applied. This promotes a brief increase in cell membrane permeability, so that there is an opportunity for pDNA to traffic into the cytoplasm in a percentage of host cells. Following transformation, bacteria are initially grown in growth medium (broth) for sufficient time so that pDNA gene expression becomes established and genes of the selectable marker are expressed. Bacteria may then be spread on an agar **selection plate** containing antibiotic compatible with the selectable marker gene so that only transformed host cells containing the independently expressing pDNA will survive.

3.2.6 Selection

Selectable markers are typically genes that code for resistance to antibiotics such as **ampicillin**, **tetracycline** and **kanamycin** (Figure 3.8). Additional selectable markers may also be used to improve the selection process, such as those related to the inactivation of β-**galactosidase** (β-**gal**) activity (***lacZ* selection**). In this case, the selection process requires pDNA to harbour an intact *lacZ* gene that codes for the first 146 amino acids of β-gal. The expression of the *lacZ* gene is probed by using the chromogenic substrate **5-bromo-4-chloro-3-indolyl-β-galactopyranoside** (**X-gal**), a colourless substance that becomes an intense blue colour due to hydrolysis caused by *lacZ* expressing β-gal enzyme (Figure 3.8). Successful ligation of heterologous DNA (from genomic DNA or cDNA) is designed to take place directly within the *lacZ* gene so that ligation must cause X-gal hydrolysis to fail (Figure 3.7). Accordingly,

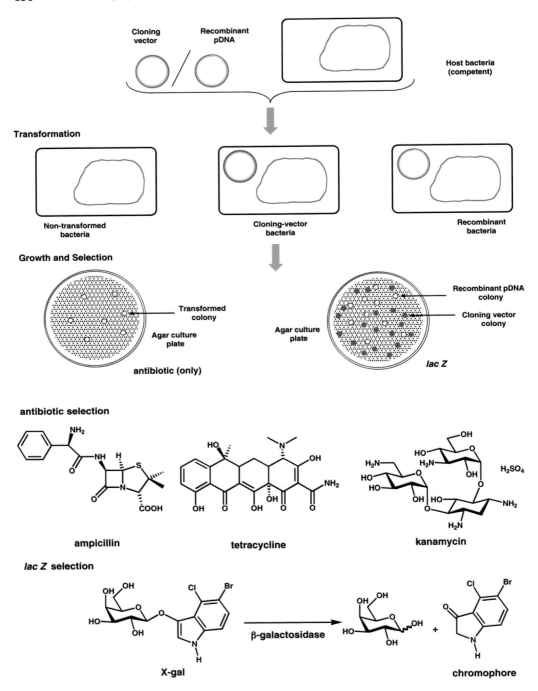

Figure 3.8 (*Continued*)

after transformation and plating on agar, X-gal-containing selection plates, those host cell colonies identified as white should possess recombinant pDNA while those host cells that have turned blue should possess only intact *lacZ*-expressing pDNA without heterologous DNA included. *LacZ* selection is not completely reliable for two reasons. First, insertions into the *lacZ* gene do not always totally inactivate the β-gal activity, and occasionally blue colonies do actually harbour recombinant pDNA. Second, occasionally white colonies do not possess recombinant pDNA but are white in colour due to β-gal inactivation caused by excision of a small part of the *lacZ* gene during clonal growth.

3.2.7 pDNA purification

DNA in all forms is generally far more thermally stable than globular proteins, and in many ways is easier to work with. The classical approach to pDNA purification of cells has been to bring about initial lysis, typically in the presence of **sodium dodecyl sulphate** (**SDS**) at a high pH. Genomic and pDNA remains in solution, while cell wall material with most of the cellular proteins are precipitated. Post-centrifugation, the lysate is then neutralised with potassium acetate. The cleared lysate containing the plasmid DNA is then extracted using **phenol/chloroform/isoamyl alcohol**, and **RNAse** is typically added to destroy any contaminating RNA. When particularly pure pDNA is required then **caesium chloride** gradient purification by **ultracentrifugation** can be used. The classical approach is quite cumbersome, time consuming and uses phenol, which is toxic and unpleasant to handle. Therefore, the preparation and purification of pDNA has become much simpler with the widespread use of alkaline lysis coupled to the **miniprep** system (Figure 3.9). The method is performed as follows: Initially clonal cells are grown at a small volume (several millilitres), typically overnight. Thereafter, the bacterial pellet is resuspended in a buffer containing RNAse, which will degrade RNA. Cells are then lysed using sodium hydroxide and SDS, causing **open-circle** genomic DNA and proteins to denature, while leaving **supercoiled** pDNA unchanged.

Figure 3.8   Selectable markers. Formation of recombinant plasmid DNA (pDNA) constructs (see **Figs 3.6** and **3.7**) is not 100% efficient such that recombinant and cloning vector pDNA (without heterologous DNA restriction fragment insert) co-exist at the end of the process. Also, host bacterial transformation is not 100% efficient either so that both transformed and non-transformed bacteria co-exist post-transformation. Both of these problems are solved by **growth and selection**. Bacterial growth is performed in the presence of antibiotic (**antibiotic selection**) on agar culture plates so that only **transformed bacteria** (1 pDNA/cell) can survive and give rise to observed colonies. Individual colonies must then be selected for further analysis of pDNA sequence to check for the presence of recombinant versus cloning vector pDNA. The *lac Z* **selection** process allows for the presence of recombinant versus cloning vector pDNA to be determined more directly on the basis that the lacZ function is disrupted in recombinant pDNA constructs and not in clonal vector pDNA. Hence if **X-gal** is included in the agar, only bacterial colonies that harbour cloning vector pDNA should develop a blue colour while those that harbour recombinant pDNA constructs should be white in colour. Individual white colonies can then be selected for further analysis of pDNA sequence. Three main selectable marker antibiotics are shown. X-gal and the effect of β-galactosidase (β-gal) on X-gal are also illustrated.

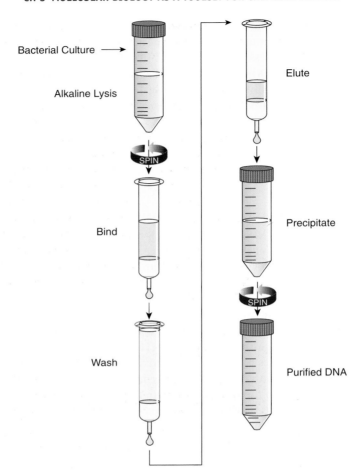

Figure 3.9 Recombinant pDNA purification. Selected transformed clonal bacterial cultures are grown in medium and the pDNA is extracted as shown. Bacterial culture is subject to **alkaline lysis**. Cellular debris and open-circle DNA is removed and pDNA purified by binding to and eluting from a silica glass fibre filter. Relatively pure pDNA may be obtained following ethanol precipitation and collection of the pellet by centrifugation (illustration of PureLink™-HiPure Plasmid Filter Kit; http://catalog.invitrogen.com/).

Potassium acetate buffer is then used to neutralise the sodium hydroxide, resulting in precipitation of potassium dodecyl sulphate, with which genomic DNA coprecipitates. The cleared supernatant is then passed through a **silica-derived glass fibre filter** frit, where pDNA is able to bind onto the silica surface in the presence of the chaotropic reagent guanidinium isothiocyanate (GuNCS). Finally, the frit is washed and pDNA eluted using a simple aqueous solution in the absence of GuNCS. This miniprep system of pDNA purification and isolation provides ample DNA for other recombinant manipulations. The method may be simply scaled up if large quantities of a particular pDNA are required. Similar guanidinium–silica frit preparation methods may also be used to purify products of a PCR amplification reaction (see Section 3.3.2), removing the enzymes and excess deoxynucleotides present at the end of the reaction.

3.2.8 Nucleic acid gel electrophoresis

Electrophoresis is the movement of charged molecules through a solid-phase medium under the influence of an electrical potential difference. In molecular biology the solid-phase media are usually **agarose** or **polyacrylamide gels**. Agarose is a naturally occurring heteroglycan, which has been described previously and is used for **agarose gel electrophoresis** (**AGE**) (Figure 3.10). Polyacrylamide is a synthetic polyamide polymer that provides the essential solid-phase medium for **polyacrylamide gel electrophoresis** (**PAGE**) (see Chapters 2 and 9). AGE is generally used for the separation of larger polydeoxynucleotides/polynucleotides (>100 bases), whereas PAGE is frequently used for the separation of smaller polydeoxynucleotides/polynucleotides or oligodeoxynucleotides/oligonucleotides (<100 bases). Therefore, for the separation of large nucleic acids, agarose is generally the solid-phase medium of choice (Figure 3.10). Agarose gels are very simple to make when compared with polyacrylamide gels. Initially, agarose is mixed with either **tris acetic acid/ethylenediaminetetraacetic acid** (**TAE**) or **tris boric acid/ethylenediaminetetraacetic acid** (**TBE**) buffer, then the heterogenous mixture is heated to dissolve the agarose, and cooled to gelation in a gel-slab mounted with a plastic comb to create sample wells. TAE results in larger agarose 'pore sizes' than TBE. Hence TAE gels are generally used to resolve DNA larger than 1000 bases, and TBE gels to resolve smaller DNA fragments. However, recovery of DNA is generally poorer from TBE–agarose gels, and therefore TAE often ends up being used for the resolution of smaller DNA fragments too.

In order to run an agarose gel, samples are mixed with a loading buffer, which contains glycerol or Ficoll to increase the density of the sample so that samples sink easily into the wells, plus mobility dyes to aid sample loading and monitoring of the electrophoretic process. After electrophoresis, DNA may be visualised by staining with **ethidium bromide** (Figure 3.11). Ethidium bromide is a base pair **intercalator** that inserts or intercalates between base pairs (maximum 1 ethidium bromide/6.5 base pairs) and in so doing acquires a substantial increase in ϕ_F and hence fluorescence intensity at I_{max} (595 nm) (see Chapter 4). Ethidium bromide is a powerful mutagen. Hence other staining procedures have been devised. These include silver, methylene blue or acridine orange staining. **Silver staining** has a similar sensitivity to ethidium bromide staining, but the former is able to give a permanent record of the gel, unlike the latter. **Methylene blue** staining is 40 times less sensitive than ethidium bromide, but causes less damage to DNA and is non-carcinogenic. **Acridine orange** is useful for differentiating **single-stranded** (**ss**) and **double-stranded** (**ds**) **DNA** since dsDNA will fluoresce green under UV light whilst ssDNA will fluoresce red. The recovery of DNA samples and fragment from electrophoresis gels is relatively simple. There were originally a wide range of methods to recover DNA from agarose gels, but methods have frequently been superseded by the use of the GuNCS miniprep method. The approach in this case here is literally to cut out the DNA

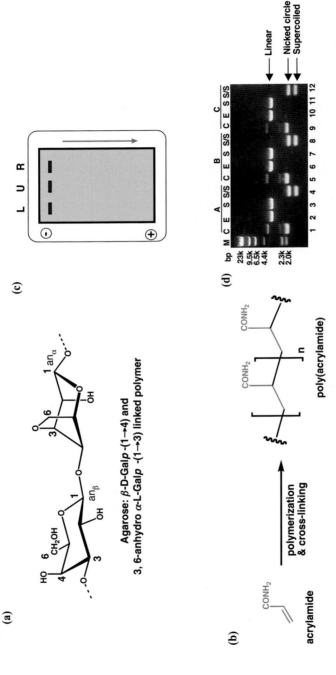

(a)

Agarose: β-D-Galp -(1→4) and
3, 6-anhydro α-L-Galp -(1→3) linked polymer

(b)

acrylamide

polymerization
& cross-linking

poly(acrylamide)

(c)

(d)

Figure 3.10 Agarose/Poly acrylamide gel electrophoresis. (a) Agarose is a heteroglycan consisting of a β-D-galactopyranose (**β-D-Galp**) and 3,6-anhydro-α-L-galactopyranose (**3,6-anhydro α -L-Galp**) **agarobiose** repeat unit. The total molecular weight is typically 120,000 Da. The heteroglycan readily forms cross-links via intermolecular double helix formation involving different agarose chain intertwined together (see Chapter 1). **(b)** Polyacrylamide is an artificial polymer prepared and cross-linked from acrylamide monomer. **(c)** Simple schematic of agarose gel electrophoresis set up with wells at the negative end for sample loading; **L: ladder; U:** untreated **purified pDNA; R: restriction cut pDNA:** arrow shows direction of movement of DNA under influence of electric field. **(d)** example of ladder, untreated purified pDNA and restriction cut pDNA run side by side. The identities of the 3 pDNA species shown in lane U are given.

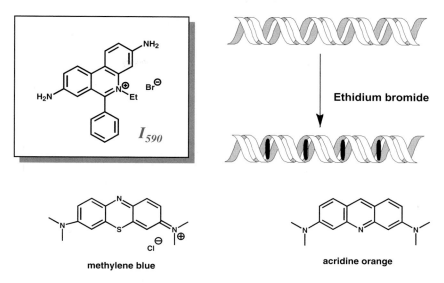

Figure 3.11 The structure of **ethidium bromide (EtBr)** (left) is planar aromatic. EtBr intercalates between plan parallel Watson-Crick base pairs causing the DNA structure to expand slightly (lengthwise). The maximum possible is 13 EtBr/nucleotide (6.5 EtBr/base pair). EtBr experiences a significant enhancement in fluorescence properties upon interaction with DNA but not otherwise. Structures of two other well-known DNA intercalator dyes are shown.

band(s) of interest and suspend in guanidinium thiocyanate buffer in order to solubilise the agarose gel before carrying on with the remainder of the purification protocol (see Subsection 3.2.7).

3.2.9 DNA sequencing

The standard method of sequencing DNA is the **chain-termination sequencing** method (Figure 3.12). In this method DNA polymerase is used for short time periods to re-build duplex DNA using the complementary DNA strand as template. The region of sequencing interest is dictated by the choice of sequencing primer that anneals by Watson–Crick base pairing to its complementary sequence in the complementary DNA strand and then acts as an initiation point for DNA sense strand polymerisation and duplex DNA rebuilding.

For many years, the standard approach was to set up four simultaneous reactions with equivalent, defined concentrations of complementary DNA strand, primer and four deoxynucleotide triphosphate (dNTP) substrates. Each reaction differed only in having a low mol per cent of a single radioactively labelled dideoxynucleotide (ddNTP) substrate (either ddATP, ddGTP, ddCTP or ddTTP). These ddNTPs possess neither 2′ nor 3′ hydroxyl group and therefore prevented further DNA polymerisation whenever they were incorporated into

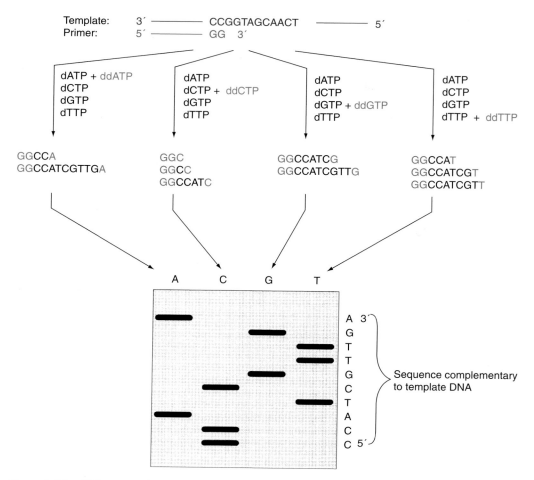

Figure 3.12   DNA sequencing requires template **single-stranded DNA (ssDNA)** and sequencing primers. A selected primer Watson-Crick base pairs to the template and four discrete template-directed DNA polymerization experiments are begun each spiked with a different **chain-terminating dideoxynucleotide** or **ddNTP** (**ddATP**, **ddCTP**, **ddGTP** or **ddTTP**). When the polymerizations take place, oligodeoxynucleotide chain synthesis is stopped wherever a ddNTP is incorporated. Hence each different experiment has different chain terminated oligodeoxynucleotide products (as illustrated). If these reactions involve radioactive ddNTPs then the products can be resolved simultaneously by **polyacrylamide gel electrophoresis** (**PAGE**) and imaged by **autoradiography** giving black bands (as above). These black bands together represent a **sequencing ladder** that is read from bottom to top identifying the DNA sequence (5′ to 3′) complementary to the template DNA, reading directly from the selected primer (Reproduced from Voet, Voet & Pratt, 1999 [Wiley] Fig. 3-23).

a growing chain. Consequently, once the designated short reaction period had come to a close, each DNA polymerisation reaction was expected to contain a range of incomplete DNA sense strands terminating in a dideoxynucleoside. Where ddATP was used, all the incomplete strands were expected to terminate in ddA, where ddGTP was used all were expected to end in ddG, where ddCTP all were supposed to ended in ddC and with ddTTP strands all terminated in ddT. The DNA sense strand products of all four reactions were then resolved side by side on polyacrylamide gel and the radioactivity visualised by photographic plate, resulting in the famous **DNA sequencing ladder**, wherein each successive ladder line going upwards in order from the bottom of the gel (shorter strands run faster) was used to identify successive deoxynucleoside residues in the deoxynucleoside sequence of sense strand DNA starting from the primer.

Nowadays, sequencing is performed with a single DNA polymerisation reaction containing all four ddNTPs differentially labelled with four different types of fluorescent label specific for each ddNTP (see Chapter 4) (Figure 3.13). The complete set of individual DNA sense strand products can now be resolved by **capillary electrophoresis** (**CE**, see Chapter 7) so that each successive fluorescent label resolved and identified from the beginning of the elution run (shorter strands run faster) is able to correlate with and identify the deoxynucleoside residue sequence of sense strand DNA starting from the primer. Read lengths are now typically from 400 to 800 deoxynucleoside residues from the primer.

3.3 Cloning and identification of genes in DNA

Now that we have briefly introduced some of the most important tools and techniques of molecular biology, we can return to the isolation, cloning and identification of genes of interest from within prokaryotic genomic DNA or eukaryotic cDNA library sequences. There are two main approaches for this.

(a) **Direct DNA cloning.** This involves 'cutting' DNA from a source (such as genomic DNA), and then 'inserting' the desired DNA into plasmid DNA that can be replicated (in effect multiple copied), usually in *E. coli.*

(b) **Polymerase chain reaction (PCR).** PCR is an enzyme-based method for amplifying (multiple copying) DNA, from either a DNA template or an RNA template (RT-PCR).

3.3.1 Direct DNA cloning

Direct DNA cloning was originally developed for the isolation and cloning of prokaryotic genes but can be used for the isolation and cloning of eukaryotic genes as well. The meaning of direct DNA cloning is the isolation and multiple copying of DNA from a source of interest

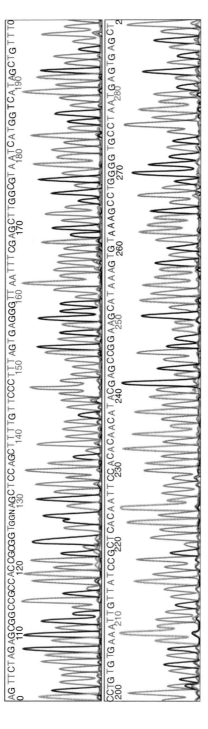

Figure 3.13 Automated DNA sequencing. When ddNTPs are differentially fluorescent-labelled, then only a single template-directed DNA polymerization reaction is required spiked with all four ddNTPs. The different length oligodeoxynucleotide products are then resolved individually by **capillary electrophoresis** and the identity of the terminating ddNTP can be identified not by horizontal position on a gel (see **Fig. 3.12**) but by colour of extrinsic fluorescence output (**red** for **ddTTP**, **blue** for **ddCTP**, **green** for **ddATP** and **cyan** for **ddGTP**) (see Chapter 4). The collective sequence of fluorescence peaks together represent another version of the **sequencing ladder** that is read from left to right identifying the DNA sequence (5' to 3') (400–800 bases) complementary to the template DNA, reading directly from the selected primer (Reproduced from Voet, Voet & Pratt, 1999 [Wiley] Fig. 3-25).

(i.e. genomic DNA primarily purified directly from a prokaryotic organism, or DNA established in a eukaryotic cDNA library). With respect to prokaryotic organisms, DNA once isolated must be cut into fragments ('shot-gun' fragments) either by chemical means or by using restriction enzymes (see Section 3.2.2). Restriction fragments of genomic DNA are then ligated into pDNA vectors (see Section 3.2.1) to create recombinant pDNA constructs. With respect to eukaryotic organisms, cDNA library components may be inserted similarly into pDNA to create alternate eukaryotic recombinant pDNA constructs.

Recombinant means that the pDNA is comprised of regions of DNA from at least two different organisms. These recombinant pDNA constructs are used in the transformation of host cells, typically *E. coli*. Multiple copying of the recombinant pDNA constructs then becomes possible with growth of the host owing to simple **DNA replication**. Since the genetic code is universal, the host is unable to distinguish recombinant DNA from self- (host) DNA, and consequently, when the host grows and divides, even the recombinant pDNA is copied. If *E. coli* cells are spread on a nutrient plate and allowed to grow, then colonies form such that each cell of a given colony originates from a single parent cell and is a **clone** of the original transformed cell. Each cell of the colony will possess recombinant pDNA (as single plasmid or multiple copy/clonal cell) containing a single, unique restriction fragment not found in any of the other *E. coli* colonies. The result then is known as a **clonal library**, since each clone harbours a unique restriction fragment from the original genomic DNA or cDNA of interest.

After making the library, there is a need to identify which of the clones contains the gene of interest. The usual way of doing this is to use a synthetic, single-stranded DNA (ssDNA) molecule known as a **probe** that is complementary to a DNA sequence in the target gene of interest. This probe will then be used to bind specifically to the target gene by Watson–Crick base pairing in a process known as **hybridisation** (Figure 3.14). If the DNA sequence is unknown, how is the probe designed? In this instance there are four general approaches.

(a) If the amino-acid sequence is known for the desired protein, then oligodeoxynucleotide hybridisation probes may be designed with reference to the genetic code (see Chapter 1).

(b) If the gene has previously been cloned from a related organism then a previously used probe (known as a **heterologous probe**) may be tried.

(c) If a protein is known to be abundant in a particular cell/tissue, then this abundance may also be reflected in its statistical abundance within a clonal library.

(d) If the protein of interest has been purified before, and an antibody has been raised against the protein, then the clonal library will have to be converted into an expression library (see later) and the presence of the desired protein is then screened using this antibody.

Clearly options (a) and (b) are much preferred since they can give unambiguous identification of a gene of interest within a very small number of clones (possibly one clone) within the clonal library.

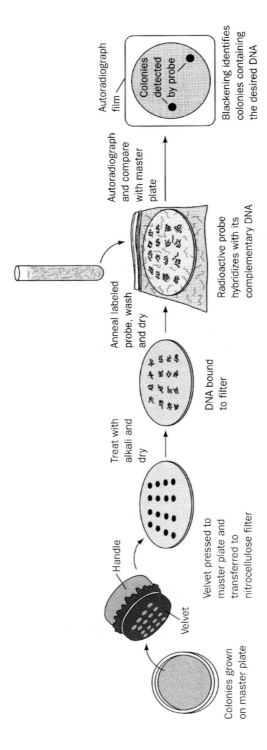

Figure 3.14 Hybridisation in **direct cloning** to identify wherein the heterologous DNA of interest can be found within a **clonal library.** DNA from each clone is isolated by treating each colony with alkali and drying. A **labelled probe** is then use to hybridise to the target in order to identify in which colony the desired gene/DNA of interest can be found (Reproduced from Voe, Voet & Pratt, 1999 [Wiley] Fig. 3-31).

3.3.2 Polymerase chain reaction

The polymerase chain reaction (PCR) has revolutionised biological research since its invention in 1986. PCR is a method for amplifying (multiple copying) DNA, from DNA or RNA sources. PCR has many applications but an important role is the isolation and cloning of eukaryotic genes from cDNA libraries. The mechanism of PCR is as follows (Figure 3.15). Duplex template DNA is identified (for instance a cDNA library) and initially brought to a very high temperature (94 °C) in order that DNA strands (sense and complementary) may dissociate, a process that is often referred to as **DNA melting** or **denaturation**. The region to be amplified is then defined by the introduction of two short oligodeoxynucleotides, known as **primers**. When the temperature is reduced to 50–60 °C, these primers are able to bind, or **anneal**, antiparallel to mutually complementary sequences in either DNA strand of the separated duplex template DNA as appropriate by Watson–Crick base pairing. The temperature is then raised to around 74 °C, optimal operating conditions for a **thermostable DNA polymerase**. This enzyme was originally purified from the hyperthermophile *Thermus aquaticus*, and hence is known as **Taq polymerase**.

Taq polymerase reconstructs duplex DNA starting from the primers annealed to either the sense or complementary strands of the original duplex DNA template. The enzyme proceeds in a $5' \rightarrow 3'$ fashion, taking the deoxynucleotide triphosphates dATP, dCTP, dGTP and dTTP (often referred to as the dNTPs) as substrates for the synthesis of DNA and the reconstruction of DNA duplex. This catalytic process is known as **extension**. From the original duplex DNA template (parent original), two new duplex or double-stranded DNA (dsDNA) copies (daughter copies) now exist, wherein one DNA strand from the parent original template is now in each of the two daughter dsDNA copies – PCR is hence a method of **semi-conservative replication**. The process of denaturing, annealing and extension may then be repeated (typically 20–30 times) and the quantity of dsDNA product expands exponentially, to result in a significant quantity of dsDNA that has been selectively amplified according to the design of the two primers.

Although PCR is powerful, it does have limitations. First, in order to design optimal primers, the base sequences of the regions bordering the target region of interest in the duplex DNA template should be known as well as possible. Second, it is difficult to amplify very large stretches of DNA. As the region of amplification is increased further and further, so is the likelihood of introducing mutations since Taq polymerase is not completely faithful (i.e., the **fidelity rate** is not 100 per cent). In practice, PCR amplifications of up to 3000 base pairs (3 kb) are performed easily, and with care and skill this may be extended up to 10 kb. An absolute limit of around 40 kb is the maximum size of region that may be amplified by PCR. However, for most practical purposes, these limits do not pose a major problem. A 6 kb length of DNA coding sequence should code for a protein of approximately 2000 amino-acid residues, which corresponds to a protein of 240 kDa, assuming an average molecular weight of 120 Da per amino-acid residue. Accordingly, one of the main advantages of PCR in the process of isolation and cloning of genes is that direct cloning may be avoided if the gene is quite well known and has been cloned from a related source previously, or else amino-acid sequences are known. In this case, heterologous probes may be used to PCR amplify a gene of interest direct from prokaryotic genomic DNA or from a eukaryotic cDNA library

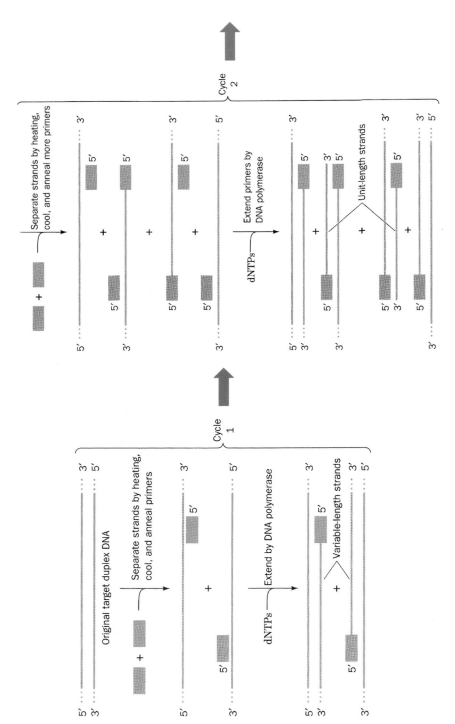

Figure 3.15 Illustration of a PCR reaction. A region of double-stranded DNA (dsDNA) for instance (from a **cDNA library**) is amplified in the following way. Strands are melted by heating and then cooled to anneal two primers. **DNA polymerase** extends from the primers in the 5′ to 3′ direction. Thereafter another round or heating, cooling and **templated DNA synthesis** take place for as many times as required for the specific **amplification** of a target DNA sequence of interest (Reproduced from Voet, Voet & Pratt, 1999 [Wiley] Fig. 3-32).

without the need for any of the previously described direct cloning procedures (see Section 3.3.1). PCR amplification then becomes a potent means to obtain quantities (μg–mg) of a gene of interest irrespective of duplex DNA template source. Obviously, a gene of interest in prokaryotic genomic DNA or eukaryotic cDNA may exceed the limits of PCR amplification, in which case there is no alternative but to effect direct cloning approaches to isolate, clone and identify a gene of interest from either genomic DNA or cDNA libraries as appropriate.

3.3.3 Gene expression and expression vectors

Following the isolation, cloning and identification of genes of interest from within genomic DNA or cDNA libraries by direct cloning or PCR amplification, the next stage is to seek high levels of gene expression and the purification of pure protein in consequence.

3.3.3.1 *Expression vectors*

Typically, proteins are expressed in *E. coli* using a pDNA expression vector (Figure 3.16) especially adapted for high-level gene expression. These pDNA expression vectors are typically around 5000 base pairs in size and have the following characteristics. As for pDNA cloning vectors, an origin of replication is still required and so is a selectable marker. The origin of replication in this case is a **dA = dT** base pair rich region also containing multiple copies of the palindromic sequence 5′-d(pGATC)-3′, which can be methylated on guanine to control replication. DNA methylation at origins of replication is a well known way to shut down replication and inactivate a pDNA vector with respect to replication. The naturally occurring origin of replication in the *E. coli* chromosome (there is only a single origin of replication in *E. coli* for the entire chromosome) is **oriC**, a 468-base-pair non-coding region that when incorporated into pDNAs supports a single copy per cell. The pre-replication complex is a protein complex that binds to oriC allowing replication of the pDNA. When this oriC (often referred to as ori) origin of replication is reduced there is less control of replication by the pre-replication complex and pDNAs are found in multiple copies per cell. The importance and application of the selectable marker for a pDNA vector have been explained already (see Section 3.2.6). Where the selectable marker confers antibiotic resistance against antibiotics such as ampicillin, kanamycin and tetracycline, then the marker is most commonly known as ***Amp**^R*, ***Kan**^R* and ***Tet**^R* respectively (although other names are used too; see Figure 3.16). *Amp*^R is the most common marker and corresponds to the gene coding for the enzyme β-**lactamase**. One other highly important region of a pDNA expression vector is the **multiple cloning site** (**MCS**). This region is prepared from a synthetic, heterologous DNA fragment engineered to contain as many unique (to the pDNA) restriction sites as possible in order to facilitate ligation of the heterologous gene of interest isolated, cloned and identified from either genomic DNA or a cDNA library by direct cloning or direct PCR amplification (see Sections 3.3.1 and 3.3.2).

There are other important regions in a pDNA expression vector that need to be mentioned as well in order to 'complete the tour'. Foremost is the **promoter**. Promoters are non-coding

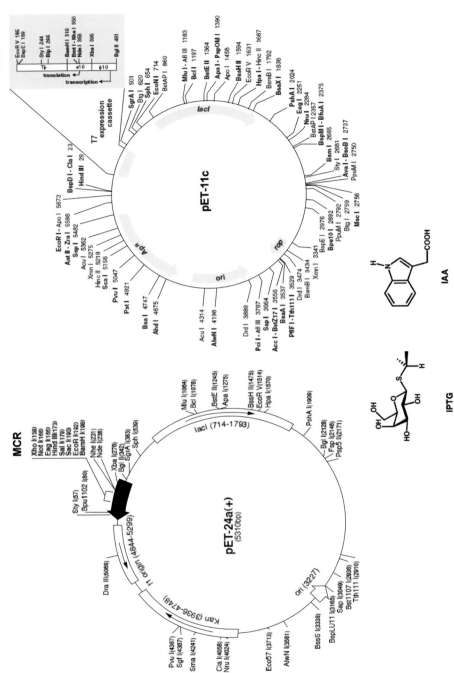

Figure 3.16 Typical commercial protein expression vectors. (a) pET-24a (+): the **origin of replication** (*ori*), **kanamycin resistance** (*Kan*; also known as *Kan^R*), and the **lactose repressor** (*lacI*) are clearly shown. So too is the **multiple cloning site** (MCR) (illustration from www.merckbiosciences.com/docs/docs/PROT/TB070.pdf). **(b)** pET-11c: *ori*, *lacI* and *MCR* are clearly visible. So too is the **ampicillin resistance** (*Ap^R*; also known as *Amp*, *Amp^R*) region. This protein expression vector also harbours a **T7 promoter** that acts as the promoter to drive the expression of heterologous DNA inserted at the MCR. Both maps have extensive restriction endonuclease mapping (illustration from www.merckbiosciences.com/docs/docs/PROT/TB042.pdf. The small molecule **isopropyl-β-D-thiogalactopyranoside (IPTG)** (reverses *lacI* repression) and **indole acetic acid (IAA)** (reverses *trp* promoter repression) are illustrated.

stretches of DNA that are located upstream (i.e. to the 5′-side of the sense strand of pDNA) of a heterologous gene of interest. The promoter region controls the transcription of the heterologous gene (5′ → 3′) into mRNA, so is a very crucial component of any pDNA expression vector. In the early years of molecular biology, a number of natural *E. coli* promoters such as the *lac* and *trp* **promoters** were discovered, as well as phage promoters such as the λp_L **promoter** of **bacteriophage** λ. More recently, artificial promoters such as the ***tac* promoter** have been created through the fusion of sequence elements derived from original promoters. Promoters may be **inducible**, suggesting that an external agent transcription can trigger transcription. For instance addition of **isopropyl-β-D-thiogalactopyranoside** (**IPTG**) to the growth medium induces transcription from the *lac* and *tac* promoters. Similarly, the addition of **indole acetic acid** (**IAA**) induces the *trp* promoter, while raising the growth temperature (briefly to 42 °C) induces the λp_L promoter by inactivating a phage-encoded repressor of transcription. A very powerful, modern promoter element is the **T7 promoter**, which needs to be used in association with bacteriophage **T7 RNA polymerase** (see below).

The enzymes responsible for transcription of DNA to mRNA are all **RNA polymerase** enzymes (or, more specifically, DNA-dependent RNA polymerases). RNA polymerases bind at promoter sequences in order to initiate transcription. Promoter structure is unique to a given RNA polymerase. Having noted this, promoters also possess common elements such as **TATA boxes** (also known as **Pribnow boxes** in prokaryotes, or **Hogness boxes** in eukaryotes). TATA boxes consist of a 10 bp deoxynucleotide region within a promoter that has a predominance of **dA = dT** base pairs. Accordingly, the duplex DNA structure in this region is primed to separate in response to RNA polymerase 'invasion', thereby allowing transcription to begin. **Transcription factors** also play a role in this process, especially in eukaryotes. These factors are defined as proteins that regulate transcription by increasing or decreasing RNA polymerase binding to promoters. Transcription takes place (5′ → 3′ direction) (see Chapter 1) until a **terminator sequence** is reached, which signals RNA polymerase dissociation. In prokaryotes, many mRNA transcripts are **polycistronic**; this means that the coding regions for several proteins are incorporated sequentially within a single primary mRNA transcript. Proteins coded for in this manner often have related functions; therefore, the co-transcribed genes are said to belong to an **operon**. **Operator sites** are found quite frequently near promoters. These are **repressor protein** binding sites, to which a repressor protein may bind in order to modulate the transcription of genes, including those of an operon. The mechanism of repression involves the physical halting of the progress of RNA polymerase transcription. Accordingly, small molecular inducers of transcription, such as IPTG and IAA (see above), are now understood to induce or promote transcription by binding to repressor proteins directly, thereby preventing these proteins from binding to operator sites and repressing transcription.

3.3.3.2 *Protein expression strategy*

There are a number of approaches for the expression of proteins in *E. coli*. A modern approach to protein expression is to make use of purpose designed pDNA expression vectors such as the pET vector family, freely available from commercial sources (Figure 3.16). This pDNA expression vector family comprises a T7 RNA polymerase promoter for transcription, hence the corresponding *E. coli* host should be a recombinant strain engineered for constitutive expression of the heterologous T7 RNA polymerase. This chromosomal T7 RNA polymerase is under control of the promoter *lacUV5*. The product of the gene *lacI* is the **lactose repressor**, which modulates transcription from this *lacUV5* promoter. IPTG is an inducer of transcription from *lac* family promoters by binding to the lactose repressor protein; therefore, when IPTG is added to recombinant *E. coli* growth medium transcription (and translation) of the T7 RNA polymerase is promoted. Correspondingly, the T7 RNA polymerase promoter in pET vectors is a hybrid of the wild-type T7 and the *lac* promoters, known as the **T7lac promoter**. This too is a *lac* family promoter and hence the presence of IPTG also induces transcription (and subsequent translation) for the heterologous gene of interest by T7 RNA polymerase as well. The pET vector family also possesses a **ribosome binding sequence (RBS)** site that provides a means for the primary mRNA transcript to attach to *E. coli* ribosomes post-transcription (see Chapter 1). The RBS site is positioned after the promoter, seven to nine deoxynucleotides upstream (i.e. before the 5′ end of gene) from the start codon of the heterologous gene of interest. This gene of interest is inserted into a pET family vector by means of the MCS, beyond which is **a transcriptional terminator site** located downstream (i.e. post 3′ end of gene) from the **stop codon** of the heterologous gene of interest. This terminator site indicates the site where the T7 RNA polymerase finishes transcription.

3.3.3.3   *Cloning for RNA synthesis*

Transcription of RNA from DNA is far simpler than translation of RNA into protein, and large RNA molecules can be synthesised using a simple *in vitro* cell free transcription system (see Chapter 2). Typically, the DNA coding for the RNA of interest is inserted into pDNA downstream of a promoter such as the **T3, T7 or Sp6 promoter**. RNA is then synthesised from the pDNA *in vitro* using the most appropriate **DNA-dependent RNA polymerase** for the promoter (i.e., **T3 RNA polymerase, T7 RNA polymerase** or **Sp6 RNA polymerase**).

3.4 Integrating cloning and expression

The main problem for the chemical biology reader first introduced to molecular biology is to piece together the many tools and techniques involved. The chemical biology reader approaching molecular biology for the first time can be particularly daunted and even put off by the substantial change in tools, techniques and language compared with chemistry. However, once learnt, molecular biology can be very useful and effective as a tool for chemical biology, which can be easily implemented with little difficulty. Here is a worked example now of cloning and expression of a protein of interest that makes use of concepts and ideas discussed in Main Sections 3.2 and 3.3.

In our example, large quantities of *E. coli* iron-superoxide dismutase, **SodB**, which is an iron-containing enzyme involved in the removal of superoxide radicals for detoxification (Figure 3.17), are required. The first objective must be to **clone** the gene from the appropriate

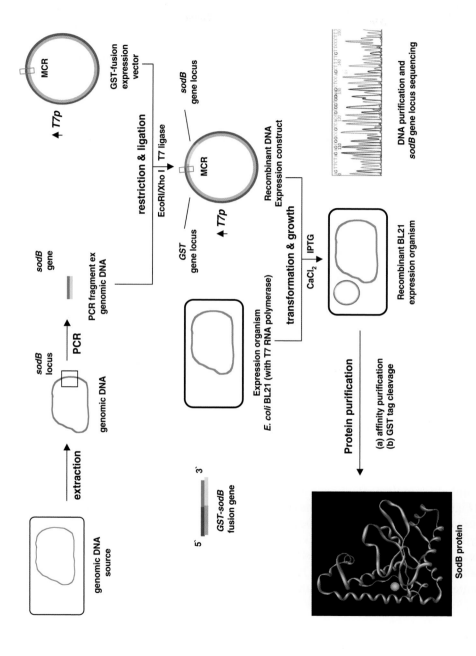

Figure 3.17 Summary of cloning from genomic DNA to GST-fusion protein expression of *E. coli* subunit **protein SodB** (pdb: **1isa**). Genomic DNA is isolated by alkaline extraction and the **sodB locus** amplified by PCR. The recombinant PCR fragment is subjected to restriction cutting and ligation into the MCR of an appropriate **GST-fusion expression vector**. After transformation of *E. coli* BL21 and growth, DNA sequencing is used to identify complete **GST-SodB** recombinant clones, then protein is purified as indicated.

organism, then to express this gene in fusion with a suitable tag to help purification and also increase the solubility of the protein product. Using web-based *E. coli* **gene databases**, basic information can be obtained about the protein and the gene: for instance, the protein is 192 amino acids (and hence is coded by 576 bases), with a molecular weight of approximately 21 kDa, and a theoretical p*I* of 5.9. Given the size of the protein, a PCR amplification strategy should be feasible and is preferred for the identification and cloning of the gene. Accordingly, the first task should be to design primers to amplify the gene from an appropriate genomic source. Within the primers, unique restriction sites must be located in order to help the easy insertion of the PCR product into a pDNA expression vector later on. Furthermore, the strategy to overcome SodB solubility problems during purification will be the introduction of an *N*-terminal GST-tag in this case so that the pDNA expression vector is expressing not the *sodB* gene but a *GST–sodB* fusion gene, giving rise to a more soluble product with translation (see Chapter 2). Hence there is a requirement that the pDNA expression vector should possess a GST-tag sequence in frame with a downstream MCS region (i.e. post 3′ end of *GST-tag* deoxynucleotide sequence) into which the PCR product can be inserted by ligation.

3.4.1 Designing forward and reverse primers

The **forward primer** (i.e. initiated before the 5′ end of the gene) is constructed with three or four deoxynucleotide residues prior to a unique Eco RI restriction site, in order to ensure that this restriction site is active since sites in terminal positions may not be usable restriction sites. Thereafter, the forward primer concludes with the first 20 deoxynucleotides (5′ → 3′) of the known *sodB* gene sequence. The Eco RI restriction site is unique to the pDNA expression vector to be used and is absent from the *sodB* gene sequence as well. The **reverse primer** (i.e. initiated before the 5′ end of the complementary gene) is also constructed with three or four deoxynucleotides prior to a unique Xho I restriction site, followed by the first 20 deoxynucleotides (5′ → 3′) of the known complementary *sodB* gene sequence. Obviously, once again, the Xho I restriction site is unique to the pDNA expression vector to be used and absent from the complementary *sodB* gene sequence.

Hence the forward primer is present to initiate sense strand DNA synthesis using the complementary (antisense) strand of DNA as a template. By contrast, the reverse primer is present to initiate complementary strand DNA synthesis using the sense strand of DNA as a template (Figure 3.15). The first few times primer design is attempted, it is usually easiest to draw out exactly what is happening to be sure of primer orientation. There is also a need to make sure that the melting temperatures of the forward and reverse primers are as similar to each other as possible by extending or shortening those deoxynucleotide stretches post the unique restriction sites, as appropriate. This is important to ensure equal levels of sense and complementary strand DNA synthesis under PCR amplification conditions.

3.4.2 PCR amplification and product isolation

PCR amplification of a gene from prokaryotic DNA is best achieved by prior isolation of **genomic DNA** from the prokaryote of interest in the following way. In this case the *sodB* gene sequence is to be amplified from *E. coli* cells. Therefore, these cells are washed with PBS buffer then heated to 95 °C for a few minutes to allow the genomic DNA to be released without degradation from DNAses. The primers can then be mixed with the released genomic DNA (or even the *E. coli* cells!), and all the necessary components for PCR amplification (*Taq* polymerase, four dNTPs, Mg^{2+}-containing buffer). Conditions and parameters may need some adjusting, most notably the melting temperatures of the primers and the number of cycles used. This melting temperature represents the temperature at which the primer is 50 per cent complexed with the template. This may be calculated from the primer sequence. However, the ideal annealing temperature is 5 °C lower than the melting temperature. If the melting temperature is too high then not enough primer will bind to template DNA. If the temperature is too low then non-specific sequences are amplified because primers will bind to similar as well as identical complementary DNA sequences. A typical number of cycles would be 25 amplification cycles. This number is important, since if there are too few amplification cycles then there may not be sufficient PCR amplification product to handle and if there are too many amplification cycles then there is serious risk of PCR-based mutations.

Following PCR amplification, a portion of the reaction mix may be run on an agarose gel to check the success of the process. If PCR has been successful, then a clean band should be visible on a stained agarose gel corresponding to the amplified *sodB* gene fragment of approximately 600 bp in length. The simplest way to purify this *sodB* gene fragment would then be by using the guanidinium isothiocyanate–silica method once again (see Section 3.2.7).

3.4.3 Ligation and transformation

Extra pDNA expression vector may be obtained if required by mini-prep preparation and digestion with Eco RI and Xho I restriction enzymes. Similarly, the *sodB* gene fragment is digested with Eco RI and Xho I restriction enzymes. In both cases, digestion should be to completion and products must be purified by agarose gel electrophoresis. After purification of the two main fragments from each digestion, the two fragments may be ligated together by means of T4 DNA ligase. In the case of our worked example, the pET pDNA expression vector was selected with the idea of ligating the PCR generated *sodB* gene fragment into the vector MCS in frame with the 3′ terminus of a *GST tag* (see above), thereby generating a new *GST–sodB* fusion gene. After ligation, the newly recombinant pDNA expression construct should be used to transform $CaCl_2$ competent *E. coli* cells, or introduced into other appropriate host cells by electroporation. For the transformation of a ligation mixture it is best to use an *E. coli* strain that has been modified so as to be particularly efficient at taking up pDNA, for example the *E. coli* DH10β strain. After transformation the cells are encouraged to grow without antibiotic for 1 h at 37 °C then spread on agar plates for antibiotic selection over a further 16 h incubation at 37 °C.

3.4.4 Validation and sequencing

Successful transformation with a recombinant pDNA expression construct should result in the appearance of a number of colonies on the antibiotic selection plate, with none appearing on the control plate. The recombinant pDNA from these colonies needs to be validated and sequenced before proceeding. In order to do this, colony samples are picked and grown in selective media (5 ml). The pDNA is then be isolated by the guanidinium isothiocyanate–silica method (as usual) and then digested with Eco RI and Xho I restriction enzymes in order to see the reappearance of two DNA fragments, one of approximately 600 bp in length. After this, the recombinant 600 bp insert comprising the *sodB* gene should be sequenced as completely as possible by DNA sequencing, using designed sequencing primers, in order to demonstrate that the *sodB* gene has been cloned successfully from genomic DNA sources without PCR errors.

3.4.5 Protein expression

Overexpression of the *GST–sodB* fusion gene is then made possible as follows. A host *E. coli* strain containing the T7 RNA polymerase is essential for optimal gene expression from the selected pDNA expression vector (pET family). Fortunately, the readily available, attenuated *E. coli* BL21 strain has just such a chromosomal copy of this heterologous enzyme, and so represents the ideal host for protein expression. Hence, post validation and sequencing of the recombinant pDNA construct, competent *E. coli* BL21 cells undergo transformation and are then grown on antibiotic selection plates in order to select for recombinant BL21 colonies. Thereafter, selected colonies may be picked, grown on a small scale until saturation (in the presence of antibiotics), then on a larger scale until the A_{600} absorbance is measured to be approximately 0.6, after which the inducer IPTG is added to induce substantial *GST–sodB* fusion gene transcription. After further cell growth for several hours, samples can be collected and analysed by SDS-PAGE for a protein overexpression band at the appropriate mass (in this case, the mass of a GST–SodB fusion protein should be 48 kDa). Assuming that this band can be seen by SDS-PAGE, then protein purification can begin (see Chapter 2).

3.4.6 Cloning and expressing from eukaryotic genes

For higher eukaryotes, the most common approach to cloning is PCR amplification from cDNA libraries in order to avoid the intron problem. Another challenge when expressing eukaryotic proteins is that eukaryotic proteins frequently do not fold properly in *E. coli* and will not be processed with the correct post-translational modifications, and therefore often other eukaryotic expression hosts must be used. Options include using yeast cells, insect cell lines or mammalian cell lines.

3.5 Site-directed mutagenesis

One powerful approach towards analysing protein structure and function is by modifying or mutating the amino-acid sequence in a directed manner and then comparing characteristics of the mutant with the wild-type proteins. Before recombinant DNA technology, a number of chemical means were used to modify specific amino acids, or crude methods such as UV radiation were used to introduce random mutations to the DNA coding sequence. However, mutagenesis has never been easier, with the applications of recombinant tools and techniques. Hence the practice of **site-directed mutagenesis** can be both PCR and non-PCR based.

3.5.1 PCR-based approaches to mutagenesis

The basic approach towards PCR-directed site-directed mutagenesis of genomic DNA is the use of primers designed with the desired mutations included. The primer should incorporate the desired **base mismatch**. If the mismatch is to be generated near the 5′ end of the gene of interest then the forward primer can include the mismatch deliberately. Similarly, if the mismatch is to be generated near the 3′ end of the gene then the reverse primer can include the mismatch instead. Hence, as the PCR reaction proceeds, Taq polymerase will end up incorporating the mismatch into the gene sequence without interruption (Figure 3.18). Should the desired mismatch involve a central gene location, the approach must be to split the PCR amplification reaction into two. Each PCR reaction uses a central forward or reverse primer containing the desired base mismatch. The result is that the gene of interest is then

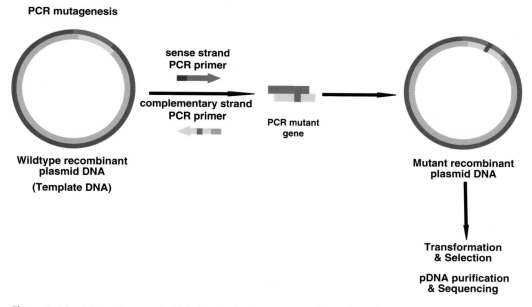

Figure 3.18 PCR mutagenesis. This is the simple way to engineer the primary structure of a protein of interest. Where desired mutations are near the 5′-terminus or the 3′-terminus or the sense strand, then the **mismatched primer technique** is used. In the illustrated case, the desired mutation is near the 3′-terminus so a normal sense strand primer is combined with a mismatched complementary strand primer containing a mutation (blue). When the PCR reaction is allowed to proceed with the **template DNA**, then the mismatch in the complementary strand primer forces a mismatch to appear in both sense and complementary strands of the final PCR amplification product resulting in a **PCR mutant gene**. Restriction cutting and ligation of the mutant PCR product into a cloning or expression vector generates a mutant recombinant pDNA construct ready for transformation and selection, then DNA purification and sequencing of correct mutant recombinant DNA.

amplified as two separate, partially overlapping, fragments, both containing the mutation. These two fragments must then be knitted back together using a further set of primers and a third PCR reaction, which will result in a **chimeric product**. Alternatively, there is the **inverse PCR** method in which two primers are introduced, both incorporating the desired base mismatch but both pointing outwards away from the centre of the gene of interest and instead pointing towards the long way round the recombinant pDNA expression construct. However, this has proven to be a very error prone method for site-directed mutagenesis and so should not be used. Hence, where the desired mismatch involves a central gene location, a non-PCR-based site-directed mutagenesis is desirable.

3.5.2 Non-PCR-based approaches to mutagenesis

Many of these approaches are patented, so it is necessary to use trade names to describe these useful approaches. Currently popular is the **Quikchange® system** (Figure 3.19). In this, two primers are designed that anneal respectively to sense and complementary strands of a parent

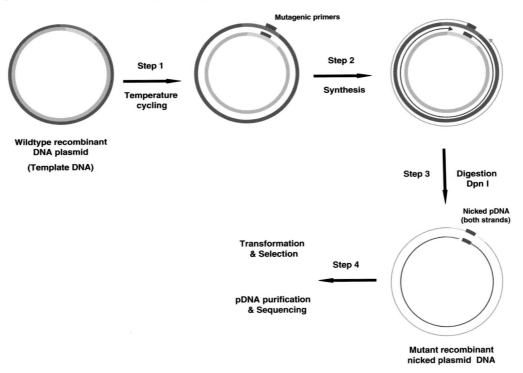

Figure 3.19   Non-PCR mutagenesis. Overview of the QuikChange® site-directed mutagenesis method; **Step 1**: denature the template DNA and anneal oligodeoxynucleotide mutagenic primers (blue) with desired mutation; **Step 2**: using the non-strand displacing action of *PfuTurbo* **DNA polymerase,** extend and incorporate the mutagenic primers resulting in nicked circular strands; **Step 3**: digest the methylated, non-mutated parental template DNA with *Dpn I*. **Step 4**: transform *E. coli* **XL1-Blue** with nicked dsDNA, ready for selection, DNA purification and sequence identification of correct correct mutant recombinant DNA (Reproduced adapted from Quikchange™ manual; www.stratagene.com/manuals/200518.pdf).

recombinant pDNA expression construct but are also appropriately modified to introduce a mutation. Necessarily, the two primers point in opposite directions. Hence, in order to effect mutations, a parent vector is introduced into a mutagenesis mixture containing the two primers, and a DNA polymerase is required to assemble a new sense and complementary DNA strand from the two primers using the complementary and sense strands as templates respectively. Both new strands are assembled with high fidelity without displacing the original oligodeoxynucleotide primers. Therefore, the result comprises mutant sense and complementary DNA daughter strands in association with corresponding wild-type complementary and sense DNA parent strands. Daughter strands are clearly distinguishable from the parent strands due to previous **adenine methylation** of the parent vector by *E. coli* (i.e., recombinant pDNA once utilised for *E. coli* transformation become methylated on both strands by their *E. coli* host cells). This methylation allows for the parent strands to be targeted for destruction in the mutagenesis mixture using the restriction enzyme **Dpn I**, which targets single-strand restriction sites, 5′-d(pGm⁶ATC)-3′, containing the *N*-6 methylated deoxyadenosine (**dm⁶A**) residue (see Chapter 1). These restriction sites are frequent enough to allow for complete digestion of the parent strands, leaving mutant daughter strands behind to generate a single mutant recombinant pDNA construct with two staggered nicks (i.e., the phosphodiester link is incomplete), one per strand. Transformation of *E. coli* once more allows these nicks to be repaired and the mutant recombinant pDNA to be replicated. There are various other technologies for site-directed mutagenesis that work by similar approaches.

4

Electronic and Vibrational Spectroscopy

4.1 Electronic and vibrational spectroscopy in chemical biology

Our first chapter on analysing structure is devoted to electronic and vibrational spectroscopy. Compared with magnetic resonance (Chapter 5), or diffraction and microscopy (Chapter 6), electronic and vibrational spectroscopy are decidedly low resolution techniques, in that atomic-level descriptions of biological macromolecular structures are all but impossible to achieve with these techniques. However, the advantage of electronic spectroscopies in particular is that they are able to provide meaningful data from very small quantities of biological macromolecules (Table 5.3). Therefore, broad brush-stroke (Å–nm range) characterisations of biological macromolecular structures can be performed in advance of the more sophisticated, but both more time and more material intensive, atomic-level structural characterisations such as X-ray diffraction (Chapter 6). Furthermore, electronic spectroscopies, and to some extent vibration spectroscopy, are also able to demonstrate the occurrence of trans-conformational changes in the structures of biological macromolecules in response to environmental changes and/or molecular interactions, so providing an additional broad brush-stroke view of biological function as well. In the case of fluorescence spectroscopy, this view can even extend up to the observations of molecular binding interactions taking place in real time in living cells. Hence, both electronic and vibrational spectroscopies represent 'first-pass' structural and even functional characterisation techniques that can contribute to a broad if not necessarily detailed initial appreciation of biological macromolecular structure and function prior to more detailed investigations. Quite often, the absence of adequate quantities of biological macromolecules for studies ensures that information from electronic and vibrational spectroscopies maybe, by default, all that is feasible to acquire and therefore currently available. Such realities ensure that electronic and vibrational spectroscopies are

Essentials of Chemical Biology   Andrew Miller and Julian Tanner
© 2008 John Wiley & Sons, Ltd

certain to play a central linking role from early structural to early functional characterisation for a long while to come!

4.2 UV–visible spectroscopy

Ultraviolet (UV)–visible light spectroscopy is one of the oldest and outwardly simplest forms of spectroscopy for the analysis of biological macromolecule structure. However, since UV–visible spectroscopy is based upon electronic excitation, the simplicity of measurement that makes the technique so attractive to use is largely cancelled out by a distinct absence of detailed theory linking measured data through to a detailed structural characterisation! In consequence, UV–visible spectroscopy is a rather blunt instrument for the analysis of biological macromolecule structure. Nonetheless, there is still structural information to be gained. The basis of UV–visible spectroscopy is that when a beam of UV or visible light of a given wavelength passes through a solution of a given solute mounted in a **cuvette** (Figure 4.1) the intensity of light may become diminished by interactions with dissolved solute or indeed solvent molecules. These interactions can be considered as inelastic collisions between photons and solute or solvent molecules, followed by **absorption** then **electronic excitation** (assuming that photon energy coincides with the energy of an acceptable **electronic transition**). The result of these interactions is that the intensity of light transmitted through the solution in the cuvette is diminished.

4.2.1 Transition dipole moments

According to the classical theory of absorption, the interaction of light with a given molecule is thought to result in the induction of dipoles through the interaction of the oscillating electric

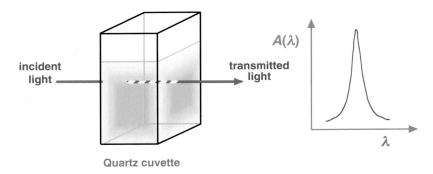

Figure 4.1   Illustration of the experimental arrangement for **UV-visible spectroscopy** where sample in a **quartz cuvette** is irradiated with monochromatic incident light at a wavelength λ and the amount of light that is absorbed at that wavelength, $A(\lambda)$, is determined by comparison between incident and transmitted light intensities. A plot of $A(\lambda)$, against wavelength λ gives us a typical absorption spectrum.

field of light with polarisable clouds of electrons. This is represented by

$$\mu_{ind} = \alpha(\nu_v) E(\nu_v) \tag{4.1}$$

where μ_{ind} is the **induced dipole moment**, $E(\nu_v)$ the **oscillating electric field of light** and $\alpha(\nu_v)$ the **electronic polarisability** of matter, the latter two a function of the **vibrational frequency of light**, ν_v. By analogy, according to quantum theory of absorption, the interaction of light with a given molecule invokes a transition dipole moment provoking the electronic excitation of a single electron from an initial wavefunction-defined state, ψ_a, to a final wavefunction defined state, ψ_b (which is by definition an electronic transition). The **transition dipole moment** invoked is given by the following expression:

$$\langle \psi_a | \bar{\mu} | \psi_b \rangle \tag{4.2}$$

Since all but one of the electrons in the given molecule remain unchanged in state as a result of electronic excitation, then only the wavefunctions involved directly in the electronic transition need be considered in defining the transition dipole moment. In the case of biological macromolecules and macromolecular assemblies, relevant wavefunctions usually correlate to lone pair orbitals, n, and π/π^* molecular orbitals such that only two main types of transition dipole moment need be considered, which are $\langle n | \bar{\mu} | \pi^* \rangle$ and $\langle \pi | \bar{\mu} | \pi^* \rangle$ respectively. The first of these transition dipole moments is in fact zero, consequently corresponding $n \rightarrow \pi^*$ electronic transitions are known as weak, **symmetry forbidden transitions**. The second of these transition dipole moments is always non-zero and consequently corresponding $\pi \rightarrow \pi^*$ transitions are known as a strong, **symmetry allowed transitions**. The symmetry allowed transitions are at least 100 times more intense than symmetry forbidden transitions.

A fall in transmittance resulting from absorption from solution in a cuvette is usually characterised in terms of **absorbance**, $A(\lambda)$, or **optical density**, $OD(\lambda)$, at the given wavelength, λ, according to the **Beer–Lambert law**:

$$A(\lambda) = c_M \varepsilon(\lambda) l \tag{4.3}$$

where l is the cuvette **path length**, c_M the **concentration** of biological macromolecule and $\varepsilon(\lambda)$ the constant of proportionality known as the **extinction coefficient**. Typically, $A(\lambda)$ is far from constant with wavelength and plotting $A(\lambda)$ as a function of λ results in a **UV–visible absorption spectrum** (Figure 4.1) that may exhibit characteristics of the solvent but will certainly exhibit characteristics of the dissolved solute. The primary reason for the variation of $A(\lambda)$ with λ is that neither dissolved solutes nor solvent molecules are able to absorb photon energy uniformly with λ. Instead, there is an extensive pattern of differential absorbance owing to the fact that the absorption characteristics of any given solute or solvent molecule are substantially dominated by **chromophores**. Chromophores are functional groups or absorbing elements (molecular structures or substructures) that absorb strongly at specific values of λ.

In general, the chromophores found typically in solutes, such as proteins, nucleic acids, carbohydrates and lipids (i.e. our biological macromolecules or macromolecular assemblies), absorb at values of $\lambda < 300$ nm, whilst structures found in water (the standard solvent) tend to absorb at values of $\lambda < 170$ nm. In fact, at $\lambda < 170$ nm water has very broad electronic absorption bands, broader than those found in most other solvents. Furthermore, water molecules also interact extensively with dissolved biological macromolecules or assemblies, leading to considerable distortions in the energies of chromophore-associated electronic transitions and hence considerable variations in the values of λ at which electronic excitations take place (see Chapter 1). Consequently, UV–visible absorption spectra of biological macromolecules in water usually take on the appearance of a collection of broad absorption peaks in the range 170–300 nm. As we shall see, UV visible spectra of globular proteins are the best understood and most widely studied.

4.2.2 UV–visible spectroscopy of proteins

Within globular proteins, the peptide links, amino-acid side-chains and disulphide bridges are the main characteristic chromophores typical in a globular protein (Table 4.1). In addition, a number of proteins may also be modified by non-peptide prosthetic groups that act as functional **cofactors** to enable protein functional activities. Such prosthetic groups are especially dominant in proteins involved in redox reactions or electron transfer processes. They have an especially rich chromophore-behaviour (Figure 4.2; Table 4.2). Both $n \rightarrow \pi^*$ and $\pi \rightarrow \pi^*$ transitions dominate throughout. Turning to amino-acid residues, tryptophan followed by tyrosine residues are much the most significant chromophores and these dominate protein absorption in the UV region. This can be very useful. At a given wavelength, when $A(\lambda)$ is less than 0.5, values of $A(\lambda)$ turn out to be proportional to macromolecular concentration, c_M. Hence, in the case of proteins, absorbance measurements made in the UV region at 280 nm, A_{280}, can be used to give a direct measure of protein concentration. Typically, protein concentrations are determined with reference to the A_{280} absorbance of the

Table 4.1 Summary of the main **Chromophore/Fluorophore residues** in proteins and nucleic acids with absorption and fluorescence characteristics given A_{max} is wavelength of maximum absorbance, ε_{max} is maximum extinction coefficient value, I_{max} is wavelength of maximum fluorescence intensity, and τ_R is radiative lifetime.

Fluorophore	Conditions	A_{max}/nm	$10^{-3} \times \varepsilon_{max}/$ $M^{-1}\ cm^{-1}$	I_{max}/nm	ϕ_F	τ_R/nsec
Tryptophan	aqueous, pH7	280	5.7	348	0.2	2.6
Tyrosine	aqueous, pH7	274	1.3	303	0.14	3.6
Phenylalanine	aqueous, pH7	257	0.2	282	0.04	6.4
Adenine	aqueous, pH7	260	13.4	321	2.6×10^{-4}	<0.02
Guanine	aqueous, pH7	275	8.1	329	3.0×10^{-4}	<0.02
Cytosine	aqueous, pH7	267	6.1	313	0.8×10^{-4}	<0.02
Uracil	aqueous, pH7	260	9.5	308	0.4×10^{-4}	<0.02

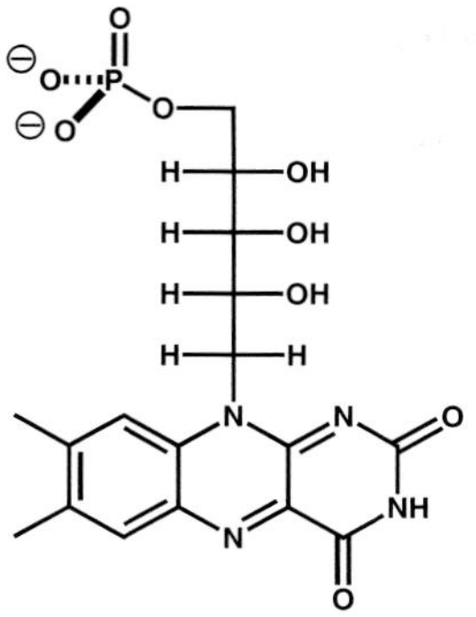

Flavin Mono Nucleotide (FMN)

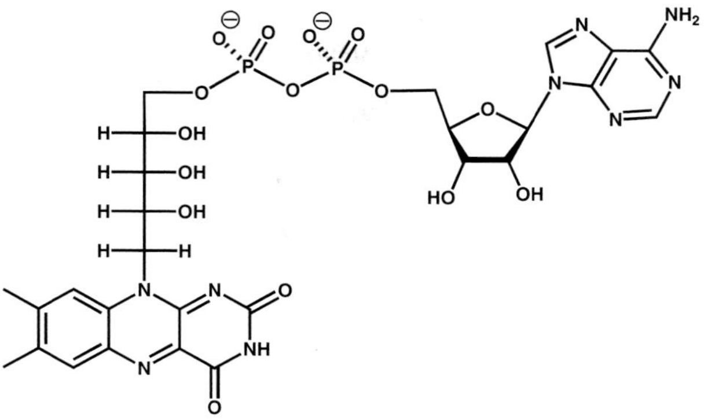

Flavin Adenine Dinucleotide (FAD)

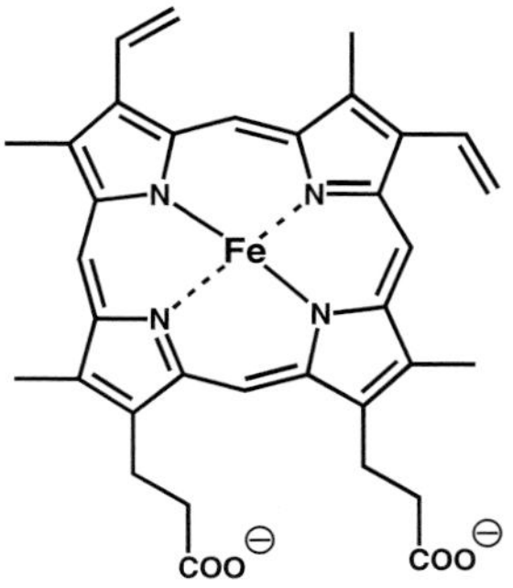

Heme

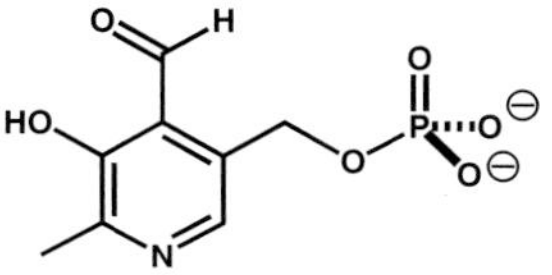

Pyridoxal Phosphate

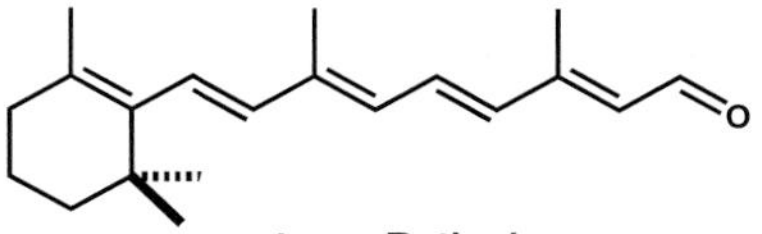

***trans*-Retinal**

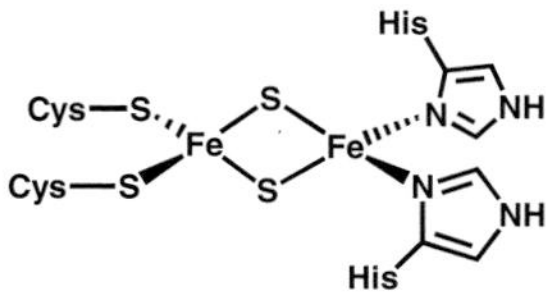

[2Fe-2S] Cluster

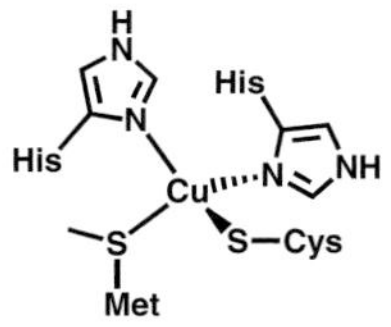

Blue Copper Centre

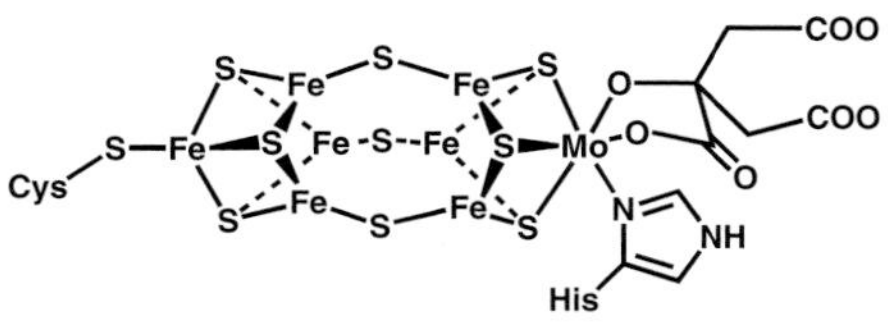

FeMo Cluster

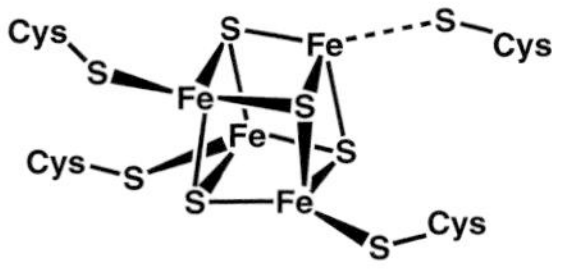

[4Fe-4S] Cluster

Figure 4.2 Structures of main **prosthetic groups** that contribute significantly to the UV-visible spectroscopy of proteins. Prosthetic groups are non amino acid-based moieties that are covalently attached to the proteins concerned and play an integral part of the structure and function of proteins to which they are covalently attached.

Table 4.2 Summary of the main **prosthetic group chromophores** found in redox-active or electron transfer proteins/enzymes with absorption characteristics given. See **Fig. 4.2** and **Table 4.1** for structures and abbreviations used in the table.

Chromophore	A_{max}/nm	$10^{-4} \times \varepsilon_{max}$/M^{-1} cm^{-1}	A_{max}/nm	$10^{-4} \times \varepsilon_{max}$/M^{-1} cm^{-1}
FMN	455	1.3	358	1.1
Blue Cu(II)	781	0.3	625	0.4
Heme Fe(II)	550	2.8		
[2Fe, 2S]	421	1.0	330	1.3
FAD	460	1.3	438	1.5
[4Fe, 4S]	570	0.4	490	0.8
Retinal	498	4.2	350	1.1
Pyridoxal	415	2.6		
FeMo	550	2.2		

solution of the protein of interest measured at a fixed concentration of 1 mg ml^{-1} (1 g l^{-1}; 0.1 per cent) (using a 1 cm path-length cuvette). This $A_{280}^{0.1}$ value may be found from the extinction coefficients of tryptophan and tyrosine amino-acid residues (i.e., ε_{max} 5700 and 1300 M^{-1} cm^{-1} respectively) together with the **molecular weight of the globular protein** concerned, M_p, according to the following equation:

$$A_{280}^{0.1} = (5700 n_{Trp} + 1300 n_{Tyr})/M_p \qquad (4.4)$$

where n_{Trp} and n_{Tyr} are the number of tryptophan and the number of tyrosine amino-acid residues per protein molecule. On average, the $A_{280}^{0.1}$ value for the majority of proteins is approximately 1.0.

4.2.3 UV–visible spectroscopy of nucleic acids

The UV–visible spectroscopy of nucleic acids is dominated by base absorption. Neither phosphodiester backbone nor β-D-ribofuranose/2'-deoxy-β-D-ribofuranose rings have any significant UV–visible absorbance above 200 nm. In comparison with absorption by the main protein chromophores (not including the prosthetic groups), absorption by each nucleic acid base (Table 4.1) is associated with more than one main $n \rightarrow \pi^*$ and $\pi \rightarrow \pi^*$ transition (in the range 200–300 nm) owing to the fact that each base has low symmetry and several hetero-atom lone pairs (see Chapter 1). Transitions for each individual base in a given nucleic acid tend to overlap and merge into a single broad, strong absorption band for the nucleic acid polymer as a whole, with an absorbance maximum, A_{max}, at 260 nm (ε_{max} 10 000 M^{-1} cm^{-1} on average per nucleotide base). In a similar way as for proteins, nucleic acid concentrations in solution may be determined by A_{260} absorbance measurements with reference to the A_{260} value of a 1 mg ml^{-1} (1 g l^{-1}; 0.1 per cent) solution of nucleic acids measured in a 1 cm path-length cuvette. Unlike for proteins, one average value of $A_{260}^{0.1}$ is sufficient to determine the concentration of most nucleic acids of interest since the bases of each nucleoside or deoxynucleoside building $A_{260}^{0.1}$ block behave as chromophores in a very similar manner. This average value may be calculated from the **average molecular weight of a nucleotide**, M_{nt}, according to the following equation:

$$A_{260}^{0.1} = 10000/M_{nt} \tag{4.5}$$

A typical value for M_{nt} is usually 330 Da.

In contrast with proteins and nucleic acids, carbohydrates and lipids possess few substantial inherent chromophores and so neither class of biological macromolecule has a particularly rich or useful UV–visible spectroscopic behaviour. Therefore, we shall focus the next section on structural versus functional information available from the UV–visible spectroscopy of proteins and nucleic acids only.

4.2.4 Structural versus functional information from UV–visible spectroscopy

In the most trivial application, UV–visible spectroscopy provides a means to assess the concentration in solution of proteins or nucleic acids. Moreover, calibrated values of A_{260} and A_{280} even provide a means to calculate approximate molecular weights according to Equations (4.4) and (4.5). However, more substantial structural information remains frustratingly difficult to deduce. Nevertheless, UV–visible spectroscopy can be a useful monitor of conformational changes in globular proteins. This is possible owing to the effects that local environment may have on the absorbance characteristics of aromatic amino-acid residue chromophores, particularly tryptophan. Aromatic amino-acid residues are responsible for clusters of $\pi \rightarrow \pi^*$ transitions absorbing strongly in the region 250–300 nm. The largest contributors to this UV–visible absorbance are tryptophan residues, with more modest contributions coming from tyrosine and phenylalanine residues (Table 4.1). Changes in the local environments of these aromatic residues can often be sufficient to change the UV–visible absorbance behaviour of some or all of these residues. This is particularly true in the event that a globular protein is subject to a range of different physical conditions and/or molecular interactions, which can lead to obvious if not substantial trans-conformational changes, which can provoke changes in local environments and thereby bring about UV–visible absorbance changes. For instance, many aromatic amino-acid residues are often 'buried' in the hydrophobic interior of a globular protein and not at the hydrophilic surface. However, situations arise where conditions change and/or molecular interactions take place that may lead to buried aromatic amino-acid residues entering more hydrophilic environments and becoming more solvent accessible as a consequence of conformational changes (and vice versa). In such events, energies of both $n \rightarrow \pi^*$ and $\pi \rightarrow \pi^*$ transitions could become altered in response to changes in the local environments of aromatic amino-acid residues. Specifically, if the local environment of an aromatic amino-acid residue changes from a hydrophobic to a more hydrophilic environment, then a corresponding change in $\varepsilon(\lambda)$ can lead to a reduction in $\pi \rightarrow \pi^*$ transition energies associated with an increase in **transition wavelength** (**red-shift**), and an increase in $n \rightarrow \pi^*$ transition energies, leading to a decrease in **transition wavelength** (**blue-shift**) (Figure 4.3). (Obviously, the reverse situation is also true if the local environmental changes are from

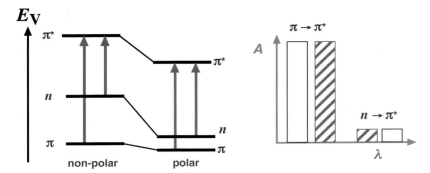

Figure 4.3 Illustration of the effect of environmental conditions on $\pi \rightarrow \pi^*$ and $n \rightarrow \pi^*$ transitions. Displacement of a **chromophore** from non-polar (white bar) to polar (red hatched bar) conditions results in a red shift of the $\pi \rightarrow \pi^*$ and a blue shift of the $n \rightarrow \pi^*$ due to a differential stabilisation of lone pairs n compared with π^*-orbitals E_V is energy.

hydrophilic to hydrophobic.) Therefore, in summary, conformational changes in globular proteins may be diagnosed by shifts in the wavelengths of $\pi \rightarrow \pi^*$ and $n \rightarrow \pi^*$ transitions provided that the aromatic chromophores (especially tryptophan) are sufficiently sensitive to the local environmental changes caused by these conformational changes. Such changes in spectroscopic signature in response to molecular interactions can be very useful to study molecular recognition and binding as well (see Chapter 7).

Protein absorption bands may also be subject to band splitting, or **perturbation**, as a result of electronic interactions between adjacent chromophores (Figure 4.4). To a first approximation, the number of individual absorption bands generated by perturbations will be equivalent to the number of interacting chromophores, although the number of bands may be considerably smaller if perturbation effects are heavily affected by relative orientations between chromophores. Such reduced perturbation effects created through electronic interactions between peptide links can be used to identify the presence of protein secondary structures

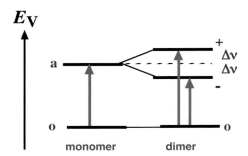

Figure 4.4 Illustration of **perturbation effects** when there are electronic interactions between chromophores. Interaction between two monomer chromophores splits the excited states into two sub-states creating two new displaced electronic transitions. There should be at least as many excited state sub-states as there are electronically interacting chromophores, however selection rules and orientation effects will diminish the number of transitions observed E_V is energy.

under some circumstances. For instance, perturbation effects will identify the presence of α-helical secondary structures in a protein. Owing to the highly regular nature of α-helical secondary structures and the extreme effect of orientation upon peptide link chromophore perturbation effects, α-helical structures are characterised by only two UV–visible $\pi \rightarrow \pi^{*}$ transitions associated with α-helix peptide links that are characterised by

(a) transition dipole moment parallel to the main helix axis

(b) transition dipole moment perpendicular to the main helix axis.

In practical terms, transition (a) is observed as a 190 nm absorption band with a shoulder at 208 nm. Transition (b) is observed only at lower wavelengths with good optical equipment. UV–visible $\pi \rightarrow \pi^{*}$ transitions involving either β-sheets or less regular structures (known broadly as **random coil**) are not subject to extensive chromophore perturbation effects and hence UV–visible spectroscopy is unable to identify the presence of either secondary structural elements directly.

Turning to nucleic acids, the potential of UV–visible spectroscopy for nucleic acid structural analysis has always been considered high in principle. The reason for this is the sheer number of base chromophores available in nucleic acids and their potential for electronic interactions. Given the high degree of structural uniformity in nucleic acids, the total absorbance $A(\lambda)$ of a given sample of nucleic acids may be given by

$$A(\lambda) = c_{nt}l \sum_{i} \chi_i \varepsilon_i(\lambda) \tag{4.6}$$

This is a variation of the Beer–Lambert law (Equation (4.3)) given above, where $\varepsilon_i(\lambda)$ is the **molar extinction coefficient of pure nucleotide monomer of type** i, c_{nt} is **total nucleotide monomer concentration** and χ_i is **the mole fraction of nucleotide monomer** of type i in the nucleic acid under investigation. Conformational changes will promote significant deviation from Equation (4.6) primarily by promoting local deviations in $\varepsilon_i(\lambda)$ values away from pure nucleotide monomer values. Local deviations in $\varepsilon_i(\lambda)$ values are primarily the result of local changes in electronic interactions between bases as a result of local geometric distortions together with some contribution from local environmental changes. In the case of nucleic acids, local environmental changes have much less effect on UV–visible $\pi \rightarrow \pi^{*}$ transitions than changes in electronic interactions between bases. The conformational flexibility of nucleic acids turns out to be too high and the resulting geometric distortions too extensive and dynamic to obtain currently meaningful structural information by UV–visible spectroscopy on secondary and tertiary structures in nucleic acids. However, the promise remains.

4.3 Circular dichroism spectroscopy

Circular dichroism (CD) spectroscopy is in many ways a more sophisticated version of UV–visible spectroscopy and is able to give substantially more structural information than may be obtained by routine UV–visible spectroscopy. Unfortunately, CD spectroscopy gives little meaningful information for carbohydrates or lipids owing to the lack of substantive chromophores in either class of biological macromolecule once again.

4.3.1 Circularly polarised light

The classical view of light is that of two coupled, mutually perpendicular oscillating fields (electric and magnetic) that propagate together. Typically, the behaviour of either field can be defined in terms of a vector known as the **electric vector** (E) and the **magnetic vector** (B) respectively (Figure 4.5). The behaviour of the electric vector is critical to electronic spectroscopy and to optical activity. Therefore, we will just concentrate on the electric vector for now. In the normal course of events, the electric vector may oscillate in any plane perpendicular to the direction of propagation. **Plane polarised light** is generated by means of a **polariser**, which restricts electric vector oscillation to a single plane (Figure 4.5). When two beams of plane polarised light are combined 90° ($\pi/2$) out of phase with respect to each other the two electric vectors combine to form a single electric vector that precesses around the direction of propagation mapping out a pathway that takes on the appearance of either a **left-** or **right-hand corkscrew**. Provided that both electric vectors are of equal magnitude then the result is either **left-** (E_L) or **right-hand** (E_R) **circularly polarised light**. If the electric vectors are of unequal magnitude then the corkscrew becomes asymmetric and the result is either **left-** or **right-hand elliptically polarised light** respectively (Figure 4.5).

4.3.2 Optical activity and circular dichroism

CD spectroscopy originates from **optical activity**. A given molecule has optical activity if light–molecule interactions are able to alter the physical properties of incident light transmitted through a sample containing that molecule. When left- and right-hand circularly polarised light beams are incident on a sample containing an optically active molecule, the sample will absorb left- and right- hand circularly polarised light to different extents during transmission (Figure 4.5). The net result of this differential absorption is to transform combined circularly polarised light into elliptically polarised light (Figure 4.5(c), (d)). Alternatively, the CD spectrum of a sample containing an optically active molecule is typically generated by exposing the sample in a CD spectrometer (Figure 4.6) to alternating beams of $E_L(\lambda)$ and $E_R(\lambda)$ generated by a **Pockels cell**, over a range of different wavelengths, λ, and then measuring the **differential absorbance**, $\Delta A(\lambda)$, at each wavelength according to

$$\Delta A(\lambda) = A_L(\lambda) - A_R(\lambda) \tag{4.7}$$

where $A_L(\lambda)$ and $A_R(\lambda)$ are the **sample absorbance of $E_L(\lambda)$ and $E_R(\lambda)$** respectively. Values of $\Delta A(\lambda)$ are typically very small and are between 0.03 and 0.003 per cent of total sample absorbance.

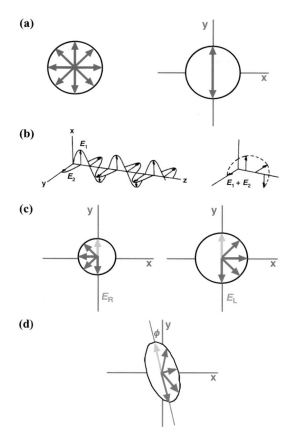

Figure 4.5 The origins of circularly polarised light and the generation of elipticity. (a) If light is viewed approaching an observer along the direction of propagation, then the **electric vector** oscillates in all possible planes (**left**) until transmission through a polariser (**right**) restricts oscillations to one plane; (b) Two **plane-polarised electric vectors** $\pi/2(90°)$ out of phase (**left**) but of equal amplitude, interact to generate a combined electric vector ($E_1 + E_2$; **right**) that maps out a helical path which can be right-handed or left-handed. This is **circularly polarised light**; (c) the combined electric vector of **right handed**, E_R, and **left-handed**, E_L, **circularly polarised light** viewed approaching an observer along the direction of propagation. E_R is shown with smaller amplitude than E_L; (d) constructive interference of E_R and E_L from (c) generates **elliptically polarised light** where the combined electric vector maps out an elliptical path which is left handed in this case. The angle ϕ is known as the **optical rotation**.

4.3.3 The circular dichroism spectrum

The most basic CD spectrum is then generated by plotting $\Delta A(\lambda)$ as a function of λ. CD spectra may be rendered in at least two other ways. The first uses the Beer–Lambert law:

$$\Delta\varepsilon(\lambda) = \varepsilon_L(\lambda) - \varepsilon_R(\lambda) = \frac{\Delta A(\lambda)}{c_M l} \tag{4.8}$$

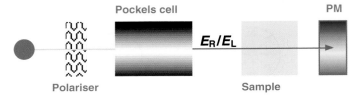

Figure 4.6 Illustration of the general experimental arrangement for circular dichroism (CD) spectroscopy. The **Polariser** and **Pockels cell** generate E_R and E_L circularly polarised light of equal amplitude at any selected wavelength λ. This is passed through a sample and **differential absorbance** between E_R and E_L is observed as a function of λ. This is a CD spectrum. Biological macromolecules (proteins and nucleic acids) are usually right handed and absorb E_R more than E_L. Hence the combination between E_R and E_L after transmission through the sample will generate left handed elliptically polarised light owing to the smaller amplitude of E_R relative to E_L (**Fig. 4.5c** and **4.5d**).

where $\varepsilon_L(\lambda)$ and $\varepsilon_R(\lambda)$ are **molar extinction coefficients corresponding to the sample absorbance of $E_L(\lambda)$ and $E_R(\lambda)$** respectively. Hence a CD spectrum may also be generated by plotting the **differential molar extinction coefficient** $\Delta\varepsilon(\lambda)$, as a function of λ. Both $\Delta A(\lambda)$ and $\Delta\varepsilon(\lambda)$ plots are related to total sample optical activity but only the first should be used if combinations of more than one optically active molecule are under investigation in the same sample, since molarity forms part of the dimensions of $\Delta\varepsilon(\lambda)$, which is difficult to define if more than one optically active type of molecule is involved in the sample. The second method relies upon transforming differential absorption data $\Delta A(\lambda)$ into **ellipticity**, $\theta(\lambda)$, and differential molar extinction coefficient $\Delta\varepsilon(\lambda)$ data into **molar ellipticity**, $[\theta(\lambda)]$, by Equations (4.9) and (4.10) respectively:

$$\theta(\lambda) = 2.303\frac{180}{4\pi}\Delta A(\lambda) \tag{4.9}$$

$$[\theta(\lambda)] = 3300\Delta\varepsilon(\lambda) \tag{4.10}$$

In the same way as for $\Delta A(\lambda)$ and $\Delta\varepsilon(\lambda)$ plots, only $\theta(\lambda)$ plots should be used if combinations of more than one optically active molecule are under investigation in the same sample, since molarity forms part of the dimensions of $[\theta(\lambda)]$, which once again is difficult to define if more than one optically active type of molecule is involved in the sample.

4.3.4 Structural versus functional information from circular dichroism spectroscopy

One of the most useful ways of using CD spectroscopy is to deduce the relative proportions of secondary structure elements in a globular or even in a fibrous protein. The main structural elements in a globular protein that can be identified separately by CD spectroscopy are defined as α-helix, β-sheets or random coil. Each main secondary structural element is right handed (see Chapter 1) and consequently absorbs $E_R(\lambda)$ more effectively than $E_L(\lambda)$ in the peptide link region, 200–230 nm, giving rise to exclusively negative values of $\Delta A(\lambda)$ or $[\theta(\lambda)]$. The CD spectrum of a sample of globular protein of interest can be assumed to be a weighted, linear combination of contributions from α-helix, β-sheets or random coil structure according to

$$[\theta(\lambda)] = \chi_\alpha[\theta_\alpha(\lambda)] + \chi_\beta[\theta_\beta(\lambda)] + \chi_r[\theta_r(\lambda)] \qquad (4.11)$$

where χ_α, χ_β and χ_r are **fractional composition terms** and $[\theta_\alpha(\lambda)]$, $[\theta_\beta(\lambda)]$ and $[\theta_r(\lambda)]$ are **molar ellipticities** measured from polypeptides in the 'pure' conformation indicated (Figure 4.7). The weakness of this equation is the quality of the molar ellipticity data. Values obtained from 'pure'-conformation polypeptides are probably not the same for secondary structure elements in complex tertiary structure environments owing to differences in polypeptide residue lengths and additional tertiary structure interactions. Nevertheless, Equation (4.11) can give meaningful data provided that the basis set of CD molar ellipticities is optimised with reference to the CD spectra of globular proteins with known χ_α, χ_β and χ_r values.

In addition to this application to globular proteins, CD spectroscopy is one of the only effective techniques for identifying the presence of left-handed P_{II}-helix structures (ΔA_{max} 225 nm) that make up the anatomy of collagen and collagen-like fibrous proteins (Figure 4.7)

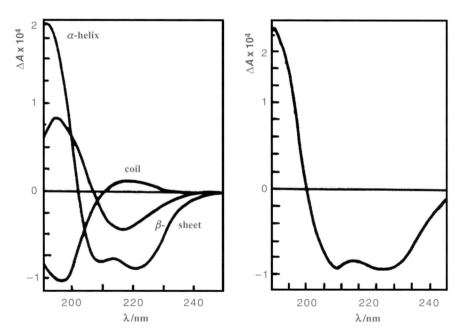

Figure 4.7 CD spectra of polypeptides in pure conformations as indicated (**left**). These form a typical basis set for the deduction of secondary structure content in a protein sample of interest by mathematical analysis of the recorded CD spectrum (**right**).

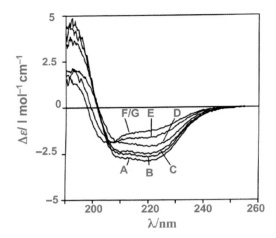

Figure 4.8   pH-Titration of a protein (heat shock protein 47 [Hsp47]) (see Chapter 7) monitored by **CD spectroscopy** in the far UV region. Far UV data possesses two **isodichroic points** (at approx. 202 and 208 nm respectively) suggesting a two stage transition between an **Alkali stable state** and an **Acid stable state** via a **transient intermediate state**. CD spectroscopy has revealed that Hsp47 will undergo reversible pH-driven trans-conformational changes. **A:** pH 7.2; **B:** pH 6.8; **C:** pH 6.4; **D:** pH 6.3; **E:** pH 6.0; **F:** pH 5.7; **G:** pH 5.0 (Reproduced from El Thaher et al., 1996, Fig. 2a).

(Chapter 1). The high degree of sensitivity of CD spectroscopy to protein secondary structure elements and changes in fractional composition of these elements ensures that CD spectroscopy is also one of the most effective techniques for observing conformational changes of a given protein in solution, either as a result of changing conditions or else through interactions with other molecules (Figure 4.8). Once again, such changes in spectroscopic signature in response to molecular interactions in particular can be very useful to study molecular recognition and binding involving proteins as well, in great detail (see Chapter 7).

The CD spectroscopy of nucleic acids is even more complex than proteins and as such has really not been explored to its fullest potential yet. CD spectra are uniquely dependent on nucleotide composition and sequence, in which base–base interaction terms need to be included. For example, the CD spectrum of dinucleotide ApG will be given by an expression in the form of

$$2[\theta_{\mathrm{ApG}}(\lambda)] = [\theta_{\mathrm{A}}(\lambda)] + [\theta_{G}(\lambda)] + I_{\mathrm{AG}}(\lambda) \tag{4.12}$$

where $[\theta_{\mathrm{A}}(\lambda)]$ and $[\theta_{G}(\lambda)]$ are **molar ellipticities** measured from pure nucleotides and $I_{\mathrm{AG}}(\lambda)$ is a **base–base interaction term**. For more complex nucleic acids, multiple terms are required to compute the CD spectrum of a sample of a nucleic acid of interest. However, given the extensive flexibility inherent in many complex nucleic acid structures, there can be considerable difficulties experienced in making reliable calculations given fluctuations in base–base interaction terms. However, the sensitivity of base–base interaction terms to nucleic acid conformation ensures that CD spectroscopy is also one of the most effective techniques for observing conformational changes of a given nucleic acid in solution either as a result of changing conditions or else through interactions with other molecules (Figure 4.9). Hence,

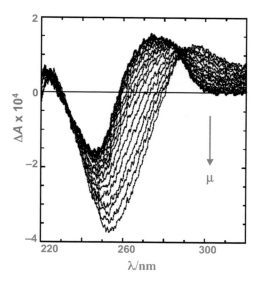

Figure 4.9 CD spectra of fixed concentration of plasmid DNA titrated with an increasing concentration of an adenoviral peptide, μ, known to template with DNA and induce condensation. Data illustrates that the peptide binding induces **base-pair tilting** and subsequent **supercoiling** (Chapters 1 and 7). Arrow shows direction of spectral increase with increasing μ peptide (Reproduced from Preuss et al., 2003, Fig. 4A).

hereto changes in spectroscopic signature in response to molecular interactions can be turned to good use in studying molecular recognition and binding events involving nucleic acids (see Chapter 7).

4.4 Vibrational spectroscopy

Infra-red (IR) spectroscopy functions to probe vibrational transitions (2000–50 000 nm; 5000–200 cm^{-1}, i.e. **wave number** – typical IR spectroscopy units) in the singlet ground electronic state of molecules. The absorption principles of IR spectroscopy are identical to those of UV–visible and CD spectroscopy. Hence the Beer–Lambert law (Equation (4.3)) applies. Moreover, absorption band intensities are determined by the transition dipole moment and there are extensive perturbation and coupling effects. Overall though, values of **molar extinction coefficients for vibrational transitions**, $\varepsilon_v(\lambda)$, are up to 10^2 times lower in magnitude than UV–visible and CD $\varepsilon(\lambda)$ values, making IR spectroscopy a much less sensitive technique.

4.4.1 Infra-red vibrational modes

In general, there has been some misunderstanding about the nature of the vibrational transitions being observed, given the way IR spectroscopy is frequently referred to in terms of functional group vibrations. In fact, observed vibrational transitions are associated with normal vibrational modes. Each normal vibrational mode will in effect include contributions (greater or smaller) from all the atoms in a molecule and not just individual functional groups, owing to the existence of heavy coupling between atoms in a vibrating molecule. Having said this, a normal vibrational mode often involves the substantive vibrations of just two bonded atoms at one location in a molecule, with little motion otherwise elsewhere. Therefore, to a first approximation, a normal vibrational mode may be said to correspond to just the atom motions in a particular type of functional group. As with UV–visible spectroscopy, the extent of IR absorption by a molecule of interest depends entirely upon the **IR transition dipole moment**, which should be non-zero for a vibrational transition to be observed. The transition dipole moment is defined by

$$\left\langle \psi_0 \phi_{\nu_R} | \bar{\mu} | \psi_0 \phi_{\nu'_R} \right\rangle \tag{4.13}$$

where ψ_0 is the **singlet ground state electronic wavefunction** and ϕ_{ν_R} and $\phi_{\nu'_R}$ are the wavefunction of the **vibrational states** (normal vibrational modes) pre- and post-absorption respectively.

4.4.2 Structural information from infra-red spectroscopy

IR spectroscopy of proteins is often seen as a technique complementary to CD spectroscopy for proteins. The IR spectroscopy of peptide links is particularly rich and useful given the extensive way in which the energies of vibrational transitions associated with the normal vibrational modes centred on atom motions within peptide links can vary substantially.

The normal vibrational modes of interest for proteins are illustrated (Table 4.3; Figure 4.10). Variations in hydrogen bonding are the primary reason for variations in the energies of vibrational transitions. Hydrogen bonding arrangements between peptide links differ markedly in pattern and strength depending upon whether peptide links are located in α-helices or β-sheets. Therefore, the energies of vibrational transitions associated with peptide links in α-helices or β-sheets can vary considerably as well. The situation could become excessively complex given the number of individual peptide links in a given protein. However, α-helices or β-sheets are highly regular and there is substantial coupling between vibrational transitions involving perturbation effects that are extremely orientation dependent. As a result, α-helices, parallel β-sheets and antiparallel β-sheets are characterised individually by just two main, unique vibrational transitions each (Table 4.3; Figure 4.10), so that the presence of any one secondary structure type can be established with relative ease in a globular protein of interest.

The IR spectroscopy of other biological macromolecules of interest is much less developed. Vibrational transitions in the region 1500–1800 cm^{-1} are associated with normal vibrational modes centred substantially on atom motions in nucleotide bases such as C=O, C=C and C=N stretching vibrations. Energies of these vibrational transitions are very sensitive to base pair formation owing to hydrogen bonding effects. However, the IR spectroscopy of nucleic acids has not so far been developed to appreciate the presence of unique vibrational transitions that identify the presence of different types of secondary or tertiary structure in nucleic acids of interest. Otherwise, the IR spectroscopy of carbohydrates and lipids is largely uninformative, except to prove the presence of functional groups.

Table 4.3 Summary of the main **vibrational transitions** corresponding to **vibrational modes** associated with the peptide links of protein secondary structural elements.

Vibration	α-helix (cm^{-1})	β-sheet (parallel) (cm^{-1})	β-sheet (anti-parallel) (cm^{-1})	Random Coil (cm^{-1})	H-bond free (cm^{-1})
N-H stretch	3290–3300	3280–3300	3280–3300		3400
Amide I	1650–1660				1670–1700
$\nu_R(0)$	1650				
$\nu_R(2\pi/n)$	1652				
$\nu_R(0,0)$		1645			
$\nu_R(\pi,0)$		1630			
$\nu_R(0,\pi)$			1685		
$\nu_R(\pi,0)$			1632		
ν_{OR}				1656	
Amide II	1540–1550				<1520
$\nu_R(0)$	1516				
$\nu_R(\pi/n)$	1546				
$\nu_R(0,0)$		1530			
$\nu_R(\pi,0)$		1550			
$\nu_R(0,\pi)$			1530		
$\nu_R(\pi,0)$					
ν_{OR}				1535	

4.4.3 Raman spectroscopy

Raman spectroscopy seeks to analyse vibrational transitions in biological macromolecules in a complementary way to IR spectroscopy. The physical basis of the technique is somewhat different as well. Initially, an intense beam of **light of frequency** ν_v is used to irradiate a sample of molecules of interest in order classically to induce oscillating dipoles of equivalent frequency in the polarisable clouds of electrons. The **time dependent magnitude of the induced dipole**, $\mu_{ind}(t)$ obeys

$$\mu_{ind}(t) = \alpha(\nu_v) E_0 \cos 2\pi \nu_v t \qquad (4.14)$$

where $\alpha(\nu_v)$ is the **time dependent electronic polarisability** and E_0 the **equilibrium electric field**. This can be divided into an **equilibrium polarisability component**, $\alpha_0(\nu_v)$, and a **nuclear oscillation component**, $\alpha_R(\nu_R)$, which is linked to the **Raman frequency** ν_R of

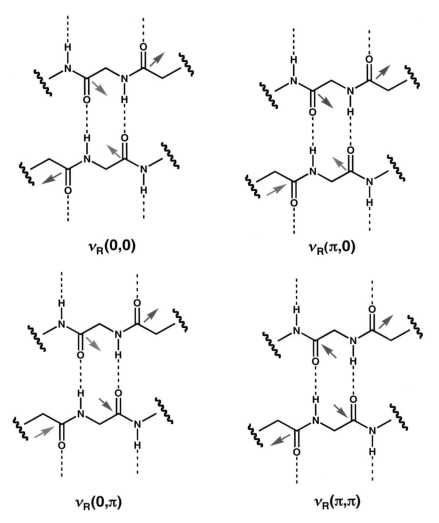

Figure 4.10 Vibrational modes of β-sheets. Each mode is differentiated by different in-plane motions and out of plane deformations above (red arrow) or below (blue arrow) the plane of the illustration.

vibrational modes in each molecule. These terms are all related according to

$$\alpha(\nu_v) = \alpha_0(\nu_v) + \alpha_R(\nu_R)\cos 2\pi\,\nu_R t \tag{4.15}$$

By substituting back into Equation (4.14), we obtain

$$\mu_{\text{ind}}(t) = [\alpha_0(\nu_v)\,E_0\cos 2\pi\,\nu_v t] + [\alpha_R(\nu_R)\,E_0\cos 2\pi\,\nu_R t\cos 2\pi\,\nu_v t] \tag{4.16}$$

where the first term in square brackets represents the induced dipole oscillating at the same frequency ν_v as the incident frequency and the second term is known as the **Raman dipole**. This equation represents the dual reality of the Raman spectroscopy experiment. When molecules of interest in a certain sample are irradiated, the vast majority develop induced dipole oscillations at the same frequency ν_v as the incident frequency and then promptly re-emit light at the same frequency in random directions. This effect is simply **classical light scattering**. However, a proportion of molecules in the same sample will funnel energy into or out of a number of normal vibrational modes before re-emission. The result is that a band of light re-emitted from the sample at frequency ν_v due to classical light scattering will be attended by smaller satellite bands at frequencies of $\nu_v + \nu_R$ (**Stokes bands**) and $\nu_v - \nu_R$ (**anti-Stokes bands**). Each pair of satellites can then be identified to assign the Raman frequency, ν_R, of each activated vibrational transition. If the frequencies ν_v (electronic oscillation) and ν_R (nuclear oscillation) are very similar, then classical light scattering effects will be minimised in favour of energy funnelling to normal vibrational modes, allowing satellite bands to dominate. This effect is known as **resonance Raman spectroscopy**.

Raman spectroscopy of proteins runs parallel to IR spectroscopy. The same vibrational transitions associated with the same normal vibrational modes centred on atom motions within peptide links are observed (Table 4.3; Figure 4.10). The same is true for the Raman spectroscopy of nucleic acids as well. Arguably, Raman spectroscopy of a globular protein of interest gives an even more precise characterisation of vibrational transitions than IR spectroscopy, allowing for the clear discrimination and identification of random coil structure as well as α-helix, parallel β-sheet and antiparallel β-sheet secondary structures.

4.5 Fluorescence spectroscopy

The basic concept of fluorescence spectroscopy is as illustrated (Figure 4.11). Molecular singlet ground state S_a is promoted to singlet excited state S_b by photon absorption. State S_b may then release a second photon by a process of spontaneous emission known as **fluorescence** to return to singlet ground state S_a. Electronic promotion to the singlet excited state involves a **vertical transition**, which inevitably places the electronically excited molecule in a high lying vibrational state. A vertical transition arises because electronic transitions occur typically in a time of 10^{-15} s, during which time the molecule is effectively static given that molecules typically vibrate in 10^{-13} s. Furthermore, a typical singlet excited state of any molecule has slightly greater physical dimensions than the singlet ground state, since the excited state is created by electronic promotion into antibonding molecular orbitals, causing an overall weakening (i.e. lengthening) of bonds. Subsequent spontaneous emission from this excited state occurs by a **second vertical transition** but only to a high lying vibrational state of the singlet ground state, given the decrease in molecular dimensions with a return to the ground electronic state. Consequently, this second vertical transition involves a smaller energy gap and hence the emission of a photon of lower frequency (higher wavelength). Therefore, fluorescence always involves the emission of a photon of lower energy than that absorbed initially.

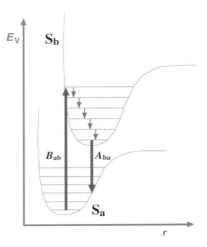

Figure 4.11   General principle of fluorescence in which **singlet ground state, S_a**, absorbs photons at a rate, B_{ab}, and enters **singlet excited state, S_b**, by **vertical transition**. Rate of re-emission, A_{ba}, is slow compared with timescale of vibration and several radiation-less transitions (grey arrows) occur between excited state vibrational states until re-emission (**fluorescence**) takes place by a second vertical transition E_V is energy and r interatomic distance.

4.5.1 Rates of emission and lifetimes

The molecular singlet ground state S_a is promoted to singlet excited state S_b at a **rate of photon absorption**, B_{ab}, related to the transition dipole moment (see Expression (4.2)) by the following equation:

$$B_{ab} = (2\pi/3\hbar^2)|\langle\psi_a|\bar{\mu}|\psi_b\rangle|^2 \tag{4.17}$$

where the squared term $|\langle\psi_a|\bar{\mu}|\psi_b\rangle|^2$ is known as the **dipole strength**, D_{ab}. Transition back to the ground state (**fluorescence**) then occurs at a **rate of spontaneous emission**, A_{ba}, that obeys the following equation:

$$A_{ba} = (8\pi h\nu_{em}^3 c^{-3})B_{ab} \tag{4.18}$$

where the term in brackets containing **Planck's constant** h, **frequency of emitted light** ν_{em} and **speed of light** c is known as the **black body radiation constant**. By combining (4.17) and (4.18), we arrive at the important expression

$$A_{ba} = (32\pi^3\nu_{em}^3/3c^3\hbar)D_{ab} \tag{4.19}$$

which demonstrates that the rate of spontaneous emission, A_{ba}, is directly proportional to ground state dipole strength, D_{ab}. In other words, the stronger the absorption, the faster is the rate of spontaneous emission A_{ba} (also known as k_F), which is related in addition to another important fluorescence property known as the **fluorescence** or **radiative lifetime**, τ_R, of the singlet excited state S_b by

$$A_{ba} = 1/\tau_R = k_F \qquad (4.20)$$

Typical values of τ_R are in the region of nanoseconds.

4.5.2 Effects of non-radiative competition processes

Fluorescence radiation is in competition with a variety of non-radiative processes that reduce the efficiency of spontaneous emission. These processes are known as **internal conversion** (rate k_{IC}), **intersystem crossing** (rate k_{IS}) and **quenching** by an external quenching agent typically denoted Q (rate $k_q[Q]$) (Figure 4.12). All these non-radiative processes reduce the efficiency of spontaneous emission by depopulating the singlet excited state. A measure of the residual efficiency of spontaneous emission is known as the **fluorescence quantum yield**, ϕ_F, which is related to all the various rate constants according to

$$\phi_F = k_F / (k_F + k_{IC} + k_{IS} + k_q[Q]) \qquad (4.21)$$

Internal conversion is a pseudo-first-order process by which the singlet excited state S_b energy is lost by collisions with solvent molecules or else by transfer between vibrational modes. Inevitably, the rate k_{IC} will increase with increasing temperature and *vice versa*. Quenching is a similar deactivation process, in which collision with solute molecules leads to loss in singlet

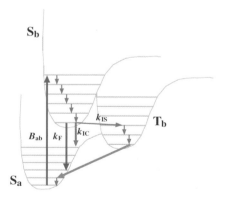

Figure 4.12   Competition between fluorescence and radiation-less processes following the promotion of singlet ground state, **S_a**, to singlet excited state, **S_b**, at a rate, **B_{ab}**. The rate of fluorescence, **$A_{ba}(k_F)$**, is unaffected by competing radiation-less processes, but the **fluorescence quantum yield**, relating to the intensity of fluorescence, is compromised by high rates of radiation-less **internal conversion (IC)**, **k_{IC}**, and of **intersystem crossing (IS)**, **k_{IS}**. IS leads to triplet excited state, **T_b**, which loses energy by transition forbidden **phosphorescent re-emission** to regenerate singlet ground state, **S_a**.

excited state S_b energy. Quenching is a second order process but can be rendered pseudo-first-order if $[Q] \gg [S_b]$. Quenching is only meaningful with solute molecules such as O_2 or I^- that are able to deactivate the singlet excited state S_b with almost every collision, in which case the rate constant k_q is at the diffusion limit (see Chapter 7). Finally, intersystem crossing relates to **forbidden spin exchange**, which involves the transformation of the singlet excited state S_b into a triplet excited state T_b that then undergoes slow but spontaneous emission in a process known as **phosphorescence** in order to return to the singlet ground state (Figure 4.12). As mentioned above, typical values of τ_R for fluorescence are in the region of nanoseconds. Equation (4.19) suggests that the stronger photon absorption by S_a becomes, the faster is the rate of spontaneous emission from S_b. Clearly, the theoretical absorption of a photon to bring about a transition from singlet ground state S_a to triplet excited state T_b must be much weaker, since the transition is forbidden. Hence $\tau_{R,Phor}$ must be considerably greater than τ_R for fluorescence. In the event, typical values of $\tau_{R,Phor}$ for phosphorescence are in the region of seconds.

4.5.3 Structural versus functional information from intrinsic fluorescence spectroscopy

The basic structural information available from intrinsic fluorescence spectroscopy of biological macromolecule structures is quite limited compared with information available from even UV–visible or even CD spectroscopy and is largely limited to globular proteins. One of the main reasons for this is that only proteins and nucleic acids possess substantial numbers of chromophores that are potentially capable of absorbing photons leading to fluorescence emission. However, not every chromophore is simultaneously a good **fluorophore** (i.e. chromophore capable of generating fluorescence emission). Indeed, the nucleic acid bases are fundamentally poor fluorophores. In proteins, only tryptophan amino-acid residues are substantial fluorophores out of the three main aromatic amino-acid chromophores. Moreover, values of ϕ_F are low in water, though values of τ_R are short, hence generally limiting fluorescence utility even further (Table 4.1).

In spite of these limitations, fluorescence spectroscopy of proteins involving **intrinsic tryptophan residue fluorescence** (excitation 295 nm) can be a useful monitor of conformational changes in globular proteins in a way similar to UV–visible spectroscopy of tryptophan residues in globular proteins. If the local environment of a tryptophan residue is changed from hydrophilic (or polar) to hydrophobic, then this leads to an increase in fluorescence emission ($\pi \to \pi^*$) transition energies associated with a decrease in transition wavelength (**blue-shift**) (typically 350–330 nm). Since the interior of such a protein may be regarded as hydrophobic whilst the exterior is hydrophilic, then we can generalise to say that interior 'buried' residues are blue-shifted compared with 'solvent-exposed' residues. Furthermore, interior 'buried' residues will not be subject to internal conversion problems caused by random collisions with water molecules, or to collisional deactivation with quenching molecules. Therefore, values of ϕ_F should increase substantially according to Equation (4.21), resulting in significantly enhanced fluorescence emission intensities. Both characteristics ensure that

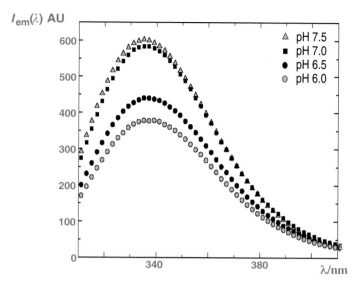

Figure 4.13   pH-Titration of protein Hsp47 monitored by **intrinsic tryptophan fluorescence spectroscopy** (excitation 295 nm). Data is also indicative of a two stage transition between an Alkali stable state and an Acid stable state via a transient intermediate state (see **Fig. 4.8**). Fluorescence spectroscopy also reveals that Hsp47 will undergo reversible pH-driven trans-conformational changes (see Chapter 7) (Reproduced from Homma et al., 2008). $I_{em}(\lambda)$ is fluorescence emission intensity.

intrinsic tryptophan fluorescence of proteins becomes a useful tool to probe changes in the conformational state of protein structure in response to changes in environmental conditions and/or the binding of other molecules (Figure 4.13).

Aside from this application, intrinsic tryptophan fluorescence may be used in combination with fluorescence quenching agents to discriminate between those tryptophan residues more surface accessible or 'solvent exposed' than others. This relies upon the **Stern–Volmer equation**

$$F_0/F = 1 + k_q[Q]\tau_0 \tag{4.22}$$

where τ_0 is $(k_F + k_{IC} + k_{IS})^{-1}$ i.e. **excited state lifetime in the absence of quencher molecule** Q, F_0 is fluorescence intensity in the absence of Q and F intensity in the presence of Q. Data may be presented graphically in the form of a **Stern–Volmer plot** (Figure 4.14) in order to deduce values of k_q. Values of k_q will appear towards the so-called diffusion limit of 10^{10} M^{-1} s^{-1} if the tryptophan is completely surface accessible, much lower if the residue is 'buried'.

4.5.4 Extrinsic fluorescence and FRET

Ultimately though, whilst intrinsic fluorescence spectroscopy of biological macromolecules appears to be rather limited, the technique of fluorescence spectroscopy becomes considerably

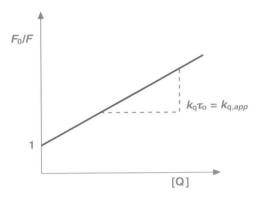

Figure 4.14   Stern-Volmer Plot to determine the rate of **fluorescence quenching** by solute molecules that function as **quenching agents, Q.** Quenching also competes with the other factors described in **Figure 4.12** to reduce fluorescence quantum yield.

more versatile if extrinsic fluorophores are combined with the biological macromolecules of interest. There is now quite an industry in these extrinsic fluorophores (Figure 4.15) as probes of biological function (see Section 4.5.5). The primary reason for this is the fact that, whilst typical electronic absorption transitions take place in 10^{-15} s and vibrations in 10^{-13} s (see Main Section 4.4), values of τ_R vary between 10^{-9} and 10^{-8} s (Table 4.4), which is a slow enough timescale to probe a huge range of biologically relevant processes, such as protonation, solvent cage relaxation, local conformational changes and other processes coupled to molecular rotation and even translation (see Chapter 7). Therefore, whilst intrinsic fluorescence spectroscopy may be a rather modest technique for structural characterisation of biological macromolecules, extrinsic fluorescence spectroscopy is an impressive tool to probe both structure and dynamics of biological macromolecules, by such techniques as **fluorescence binding titration experiments** for the characterisation of molecular

Table 4.4   Summary of the main extrinsic fluorophores that may be combined with proteins or nucleic acids. Main absorption and fluorescence characteristics are given. See **Fig. 4.15** and **Table 4.1** for structure abbreviations and other abbreviations used in the table.

Fluorophore	A_{max}/nm	$10^{-3} \times \varepsilon_{max}$/M^{-1} cm^{-1}	I_{max}/nm	ϕ_F	τ_R/nsec
DnsCl	330	3.4	510	0.1	13
1,5-I-AEDANS	360	6.8	480	0.5	15
FITC	495	42	516	0.3	4
ANS	374	6.8	454	0.98	16
Pyrene	342	40	383	0.25	100
EtAd	300	2.6	410	0.40	26
EtBr	515	3.8	600	1	26.5

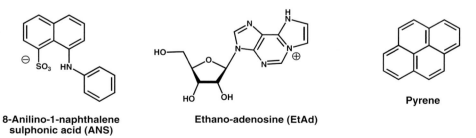

Dansyl Chloride (DnsCl)

Fluorescein Isothiocyanate (FITC)

Tetramethyl Rhodamine (TAMRA)

Oregon Green 488 Carboxylic

**5-[2-(2-iodoacetamido)ethylamino]-
1-naphthalenesulfonic acid
(1, 5-I-AEDANS)**

Ethidium Bromide (EtBr)

**8-Anilino-1-naphthalene
sulphonic acid (ANS)**

Ethano-adenosine (EtAd)

Pyrene

Figure 4.15 Structures of some useful extrinsic fluorophores that may be chemically combined with a biological macromolecule of interest for structure and/or function investigations.

recognition and binding events (see Chapter 7), and **fluorescence resonance energy transfer** (**FRET**) experiments.

FRET experiments involve complementary pairs of fluorophores that are matched to allow coupling to take place between the **fluorescence emission transition dipole moment** of a given **donor fluorophore** and the **absorption transition dipole moment** of a corresponding **acceptor fluorophore**, provided that donor and acceptor are sufficiently close in space. This

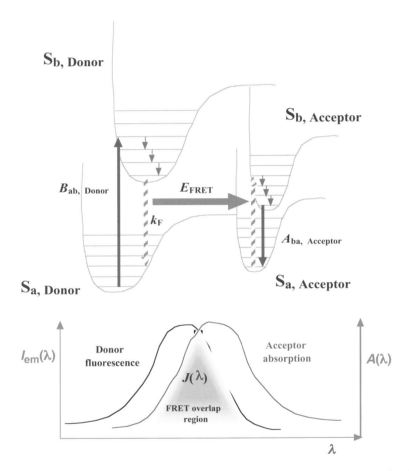

Figure 4.16 Schematic to show the principles of **fluorescence resonance energy transfer** (**FRET**). *Top diagram* illustrates the process of **resonance energy transfer** made possible by **coupling** of the **fluorescence emission transition dipole** moment of a given **Donor fluorophore** with an **absorption transition dipole moment** of a corresponding **Acceptor fluorophore**. This process typically leads to **Acceptor fluorescence**. *Bottom diagram* illustrates the **spectral overlap J(λ)** between the fluorescence emission spectrum of a Donor and the absorption spectrum of a corresponding Acceptor. Assuming that both Donor and Acceptor fluorophores are also close together in space (10–75 Å) and in good relative orientation, then this spectral overlap is essential according to equation 4.24 in order to allow transition dipole moment coupling and subsequent resonance energy transfer to take place, leading to Acceptor fluorescence.

process is typically followed by acceptor fluorescence (Figure 4.16). In other words, provided that a donor and an acceptor fluorophore are close enough together in space, then the absorption of a photon by a donor fluorophore can be effectively converted into fluorescence emission from the corresponding acceptor fluorophore by resonance energy transfer between the two fluorophores through space. The **efficiency of the FRET process**, E_{FRET}, is dependent upon the distance between the two fluorophores according to the following equation:

$$E_{FRET} = 1/[1 + (R_F/R_0)^6] \tag{4.23}$$

where R_F is the **inter fluorophore distance** and R_0 is the standard **Förster length** for a given donor–acceptor pair (see Chapter 8). The orientation dependence is revealed in the equation for the Förster length

$$R_0 = [8.8 \times 10^{-28} \phi_D \kappa^2 n_R^{-4} J(\lambda)]^{1/6} \tag{4.24}$$

where ϕ_D is the **fluorescence quantum yield of the donor**, n_R is the **refractive index** of the medium, κ is an **orientation parameter** (varying from zero to four, but typically set to 0.667 to represent the likelihood of random relative orientations between fluorophores) and $J(\lambda)$ is a **spectral overlap parameter**, which governs the overlap between the donor fluorescence emission spectrum and the absorption spectrum of the corresponding acceptor. Clearly, successful transition dipole moment coupling leading to resonant energy transfer and acceptor fluorescence relies uniquely upon good spectral overlap, short distances between donor and acceptor fluorophores (10–75 Å) and optimal relative orientations (collinear is best). Accordingly, FRET effects between complementary pairs of largely extrinsic donor and acceptor fluorophores (Table 4.5) can be employed as a powerful tool for studying the formation of complexes involving different biological macromolecules (see Chapter 7), even in real time within living cells (see Section 4.5.5), but also for interpreting the significance of specific intramolecular motions and normal vibrational modes within single biological macromolecules (see Section 4.5.6)!

Table 4.5 Summary of simple **Donor** and **Acceptor fluorophores** competent for FRET studies. See **Fig. 4.15** for structures and abbreviations used in the table.

Donor Fluorophore	Acceptor Fluorophore
DnsCl	FITC
FITC	TAMRA
1,5-I-AEDANS	FITC
Tryptophan (amino acid residue)	1,5-I-AEDANS
Tryptophan (amino acid residue)	DnsCl

4.5.5 Probing biological macromolecule functions with extrinsic fluorescence

Extrinsic chemical probes increasingly provide powerful means to study the dynamics and function of biological macromolecules and assemblies in biology. Of these, extrinsic fluorescent probes are amongst the most potent and useful. Therefore, this section will be devoted to understanding their addition and potential uses. The addition of such probes requires **chemoselective coupling** or **bioconjugation** involving activated fluorescent probe molecules on the one hand and biological macromolecules or macromolecular lipid assemblies of interest on the other hand. A major constraint on all bioconjugation coupling reactions is that they should commonly be possible to perform in an aqueous environment at around room temperature, under buffer conditions at around neutral pH.

4.5.5.1 Chemical conjugation of extrinsic fluorescent probes

One of the most common approaches to the bioconjugation of fluorescent probes is the use of **amine-reactive probes** to combine with free primary amine functional groups found in proteins, peptides, oligonucleotides and even lipids. In proteins, target functional groups may be an N-terminal α-amino group or the ε-amino side-chain group of lysine amino-acid residues (see Chapter 1). The same is true in peptides, while aminosugars are found in oligosaccharides (see Chapter 1). In the case of lipids, the 2-aminoethyl side-chains of phosphatidylethanolamines (see Chapter 1) are ideal attachment points for amine-reactive probes. Bioconjugation involving amine functional groups typically takes place best under mildly alkali conditions, when these groups are substantially unprotonated (pH 8.5–9.5). The N-terminal α-amino group of an oligo- or polypeptide can bioconjugate under more neutral pH conditions given the fact that N-terminal α-amino groups are more acidic than ε-amino side-chain groups, and have lower pK_d^A values (see Chapter 8; also known as pK_a values).

Succinimidyl esters are an excellent first choice to activate amine-reactive probes, but their low solubility has led to the alternative use of sulphonyl chlorides (Figure 4.17). The resultant sulphonamide link is extremely stable, even more stable than an amide link, and will survive even complete protein hydrolysis – a property that can be exploited in protein analysis. The disadvantage of sulphonyl chlorides is that they are unstable in aqueous buffers under mildly alkaline conditions (typically the pH required for the reaction with aliphatic amine!). Hence extreme care must be taken to perform bioconjugations with sulphonyl chlorides at low temperatures (approx 4 °C). Alternatively, amine-reactive probes may be equipped with isothiocyanate 'traps', from which thiourea links are formed post-reaction with amine functional groups, or with aldehydes, from which Schiff's base links can be formed with amine functional groups (Figure 4.17).

An alternative approach to bioconjugation of fluorescent probes is the use of **thiol-reactive probes** to combine with free thiol functional groups typically found in proteins and peptides (involving reduced cysteine amino-acid residues), although they could be added to oligonucleotides, oligosaccharides and even lipids if required as well on the assumption that thiol functional groups are present. Thiol-reactive moieties are typically alkylating reagents

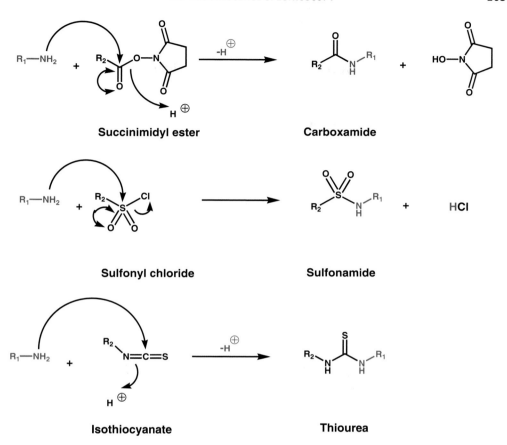

Succinimidyl ester   **Carboxamide**

Sulfonyl chloride   **Sulfonamide**

Isothiocyanate   **Thiourea**

Figure 4.17 Amine reactive probes. Succinimidyl esters, **sulfonyl chlorides** and **isothiocyanates** can all be used to react with amines in biological macromolecules and lipids.

such as **iodoacetamides, maleimides, alkylhalides** or **halidomethylketones** (Figure 4.18). Maleimides are probably the first choice as cysteine modifying reagents. Maleimides (usually used as *N*-**ethylmaleimide, NEM**) react quite selectively with cysteine residues in oligo- and polypeptides to form **thioethers** (Figure 4.18). In comparison, iodoacetamides react readily with thiols to form thioethers (Figure 4.18), but are also capable of over-reaction such as with methionine, histidine or even tyrosine residues in oligo- and polypeptides. More control can be exercised again using thiol-exchange reactions (Figure 4.18). Overall, the stability of thiol-reactive probes post-bioconjugation is lower than that of amine-reactive probes. Hence there is a trade-off between stability and the lack of chemo-selectivity comparing thiol-reactive probes to amine-reactive probes.

In addition, bioconjugation of fluorescent probes may be enabled through a variety of functional group activation chemistries as a means to facilitate bioconjugation. For instance, **carboxyl-reactive probes** can combine with carboxyl groups in proteins, peptides,

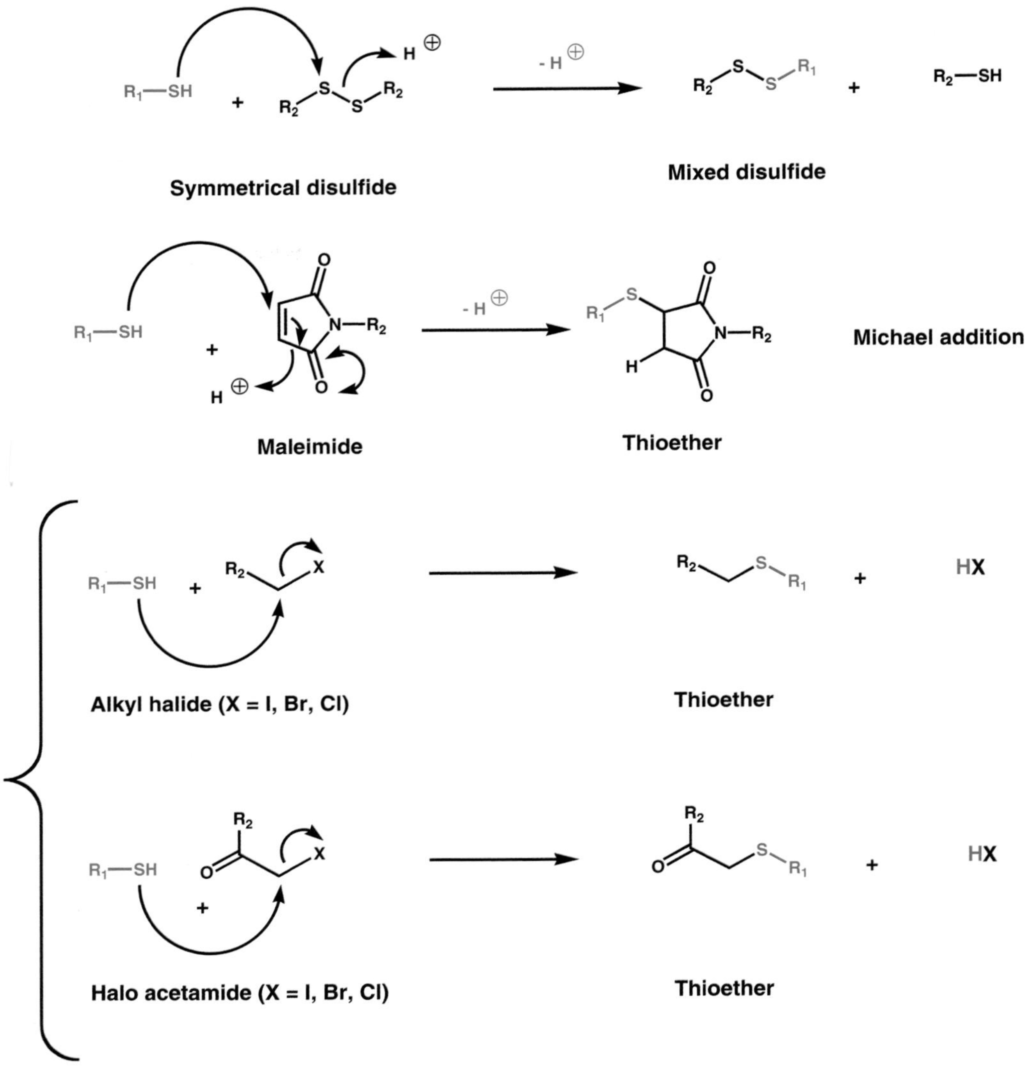

Figure 4.18 Thiol reactive probes. Alkyl halides, maleimides and **symmetric disulfides** can all be used to react with thiols in biological macromolecules and lipids.

oligonucleotides and lipids, post-activation with water-soluble carbodiimides such as **1-ethyl-3-(3-dimethylamino-propyl)carbodiimide** (**EDAC**) (Figure 4.19). EDAC combines with carboxyl groups, resulting in an unstable intermediate – an *O*-acylisourea that rapidly reacts with an amino functional group (either an amine or hydrazine) belonging to a carboxyl-reactive probe. The presence of **N-hydroxysulphosuccinimide** improves the coupling efficiency. Alternatively, fluorescent probes with carboxyl groups could be activated with EDAC for the reverse bioconjugation of the probe with amine functional groups in proteins, peptides,

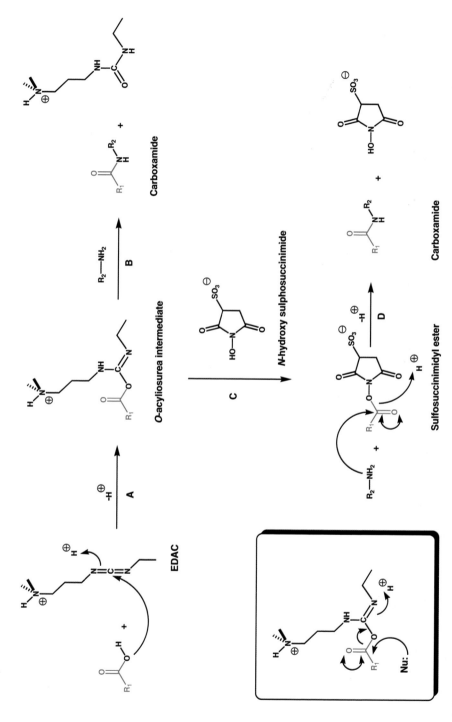

Figure 4.19 Carboxylic acid reactive probes. Stabilization of an unstable *O*-acylisourea intermediate by use of *N*-hydroxysulphosuccinimide during the carbodiimide-activated combination of a carboxylic acid with a primary amine. Reaction normally occurs by steps **A** and **B**. With *N*-hydroxysulphosuccinimide the reaction now takes place by steps **A**, **C** and **D**.

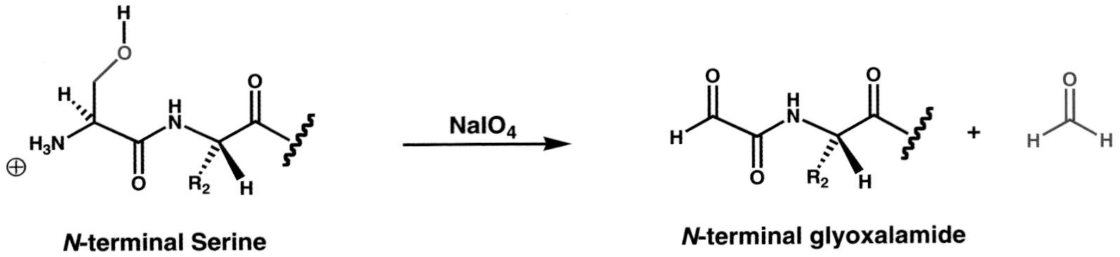

Figure 4.20   Terminal serine reactive probes. Sodium periodate oxidation of *N*-terminal serine.

oligonucleotides and lipids. Other highly selective bioconjugations to probes are made possible in oligo- or polypeptides in other ways. For instance, *N*-terminal serine or threonine residues of an oligo- or polypeptide can be selectively oxidised by oxidative cleavage to give aldehydes (Figure 4.20), which are primed for bioconjugation to fluorescent probes with amines or hydrazines. Furthermore, tyrosine residues can sometimes be selectively modified by *ortho*-nitration using tetranitromethane followed by reduction to form an aminotyrosine (Figure 4.21). Alternatively, a particularly innovative approach is to use a purified enzyme (**transglutaminase**) to specifically modify glutamine residues with amine-containing probes in the primary amide functional group (Figure 4.22). The presence of an aliphatic spacer between the amine functional group and the fluorescent probe increases reaction efficacy, especially when a cadaverine spacer is used (as shown).

One extreme view of chemical introduction of an extrinsic fluorescent probe is found in the case of the alanine derivative of the fluorophore **6-dimethylamino-2-acylnaphthalene (DAN)** (Figure 4.23). This derivative fluorophore, given the trivial name **Aladan**, is incorporated into a polypeptide by solid-phase synthetic chemistry (although a molecular biology technique known as **nonsense suppression** is now available for the introduction of unnatural amino-acid residues into recombinant proteins). The fluorescent emission maximum (I_{max}) of Aladan shifts dramatically on different solvent exposures, from 409 nm in heptane to 542 nm in water, yet at the same time remains only mildly changed by variations in pH or salt concentration. This compares to a maximum environment-mediated shift of around 40 nm for intrinsic tryptophan fluorescence. In addition, there is little spectral overlap between extrinsic Aladan fluorescence and intrinsic fluorescence from tryptophan or tyrosine.

4.5.5.2   *Biological conjugation of extrinsic fluorescent probes*

The chemical approaches to bioconjugation rely upon the chemoselective reactivity of extrinsic fluorescent probes combining with isolated biological macromolecules or lipids. In the case of proteins, recombinant technologies allow for more biological approaches to fluorescent tagging *in situ*, in cells. This carries great advantages for work in a cellular system since a protein may be specifically labelled and observed within the cellular context. First and foremost of the biological approaches is to express a recombinant protein of interest in

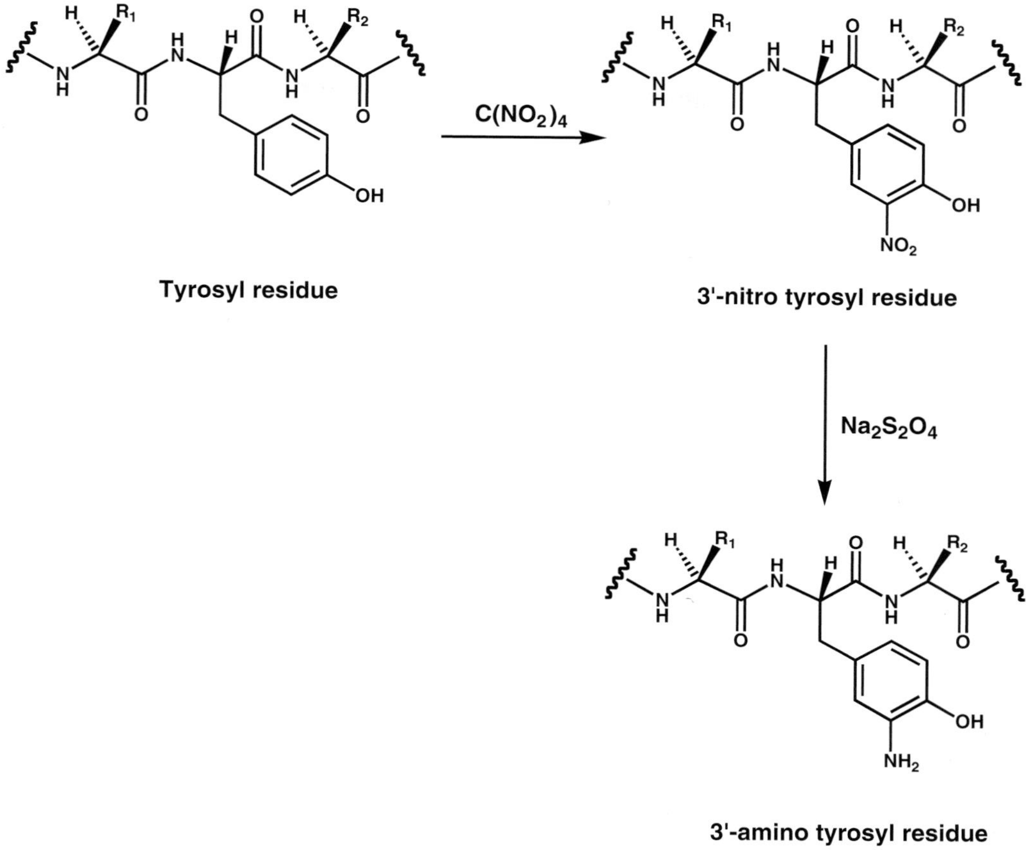

Tyrosyl residue

3'-nitro tyrosyl residue

3'-amino tyrosyl residue

Figure 4.21 Tyrosine reactive probes. Nitration of tyrosine by reaction with **tetranitromethane**, followed by reduction with sodium dithionite, to yield an *o*-aminotyrosine.

a cell as a chimeric or fusion protein in which the protein of interest is expressed conjoined (at the *N*- or *C*-terminus as appropriate) to another whole protein with fluorescent properties. The fluorescent protein most used in fusion proteins is **green fluorescent protein** (**GFP**) from the **jellyfish *Aequorea victoria***. GFP comprises 238 amino-acid residues and is capable of absorbing blue light (A_{max} 395 nm) only to fluoresce green light (I_{max} 509 nm). The protein has no extrinsic prosthetic group or cofactor to act as a fluorophore. Instead, a **p-hydroxybenzylideneimidazolinone fluorophore** is created by direct autocatalytic chemical cyclisation of amino-acid residues Ser65, Tyr66 and Gly67 (Figure 4.24). In effect, GFP assembles its own fluorescent cofactor from its own primary structure! This fluorescent cofactor is protected within a cylindrical structure consisting of 11 strands of β-sheet with α-helix at each end, a structure that has been christened the β-**can**. Since the fluorescent cofactor is amino-acid residue derived, then the reader should not be surprised to learn that variations in and around the crucial amino acid sequence can lead to other blue, cyan and yellow

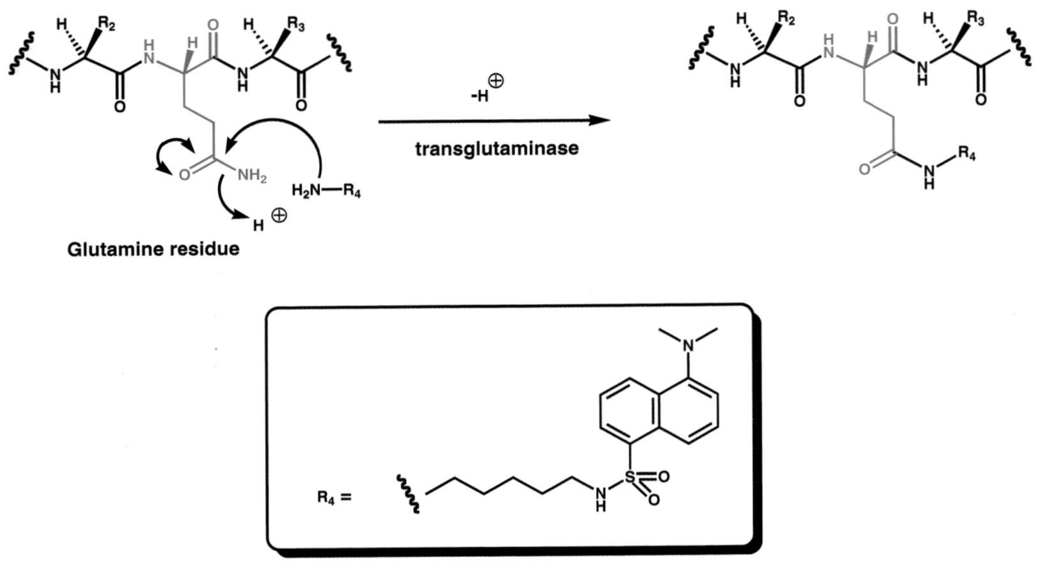

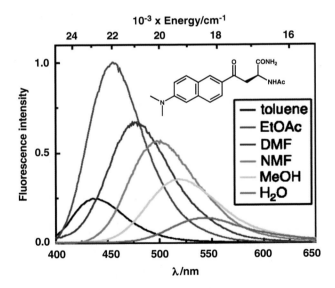

Figure 4.22   Transamidation of glutamine. Transglutaminase-mediated labeling of a protein using dansyl cadaverine.

Figure 4.23   Fluorescence of non-natural amino acid Aladan. The figure demonstrates how Aladan fluorescence signal is strongly dependent on the hydrophobicity/hydrophilicity of the surrounding solvent, showing why it is an excellent probe of environment (Reproduced from Cohen et al., 2002, Fig. 1).

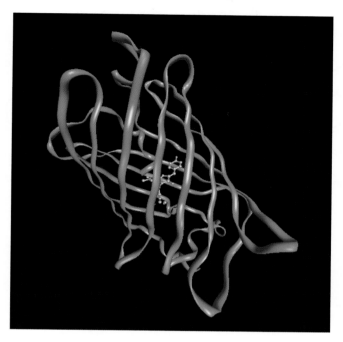

Figure 4.24 **Green Fluorescence Protein** (**GFP**) (Aequorea victoria) **Ribbon display structure** of GFP, showing 11 β-strands forming a hollow cylinder through which is threaded a helix bearing the chromophore, constructed from amino acid residues Ser65, Tyr66 and Gly67, shown in **ball-and-stick representation** (pdb: **1emb**).

fluorescent protein variants (known as BFP, CFP and YFP respectively). A further alternative to GFP is **DsRed**, which is naturally found in the coral *Discosoma*. Wild-type DsRed is an obligate tetramer but mutant DsRed proteins that are monomeric can now be used in place of GFP in fusion proteins.

Biological and chemical approaches can be combined to yield similar possibilities to the fusion protein approach described above. A tetracysteine motif (**CCXXCC**; where X is a non-cysteine amino-acid residue) can be engineered into any protein of interest at any required position, in principle (see Chapter 3). This motif is highly selective for binding to biarsenical fluorophores based upon fluorescein. Biarsenical fluorophores are able to permeate cells and remain non-fluorescent until chelated by the tetracysteine motif (Figure 4.25). Biarsenical fluorophores are particularly partial to being across a α-helix with the molecular plane oriented perpendicular to the direction of the helix. Hence, using such fluorophores, an engineered protein of interest can be expressed in cells *in situ* then tagged *in situ* by any one of a whole range of biarsenical dyes with slightly different structures that are able to fluoresce at different wavelengths.

A final biological approach to extrinsic labelling that is worth noting for the interested chemical biology reader is the use of cyanine (Cy) dyes (in particular Cy3 and Cy5). At first sight these look complex, but they can be introduced into DNA by a method known as **nick**

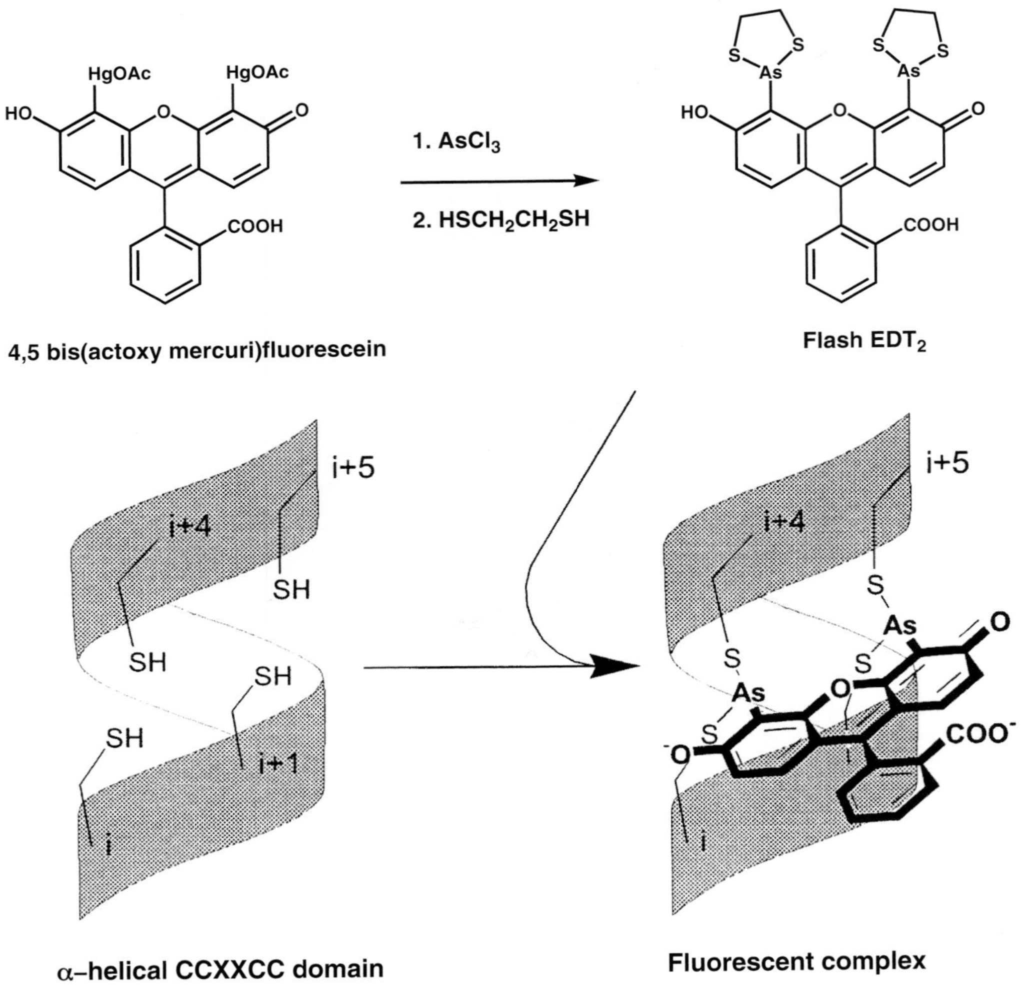
HgOAc
HgOAc
HO
O
O
COOH
1. AsCl3
2. HSCH2CH2SH
S
S
As
HO
O
O
COOH
4,5 bis(actoxy mercuri)fluorescein
Flash EDT2
i+5
i+4
SH
SH
SH
SH
i+1
i
α-helical CCXXCC domain
i+5
i+4
S
As
O
S
S
As
O
S
COO-
-O
i
Fluorescent complex

Figure 4.25 Biarsenical ligands. Synthesis of **Flash EDT$_2$** and proposed structure of its complex with an α-helical tetracysteine-containing peptide or protein domain. The structure is drawn with the i and $i+4$ thiols bridged by one arsenic and the $i+1$ and $i+5$ thiols bridged by the other (Reproduced from Griffin et al., 1998, Fig. 1).

translation. According to this method, random nicks (or single-strand breaks, i.e. random hydrolyses of phosphodiester links) are introduced into DNA and then repaired using the so-called Klenow fragment of DNA polymerase I accessing dATP, dGTP and dCTP as repair substrates together with dRTP, where R is uridine substituted at position 5 on the pyrimidine ring with cyanine dye (Figure 4.26). During the repair process, dRTP is used in place of dTTP to repair dA=dT base pairs. The value of this labelling process is that the amount of nick translation performed can be adjusted to ensure that DNA remains almost completely functional with respect to transcription.

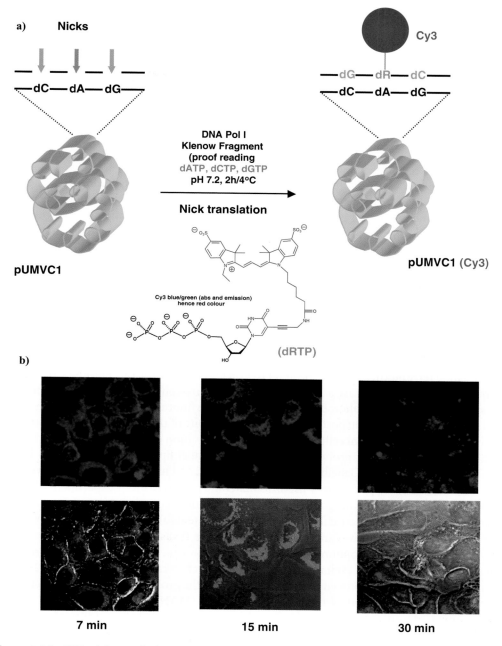

Figure 4.26 DNA nick translation. (a) Plasmid DNA (pDNA; **pUMVC1**) labelling with **Cy3 cyanine dye** was accomplished as shown above by means of an enzymatic procedure. **(b)** The dye-labelled pDNA was then combined into nanometric particles known as **liposome:mu:pDNA particles** wherein the lipid:mu:pDNA ratio was 12:0.6:1 (w/w/w). These particles (approx 120 nm in diameter) were added to human tracheal epithelial (HTE) cells and incubated for just 2 mins with cells before DNA movements were monitored with time by microscopy. Bottom-line images are same as top-line images except for superposition of cell contrast image to demonstrate sub-cellular localization. DNA enters the nucleus in approx. 30 min (adapted from Keller et al., 2003, Fig. 4). Scale as per **Fig. 4.27b**.

4.5.5.3   Selecting extrinsic fluorescent probes

The selection of extrinsic fluorescent probe is driven by the consideration of which biological macromolecule or lipid is to be labelled, the requirement for compatibility between the intended fluorescent probe (in terms of solubility in water, pH sensitivity and so on) and the properties of the molecule to be labelled. Also, choice of the fluorescent probe should be consistent with experimental objectives. For instance, FRET experiments require that extrinsic donor and acceptor fluorophores should be properly matched for their capacity to participate in the FRET effect (see Section 4.5.4).

One of the first extrinsic fluorophores to be developed was **dansyl chloride**, which first emerged in 1951. Dansyl chloride is an amine-reactive probe that is non-fluorescent until bound to amine functional groups with the creation of a sulphonamide link (Figures 4.15 and 4.17). This probe has proven particularly useful in binding interaction experiments since the values of I_{max} and ϕ_F are so sensitive to environment (see Chapter 7). There is a substantial blue-shift (ca. 20–30 nm) and an increase in ϕ_F as a consequence of the transfer of the probe from a more hydrophilic to a more hydrophobic environment, such as the transfer from bulk aqueous conditions to a hydrophobic binding region in a protein (see Figure 4.3, to understand the spectral changes which are equivalent). Subsequently, **fluorescein** was developed, which has proved to be a very popular extrinsic fluorophore available in several reactive probe forms that all absorb strongly (494 nm, close to the 488 nm wavelength of the argon-ion laser), fluoresce strongly and are readily water soluble. Direct derivatives of fluorescein include **tetramethyl rhodamine** and **Oregon green** (Figure 4.15). Fluorescein and these corresponding derivatives are a mainstay of many fluorescent probe experiments, but they do suffer from significant photobleaching, pH-sensitive fluorescence, broad emission spectra and fluorescence quenching post-bioconjugation. In spite of these problems, fluorescein and derivatives can give excellent cellular tracking and localisation data in cells, particularly where these extrinsic fluorescent probes have been used to label lipids and oligopeptides in conjunction with cyanine dye labelling of DNA (Figure 4.27). Fluorescein and derivatives, with cyanine dyes, have also proven very useful as matching probes in FRET experiments designed to investigate real time bending, folding and conformational dynamics in isolated biological macromolecule systems, particular those involving proteins and nucleic acids (Figure 4.28).

Fluorescein and derivatives are complemented by the **Texas red** fluorophore, a useful long wavelength extrinsic fluorophore (Figure 4.29). By contrast, coumarin derivatives are useful for shorter UV wavelength excitation, as are **pyrenes** such as **cascade blue** (Figure 4.29). One extrinsic fluorophore has proven particularly useful for the probe labelling of oligonucleotides or even nucleotides, namely N-methylanthranilic acid (**MANT**). This is considered a 'small probe' prepared from the alcohol-reactive probe precursor N-methylisatoic anhydride, which appears to combine with 2′-hydroxyl groups of β-D-ribofuranose rings, introducing the fluorescent MANT moiety without appearing to impair the functional binding behaviour of oligonucleotides or nucleotides (Figures 4.29 and 4.30). Increasingly, the tendency in fluorescent probe design has been to make designs flexible in order that precise wavelengths of absorption and emission can be tailored to requirements by subtle changes in selected structural parameters. For instance, **Alexa Fluor** probes can be tailored to cover a huge range of wavelengths and can be very good choices in many kinds of application. The most widely used Alexa Fluor dye is Alexa Fluor 488 (the number represents the excitation wavelength)

a)

FAM-**Lp24**

Cy5 red (abs and emission)
hence blue colour

Substrate for Cy5
Labelling **of pUMVC1**

TAMRA-**mu**

N—Met - (Arg)$_2$ -Ala -(His)$_2$ -(Arg)$_4$ -Ala -Ser -His -(Arg)$_2$ -Met -Arg -(Gly)$_2$-OH

b)

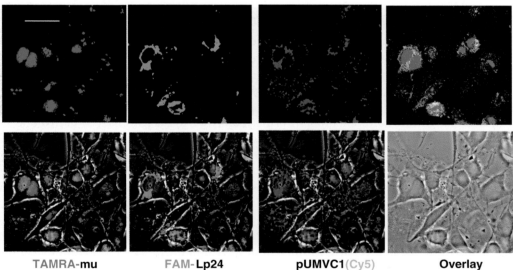

| TAMRA-**mu** | FAM-**Lp24** | **pUMVC1**(Cy5) | **Overlay** |

Figure 4.27   Multiple labelling. (a) Plasmid DNA (pDNA; **pUMVC1**) labelled with **Cy5 cyanine dye** (see **Fig. 4.26**), mu peptide labelled with Tetramethyl rhodamine (TAMRA) by α-N -capping (see **Fig. 4.17**); fluorescein (FAM) labelling of lipid (see Fig. 4.17) **(b)** All three labelled components were then combined together into three-fold labelled liposome:mu:pDNA particles wherein the lipid:mu:pDNA ratio was 12:0.6:1 (w/w/w). These particles (approx 120 nm in diameter) were added to human tracheal epithelial (HTE) cells and incubated for 15 mins with cells before three-fold analysis by microscopy. Bottom-line images are same as top-line images except for superposition of cell contrast image to demonstrate sub-cellular localization. Mu peptide enters the nucleus in 15 min. The other components remain in the cytosol (adapted from Keller et al., 2003, Fig. 3A) Bar is 10 μm.

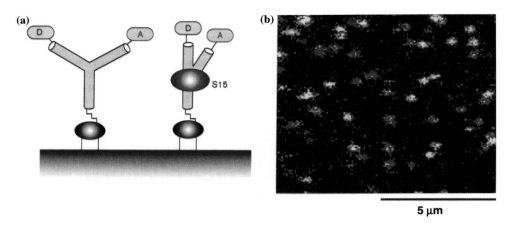

Figure 4.28   Protein Induced Folding of RNA. (a) Schematic to show RNA junction ("Y" shape cylinders) attached to glass surface at one end and with a **FRET donor-D (fluorescein)** on one arm of the "Y" and a **FRET acceptor-A (Cy 3 dye)** on the other arm of the "Y". Binding of ribosomal protein S15 brings arms of the "Y" close enough for a meaningful FRET effect to be observable. (b) Glass slide with multiple RNA junction molecules is irradiated at 488 nm. If protein induced folding of RNA takes place, then donor-D fluorescence (green) is quenched though absorption by acceptor-A leaving red dye colour. Both folding and unfolded junctions appear to be present (adapted from Lilley and Wilson, 2000, Fig. 4).

(Figure 4.29). In contrast, **BODIPY** probes have a quite different structure, but once again can be tailored to cover a large range of wavelengths (Figure 4.31). Relatively speaking, the BODIPY probes are less hydrophilic than the Alexa Fluor probes and BODIPY molecules have no net charge. Hence they are membrane permeable and may enter cells freely, in the same way as extrinsic biarsenical fluorescent probes. Furthermore, BODIPY tagging has also been found to have very little impact upon the electrophoretic mobility of labelled molecules; consequently, BODIPY probes have become integral to modern day, automated DNA sequencing (see Chapter 3). The small size of BODIPY probes also makes them potentially useful alternative fluorescent labels for small molecules such as oligonucleotides or nucleotides, in place of MANT labels.

Aladan substitution of internal core amino-acid residues provides an approach to characterise the physical characteristics of protein cores. Steady-state fluorescence alone can provide initial insight to the immediate environment of Aladan in the protein core. However, **time-resolved fluorescence spectroscopy** can be used to understand variations in protein core composition and structure as a function of time through the characterisation of Aladan fluorescence intensity and I_{max} changes that are caused by small fluctuations in the relative permittivity, ε, of the protein interior with time (fs–ps timescale). Such spectroscopy is possible since fluorescence lifetimes, τ_R, are typically in the ns range (see Section 4.5). Also, time-resolved fluorescence spectroscopy can be performed with non-covalently linked extrinsic fluorophores such as **ethidium bromide (EtBr)**. This fluorophore intercalates between the bases of DNA or RNA double helix and in so doing acquires a substantial increase in ϕ_F and hence fluorescence intensity at I_{max} (595 nm). Should there be a disruption or collapse in double-helical structure, then intercalation fails and fluorescent intensity drops

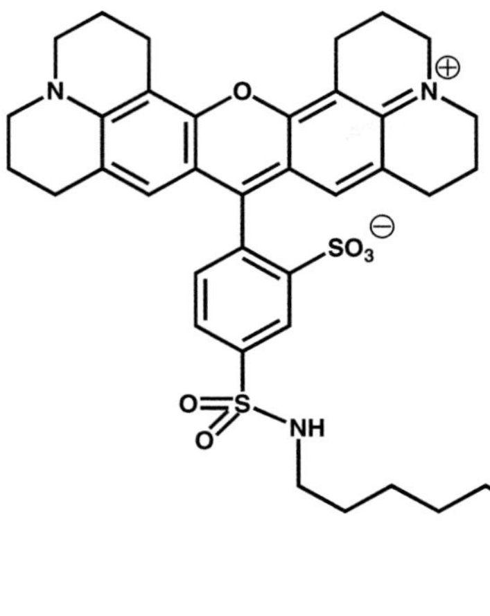

Texas Red-X, succinimidyl ester

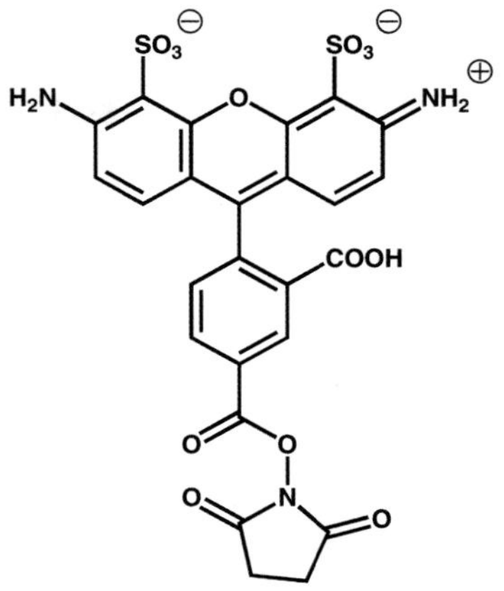

AlexaFluor 488, succinimidyl ester

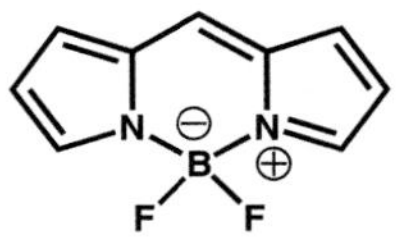

BODIPY, 4,4-difluoro-4-bora-3a, 4a-diaza-s-indacene

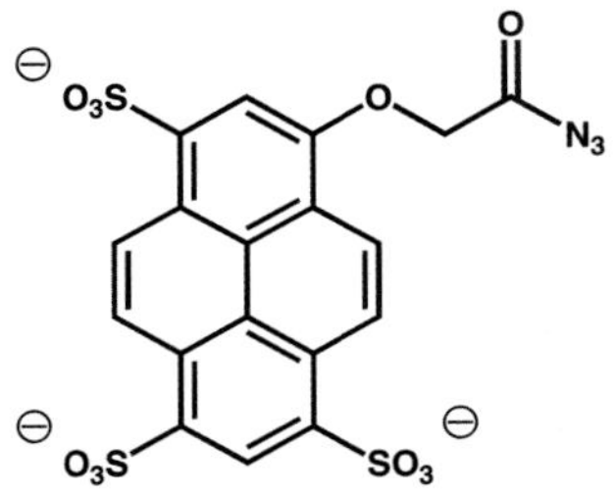

Cascade Blue Acetyl Azide

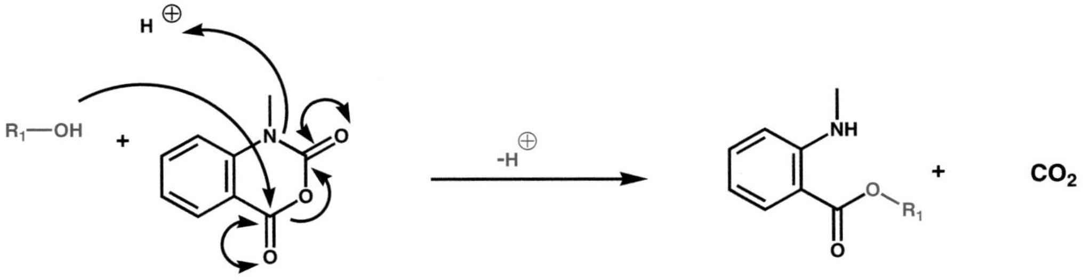

N-methylisatoic anhydride

R_1—OH + $-H^{\oplus}$ →   **N-methylanthranilic acid (N-MANT)** + CO_2

Figure 4.29 **Newer generation** of fluorescent probes and tags.

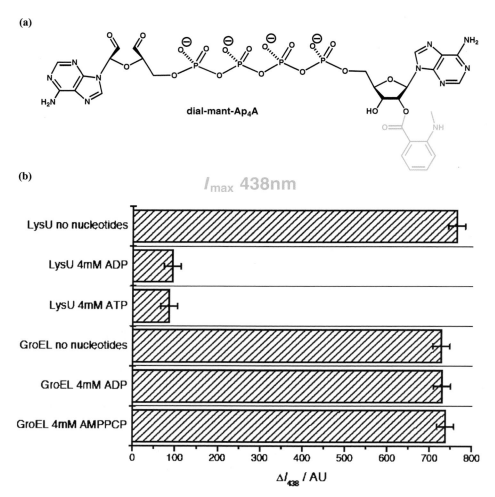

Figure 4.30 Flourescence binding competition. (a) Structure of **dial-mant-Ap₄A probe.** (b) Fluorescence binding data when two different proteins are incubated with the probe in the presence and absence of putative site-specfic competitive binders. In the case of **LysU protein** (see Chapters 6, 7 and 8), adenosine 5′-diphosphate (ADP) and adenosine 5′-triphosphate (ATP) are competitive binders and reduce probe binding to basal levels. In the case of **molecule chaperone protein GroEL** (see Chapters 6 and 7) the probe is binding allosteric to adenosine 5′-diphosphate (ADP) and adenosine 5′-[λ,-methylene]-triphosphate (AMPPCP) (Reproduced from Wright et al., 2006, Fig. 2c).

instantaneously. Accordingly, extrinsic EtBr fluorescence becomes an ideal probe to study the rates of structural collapse and templating of DNA (or RNA) mediated by strongly cationic entities such as certain peptides or proteins (ms–s timescale) (Figure 4.32).

Where proteins are concerned, the use of GFP or GFP variants (e.g. BFP, CFP, YFP and DsRed) in fusion with proteins of interest is becoming increasingly useful where cellular imaging is concerned using **fluorescence microscopy**. On the assumption that a GFP or GFP-variant fusion protein retains the biological activities and functions as the wild-type

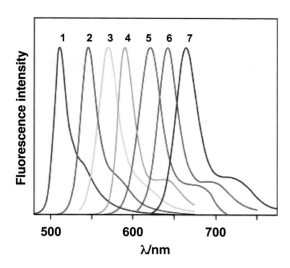

Figure 4.31 BODIPY Dyes. Normalized fluorescence emission spectra of (**1**) BODIPY FL; (**2**) BODIPY R6G; (**3**) BODIPY TMR; (**4**) BODIPY 581/591; (**5**) BODIPY TR; (**6**) BODIPY 630/650; (**7**) BODIPY 650/665 fluorophores in methanol (Reproduced from Molecular Probes Handbook, Fig. 1.37).

protein of interest (at least to a reasonable extent), then the attached fluorescent protein allows for meaningful *in situ* tracking and localisation of this protein of interest in cells (Figure 4.33), provided that the wavelengths of absorption and emission are clearly distinct from those of other fluorophores present. This is especially important if multiple individual proteins of interest are under observation simultaneously. Moreover, GFP and GFP variant fusions also offer a powerful way to identify functional binding partners in cells by FRET. In this case, obviously the GFP or GFP variant associated with each potential binding partner protein of interest should be properly matched with the GFP or GFP variant fused with the original protein of interest in order for the FRET effect to be properly observed when binding events take place (see Section 4.5.4).

The corresponding use of biarsenical fluorophore probes is clearly just as diverse but less invasive than the use of GFP or GFP variant fusions. Proteins of interest can be just as easily tracked in cells *in situ* and localised using biarsenical fluorophores. Furthermore, this approach lends itself very easily to differential fluorescent tagging of multiple proteins of interest in one cell, and therefore the identification and visualisation of functional binding partners in cells by FRET experiments, subject to the usual condition that fluorophores are matched to enable the FRET effect to be observed when binding events take place. Moreover, biarsenical fluorophore tags remain fluorescent post protein denaturation during electrophoresis for instance (provided no reductive dithiols are used in the preparation of the protein) (see Chapter 2), and the tags may even be used for affinity chromatography. In the latest manifestation of the technique, known as **chromophore-assisted light inactivation (CALI)**, strong illumination of the red biarsenical fluorophore **ReASH**, post chelation to proteins of interest in cells, creates short lived oxygen radicals that are able to inactivate nearby proteins. Such approaches illustrate how light can be used not only to observe molecules, but to actually control and elucidate molecular function in a real cellular context.

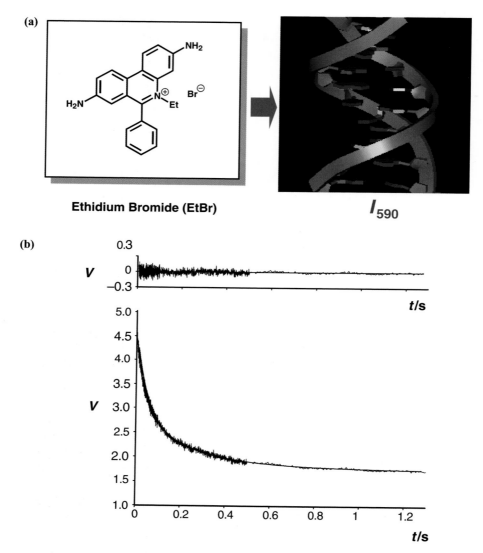

(a)

Ethidium Bromide (EtBr)

I_{590}

(b)

Figure 4.32   Flourescence exclusion. (a) Ethidium bromide (EtBr) becomes a strong fluorophore through intercallation between DNA bases. **(b)** When DNA is condensed with increasing concentrations of mu peptide (from the adenoviral core) then EtBr is excluded instantaneously causing fluoresence intensity to drop. At mu:pDNA ratios of 0.6 (w/w) condensation as measured by EtBr exclusion rates are rapid and reproducible. Mu peptide has a **template-condensation effect** on pDNA and the rates of EtBr exclusion suggest a condensation process similar in type and speed to single-domain protein folding. The top represents the control, the bottom represents the change in EtBr fluorescence signal (as voltage V) with time t [Reproduced from Tecle et al., 2003, Fig. 1A].

eGFP-*C*-terminal tags

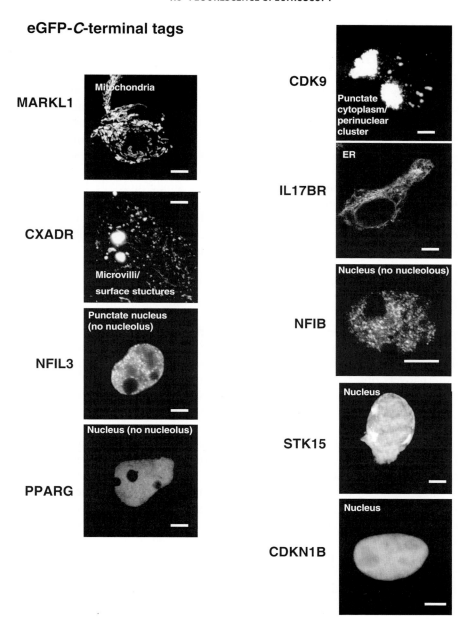

Figure 4.33 GFP-taging. Complete range of fusion proteins generated by **C-terminal fusion of green fluorescence protein** (**GFP**) (see **Fig. 4.24**) with selection of human proteins expressed by genes from the human genome mapping project. Fusion genes are generated in plasmid DNA (see Chapter 3) and used to transform mammalian cell line by a process of **reverse transfection**. Subcellular localization of fusion gene products are then observed by microscopy. All proteins appear in their expected locations given their known functions (adapted from Palmer and Freeman, 2004, Figs. 2 & 3) Bar is 10 μm.

4.5.6 Fluorescence single-molecule spectroscopy (SMS)

All the techniques described elsewhere in this chapter measure the average behaviour of ensembles of molecules. Now single-molecule investigations are becoming possible. Such investigations allow for the dynamic observation of single molecules, thereby revealing behaviour that is often hidden in most studies of biological macromolecular structure and dynamics. Observation of the ensemble (i.e. most techniques used in chemistry) reveals no information about the spread and inhomogeneity in **an experimental trajectory**. Single-molecule experiments can provide a great deal of otherwise intractable, and sometimes surprising, information regarding time trajectories and reaction pathways of biomolecules. Fluctuations and flickering are often observed at the single-molecule level that would otherwise be obscured in ensemble experiments.

Single-molecule observations are clearly demanding. To observe a single absorbing molecule within trillions of solvent or matrix molecules represents a significant technical problem. In order for this to be possible, two conditions should be fulfilled:

(a) laser beam excitation should be target specific for the biological macromolecule;

(b) post-excitation, biological macromolecule emission should exceed background.

The simplest approach to meet both conditions is either to immobilise a target biological macromolecule of interest on a surface, or else restrict (Brownian) motion (see Chapter 7) of the target by making observations in the presence of a gel to substantially attenuate Brownian motion. Alternatively, observations can be made in a flow cell so that photonic bursts of light are generated and observed as biological macromolecules flow through an incident, excitation beam. To meet condition (a), the use of defined wavelength laser beams, also controlled in direction, ensures that an appropriate, matching fluorescent probe can be selected with precision. Meeting condition (b) is more complex. Typically, fluorescence emission is only a tiny fraction of the incident energy used for the excitation, so efficient fluorescence detection is critical for single-molecule fluorescence spectroscopy. A number of factors can be considered to reduce background so that single-molecule detection becomes possible. For instance, small sample volume, high efficiency optics and the prebleaching of buffers are all helpful. The fluorescent probe should also exhibit a high value of ϕ_F and of D_{ab} (corresponding to an allowed electronic absorption transition) collected over a large absorption cross-section. In all these respects, GFP fusion proteins of interest appear to be excellent subjects for single-molecule detection of proteins.

The power of single-molecule detection should become obvious with reference to example. The range of observations that can be made using single-molecule spectroscopy is illustrated.

(a) The simplest experiment is to observe the position and positional fluctuation of a biological macromolecule of interest. Since the emission wavelength is far greater than the size of the biological macromolecule, each molecule acts as a point light source for fluorescence emission. Observing the position of the biological macromolecule provides a technique for observing protein movements (Figure 4.34(A)) (e.g. diffusion of lipid molecules within membranes or the diffusion of molecules within gels or sols).

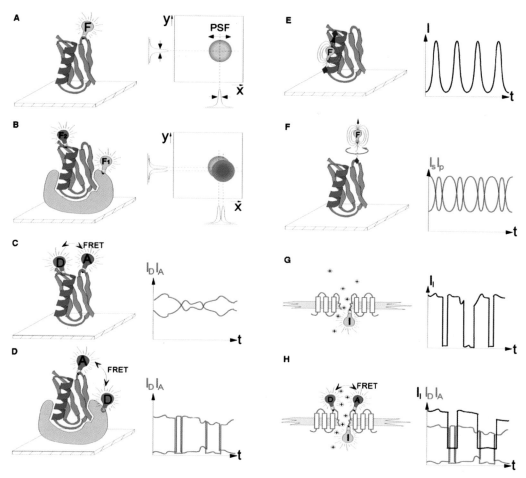

Figure 4.34 Fluorescence spectroscopy of single biomolecules (A) Localization of a macromolecule labeled with a **single fluorophore F** with nanometer accuracy. The **point-spread-function (PSF)** can be localized within a few tenths of a nanometer. (B) Colocalization of two macromolecules labeled with two **noninteracting fluorophores**, **F1** and **F2**. Their distance can be measured by subtracting the center positions of the two PSFs. (C) Intramolecular detection of **conformational changes by spFRET**. D and A are donor and acceptor; I_D and I_A are donor and acceptor emission intensities; t is time. (D) Dynamic colocalization and detection of association or dissociation by intermolecular spFRET. Donor and acceptor intensities are anticorrelated both in (C) and (D). (E) The **orientation** of a single immobilized dipole can be **determined by modulating the excitation polarization**. The fluorescence emission follows the angle modulation. (F) The **orientational freedom of motion** of a tethered fluorophore can be measured by modulating the excitation polarization and analyzing the emission at orthogonal s and p polarization detectors. I_S and I_P are emission intensities of s and p detectors. (G) Ion channel labeled with a **fluorescence indicator I**. Fluctuations in its intensity I report on local ion concentration changes. (H) Combination of (C) and (G). D and A report on conformational changes whereas I reports on ion flux (Reproduced from Weiss, 1999, Fig. 1) Labeling schemes (left) and physical observables (right).

(b) Two biological macromolecules of interest can be labelled with 'non-interacting' fluorophores. The relative positions of the two molecules can then be monitored to observe protein interactions in real time (Figure 4.34(B)) (e.g., binding or catalysis can be directly observed in this way).

(c) Two biological macromolecules of interest (with 'interacting' fluorophores, that come periodically within 2–8 nm of each other) can be probed using single-molecule fluorescence resonance energy transfer (FRET) experiments to observe motion in real time (Figure 4.34(C), (D), (H)), (e.g. intramolecular movements in response to conditions and other molecules, binding interactions and effects of binding upon intermolecular movements, the effects of intramolecular motion on function such as ion channel opening and closing).

(d) A biological macromolecule with single attached chromophore can be observed using plane-polarised fluorescence light to demonstrate local motion in real time by observing changes in fluorescence emission intensity with time as the orientations of absorption and emission transition dipoles vary through motion (Figure 4.34(E), (F), (G)) (e.g. protein tumbling, discrete intramolecular rotations, ion channel opening and closing).

Without doubt, single-molecule fluorescence spectroscopy is a growing field and many of the technical barriers to entry are now removed or understood so can be solved. When combined with many of the other single-molecule techniques available such as atomic force microscopy (see Chapter 6), then the impact of single-molecule detections and analyses can only become more influential, particularly where output from single-molecule techniques is sufficiently robust, reproducible and species independent that single-molecule measurements can be related to single-cell behaviour and even multi-cellular behaviour. Studies on ion channels and ion channel behaviour certainly have this potential, particularly when linked together with electrophysiological investigations of brain matter. Single-molecule fluorescence spectroscopy is sure to become increasingly influential.

4.6 Probing metal centres by absorption spectroscopy

X-ray absorption may also be used to probe the immediate environment of specific metal atom centres in biological macromolecules of interest. X-rays typically have energies ranging from 500 eV to 500 keV, equivalent to wavelengths from 25 to 0.25 Å. The absorption of X-rays obeys the following equation:

$$I_x = I_{x0} \exp(-\mu_{ab}x) \tag{4.25}$$

where I_{x0} is the **incident x-ray intensity**, I_x is the **transmitted intensity**, μ_{ab} an **X-ray absorption coefficient** and x is the path length. Light at this energy and wavelength is so energetic that absorption of photons can only take place by means of the **photo-electric effect**. According to this effect, absorption occurs when the energy of an incident X-ray photon exceeds the orbital energy of a core electron, allowing the X-ray photon to be absorbed and a

photo-electron to be ejected. However, only atoms with atomic numbers between 20 and 65 are subject to the photo-electric effect with X-ray photons, hence the X-ray absorption spectrum of molecules, liquids and solids is dominated by metal atom absorption. The X-ray absorption spectrum is known as the **X-ray absorption fine structure (XAFS)** spectrum of a biological macromolecule of interest. XAFS spectra are very sensitive to oxidation and coordination state of atoms involved. Moreover, XAFS spectra can yield significant detail about distances (0.02–4 Å) from metal atoms to surrounding atoms, and even identify these surrounding atoms. Unfortunately, spectral information is always averaged over all the metal atoms of a given type in a biological macromolecule of interest. Therefore, the technique of X-ray absorption is most useful only when the biological macromolecule of interest contains a single metal atom of a given type or at most only a modest cluster of atoms of the same type.

The typical XAFS spectrum is punctuated by the appearance of sharp edges from which two X-ray spectroscopy techniques take their names, namely **X-ray absorption near edge spectroscopy (XANES)** and **extended X-ray absorption fine structure spectroscopy (EXAFS)**, referring to the region of spectral oscillation further from an edge. Each edge corresponds to enhanced X-ray absorption caused by the photo-electric effect and the emission of a photo-electron. Accordingly, the energy of each edge should be metal atom type dependent, and identifiable with X-ray absorption by a given metal atom or a modest metal atom cluster of the same (Figure 4.35). XANES then gives some qualitative insights into the metal atom oxidation state and coordination chemistry whilst EXAFS analysis gives deeper insights into coordination number, neighbouring atom identities and inter-atomic distances involved. There is a much deeper understanding of EXAFS, so in practice XANES is used only as a qualitative metal atom fingerprint, while EXAFS analysis provides more quantitative information.

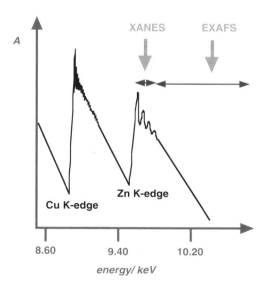

Figure 4.35   X-ray Absorption Spectrum of Cu,Zn-metallothionein. The copper and zinc K-edges are observed and the **XANES** and **EXAFS regions** are shown for the zinc K-edge.

5
Magnetic Resonance

5.1 Magnetic resonance in chemical biology

Since chemical biology is about understanding the way biology works at the molecular level, then access to detailed three-dimensional structures of biological macromolecules is indispensable. In Chapter 4, the chemical biology reader was introduced to the contribution that electronic spectroscopy can make to an understanding of structure and even function of biological macromolecules. However, electronic spectroscopies, although promising, are unable to give us a truly atomic-level description of any biological macromolecular structure. Therefore, in Chapters 5 and 6 the chemical biology reader will be brought face to face with those key, central techniques that have the capacity to generate meaningful atomic-level structures on which an atomic level of functional understanding can be built! All the techniques that will be discussed are surprisingly complementary both in theory and in application. All of these techniques are now totally fundamental to the effective practice of chemical biology.

Here, Chapter 5 is devoted to the contribution that magnetic resonance can make in deriving and understanding the structures of biological macromolecules. In particular, nuclear magnetic resonance (NMR) spectroscopy has been one the most beloved and powerful techniques of structural analysis used by chemists. Nowadays, the theory and the quality of instrumentation have developed to the point that NMR spectroscopy is also completely relevant and applicable to chemical biology research. Although the history of NMR spectroscopy has been dominated by the analysis of small molecule structures (<1000 Da), the structural characterisation of biological macromolecules, in particular of globular proteins, is now fast becoming routine. In writing this chapter, the intention has been to focus on and provide an explanation of the main theories and ideas that underpin the use of NMR spectroscopy in chemical biology research. This is because NMR spectroscopy is fast becoming a generic technique for the determination of three-dimensional structure at atomic-level resolution, so that the three-dimensional structures of many globular proteins, nucleic acids, carbohydrates

Essentials of Chemical Biology   Andrew Miller and Julian Tanner
© 2008 John Wiley & Sons, Ltd

and macromolecular lipid assemblies, as described in Chapter 1, can be readily accessible using this technique. In this chapter, we shall be making the leap all the way from the simple underlying quantum mechanical theory of NMR spectroscopy to the multidimensional NMR spectroscopy that forms the basis of what is also known today as biological NMR spectroscopy!

5.2 Key principles of NMR

This section deals with basic quantum mechanical theory in NMR. For some readers, this may be surplus to requirements. However, in our view, an appreciation of the quantum mechanical theory behind NMR spectroscopy is essential in order to understand the subsequent principles of biological NMR spectroscopy. So unless the reader is truly familiar with the quantum level NMR theory, please read on!

5.2.1 Spin angular momentum

In quantum mechanics, each nucleus of an atom possesses the property of **spin**. In other words, each nucleus behaves as if it were a child's spinning top or a gyroscope, spinning freely in one position located on a smooth surface. The top rotates about its main axis whilst at the same time precessing (Figure 5.1). Each nucleus also functions like a tiny bar magnet radiating magnetic force lines. Hence, we shall define a nucleus as a precessing, rotating, miniature bar magnet (Figure 5.2). The kinetic energy of the spin is defined in terms of **angular momentum**, J, a quantity that is represented in the form of a vector whose length reflects magnitude and whose orientation reflects direction of spin (i.e. relative to a predefined axis). In the world of quantum mechanics, the **angular momentum vector** is quantised with allowed magnitude defined by a **spin quantum number**, I, as represented by

$$J = [I(I+1)]^{1/2}\,\hbar \tag{5.1}$$

where h is Planck's constant. The spin quantum number also defines the number of allowed orientations that the spin **angular momentum vector** may adopt relative to a predefined reference axis. This number is equivalent to $2I + 1$. For instance, a proton (^1H nucleus) that has a spin quantum number of 1/2 will have just two allowed orientations with respect to the predefined reference axis. Each of these distinct orientations is known as a **spin state**.

There is one further consequence of quantum mechanics; according to the Heisenberg uncertainty principle an atomic or sub-atomic particle cannot simultaneously have both position and momentum defined. Therefore, the angular momentum vector associated with each spin state cannot align with the predefined reference axis but must reside off axis. This condition results in precessional cones, one cone per spin state, as shown for a proton (Figure 5.3). Individually, each precessional cone may be described as a surface representing all the possible orientations that the spin angular momentum vector can adopt in order to satisfy the requirements of quantum mechanics. Alternatively, each cone can be thought of as

Figure 5.1 Child's spinning top simultaneously rotating around its own primary axis but also precessing around a central axis of gyration.

mapping out the path traversed by the angular momentum vector as it precesses in an even sweep around the predefined reference axis at a fixed frequency.

In the absence of an externally applied magnetic field, reference axes for each spinning nucleus are arbitrary and spin states of a given nucleus are also **degenerate** (i.e. of the same energy). However, when an external magnetic field is applied then the direction of the external field becomes the reference axis (usually defined as the z-axis) for every spinning nucleus within the influence of this applied field. Interactions between the inherent magnetic field associated with each spin state and the external magnetic field create a situation in which different spin states that may be occupied by a given nucleus now possess inherently different energies. This situation is known as **lifting the degeneracy** and is a familiar concept in spectroscopy, where externally applied electric or magnetic fields are used routinely to generate energy differences between otherwise degenerate quantum states. Energy differences between

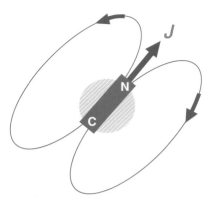

Figure 5.2   Spinning nucleus with angular momentum J behaves as a **minature bar magnet** that projects a magnetic field out into the local environment.

spin states are usually small and represented by the energy content of a single radio-frequency photon. Such modest energy differences are the entire basis of NMR spectroscopy!

5.2.2 Magnetic moment

The inherent magnetic field strength associated with any given spin state is represented by a **magnetic moment**, μ_z, that is proportional to the **component of spin angular momentum**, J_z, which each spin state projects upon the reference z-axis, defined above as the direction of the externally applied magnetic field. Since spin angular momentum is quantised in terms

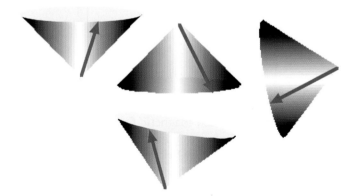

Figure 5.3   Depiction of four spinning nuclei. Spinning nuclei simultaneously spin and precess at a **Lamor frequency**, $\nu_{L'}$ therefore angular momentum vectors (red arrows) map out precessional cones. In the absence of any external magnetic field, vectors align relative to arbitrary z-axes. According to quantum mechanical rules, magnitude of angular momentum J is determined by spin quantum number I and a spinning nucleus can exist in any one of $2I + 1$ spin states.

of magnitude and orientation according to the spin quantum number, I, then z-axis components are similarly quantised. Each allowed z-axis component is represented by an individual **magnetic quantum number**, m_I, according to

$$J_z = m_I \hbar \tag{5.2}$$

In order to satisfy the requirement that the number of allowed spin states be equivalent to $2I + 1$, then the allowed values of m_I are equivalent to the series $I, I-1, \ldots, -I$. Hence in the case of a ^1H nucleus, whose spin quantum number is 1/2, the allowed values of m_I are $+1/2$ and $-1/2$. By convention, magnetic quantum numbers denoted with a '+' sign are said to align in generally the same direction as the reference z-axis and those denoted with a '−' sign are said to align in generally the opposite direction. This situation is illustrated for a ^1H nucleus (Figure 5.4). Both possible states are illustrated on the same diagram with precessional cones included, the spin state aligned with the applied magnetic field (reference z-axis) ($m_I +1/2$) is known by convention as the α **state**, the spin state aligned against the applied magnetic field ($m_I -1/2$) is known as the β **state**.

Magnetic moment relates directly to the allowed z-axis component of angular momentum of any given spin state of a nucleus according to

$$\mu_z = \gamma m_I \hbar \tag{5.3}$$

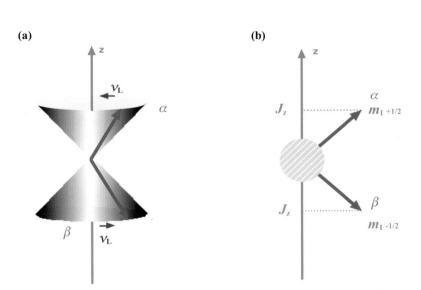

Figure 5.4 Depictions of the two different **allowed spin states of spinning nucleus** of I 1/2 (e.g., ^1H -nucleus). Reference z-axis is supplied by **external magnetic field** and angular momentum vectors (and precessional cones) align with ($m_I + 1/2$; α-**state**) or against ($m_I -1/2$; β-**state**) the field direction. **Degeneracy** between the two allowed ($2I + 1$) spin states is **lifted** by interaction between intrinsic magnetic fields of these spin states and the external field.

where γ is known as the **gyromagnetic ratio**, which in turn is defined by

$$\gamma = \frac{g_I \mu_N}{\hbar} \tag{5.4}$$

in which g_I is known as the **nuclear g-factor** and μ_N the **nuclear magneton**. The nuclear magneton is further defined by

$$\mu_N = \frac{e\hbar}{2m_p} \tag{5.5}$$

where m_p is the **mass of a proton**. Substitution of Equation (5.4) into (5.3) gives

$$\mu_z = m_I g_I \mu_N \tag{5.6}$$

5.2.3 Quantum mechanical description of NMR

The energy differences between different spin states are created by the differential way in which the magnetic moments of given spin states interact with the **applied magnetic field**, B_z. The **interaction energy** attributable to any given spin state, E_{m_I}, is defined by the product given in

$$E_{m_I} = -\mu_z B_z \tag{5.7}$$

Usually, the nuclear g-factor, g_I, is greater than unity and the ratio γ is positive (Table 5.1). Therefore, taking the ^1H nucleus as an example once more, the magnetic moment μ_z is positive for the α state and negative for the β state according to Equation (5.6). Consequently, the α state becomes more stable than the β state by interaction with the applied magnetic field, according to Equation (5.7). This situation is illustrated in the form of an energy level diagram (Figure 5.5) where the **energy difference**, ΔE, between these two states is then given

Table 5.1 Summary of all the main spin active (I 1/2) nuclei observed in the biomolecular NMR spectroscopy of biological macromolecules. Note that γ is proportional to the nuclear g-factor, g_I.

Isotope	Spin (I)	Natural Abundance (%)	$10^7 \times \gamma/$ rad s^{-1} T^{-1}	Relative sensitivity	NMR frequency (ν_L) at 2.35 T (field strength)
^1H	1/2	99.98	26.75	1.00	100.00
^{13}C	1/2	1.11	6.73	1.59×10^{-2}	25.14
^{15}N	1/2	0.37	-2.71	1.04×10^{-3}	10.13
^{19}F	1/2	100	25.18	0.83	94.08
^{31}P	1/2	100	10.84	6.63×10^{-2}	40.48
^{113}Cd	1/2	12.26	-5.96	1.09×10^{-3}	22.18

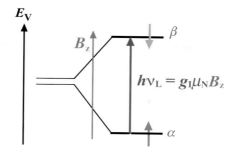

Figure 5.5 **Lifting the degeneracy** between the two allowed $(2I + 1)$ spin states of I 1/2 nucleus (*e.g.*, ^1H -nucleus) by application of an **external magnetic field, B_z.** Two spin states are illustrated by arrows (orange) aligned with (α-**state**) or against (β-**state**) the field direction. A **vertical spin state transition** is shown (red arrow) along with the resonance condition for inter-conversion of α- to β-**state**.

by a further equation

$$\Delta E = E^{\beta}_{-1/2} - E^{\alpha}_{1/2} = g_I \mu_N B_z \tag{5.8}$$

NMR spectroscopy relies on the fact that transitions from lower to higher energy spin states may be accomplished by interaction with radio-frequency photons. When photon energy is equivalent to spin state energy differences, then resonance coupling between nuclear spin and radiation leads to photon absorption and spin–spin transition. The frequency of absorption at resonance is sometimes known as the **Larmor frequency**, ν_L. Hence the resonance condition for NMR spectroscopy can be given in the form of

$$\Delta E = h\nu_L = g_I \mu_N B_z \tag{5.9}$$

This resonance condition (Equation (5.9)) is such that ν_L is directly proportional to external magnetic field strength, B_z, and to the size of the nuclear g-factor, g_I. The Larmor frequency, ν_L, has also been linked to the frequency with which spin angular momentum vectors associated with given associated spin states are said to precess evenly around precession cones of the type illustrated above (Figure 5.4). Therefore, ν_L may be alternatively called the **Larmor precession frequency**. In such a model, all states that could be occupied by a given nucleus subject to a given external magnetic field will possess the same precession frequency. For a given nucleus this frequency will be set in proportion to the nuclear g-factor, g_I, but be modulated in direct proportion to the size of the external magnetic field strength, B_z. A summary of some nuclear g-factors and spin quantum numbers for a range of different nuclei is given in Table 5.1.

5.2.4 Chemical shift and coupling

There are two aspects to NMR spectroscopy that have made it an extremely valuable spectroscopic technique. The first is the phenomenon of **chemical shift**, and the second that of **spin–spin coupling**. These topics will be covered very briefly in turn.

5.2.4.1   *Chemical shift*

Chemical shift may be thought of as the manner in which the resonance frequencies, ν_L, of nuclei that are part of molecular structures vary in a systematic and reproducible way in response to local chemical environment. According to Equation (5.9), changes in external magnetic field strength experienced by a given nucleus must have a direct affect on the energy difference between nuclear spin states leading to a proportionate change in resonance frequency, ν_L. Chemical shift arises because the strength of the effective external magnetic field experienced by any nucleus in a molecular structure appears to vary in response to local movements in neighbouring electron density. In other words, local electronic effects have direct and reproducible effects on ν_L values. Electronic effects are both **shielding** and **deshielding** in character. Shielding effects are generated by the tendency of an external magnetic field to induce electron density to 'circulate' in such a way as to create a local magnetic field in opposition to the applied field. The effective external magnetic field experienced by any such nucleus is then modulated according to

$$B_{\mathrm{eff},z} = B_z(1 - \sigma_N) \qquad\qquad (5.10)$$

where $B_{\mathrm{eff},z}$ is the effective field experienced by the nucleus and shielding is characterised by the **shielding parameter**, σ_N, also known as the **chemical shift tensor**. Deshielding arises out of hetero-atom σ-bond inductive effects and π-bond ring current effects. The former effect reduces local electron density around a given nucleus, hence increasing the effective field and hence ν_L. The latter effect creates local magnetic fields that cooperate with the applied field to increase the effective external magnetic field experienced by nuclei and hence their ν_L values (Figure 5.6). Together, shielding and deshielding effects are primarily responsible for ensuring that ν_L values vary as a direct consequence of local chemical environment and are therefore a direct indication of the nature of this chemical environment. In order to ensure

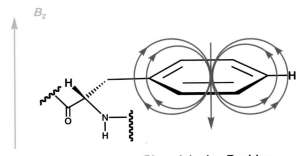

Phenylalanine Residue

Figure 5.6   **Ring currents** are generated by delocalised electron clouds that circulate in such a direction as to create a local magnetic field (**red** arrow) that opposes the effect of the external magnetic field, B_z (**light blue** arrow). In aromatic systems, ring current enhances magnetic field experienced by attached [1]H-nuclei causing enhanced **deshielding**.

that variation in ν_L values as a function of local chemical environment is standardised between NMR experiments and NMR spectrometers, the δ **chemical shift scale** was introduced. This scale is defined by Equation (5.11) in parts per million (ppm):

$$\delta = \frac{\nu_L - \nu_0}{\nu_0} \times 10^6 (\text{ppm}) \tag{5.11}$$

where ν_0 is the **operating frequency** (in MHz) of the NMR spectrometer and ν_L the resonance frequency of a nucleus of interest. Typically chemical shift ranges are small compared with ν_0, therefore ^1H-NMR spectra are recorded over the range 0–12 ppm, ^{13}C-NMR spectra over the range 0–200 ppm and ^{15}N-NMR spectra over the range 1–200 ppm. The nuclei in most biologically relevant molecules will resonate within these ranges with very few exceptions. The δ chemical shift scale is universal and detection of a signal at a given δ value provides a very potent indication of local chemical environment and even functional group locality, as shown (Figure 5.7). The scale is arbitrary and given from a reference value – for instance, in ^1H-NMR spectra the methyl signal of tetramethylsilane (TMS) is set to 0 ppm.

5.2.4.2 Spin–spin coupling

Spin–spin coupling effects on ν_L values are subtler than chemical shift effects but provide a great deal more information about the structure of the local chemical environment than suggested by the gross δ value. In short, electrons, like nuclei, have the property of spin represented by a spin quantum number, I, of 1/2. Therefore, spin pairing will take place between a given nucleus and the electrons of all associated bonds. Consequently, the spin state of this nucleus will be communicated with and have a direct local effect on the spin state of other nuclei related to the first through-bond. This is known as **scalar spin–spin coupling**. The **electron-coupled spin–spin interaction energy**, $E_{\mathscr{J}}$, is given by

$$E_{\mathscr{J}} = h \mathscr{J} I_i I_j \tag{5.12}$$

where I_i and I_j are the spin quantum numbers of spin–spin coupled nuclei, and $\mathscr{J}$ is the **scalar coupling constant** (in Hz). Each group of nuclei interrelated by spin–spin coupling is known as a **spin system**. Spin–spin coupling ensures that the spin states of each resonating nucleus in a spin system are evenly split into a number of spin microstates usually closely similar in energy to the parent spin states. This situation is illustrated for two cases where a ^1H nucleus is coupled with one and then two ^1H nuclei respectively (Figure 5.8). A practical consequence of spin–spin coupling is that the resonance frequency lines of each nucleus are also evenly split into a number of usually closely related resonance frequency lines, each one of which correlates to an allowed spin–spin transition between a lower energy and a higher energy spin microstate (Figure 5.8).

There is a general rule that for each spin state of a resonating nucleus, the number of spin-coupled microstates that are generated by spin–spin coupling with n identical neighbouring nuclei is $(2I + 1)^n$, although the number of allowed spin–spin transitions is only

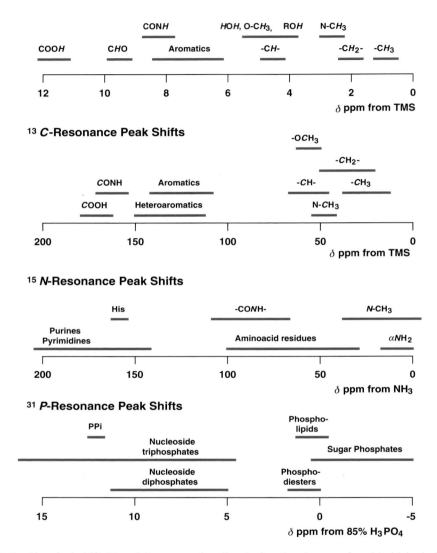

Figure 5.7   Chemical shift (δ scale) summary for all main functional groups found in biological macro-molecules for all main **I 1/2** nuclei used to probe structure by NMR spectroscopy. **TMS; tetramethylsilane.**

$2nI + 1$, where I is the spin quantum number of the neighbouring nuclei in each case. The reason for this is that quantum mechanical selection rules require that there be no changes in the nuclear spin states of coupled nuclei during a given spin–spin transition between two microstates of a given resonating nucleus. So, for instance, if a resonating nucleus ($I = 1/2$) is coupled with one neighbouring nucleus ($I = 1/2$) then although four spin-coupled microstates are generated in total only two resonance frequency lines (known

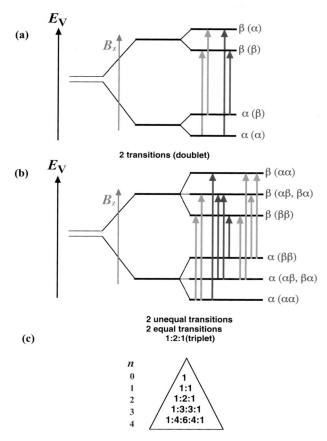

Figure 5.8 The **formation of spin microstates in response to spin-spin nuclear coupling.** (a) Coupling of spinning nucleus of $I = 1/2$ (e.g., ^1H-nucleus) with one neighbouring spinning nucleus of $I = 1/2$ (e.g., ^1H-nucleus). Two **new microstates** are formed from each main spin state (right). Two spin microstate transitions are allowed (red arrows) and two transitions disallowed (grey arrows); **(b)** Coupling of spinning nucleus of $I = 1/2$ (e.g., ^1H-nucleus) with two equivalent neighbouring nuclei of $I = 1/2$ (e.g., ^1H-nucleus). Four new microstates are formed from each main spin state (right). Four spin microstate transitions (two degenerate) are allowed (red arrows) and twelve transitions disallowed (six shown; grey arrows); **(c)** **Pascal's triangle**, a useful nemonic with which to remember the number and intensity of resonance signals that result from spin-spin coupling of n equivalent nuclei of $I = 1/2$ with a main spinning nucleus of $I = 1/2$.

as a doublet) will result from allowed spin–spin transitions (Figure 5.8). Similarly, if two identical neighbouring nuclei ($I = 1/2$) are involved then three resonance frequency lines will result (triplet). Furthermore, if four identical neighbouring nuclei ($I = 1/2$) are involved then five resonance frequency lines will result (quintet) and so on. The spacing between lines is given by $\mathscr{J}$, the scalar coupling constant (in Hz), and the number and relative intensities follow a distribution denoted by Pascal's triangle to a first approximation (Figure 5.8). These intensity patterns actually correlate directly with the number of allowed spin–spin transitions between microstates that are coincidentally degenerate. For example, when a resonating nucleus ($I = 1/2$) is coupled with two identical neighbouring nuclei ($I = 1/2$) then inspection of the appropriate spin splitting diagram shows that there are actually four allowed spin–spin transitions between the eight spin-coupled microstates generated, of which two transitions are degenerate, hence the appearance of three resonance frequency lines in the 1:2:1 intensity ratio characteristic of an NMR triplet (Figure 5.8). An important point to be aware of is that these rules only apply when $\mathcal{J} \ll \delta$ (in Hz).

Typically in most organic and biological macromolecules nuclei spin–spin coupling takes place through one, two, three and possibly four consecutive covalent bonds. Such spin–spin coupling behaviour may be called $^1\mathcal{J}$ (**single-bond**), $^2\mathcal{J}$ (**geminal**), $^3\mathcal{J}$ (**vicinal**) and $^4\mathcal{J}$ (**long range**) **coupling** respectively. The magnitudes of coupling constants vary substantially (Table 5.2). By definition, spin systems are clusters of spin-coupled nuclei that are prevented from spin-coupling, or are otherwise unable to spin-couple, with neighbouring spin systems. There can be an enormous number of varieties of spin systems. For this reason, NMR spectroscopists frequently use a shorthand alphabetic nomenclature to denote the given type of spin system

Table 5.2 Summary of main homo- (^1H-^1H) and heteronuclear spin-spin coupling constants relevant to the biomolecular NMR spectroscopy of biological macromolecules.

^1H-^1H Coupling		
$^2\mathcal{J}$ (geminal)	^1H-C-^1H	−12 to −15Hz
$^3\mathcal{J}$ (vicinal)	^1H-C-C-^1H	2 to 14Hz
	^1H-C=C-^1H	10Hz (cis); 17Hz (trans)
	^1H-N-C-^1H	1 to 10 Hz
		0.5 to 3 Hz (long range)
^1H-^{13}C Coupling		
$^1\mathcal{J}$	^1H-^{13}C-(sp^3)	110-130Hz
$^2\mathcal{J}$	^1H-C-^{13}C	5Hz
	^1H-C=^{13}C	2Hz
^1H-^{15}N Coupling		
$^1\mathcal{J}$	^1H-^{15}N	89 to 95Hz
$^2\mathcal{J}$	^1H-C-^{15}N	15 to 23Hz
^1H-^{31}P Coupling		
$^2\mathcal{J}$	^1H-O-^{31}P	15 to 25Hz
$^3\mathcal{J}$	^1H-C-O-^{31}P	2 to 20Hz
^{31}P-^{31}P Coupling		
$^2\mathcal{J}$	^{31}P-O-^{31}P	10 to 30Hz
^1H-^{19}F Coupling		
$^2\mathcal{J}$	^1H-C-^{19}F	40 to 50Hz
$^3\mathcal{J}$	^1H-C-C-^{19}F	5 to 20Hz

under investigation. Initially, a set of reference nuclei are initially denoted A_n, where n is the number of chemically equivalent reference nuclei involved. Spin-coupled nuclei are then denoted as follows. If their resonance frequencies are close to the resonance frequencies of the reference nuclei then the letter codes B_n, usually followed by C_n, are used. Alternatively, if their resonance frequencies are very far from the resonance frequencies of the reference nuclei then the letter codes X_n, usually followed by Y_n, are employed. If the reference nuclei are coupled with two sets of chemically equivalent nuclei all of which have substantially different resonance frequencies from each other then the letter code M_n may be used. For instance, $CHCl_2$–CH_2Br would be described as an AB_2 spin system; CH_2Br–CF_3 would be described as an A_2X_3 spin system and $^{13}CHF_3$ as an AMX_3 spin system. We will use this nomenclature later on in this chapter when looking at spin systems found in biological macromolecules such as the polypeptides or proteins.

5.2.5 Vector description of NMR

On the whole, NMR spectroscopy is a very insensitive technique. The reason is that NMR spectroscopy relies on observing transitions from lower to higher energy spin states. Unfortunately, sensitivity relies on there being a substantial population difference between nuclei in lower energy states and those in higher energy states. However, owing to the very slight energy differences between high and low energy spin states population differences are frequently small, with the result that NMR spectroscopy requires a large population of nuclei in order to observe any significant photon absorption at all. Compare the amounts of material typically required to observe an NMR spectrum compared with other techniques described previously (Table 5.3). For instance, if a Boltzmann distribution is calculated corresponding to the distribution of ^1H nuclei between α- and β-spin states using

$$N_\beta / N_\alpha = \exp(-h\nu_L / kT) \tag{5.13}$$

assuming that $h\nu_L / kT$ is approximately 7×10^{-5} for a population of ^1H nuclei at a temperature of 300 K and an external magnetic field strength of 10 T, the **population difference** N_β / N_α is

Table 5.3 Summary of approximate quantities of biological macromolecules required in order to realise complete structural characterisation using the indicated types of technique.

Type of Structural Analysis Technique	Approximate Quantities Required for Structural Analysis
Electronic (Chap 4)	μg-mg
Vibrational (Chap 4)	mg
Magnetic Resonance (Chap 5)	mg-100mg
X-ray Crystallography (Chap 6)	mg-g
Mass (Chap 9)	ng

only slightly greater than unity. Since ν_L is a function of the nuclear g-factor, then the smaller the g_I of a given nucleus the smaller still would be the population difference. The only way to reverse this situation is to increase external magnetic field strength, B_z, and in so doing increase ν_L in proportion.

Nevertheless, there is usually a significant enough population between lower and higher energy spin states for NMR spectroscopy to be viable. This population difference averaged over a whole sample population of nuclei subject to an external applied magnetic field must necessarily result in a net alignment of spin states in the direction of the external applied magnetic field (reference z-axis). This leads to a net sample magnetisation in the direction of the external applied magnetic field whose magnitude is determined by the vector sum over all the magnetic moments of the sample population of nuclei under observation. This net magnetisation, M, is frequently referred to as the **bulk magnetisation vector** (Figure 5.9). The existence of M allows for **Fourier transform (FT)-NMR spectroscopy** to be performed. FT-NMR spectroscopy is the basis of all modern NMR spectroscopy.

In the simplest possible FT-NMR experiment, the resting sample is comprised of a homogeneous sample population of nuclei precessing at a uniform value of ν_L with a steady state value of M. If this sample is then subject to a **circularly polarised radio-frequency pulse** of frequency ν_L along the x-axis, then the NMR resonance condition is satisfied (Equation (5.9)) and M is able to precess towards the xy-plane. The pulse duration is sufficient only for M to precess through $90°$ and lie exclusively in the xy-plane. For this reason, such a pulse is referred to as a **$90°_x$-pulse**. The bulk magnetisation vector now lies along the y-axis and begins to disperse in the xy-plane with time. The component of the bulk magnetisation vector as it evolves with time along the y-axis is usually referred to as **transverse magnetisation** or **coherence**, $M_y(t)$. **Spin–spin relaxation** (see Section 5.2.6) is primarily responsible for the evolution of $M_y(t)$. This evolution is observed by a radio-frequency receiver coil mounted coaxial with the y-axis, acquired and then stored as a digitised radio-frequency signal that

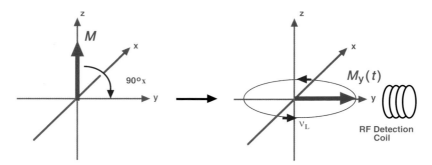

Figure 5.9 Vector model of NMR spectroscopy. Bulk magnetisation vector **M** is result of complete summation over all z-axis components of magnetic momenta across entire population of spinning nuclei aligned by external magnetic field. Illustration is drawn assuming all nuclei to be **I** 1/2 (*e.g.*, ^1H-nuclei), chemically equivalent hence precessing with an equivalent Lamor frequency, ν_L, but without spin-spin coupling. A circular radio frequency pulse is applied along the x-axis (**$90°_x$ pulse**) (**left**) and transverse magnetisation, $M_y(t)$ is realised along the y-axis where radio frequency (**RF**) changes in magnetisation are observed, acquired and stored digitally with time by means of the detection coil.

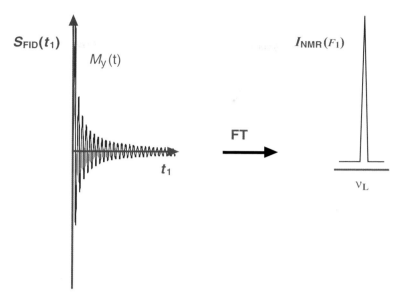

Figure 5.10 Radio frequency variation of $M_y(t)$ **transverse magnetisation** observed, acquired and stored digitally with time is known as a **Free Induction Decay (FID)**. Stored FID either singly or averaged, are processed by **fourier series transformation** (**FT**) from time domain signal information, $S_{FID}(t_1)$, into frequency domain (spectral) information, $I_{NMR}(F_1)$. Only chemically equivalent nuclei without spin-spin coupling and with an equivalent Lamor frequency, v_L, are being observed here hence only a single signal will result of frequency v_L.

varies as a function of time. This digitised radio-frequency signal is known as a **free induction decay** (**FID**) (Figure 5.10).

Spin–spin relaxation ensures that $M_y(t)$ evolves eventually to zero with time, whilst the original steady state bulk magnetisation vector, M, is regenerated by another relaxation process known as **spin–lattice relaxation** (see Section 5.2.6). After M is fully regenerated, a second 90° pulse is then applied and a second more or less identical FID may be observed, acquired and stored. This process may be repeated for as many FIDs as are required and then the averaged FID data set is subject to Fourier series transformation. This is an immensely complicated process but the actual transformation is straightforward to understand. In short, Fourier series transformation means inverting time domain data (FID data) into frequency domain data (NMR spectrum). In the case of our highly simplified FT-NMR experiment described above, this process will lead to the realisation of an NMR spectrum from the illustrated FID with a single peak corresponding to a resonance frequency of v_L (Figure 5.10). In the more usual case, M is a complex vector sum of a wide range of different nuclei in states precessing at different v_L frequencies owing to a raft of different spin–spin coupling and shielding/deshielding effects. Corresponding FIDs are therefore significantly more complex but Fourier series transformation will readily result in a clear NMR spectrum from each FID family provided that there are not too many overlapping v_L frequencies associated with nuclei in chemically different but accidentally degenerate spin states.

5.2.6 Spin–lattice and spin–spin relaxation

As indicated (Section 5.2.5), successful acquisition of multiple FIDs depends upon the ability of a sample population of nuclei to recover steady state equilibrium between radio-frequency pulses. Recovery to equilibrium between pulses relies upon the two main relaxation processes mentioned above, namely spin–lattice and spin–spin relaxation (see Section 5.2.5). Spin–lattice relaxation is associated with relaying spin energy to the surroundings by such mechanisms as through-space **dipolar coupling** (see Section 5.2.7). This same spin–lattice relaxation is primarily responsible for the restoration of the bulk magnetisation vector, M, to its original magnitude and position along the z-axis. The component of the bulk magnetisation vector as it recovers with time along the z-axis is referred to as **longitudinal magnetisation** or **polarisation**, $M_z(t)$. $M_z(t)$ obeys the following proportionality:

$$M_z(t) \propto 1 - \exp(-t/T_1) \tag{5.14}$$

where t is time and T_1 the **longitudinal relaxation time constant**. By contrast, spin–spin relaxation is associated with the exchange of spin energies between spin-coupled nuclei over one nuclear transition (**single quantum coherence**) or sometimes over several nuclear transitions (**multiple quantum coherence**) as appropriate. This process is also known as **coherence transfer**. Spin–spin relaxation acts as an indirect mechanism to regenerate the steady state bulk magnetisation vector, M. **Transverse magnetisation** or **coherence**, $M_y(t)$, obeys the proportionality

$$M_y(t) \propto \exp(-t/T_2) \tag{5.15}$$

where t is time and T_2 the **transverse relaxation time constant**. The transverse relaxation time constant not only has a direct impact on $M_y(t)$ but also has an impact on spectral resolution. **Spectral line width at half peak intensity**, $\Delta \nu_{L,1/2}$, is given according to

$$\Delta \nu_{L,1/2} = 1/\pi T_2 \tag{5.16}$$

indicating that the smaller the value of T_2, the greater will be the corresponding spectral line width and the worse the spectral resolution. In fact this expression represents yet another meeting with the Heisenberg uncertainty principle; in other words, as certainty in time increases, uncertainty in frequency also increases. Equation (5.16) is very important for the NMR spectroscopy of biological macromolecules. Many such biological macromolecules are more than large enough and are comprised of more than sufficient spin-coupled nuclei to ensure that T_2 values are very small, leading to substantial line broadening with loss of spectral resolution. This is critical. Without adequate solutions to the 'T_2-relaxation problem', NMR spectroscopy of biological macromolecules is technically impossible. Fortunately, there has been ample innovation in NMR spectroscopy over the years to solve this problem, as will be revealed shortly, in the process bringing biological NMR spectroscopy to life!

5.2.7 Nuclear Overhauser effect

Before moving forward, the chemical biology reader should appreciate that $M_z(t)$ polarisation and recovery towards steady state bulk magnetisation M by spin–lattice relaxation are primarily indicative of changes in the levels of spin state occupancy. By contrast, $M_y(t)$ coherence and evolution by spin–spin relaxation are both primarily indicative of transitions between spin state energy levels. In this context, the **nuclear Overhauser effect (NOE)** is a very important through-space effect in NMR spectroscopy that results directly from **dipolar coupling-mediated spin–lattice relaxation**.

Through-space dipolar coupling originates from the fact that each nucleus is like a precessing, rotating, miniature bar magnet (see Section 5.2.1). Another description for a bar magnet is a dipole. Therefore, nuclei are capable of the equivalent of non-bonded dipole-induced dipole interactions through space. Such **dipolar coupling** has no effect upon the number and relative energies of spin states, but does influence the relative levels of spin state occupancy, leading to changes in NMR signal intensities. Therefore, *NOE may be defined as a change in intensity of an NMR signal originating from a given reference nucleus that is dipolar coupled with other nuclei whose spin–spin transitions have been perturbed.* Perturbation means saturation in this context. Hence a change in signal intensity from a reference nucleus of interest should be observed if there is selective irradiation of the dipolar-coupled nuclei. By way of illustration, if two nuclei A and X are close together in space, then irradiation of X should provoke an NOE modulation of the **signal intensity** (S_A) emanating from nucleus A according to the proportionality

$$\frac{S_A}{S_{A_0}} \propto \frac{T_1}{T_{1,\text{dip–dip}}} \qquad (5.17)$$

where S_{A_0} represents the **signal intensity prior to irradiation of** X and $T_{1,\text{dip–dip}}$ the **longitudinal relaxation time constant related** to that component of spin–lattice relaxation associated with **through-space dipolar coupling**. Critically, the term $T_{1,\text{dip–dip}}$ contains an $1/r^6$ dependency characteristic of dipolar-coupling effects and reflects the fact that NOEs must also be subject to the same $1/r^6$ dependency, where r is the inter-nuclear distance in this case. In other words, as two dipolar coupled nuclei become closer $T_{1,\text{dip–dip}}$ becomes shorter, and change in S_A intensity must increase in proportion. Please note that dipole–dipole interactions in general obey a $1/r^6$ dependency (see Main Section 1.6), and so have little influence beyond 5.0 Å. Accordingly, the magnitude of NOEs can be a powerful tool for showing the proximity of nuclei to each other through space. Typically NOEs are grouped into three types:

(a) **strong NOEs** correlating with inter-nuclear distances of between 1.8 and 2.7 Å

(b) **medium NOEs** correlating with distances of 1.8–3.3 Å

(c) **weak NOEs** correlating with distances of 1.8–5.0 Å.

Hopefully, the reader can now see that in the battle for accurate structural determination of biological macromolecules with their complex three-dimensional structures the NOE effect is a potentially very powerful tool indeed. In fact, we would go so far as to say that NOE determinations are probably the cornerstone of structure determination experiments by biological NMR spectroscopy once T_2 relaxation problems have been solved!

5.3 Two-dimensional NMR

Armed with a basic knowledge of FT-NMR spectroscopy and NOE theory, we are now in a position to scale the heights of multidimensional NMR spectroscopy. If you have been tempted to skip Main Section 5.2, please at least be secure about the information in Sections 5.2.6 and 5.2.7 before continuing! Before embarking upon a discussion of multidimensional NMR spectroscopy, we shall need to redefine simple FT-NMR spectroscopy experiments described this for (Figures 5.9, 5.10), as one dimensional (1D) NMR experiments that consist of only a single time domain of detection and signal acquisition (t_1) following the application of radio-frequency pulse(s). An alternative diagrammatic representation of a general 1D NMR experiment is shown in Figure 5.11. Alternatively this could be expressed as

$$preparation - t_1(acquire)$$

Fourier series transformation of time domain data, $S_{FID}(t_1)$, into frequency domain signal intensity data $I_{NMR}(F_1)$ then yields a characteristic classical 1D NMR spectrum.

On the basis of this, two-dimensional (2D) NMR spectroscopy experiments can be defined as experiments that involve one time domain for signal evolution (t_1) and an additional time domain for detection and signal acquisition (t_2) together with appropriate radio-frequency

1D Pulse Sequence

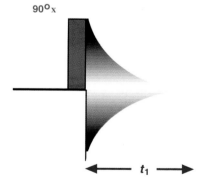

Figure 5.11 Alternative diagrammatic **representation of general FT 1D NMR experiment**. There is a single 90° pulse then signal observation and acquisition in time domain t_1 prior to fourier series transformation of time domain signal information $S_{FID}(t_1)$ into frequency domain (spectral intensity) information, $I_{NMR}(F_1)$.

pulse sequences. The basic experimental form can be expressed as

$$\text{preparation} - t_1 - M_1 - t_2(\text{acquire})$$

where M_1 is an **optional mixing period**. Fourier series transformation of time domain data, $S_{FID}(t_1, t_2)$, into frequency domain signal intensity data $I_{NMR}(F_1, F_2)$ then yields an impressive range of possible 2D NMR spectra. There are three basic types of two-dimensional (2D) NMR spectroscopy experiments that will need to be considered here, each of which has a slightly different sequence of pulses, but always involves two time domains t_1 and t_2. The simplest is **correlated spectroscopy (COSY)**, followed by **total correlation spectroscopy (TOCSY)** and then **nuclear Overhauser effect spectroscopy (NOESY)**.

5.3.1 Homonuclear 2D COSY and TOCSY experiments

The pulse sequence of a general 2D COSY experiment is shown in Figure 5.12. In time t_1, transverse magnetisation is generated that evolves with chemical shift. **Coherence transfer** between spin-coupled nuclei then takes place during the second pulse; afterwards, final coherence is observed and acquired over time t_2. The coherence transfer between spin–spin coupled nuclei is the key element since the purpose of this experiment is to determine those homonuclei of interest (e.g. $^1H-^1H$, $^{13}C-^{13}C$) that are $^1\mathscr{J}$, $^2\mathscr{J}$ or $^3\mathscr{J}$ spin–spin coupled with respect to each other in a molecule of interest, although for practical purposes COSY experiments are usually limited to $^3\mathscr{J}$ $^1H-^1H$, homonuclear spin–spin coupling.

The appearance of a typical homonuclear 2D COSY experimental spectrum is shown in Figure 5.13. This general appearance shares many common features with other 2D NMR spectra, as we shall see. The spectrum takes the form of a contour map plotted as a function of frequencies F_1 and F_2 (both in ppm). Resonance frequency lines have now given way to peaks, whose intensity and cross-sectional area are represented by contour lines in the same way that mountains or valleys are depicted on a geographical survey map. The diagonal cross-section of the spectral contour map is equivalent to the 1D NMR spectrum of the given sample under investigation. Critically, cross-peaks also exist in the spectral contour map that are generated by coherence transfer and therefore allow for the identification of nuclei that are spin-coupled by triangulation with the diagonal (Figure 5.13).

The TOCSY experiment bears many features in common with the COSY experiment except for one key essential. A general TOCSY experiment is represented for comparison (Figure 5.12). The key essential is inclusion of a mixing period (denoted τ_m or M_1) involving **spin locking**. Spin locking allows **polarisation transfer** to take place between homonuclei by rendering their spin states temporarily equivalent in order to allow for 'isotropic mixing'. This is not quite the same as through-space dipolar-coupling-mediated effects that manifest themselves in NOEs. Instead, polarisation transfer is a form of 'warming up' or 'increasing the spin temperature' of spin-coupled nuclei ($^1\mathscr{J}$, $^2\mathscr{J}$, $^3\mathscr{J}$, $^4\mathscr{J}$ etc.) by enhancing spin state energy level population imbalances leading to enhanced signal intensities and longer range spin–spin coupling effects. Hence in time t_1 coherence is generated that evolves with chemical shift. Polarisation transfer between spin–spin-coupled nuclei then takes place

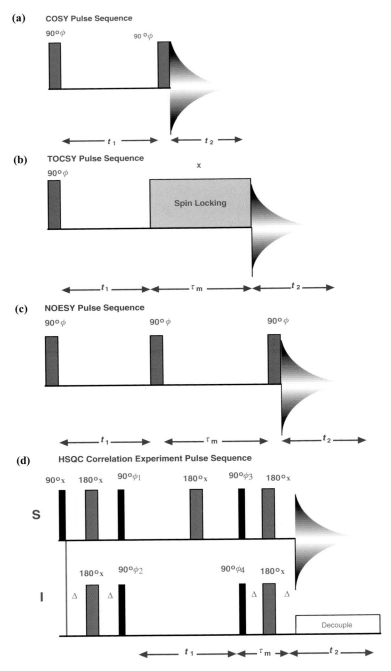

Figure 5.12 Diagrammatic **representation of general FT 2D NMR experiments** involving multiple 90° pulses with signal observation and acquisition in time domain t_2 prior to fourier series transformation of time domain information $S_{FID}(t_1, t_2)$ into frequency domain (spectral intensity) information, $I_{NMR}(F_1, F_2)$. Experiments shown are homonuclear (**a**) **COSY**, (**b**) **TOCSY** and (**c**) **NOESY** experiments. Typical heteronuclear correlation experiment (**d**) is also shown comprising complex sequence of multiple 90° and 180° pulses involving **source nuclei I** and **destination nuclei S**.

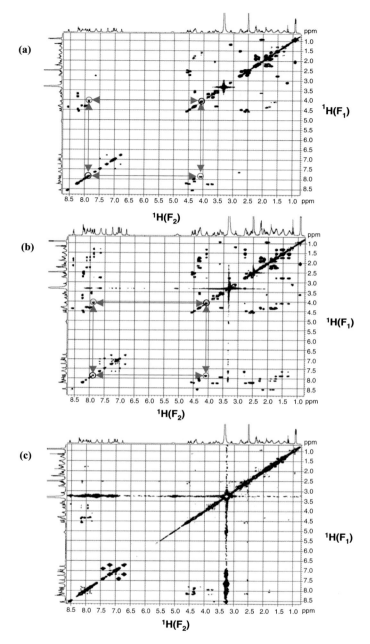

Figure 5.13 Actual I_{NMR} (F_1, F_2) spectral output ^1H-^1H homonuclear (**a**) COSY, (**b**) TOCSY and (**c**) NOESY experiments obtained with a peptide of sequence **VQGEESNDK** (Boraschi loop of Interleukin-1β) (see Chapter 7). Output is in the form of **contour maps** in which peak intensity is indicated by the density of contour lines (in the same way that contour lines represent peaks and valleys in geographical survey maps). In all cases, the diagonal (running from top right to bottom left) reproduces an original 1D spectrum of the molecule under investigation. Triangulation using off-diagonal peaks (**red circles**) identifies those on-diagonal peaks (**blue circles**) that are correlated either through-bond for COSY and TOCSY or through-space for NOESY.

during time τ_m and afterwards final coherence is observed and acquired during t_2. As a rule of thumb, the longer is τ_m, the longer the distance of polarisation transfer between spin-coupled nuclei although transfers involving $^4\mathcal{J}$ spin-coupled nuclei usually represent a practical maximum. The main practical difference of polarisation transfer rather than coherence transfer is that many more cross-peaks are generated in the spectral contour map, which allow for the identification of long range as well as short range spin-coupled nuclei by triangulation with the diagonal (Figure 5.13). TOCSY is powerful for the identification of individual spin systems and in a more advanced form is valuable for the identification of homonuclear ^1H–^1H spin systems in biological macromolecules. For instance, each amino-acid residue in a polypeptide represents such an individual homonuclear ^1H–^1H spin system that can be separately identified and resonance assigned (see Section 5.5.1).

5.3.2 Heteronuclear correlation experiments

Heteronuclear correlation experiments obey the same principles as homonuclear correlation experiments but require more complex execution. The problem with any type of heteronuclear NMR experiment is that heteronuclei have different nuclear g-factors, g_I, and as a result have substantially different sensitivities given wide potential variations in spin state energy level populations. This situation arises because values of g_I are directly proportional to the Larmor precession frequency, ν_L (according to Equation (5.9)), and as values of ν_L decline so too does the spin state population imbalance between spin states (according to the Boltzmann Equation (5.13)). In other words, the smaller is g_I, the less is the population difference between spin states and hence the less sensitive is the nucleus concerned. Nevertheless, spin–spin coupling relationships are possible between any number of spin-active nuclei such as ^1H, ^{13}C, ^{15}N, ^{31}P or ^{19}F, making heteronuclear correlation experiments potentially very valuable. The pulse sequence of a 2D **heteronuclear single quantum coherence (HSQC)** correlation experiment is shown to illustrate the additional complexity required in the pulse sequence relative to the pulse sequences of the homonuclear correlation experiments (Figure 5.12). This HSQC correlation experiment requires that there is a preparation period during which nuclei with the highest nuclear g-factor (or γ ratio) are subjected to radio-frequency pulses in order to effect polarisation transfer to spin-coupled **source nuclei** I, with the lower nuclear g-factor (or γ ratio). Thereafter, in time t_1, transverse magnetisation is generated involving nuclei I that evolves with chemical shift. Additional pulse sequences during time τ_m then ensure reverse magnetisation transfer from I to spin-coupled **destination heteronuclei** S, and afterwards final coherence is observed involving nuclei S and acquired during t_2. The HSQC experiment is routinely used to identify heteronuclear $^1\mathcal{J}$ spin–spin coupled nuclei such as ^1H–^{13}C or ^1H–^{15}N pairs, and is the basis of many so-called double-resonance experiments used for the structural determination of proteins and of other biological macromolecules, as we shall see later. A variation on the HSQC experiment is the heteronuclear multiple bond correlation (HMBC) experiment. This is a sensitive technique that may be used to identify heteronuclear $^2\mathcal{J}$ and $^3\mathcal{J}$ spin–spin coupled nuclei.

5.3.3 NOESY experiments

2D NOESY experiments are one further variation on the 2D NMR theme. The general 2D NOESY experiment is illustrated in Figure 5.12. The most important feature of the 2D NOESY experiment is the generation of spectral contour map whose cross-peaks are generated in response to NOEs resulting directly from dipolar coupling-mediated spin–lattice relaxation between nearest neighbour nuclei through space. In this case, a variable length mixing period (denoted τ_m or M_1) is used to allow polarisation transfer to take place under the influence of dipolar coupling. This effect is also known as **cross-relaxation**. Hence, in time t_1 transverse magnetisation is generated that evolves with chemical shift. Cross-relaxation then takes place during time τ_m and afterwards final coherence is observed and acquired as function of time t_2. As indicated, cross-peaks are generated by cross-relaxation in the spectral contour map that allow for the identification of dipolar-coupled nuclei close together in space (<5 Å) by triangulation with the diagonal (Figure 5.13). The value of τ_m appropriate for a given molecule is directly related to its molecular rotation or tumbling rate, which is related in turn to molecular weight. The larger the molecule, the smaller should be the value of τ_m. Both homonuclear and heteronuclear 2D-NOESY experiments are well known. The value of NOESY experiments for determination of quantitative distance information and hence the three-dimensional conformation and structure of biological molecules has already been suggested very strongly. As with correlation experiments, heteronuclear NOEs also exist and are observed by HOESY experiments!

5.4 Multi-dimensional NMR

So now at last we have arrived at the techniques that will underpin the majority of biological NMR spectroscopy and subsequent biological macromolecule three-dimensional structure determination. Key to all techniques are the concepts of polarisation transfer ($M_z(t)$-related longitudinal magnetisation transfers), cross-relaxation (through-space polarisation transfers enabled by through-space dipolar coupling) and coherence transfer ($M_y(t)$-related transverse magnetisation transfers). Clearly, these concepts have all been introduced before, but please try to appreciate doubly the differences between them before advancing further forward into this Main Section!

5.4.1 Basic principles of 3D experiments

Most 3D experiments are heteronuclear experiments and may be regarded as more sophisticated versions of the 2D HSQC correlation experiment (see Section 5.3.2). A representation of the general 3D correlation experiment concept is shown in Figure 5.14. Alternatively this can be expressed as

$$\text{preparation} - t_1 - M_1 - t_2 - M_2 - t_3(\text{acquire})$$

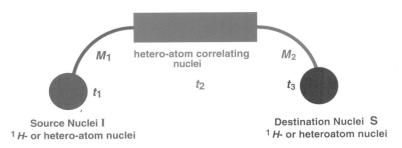

Figure 5.14 Cartoon diagram to represent general structure of 3D correlation experiments. Pulse sequences are employed to generate transverse magnetisation in **Source Nuclei I**, that evolves according to chemical shift in time t_1, prior to magnetisation transfer to correlating nuclei in period M_1. Further pulse sequences promote transverse magnetisation in the correlating nuclei that evolves according to chemical shift in time t_2, prior to final magnetisation transfer to **Destination Nuclei S** in period M_2. Final pulse sequence generates transverse magnetisation in the Destination Nuclei S that is observed, acquired and digitised in time t_3. Fourier series transformation is then used to transform time domain signal information $S_{FID}(t_1, t_2, t_3)$ into frequency domain (spectral intensity) information, $I_{NMR}(F_1, F_2, F_3)$.

where M_1 and M_2 are mixing periods. Fourier series transformation of time domain data $S_{FID}(t_1, t_2, t_3)$ into frequency domain signal intensity data $I_{NMR}(F_1, F_2, F_3)$ results in an extensive array of data from each experiment. The concept may sound simple enough and hopefully so! However, it would be inappropriate to deny the fact that the actual complexity involved in a 3D correlation experiment is a sizeable step up even in comparison with the 2D HSQC correlation experiment (Figure 5.12).

5.4.2 Correlation experiments

By way of example, look at the actual pulse sequence for a 'routine' **3D HNCA correlation experiment** used to probe polypeptide structure (Figure 5.15) (see Section 5.5.1 for further detail). If the pulse sequence looks complex enough, then have a thought for the data presentation and analysis from such an experiment! Such a 3D correlation experiment generates intensity data $I_{NMR}(F_1, F_2, F_3)$ emanating from the **triple resonance** of three entirely different populations of nuclei, in this case ^{15}N, $^{13}C_\alpha$ and ^1H nuclei. In principle, if all the data were to be displayed at once then this would require a four-dimensional means of representation. This is clearly not possible, so data from 3D correlation experiments is normally plotted as a stack or cube of individual 2D correlation experiments. For instance, $I_{NMR}(F_1, F_2, F_3)$ data could be realised as a stack of 2D $I_{NMR}(F_1, F_3)$ contour plots (F_1 and F_3 both in ppm), all corresponding to a different value of F_2 (F_2 also in ppm) (Figure 5.16). Alternatively, $I_{NMR}(F_1, F_2, F_3)$ data could be realised as a stack of 2D $I_{NMR}(F_1, F_2)$ contour plots, all corresponding to a different value of F_3, and so on. There can be substantial flexibility in the presentation of data from 3D correlation experiments depending upon strategy and need. However, the primary need must always be to resolve signals adequately so that any nucleus of interest possesses a unique and unambiguous resonance assignment. In the case of the biomolecular

HNCA Pulse Sequence

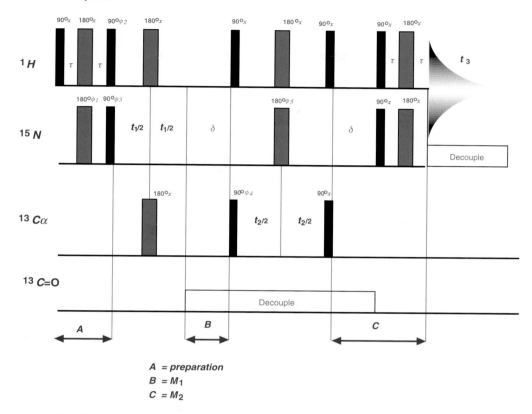

A = preparation
B = M_1
C = M_2

Figure 5.15 Diagrammatic **representation of HNCA FT 3D NMR correlation experiment** involving multiple 90° and 180° pulses with signal observation and acquisition in time domain t_3 prior to fourier series transformation of time domain signal information $S_{FID}(t_1, t_2, t_3)$ into frequency domain (spectral intensity) information, $I_{NMR}(F_1, F_2, F_3)$.

NMR spectroscopy of biological macromolecules, $I_{NMR}(F_1, F_2, F_3)$ data from 3D correlation experiments is normally sufficient to achieve this. For instance, the output of the 3D HNCA correlation experiment should ensure that every ^1HN nucleus in a protein under investigation has a unique and unambiguous resonance assignment defined in the first instance by its ^1H chemical shift but also by the chemical shifts of spin-coupled/correlated $^{13}C_\alpha$ and $H^{15}N$ nuclei. In effect, each ^1HN nucleus is referenced by a completely unique 3D address, ^1HN$(F_{15N}, F_{13C}, F_{1H})$, defined by three resonance frequencies.

5.4.3 Basic principles of 4D experiments

Increasingly, however, as the demands on biomolecular NMR spectroscopy increase, even 3D correlation experiments may not provide sufficient frequency information for any nucleus

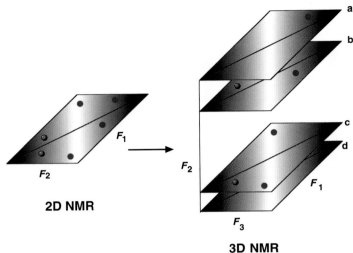

2D NMR

3D NMR

3D cube of F_1-F_3 contour plots

Figure 5.16 Diagrammatic representation of presentation of data from FT 3D NMR correlation experiments. In this representation, frequency domain (spectral) information, I_{NMR} (F_1, F_2, F_3) is plotted as a stack or cube of 2D NMR I_{NMR}(F_1, F_3) contour plots, each plot resolved at a different value of F_2. Frequency resolution is done to aid resolution of individual resonance signals in order to achieve unique and unambiguous assignment of resonance signals to resonating nuclei.

of interest to possess unique and unambiguous resonance characteristics. In this instance, there is an absolute need for more frequency information, hence a 4D correlation experiment is required. In principle this is merely an extension of the 3D principle to involve another resonating population of nuclei and another frequency domain. A representation of the general 4D correlation experiment concept is shown in Figure 5.17. Alternatively this can be

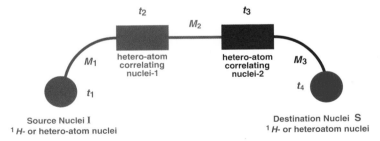

Figure 5.17 Cartoon diagram to represent general structure of 4D correlation experiments. This is the same as for 3D correlation experiments (**Fig. 5.14**) except that an extra resonant population of heteroatom nuclei are involved in generation of transverse magnetisation (in time t_3) and magnetisation transfer (during M_3). Final pulse sequence generates transverse magnetisation in the Destination Nuclei S that is observed, acquired and digitised in time t_4. Fourier series transformation is used to transform time domain signal information S_{FID} (t_1, t_2, t_3, t_4) into frequency domain (spectral intensity) information, I_{NMR}(F_1, F_2, F_3, F_4).

expressed as

$$\text{preparation} - t_1 - M_1 - t_2 - M_2 - t_3 - M_3 - t_4(\text{acquire})$$

where M_1, M_2 and M_3 are mixing periods. Fourier series transformation of time domain data $S_{\text{FID}}(t_1, t_2, t_3, t_4)$ into frequency domain signal intensity data $I_{\text{NMR}}(F_1, F_2, F_3, F_4)$ results in an even larger array of data from each experiment than obtained in the typical 3D experiment. In principle, if all the data were to be displayed at once then this would require a five-dimensional means of representation! Since this is absolutely out of the question, data from 4D correlation experiments is normally plotted as a stack or cube of individual 2D correlation experiments in the same way as data from 3D correlation experiments. The only difference is that there is one more frequency to consider, so for instance $I_{\text{NMR}}(F_1, F_2, F_3, F_4)$ data could be realised as a stack of 2D $I_{\text{NMR}}(F_1, F_4)$ contour plots (F_1 and F_4 both in ppm), all corresponding to different pairs of F_2 and F_3 values (F_2 and F_3 also in ppm) (Figure 5.18). Obviously there are numerous possibilities for plotting the data in other different ways, again depending upon strategy and need. Nevertheless, after data analysis the main result should be that any nucleus of interest is referenced with a 4D address defined by four resonance frequencies, that should in all but a few instances represent a unique and unambiguous resonance assignment. However, where this does not happen there is always the possibility of advancing to 5D correlation experiments!

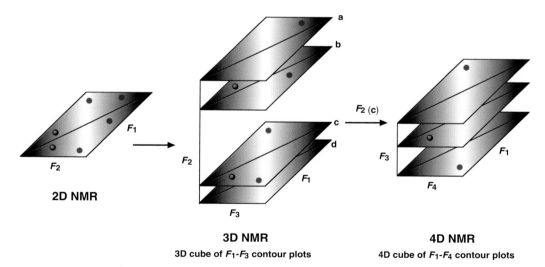

2D NMR

3D NMR
3D cube of F_1-F_3 contour plots

4D NMR
4D cube of F_1-F_4 contour plots

Figure 5.18 Diagrammatic representation of presentation of data from FT 4D NMR correlation experiments. In this representation, frequency domain (spectral) information, $I_{\text{NMR}}(F_1, F_2, F_3, F_4)$ is plotted as a stack or cube of 2D NMR $I_{\text{NMR}}(F_1, F_4)$ contour plots, each plot resolved at a different value of F_2 and also F_3. Double frequency resolution is carried out when single frequency resolution fails to achieve proper signal resolution and/or unique and unambiguous assignment of resonance signals to resonating nuclei.

5.5 Biological macromolecule structural information

Derivation of biological macromolecular structure by NMR spectroscopy involves the application of a variety of multidimensional NMR spectroscopy experiments, many of which are beyond the scope of this chapter. Nevertheless, there are some basic principles and ideas that the chemical biology reader should be aware of, which we shall attempt to cover. These basic principles and ideas pull very heavily on the discussion in Main Sections 5.3 and 5.4 above. In brief, the structural characterisation of a biological macromolecule by NMR spectroscopy draws upon a similar approach in every single case. The key objectives are the following.

(a) Unambiguous assignment of all possible resonance frequency peaks in biomolecular NMR spectra to all possible resonating nuclei; ^1H nuclei assignments are especially important, including the identification of spin systems.

(b) Identification of all possible nearest neighbour ^1H nuclei through space by NOESY experiments; the identification of long distance neighbours with quantitative inter-nuclear distance is most important.

(c) Determination of structure by energy minimisation employing through-space constraints from NOESY experiments (long distance neighbours are essential for accurate energy minimisation) as well as angular constraints from coupling constant values.

Each of these key objectives must be achieved successfully and in sequence, otherwise structure determination will itself be unsuccessful.

5.5.1 Analysing protein structures

1D and 2D NMR spectra of proteins are virtually impossible to interpret and assign. Typically, polypeptides (>5 kDa) have very short T_2 values, resulting in broad, low resolution spectral lines or peaks, respectively (see Equation (5.16)). Furthermore, proteins themselves are biological macromolecular polymers involving amino-acid residue building blocks of broadly similar structure and therefore chemical shift characteristics (see Chapter 1). Consequently, 1D and 2D biological NMR spectra of proteins possess an enormous amount of overlapping chemical shift data emanating from almost identical or closely similar amino-acid residue spin systems. Having said this, for low molecular weight proteins comprising fewer than 50 amino-acid residues a structure may be determined from 2D NMR spectroscopic data alone. However, for proteins of greater molecular weight, extensive signal overlap and low resolution can only be solved with 3D and occasionally 4D correlation experiments.

If we are to take full advantage of 3D and 4D experiments though, molecular biology techniques (Chapter 3) must be used to ensure that the protein of interest is effectively universally labelled with spin-active nuclei, in order to avoid the serious sensitivity problem created by the fact that spin-active nuclei of interest are normally found only in low natural abundance (a few per cent). As a general rule of thumb, where a protein is comprised of between 50

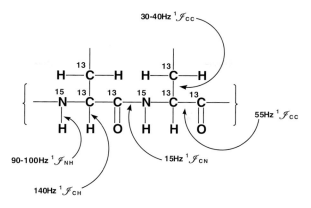

Figure 5.19 Summary of network of large heteronuclear $^1\mathcal{J}$ coupling constants created by universal labelling of protein of interest with ^{13}C- and ^{15}N-nuclei.

and 80 amino-acid residues 3D experiments involving ^{15}N labelling should suffice. Where more than 80 amino-acid residues are involved, combinations of 3D and 4D experiments are essential and require both ^{15}N and ^{13}C labelling. Depending upon the labelling pattern required, universal ^{15}N and/or ^{13}C labelling is accomplished by over-expression of the trans-gene for the protein of interest in a recombinant organism (usually bacteria) that are grown in minimal medium containing $^{15}NH_4^+$ ions and/or $[^{13}C]$-glucose (see Chapter 3). Labelled proteins of interest are then isolated pure for analysis by standard purification protocols (see Chapter 2). Having carefully prepared such a sample, both 3D and 4D versions of COSY, TOCSY and NOESY correlation experiments (3D and 4D correlation experiments) are then made possible by a viable network of large heteronuclear $^1\mathcal{J}$ spin–spin coupling constants. These enable intense homo- and hetero-nuclear coherence and polarisation transfers to take place, not to mention cross-relaxation (polarisation transfer under the influence of dipolar coupling) (Figure 5.19). Usually, the following sequence of operations is carried out.

(a) 3D/4D correlation experiments are performed to obtain the unique and unambiguous resonance assignment of the ^1H nuclei of all the amino-acid residues in the protein of interest (**spin-system analysis**) Protein amino-acid residue spin systems are summarised (Table 5.4). Obviously, with small proteins (<50 amino-acid residues) 2D correlation experiments should suffice for this task.

(b) 3D/4D correlation experiments such as **HNCA, HNCO, HCACO** and **HCA(CO)N** experiments in particular (see below) are performed to determine neighbouring amino-acid residue spin systems and relative connectivities between spin systems. Previous knowledge of the amino-acid residue sequence and the judicious use of the most appropriate correlation experiments are essential in order to match spin systems with actual amino-acid residues in the sequence and also to generate unambiguous resonance assignments of the ^1H and other hetero-atomic nuclei of the peptide links that attach these residues together.

Table 5.4 **Spin System summary** for all main L-α-amino acid residues found in proteins. By convention **X** is the $^{1}HC_{\alpha}$-nucleus of each residue. For each side chain, **A** denotes the ^{1}H-nucleus/nuclei furthest from $^{1}HC_{\alpha}$. Otherwise, letters close to **A** in the alphabet imply that subsequent nucleus/nuclei in the chain are of similar chemical shift characteristics to the **A** nucleus, letters in the middle of the alphabet imply chemical shift characteristics intermediate between **A** and **X** nuclei, letters close to the end of the alphabet imply chemical shift characteristics close to the **X**-nucleus ($^{1}HC_{\alpha}$). The use of the "+" sign indicates separate spin systems.

Common Amino Acid Systems

R	Name	Spin System	R	Name	Spin System
H—	Gly (G)	AX		Tyr (Y)	AMX + AA'XX'
Me—	Ala (A)	A_3X		Ser (S)	AMX
	Val (V)	A_3B_3MX		Thr (T)	A_3MX
	Leu (L)	A_3B_3MPTX		Cys (C)	AMX
	Ile (I)	$A_3MPT(B_3)X$		Asp (D)	AMX
	Phe (F)	AMX + AMM'XX'		Asn (N)	AMX
	Trp (W)	AMX + A(X)MP + A		Glu (E)	AM(PT)X
	Met (M)	AM(PT)X + A_3		Gln (Q)	AM(PT)X
	Pro (P)	$A_2(T)_2MPX$		Lys (K)	$A_2(F_2T_2)MPX$
				Arg (R)	$A_2(T_2)MPX$
				His (H)	AMX + AX

(c) 3D/4D NOESY experiments can also be used to identify neighbouring amino-acid residue spin systems in a polypeptide chain (**short range distance constraint analysis**). However, they are much more critical for the identification of spin systems that are in close spatial proximity to each other in the polypeptide chain, but separated in terms of sequence (**long range distance constraint analysis**). NOESY experiments rely heavily on extensive unambiguous assignments of as many ^1H and other hetero-atomic nuclei in a protein as possible. Therefore, (a) and (b) must be completed as far as possible before (c). Again, for small proteins (<50 amino-acid residues), 2D NOESY experiments should suffice.

(d) Various experiments can be performed to analyse for coupling constants, in particular $^3\mathcal{J}$ ^1H–^1H homonuclear and $^3\mathcal{J}$ ^1H–^{15}N heteronuclear constants that establish amino-acid residue spin-system and backbone conformations (**angular constraint analysis**). These experiments provide supplemental information to experiments described under (c) and contribute towards accurate structure determination at the computational stage (see below).

5.5.1.1   3D COSY and TOCSY experiments on proteins

Multidimensional correlation experiments can be arduous to analyse at the best of times. Therefore, any practitioner of biomolecular NMR spectroscopy will want to do the minimum number of experiments to achieve unique and unambiguous resonance assignment of as many amino-acid residue ^1H nuclei as necessary in order to enable the critical NOESY experiments. Two of the simplest 3D correlation experiments that have been used are **3D ^1H–^{15}N TOCSY-HSQC** and **3D HCCH COSY/TOCSY**. Such 3D correlation experiments are known as **double-resonance** experiments in that they generate intensity data $I(F_1, F_2, F_3)$ emanating from the double resonance of two entirely different populations of nuclei, either ^1H and ^{15}N nuclei, or ^1H and $^{13}C_\alpha$ nuclei respectively.

The workings of the 3D ^1H–^{15}N TOCSY-HSQC experiment are illustrated diagrammatically in Figure 5.20. The pulse sequence is designed to develop transverse magnetisation in aliphatic ^1H nuclei (specifically C_α-^1H atoms) (**source nuclei I**) (F_1) that evolves according to chemical shift. Spin–spin coupling then enables coherence transfer involving both intra- and inter-amino-acid residue $^1H^{15}N$ nuclei. **Heteronuclear multiple and single quantum coherence** (**HMQC/HSQC**) is generated involving ^{15}N nuclei (**correlating heteronuclei**) (F_2) that is subsequently converted back into transverse magnetisation involving $^1H^{15}N$ nuclei. $^1H^{15}N$ magnetisation becomes modulated by the chemical shift of the directly attached ^{15}N nuclei and then final coherence is observed involving $^1H^{15}N$ nuclei (**destination nuclei S**) (F_3). Spectral data is usually displayed in the form of individual ^1H–^1H frequency (F_1 and F_3) contour maps resolved at different ^{15}N frequencies (F_2) (all in ppm) (Figure 5.21). Vertically correlated cross-peaks allow for the assignment of neighbouring amino-acid residue C_α-^1H ($i, i - 1$) and $^1H^{15}N$ (i) resonance signals, as a function of ^{15}N chemical shift.

By comparison, 3D *HCCH* COSY experiments are a little simpler (Figure 5.22). An initial pulse develops transverse magnetisation in aliphatic ^1H nuclei (specifically $^{13}C_\alpha$-^1H atoms) (**source nuclei I**) (F_1) that evolves according to chemical shift before polarisation transfer

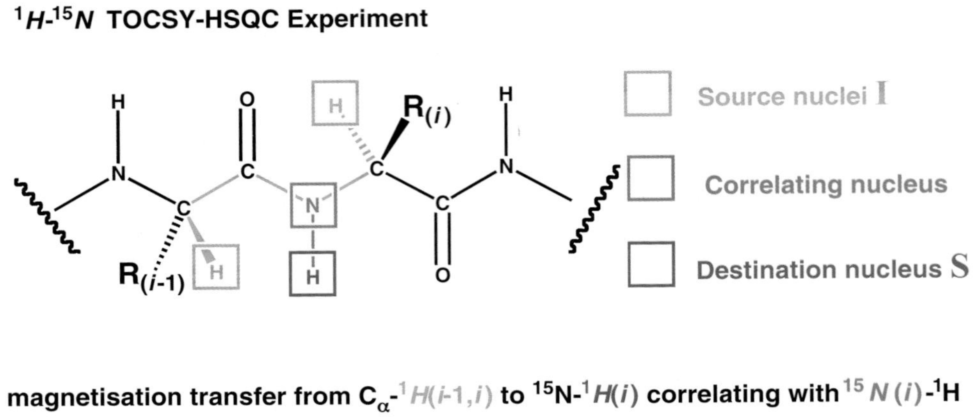

^1H-^{15}N TOCSY-HSQC Experiment

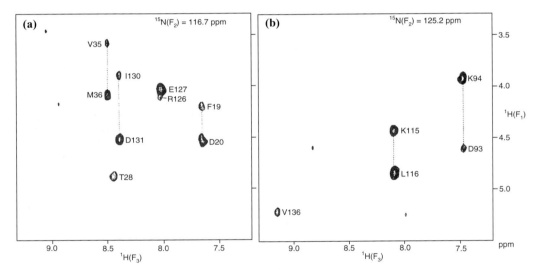

magnetisation transfer from C_α-$^1H(i$-$1,i)$ to ^{15}N-$^1H(i)$ correlating with $^{15}N(i)$-^1H

Figure 5.20   Diagrammatic summary of the 3D ^1H-^{15}N TOCSY-HSQC double resonance experiment. Colour notation is identical with **Fig. 5.14**.

Figure 5.21   Two 2D ^1H-^1H contour maps $[I_{NMR}(F_1, F_3)]$ obtained by a ^1H-^{15}N TOCSY-HSQC double resonance experiment involving the small globular protein calmodulin, where each plot is resolved at different ^{15}N-chemical shifts (F_2). Peaks indicate intra-residue correlations between ^1H-resonance signals at the given ^{15}N-chemical shift (F_2). Peaks aligned along the same verticals also suggest inter-residue correlations at the given ^{15}N-chemical shift (F_2). Hence ^1H-^{15}N TOCSY-HSQC experiments can provide unique and unambiguous resonance assignments plus **vertical** correlations between pairs of source $C_\alpha{}^1H$ nuclei (i-1 and i-residues) (F_1) and neighbouring destination nuclei $^{15}N^1H$ (i-residue) (F_3) (adapted from Kay et al., 1991, Fig. 2).

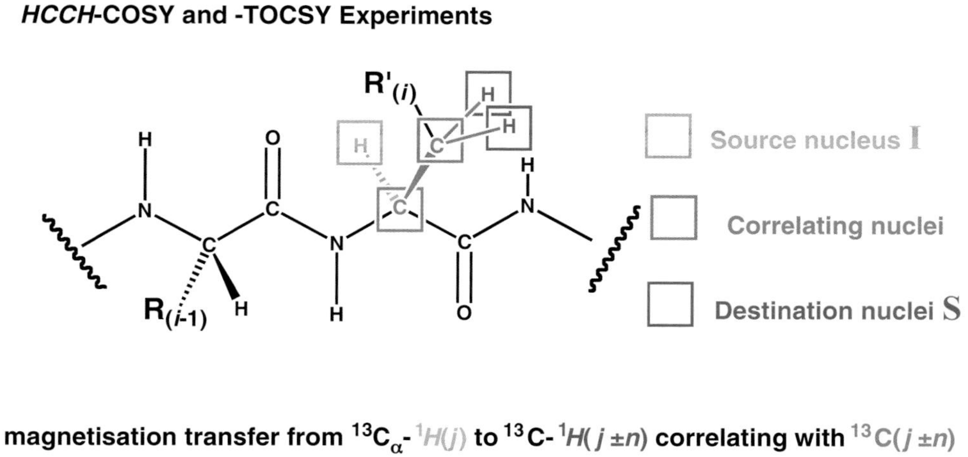

HCCH-COSY and -TOCSY Experiments

magnetisation transfer from $^{13}C_\alpha$-$^1H(j)$ to ^{13}C-$^1H(j \pm n)$ correlating with $^{13}C(j \pm n)$

Figure 5.22 Diagrammatic summary of the 3D *HCCH*-COSY and TOCSY double resonance experiments. Colour notation is identical with **Fig. 5.14**.

is enabled to $^1\mathcal{J}_{CH}$-coupled ^{13}C nuclei. Transverse magnetisation is developed involving these directly $^1\mathcal{J}_{CH}$-coupled ^{13}C nuclei and spin–spin $^1\mathcal{J}_{CC}$ coupling then enables coherence transfer between adjacent ^{13}C nuclei for the development of further transverse magnetisation involving ^{13}C nuclei (all correlating heteronuclei) (F_2). Finally, reverse magnetisation transfer is enabled to aliphatic ^1H nuclei (especially $^1H^{13}C_\beta$ atoms) and final coherence is observed involving $^1H^{13}C$ nuclei (**destination nuclei S**) (F_3). The 3D *HCCH* TOCSY experiment is very similar but pulse sequences are adapted to allow for more extensive magnetisation transfer between $^1\mathcal{J}_{CC}$-coupled ^{13}C nuclei. In both cases, spectral data is displayed in the form of individual ^1H–^1H frequency (F_1 and F_3) contour maps resolved at different ^{13}C frequencies (F_2) (all in ppm) (Figure 5.23). Horizontally correlated cross-peaks allow for the ^1H assignment of amino-acid residue spin systems starting from $^{13}C_\alpha$-^1H resonance signals, as a function of ^{13}C chemical shift.

5.5.1.2   3D HNCA experiment on proteins

The HNCA experiment has been described in detail already and need not be discussed much further here (see Section 5.4.2), except to note that the HNCA experiment is a **triple-resonance** experiment in that it generates intensity data $I_{NMR}(F_1, F_2, F_3)$ emanating from the triple resonance of three entirely different populations of ^{15}N, $^{13}C_\alpha$ and ^1H nuclei. The workings of the 3D HNCA experiment are illustrated diagrammatically in Figure 5.24. Frequently, HNCA spectral data is displayed in the form of individual ^{13}C-, ^1H-frequency (F_2 and F_3) contour maps resolved at different ^{15}N frequencies (F_1) (all in ppm). However, data could equally well be plotted in the form of ^{15}N-, ^1H-frequency (F_1 and F_3) contour maps if this were more helpful for assignment purposes. Usually the HNCA experiment is combined with other 3D correlation experiments with names such as **HNCO**, **HCACO** and

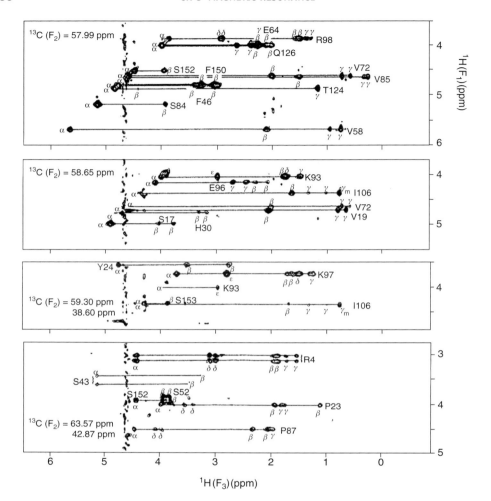

Figure 5.23 Four 2D ^1H-^1H contour maps $[I_{NMR}(F_1, F_3)]$ obtained by a *HCCH*-TOCSY double resonance experiment involving the globular protein interleukin-1β, where each plot is resolved at different ^{13}C-chemical shifts (F_2). Peaks indicate intra-residue correlations between ^1H-resonance signals at the given ^{13}C-chemical shift (F_2). Peaks aligned along the same horizontals also suggest intra-residue side-chain correlations at the given ^{13}C-chemical shift (F_2). Hence *HCCH*-TOCSY experiments provide unique and unambiguous resonance assignments plus **horizontal** correlations between C_α^1H (j) source nuclei (F_1) and neighbouring intra-residue C_β^1H ($j + 1$), C_γ^1H ($j + 2$), C_δ^1H ($j + 3$) up to C_ε^1H ($j + 4$) destination nuclei (F_3) (adapted from Clore et al., 1990, Fig. 7).

HCA(CO)N experiments. These names are deliberately descriptive and should suggest the correlations that these experiments are intended to establish by analogy with the HNCA experiment described here. All these correlation experiments acting in concert are designed to ensure optimal and mostly complete, unique and unambiguous assignments of ^1H-resonance peaks to ^1H nuclei in given protein NMR spectra. This level of information is usually sufficient

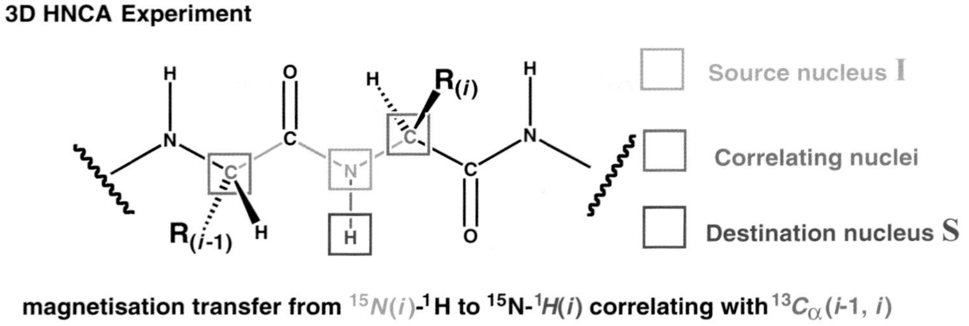

3D HNCA Experiment

magnetisation transfer from $^{15}N(i)$-^{1}H to ^{15}N-$^1H(i)$ correlating with $^{13}C_\alpha(i\text{-}1, i)$

Figure 5.24 Diagrammatic summary of the 3D HNCA triple resonance experiment. Colour notation is identical with **Fig. 5.14**. This triple resonance experiment is usually used to establish intra-residue correlations between $^{13}C_\alpha$, $^{15}N\,^1$H and $^{15}N^1H$ resonance signals in conjunction with ^1H-^{15}N TOCSY-HSQC experiments. The experiment generates unique and unambiguous resonance assignments plus correlations between source $^{15}N\,^1$H nuclei (i-residues) (F_1) and neighbouring correlating $^{13}C_\alpha$ nuclei (i-1 and i-residues) (F_2) or destination $^{15}N\,^1H$ nuclei (i-residues) (F_3). For instance if F_2 and F_3 data are plotted, the output looks like **Fig. 5.21**, with **vertical** correlations between pairs of correlating $^{13}C_\alpha$ nuclei (i-1 and i-residues) (F_2) and neighbouring destination $^{15}N\,^1H$ nuclei (i-residues) (F_3) at given ^{15}N-chemical shifts (F_1).

provided that there are enough assignments to allow for adequate NOE experiments to be conducted.

5.5.1.3   3D and 4D NOESY experiments on proteins

Both 3D and 4D NOESY experiments are the focal objective of protein NMR spectroscopy and play the key role in knitting ^1H-assignment data into a form suitable for calculating protein three-dimensional structure. Protein structures show a wealth of short range NOEs between nearest neighbour amino-acid residues in a polypeptide chain. These short range NOEs can be weak, medium or strong and are highly diagnostic of secondary structure localisation (Figure 5.25). These allow for the determination of the likely secondary structure localisation of each amino-acid residue in a protein. This is obviously an essential prerequisite prior to generating a three-dimensional protein structure from NMR spectral data. Peptide link NH groups are critical in generating all these structure-determining short range NOEs. However, the real bases of three-dimensional protein structure determination are long range NOEs. In this respect, 3D and 4D NOESY experiments are critical.

The **3D HMQC-NOESY-HMQC (HSQC)** experiment together with **4D $^{13}C/^{15}N$-edited NOESY** and $^{13}C/^{13}C$-edited NOESY experiments are primarily used to identify long range NOEs between amino-acid residues. The HMQC-NOESY-HMQC (HSQC) experiment operates in the following way. Pulses develop initial transverse magnetisation involving ^{15}N nuclei (**source nuclei I**) (F_1) followed by the development of heteronuclear multiple and single quantum coherence (HMQC/HSQC) involving $^1H^{15}N$ nuclei. $^1H^{15}N$ magnetisation becomes modulated by the chemical shift of the directly attached ^{15}N nuclei. During the subsequent

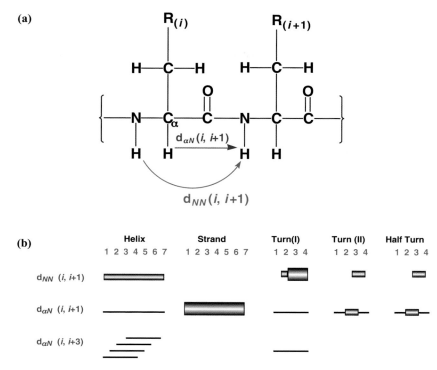

Figure 5.25 Diagrammatic illustration of the two main short range distances over which NOE distances may be seen in an organised polypeptide chain (**a**). Short range NOEs involving NH and C$_\alpha$$H$ protons are classically indicative of secondary structures as illustrated by the different patterns of short range NOEs that are developed by various different secondary structure elements (**b**). NOEs are classified as strong, medium or weak as reflected by the thickness of each band shown.

NOESY mixing period, τ_m, $^1H^{15}N$ magnetisation is transferred by cross-relaxation to immediate spatial $^1H^{15}N$ neighbours and becomes converted into further HMQC/HSQC involving $^1H^{15}N$ nuclei (**correlating nuclei**) (F_2). Final coherence is observed involving $^1H^{15}N$ nuclei (**destination nuclei S**) (F_3) (Figure 5.26). Spectral data may be presented in a number of ways, for instance in the form of individual ^{15}N–^{15}N frequency (F_1 and F_2) contour maps resolved according to different ^1H frequencies (F_3) (Figure 5.27). Each cross-peak identifies with impeccable resolution both short and long range NOEs from spatially close peptide link $^1H^{15}N$ nuclei and $^1H^{15}N$ nuclei that have unique and unambiguous resonance assignments as a result of extensive assignment experiments performed in advance (see 5.5.1.1 and 5.5.1.2).

4D $^{13}C/^{15}N$-edited NOESY and $^{13}C/^{13}C$-edited NOESY experiments are essentially the same except for one main difference. In the case of the 4D $^{13}C/^{15}N$-edited NOESY experiment pulses develop initial transverse magnetisation involving ^{13}C nuclei (**source nuclei I**) (F_1) followed by the development of HMQC/HSQC involving $^1H^{13}C$ nuclei (**correlating nuclei**) (F_2). Thereafter, there is a subsequent NOESY mixing period, τ_m, and $^1H^{13}C$ magnetisation is transferred by cross-relaxation to immediate spatial $^1H^{15}N$ neighbours then develops into

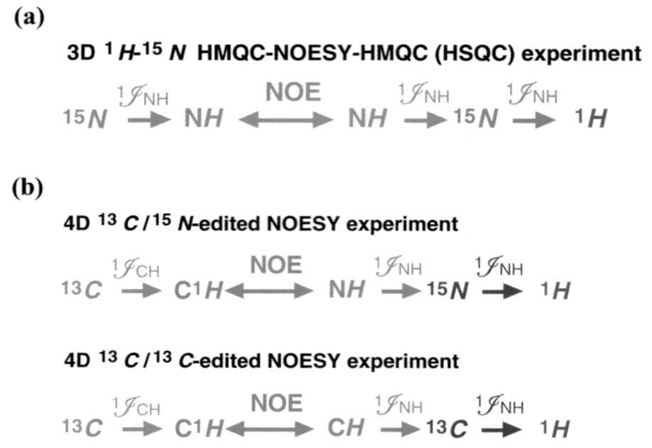

(a)

3D ^1H-^{15}N HMQC-NOESY-HMQC (HSQC) experiment

$$15N \xrightarrow{{}^1\mathscr{J}_{NH}} NH \xleftrightarrow{NOE} NH \xrightarrow{{}^1\mathscr{J}_{NH}} 15N \xrightarrow{{}^1\mathscr{J}_{NH}} 1H$$

(b)

4D ^{13}C/^{15}N-edited NOESY experiment

$$13C \xrightarrow{{}^1\mathscr{J}_{CH}} C1H \xleftrightarrow{NOE} NH \xrightarrow{{}^1\mathscr{J}_{NH}} 15N \xrightarrow{{}^1\mathscr{J}_{NH}} 1H$$

4D ^{13}C/^{13}C-edited NOESY experiment

$$13C \xrightarrow{{}^1\mathscr{J}_{CH}} C1H \xleftrightarrow{NOE} CH \xrightarrow{{}^1\mathscr{J}_{NH}} 13C \xrightarrow{{}^1\mathscr{J}_{NH}} 1H$$

Figure 5.26 Diagrammatic **summary of multidimensional NOESY experiments**. (a) 3D ^1H-^{15}N HMQC-NOESY-HMQC (HSQC) experiment; (b) 4D ^{13}C/^{15}N-edited and ^{13}C/^{13}C-edited NOESY experiments. Colour notation is identical with **Fig. 5.17**.

further HMQC/HSQC involving $^1H^{15}N$ nuclei (**correlating nuclei**) (F_3). Final coherence is observed involving $^1H^{15}$N nuclei (**destination nuclei S**) (F_4) (Figure 5.26). The ^{13}C/^{13}C-edited NOESY experiment is broadly similar to the ^{13}C/^{15}N-edited NOESY experiment except that magnetisation transfer under the influence of cross-relaxation occurs to nearest neighbour $^1H^{13}C$ nuclei instead of $^1H^{15}$N nuclei, so that ^{13}C nuclei also become second correlating nuclei (F_3) and $^1H^{13}C$ nuclei destination nuclei (F_4) (Figure 5.26).

5.5.1.4 Energy minimisations

The more constraints that are available from NMR data, the more accurate the resulting energy minimised structure will be. Both short and long range NOE data are interpolated by energy minimisation calculations as through-space constraints in order to derive a final protein structure. The other main types of constraint in use are angular constraints, deriving from $^3\mathscr{J}^1H$–^1H homonuclear and $^3\mathscr{J}^1H$–^{15}N heteronuclear constant data, and distance constraints that derive from chemical shift data, which demonstrates the existence of hydrogen bonds and residual dipolar coupling. Energy minimisation is beyond the scope of this book (at this stage at least!) so will not be described further except to say that the process can be imprecise and the number of long range distance constraints heavily influences the accuracy of the structural output. In consideration of this, NMR energy minimised structures are usually presented *in toto* in the form of an **ensemble** or **family** of different minimised structures that derive from the same basis set of short and long range NOE data. The average of this family usually compares very closely with the protein structure when available as determined by X-ray crystallography (Figure 5.28). Any major differences between derived structures from the two techniques are generally the result of dynamic regions within a protein structure that are typically 'frozen' in place within a crystal environment.

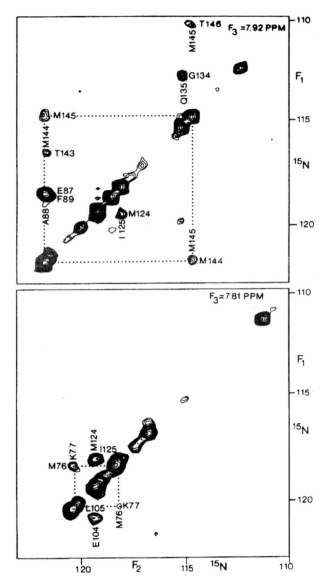

Figure 5.27 Two 2D ^{15}N-^{15}N contour maps [$I_{NMR}(F_1, F_2)$] obtained by a ^1H-^{15}N HMQC-NOESY-HMQC (HSQC) double resonance experiment involving the small globular protein calmodulin, where each plot is resolved at different ^1H-chemical shifts (F_3). Off-diagonal peaks indicate inter-residue through-space correlations between ^{15}N-resonance signals at the given ^1H-chemical shift (F_3). Hence ^1H-^{15}N HMQC-NOESY-HMQC (HSQC) double resonance experiments can provide unique and unambiguous indications of inter-residue proximities by through-space NOE correlations between pairs of ^{15}N ^1H resonance signals. The appearance of symmetrical peaks (see triangulations above) occurs when NOEs are observed between NH systems of amino acid residues with essentially identical chemical shifts to each other (adapted from *J. Am. Chem. Soc.*, 1990, **112**, 9020–9022 Fig. 2).

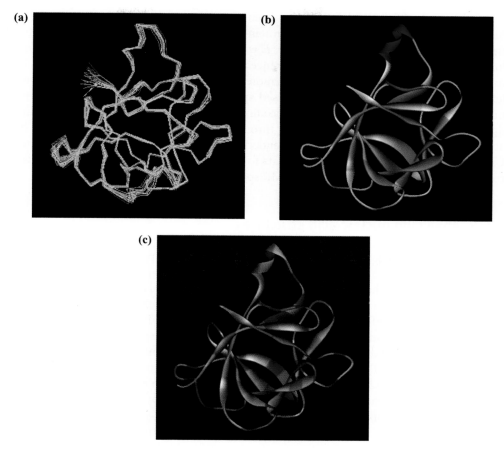

Figure 5.28 NOE distance constraints are used to determine 3D structure of a protein by energy minimisation. (a) Gives a representation of an **ensemble** (family) **of structures** for **Interleukin 1β** produced by energy minimisation with all available NOE distance constraints. The average structure is shown in the form of a **ribbon display structure** (b) (pdb: **7i1b**) which agrees very well with the X-ray crystal structure of the protein (c). The X-ray structure (pdb: **1i1b**) is also illustrated in the form of a **ribbon display structure** but with every different amino acid residue given in a different colour.

5.5.1.5 Techniques for overcoming the molecular weight limit

From Equation (5.16) it should be obvious that there comes a point when a protein becomes sufficiently large that corresponding T_2 values become sufficiently small for the resulting linewidth to become too broad for any structural determination to be possible. No matter how high a magnetic field is used, or how many dimensions of experiments are employed, the broad peaks will simply not resolve. Typically, the rule of thumb is that the upper molecular weight limit for protein structure determination is 30 kDa, above which T_2 values are too small for peak-to-peak resolution owing to excessive spectral line broadening. This molecular weight limit is low and for a long time has been seen to be a major blockage to progress in the biomolecular NMR characterisation of protein structure. However, there is now hope for the future! The partial or full replacement of ^1H with ^2H nuclei has been found to result in both longer T_2 values and a reduction in coherence transfer involving $^{13}C_\alpha$ nuclei. Simpler, easier to interpret, spectra are the result. Furthermore, a new class of experiment has been invented, known as **transverse-relaxation-optimised spectroscopy** (**TROSY**). TROSY experiments involve the suppression of transverse relaxation by interference in the processes of dipole–dipole coupling and spin–spin coupling through **chemical shift anisotropy** (**CSA**), hence artificially increasing T_2 values, thereby rendering previously undetectable peaks observable. Using these new techniques, structural data for even very large proteins (>100 kDa) is now coming within reach of the biological NMR spectroscopist!

5.5.2 Analysing nucleic acid structures

Nucleic acid NMR spectroscopy is less developed than that of proteins, but many synthetic oligodeoxynucleotides and oligonucleotides have been studied in solution as models of single DNA or RNA strands, hairpins, regular short duplexes, triplexes and even quadruplexes, not to mention structures with irregular bends, bulges or other distorted shapes (see Chapter 1). In all these cases, NMR characterisation is aided by the highly regular nature of nucleic secondary structure, and encouraged by the almost complete absence of X-ray crystal structure information involving such structural features. Since there are only five main bases (including uracil) in nucleic acids, then the assignments of ^1H-resonance signals to ^1H nuclei in individual deoxynucleotide or nucleotide residues of a DNA or RNA chain is generally easier to achieve than with proteins. Accordingly, nucleic acid NMR spectroscopy begins with just occasional 2D-TOCSY experiments for the unambiguous assignment of ^1H-resonance signals in residues followed by 2D-NOESY experiments in order to detect a small number of key intra- and inter-residue ^1H–^1H distances (<4.5 Å) that dominate nucleic acid structure (Figure 5.29). Residue connectivities, relative conformations and even three-dimensional DNA or RNA structures can then be determined directly with ease by energy minimisation using this limited basis set of short range NOE data (see 5.5.1.4). If appropriate, 2D-NOESY experiments may also be supplemented by ^{31}P-edited 3D experiments where oligodeoxy- or oligonucleotides over 25 bp are involved, in order to supplement this limited basis set with additional NOE distance constraints. Labelling with ^{15}N-, ^{13-}C- and ^2H nuclei may allow for further multidimensional experiments, which could theoretically allow the size limit to rise to around 120 bp.

5.5.3 Analysing carbohydrate structures

Carbohydrate NMR spectroscopy is much less developed even than nucleic acid NMR spectroscopy. However, assignments of aliphatic ^1H-resonance signals in glycosidic residues are possible using routine 2D-TOCSY and COSY experiments. Hydroxyl ^1H nuclei are then assigned by 1D or 2D-NOESY experiments. Finally, glycosidic residue connectivities and relative conformations may be identified making use of 2D-NOESY experiments to detect a

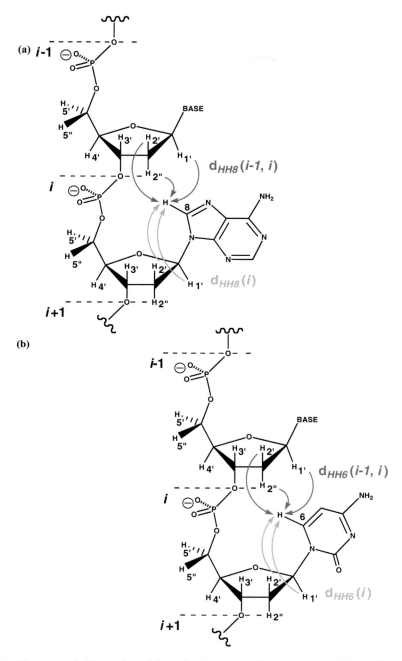

Figure 5.29 Diagrammatic illustration of the main short range distances over which NOE distances may be used to determine structure by NMR in an organised oligodeoxynucleotide (or oligonucleotide) single chain or duplex. Note that there are three main types of d_{HH8} (*i-1*, *i*) (purine) (**a**) or d_{HH6} (*i-1*, *i*) (pyrimidine) (**b**) distances and two main types of d_{HH8} (*i*) (purine) (**a**) or d_{HH6} (*i*) (pyrimidine) (**b**) distances.

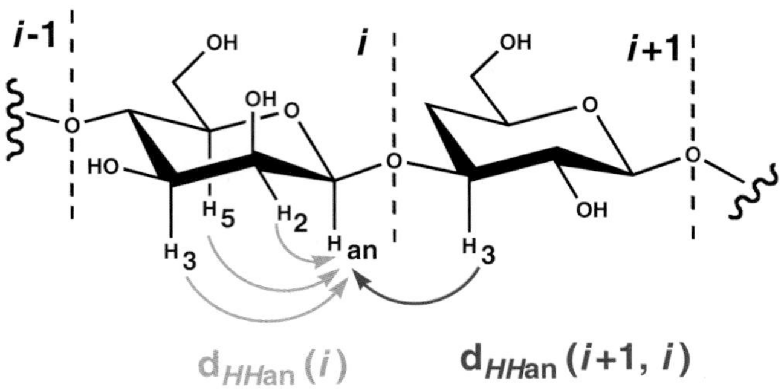

Figure 5.30 Diagrammatic illustration of the main short range distances over which NOE distances may be seen in an organised oligosaccharide chain. Note that there are three main types of d_{HHan} (i) and one main type of d_{HHan} ($i + 1$, i) distance.

select number of intra -and inter-residue $^1H–^1H$ distances emanating from glycosidic linkages which form a selected basis set for structural determination by energy minimisation (Figure 5.30). A primary problem with oligosaccharide NMR spectroscopy is the extensive flexibility and conformational irregularities found in glycosidic linkages. The other problem is that glycosidic residues show only a very narrow chemical shift anisotropy (dispersion) owing to their closely similar chemical structures. Accordingly, carbohydrate NMR spectroscopy requires the use of very high field NMR spectrometers (>600 MHz) so that there are sufficient numbers of data points (in Hz per p.p.m.) (see Equation (5.11)) to resolve glycosidic residue resonance signals adequately in the critical spectral window (δ_H 2–5 p.p.m.).

5.5.4 Analysing lipid assembly structures

Macromolecular lipid assemblies represent a completely different challenge for NMR spectroscopy. In fact, there is a very strong requirement for either 1D ^2H-NMR or ^{31}P-NMR spectroscopy. However, since phospholipids dominate biological macromolecular assemblies, then ^{31}P-NMR spectroscopy is especially ideal given that the spin quantum number I of ^{31}P nuclei is 1/2, and the ^{31}P natural abundance is essentially 100%. Furthermore, the chemical shift anisotropy (dispersion) is relatively large (see Figure 5.7), and $^1H–^{31}P$ $^1\mathcal{J}$ coupling constants are large enough to diagnose structural changes within lipid assemblies (Table 5.2). Different macromolecular lipid assemblies exhibit significant differences in the motions of phospholipids that are mirrored by measurable differences in ^{31}P-NMR spectra. This is especially true for the critical $L_{\alpha,I}–H_{II}$ transition that is characteristic of membrane fusion events.

5.6 EPR spectroscopy; key principles

Electron paramagnetic resonance (EPR) spectroscopy is really in a very primitive state compared with NMR spectroscopy even though the bedrock principles are in fact very similar!

Therefore, biological EPR spectroscopy is much less developed and much less important than biological NMR spectroscopy. Nevertheless, EPR spectroscopy is included in order to complete properly this chapter on magnetic resonance. In the same way as each nucleus of an atom possesses the property of spin, so too does each electron. As a result, each electron too behaves as if it were a precessing, rotating, miniature bar magnet with **angular momentum**, J_e, also represented in the form of a vector whose length reflects magnitude and whose orientation reflects direction of spin. Magnitude is quantised with allowed magnitude defined by a **electron spin quantum number**, I_e, as represented by

$$J_e = [I_e(I_e + 1)]^{1/2}\hbar \tag{5.18}$$

The electron spin quantum number also defines the number of allowed **spin states** that may exist. This number is equivalent to $2I_e + 1$. In the case of the electron, I_e is 1/2 therefore there are only two allowed spin states that are initially degenerate. Since spin angular momentum is quantised in terms of magnitude and orientation according to the electron spin quantum number, I_e, then **z-axis components of angular momentum** J_z^e are similarly quantised. Each allowed z-axis component is represented by an individual **magnetic spin quantum number**, m_s, according to

$$J_z^e = m_s\hbar \tag{5.19}$$

In order to satisfy the requirement that the number of allowed spin states be equivalent to $2I_e + 1$, allowed values of m_s can only be $+1/2$ and $-1/2$. As with nuclei, when an external magnetic field is applied the two electron spin states all orientate with respect to the field (z-axis) either with the field direction ($m_s +1/2$) or against the field direction ($m_s -1/2$) (Figure 5.31). In the process, spin state degeneracy is lifted. By convention, the first state is known as the α **state** and the second as the β **state**.

The inherent magnetic field strength associated with any given electron spin state is represented by a **electron magnetic moment**, μ_z^e, that is proportional to J_z^e according to

$$\mu_z^e = \gamma_e m_s\hbar \tag{5.20}$$

where γ_e is known as the **electron magnetogyric ratio**, which in turn is defined by

$$\gamma_e = -\frac{g_e\mu_B}{\hbar} \tag{5.21}$$

in which g_e is known as the g **factor** and μ_B the **Bohr magneton**. The electron magnetogyric ratio differs from the nuclear equivalent (Equation (5.4)) on the basis that nucleus and electron are oppositely charged and hence the electron bar magnet points in the reverse direction to that of a nucleus, thereby reversing the direction of the electron magnetic moment with respect to nuclear magnetic moment (see Figure 5.2). The Bohr magneton is

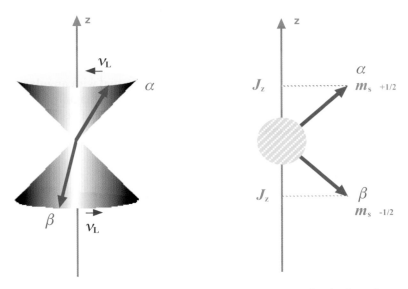

Figure 5.31   Depictions of the two different allowed spin states of spinning electron (I_e 1/2). Reference z-axis is supplied by **external magnetic field** and angular momentum vectors (and precessional cones) align with ($m_s + 1/2$; α-state) or against ($m_s - 1/2$; β-state) the field direction. **Degeneracy** between the two allowed spin states is **lifted** by interaction between intrinsic magnetic fields of these spin states and the external field. The β-state is more stable than the α-state for a spinning electron since γ_e is negative.

further defined by

$$\mu_B = \frac{e\hbar}{2m_e} \tag{5.22}$$

where m_e is the **mass of an electron**. Substitution of Equation (5.21) into (5.20) gives

$$\mu_z^e = -m_s g_e \mu_B \tag{5.23}$$

5.6.1 Quantum mechanical description of EPR

The energy differences between different spin states are created by the differential way in which the magnetic moments of given spin states interact with the applied magnetic field, B_z. The **interaction energy** attributable to either spin state E_{m_s} is defined by the product

$$E_{m_s} = -\mu_z^e B_z \tag{5.24}$$

In comparison with most nuclei, the g-factor is positive but the ratio γ_e is negative. Hence the magnetic moment μ_z^e is positive for the β state and negative for the α state according to

Equation (5.23). Consequently, the β state becomes more stable than the α state by interaction with the applied magnetic field, according to Equation (5.24). The **energy difference**, ΔE, between the α and β states is given by

$$\Delta E = E^{\alpha}_{1/2} - E^{\beta}_{-1/2} = g_e \mu_B B_z \tag{5.25}$$

Clearly this situation (Figure 5.31) is opposite to the situation found with the ^1H nucleus for instance. Hence the resonance condition for EPR spectroscopy is given by

$$\Delta E = h\nu_L = g_e \mu_B B_z \tag{5.26}$$

where the Larmor frequency, ν_L, now lies in the microwave frequency range, typically 10 GHz (wavelength 3 cm) at a magnetic field of approximately 0.3 T.

5.6.2 g-value

In contrast with NMR spectroscopy, EPR spectroscopy is limited to systems in which there is an unpaired electron such as organic radicals or transition metals. Otherwise, the technique is spectroscopically silent. Typically in an NMR experiment, magnetic field is kept constant and frequency is varied. In EPR spectroscopy, frequency is kept constant and field is varied instead. Consequently, differences in spin state energies and hence resonance condition due to electron position and environment cannot be diagnosed by NMR style chemical shift since this is a frequency-based concept. Instead, an alternative concept needs to be originated, which is the concept of the **g-value**.

Variations in g-values arise because the strength of the effective external magnetic field experienced by any electron in a molecular structure appears to vary in response to local movements in neighbouring electron density. In other words, local electronic effects have direct and reproducible effects on ν_L values. Electronic effects are both shielding and deshielding in character, as with NMR. The effective external magnetic field experienced by any such electron is then modulated according to

$$B_{eff,z} = B_z(1 - \sigma_e) \tag{5.27}$$

where $B_{eff,z}$ is the effective field experienced by the electron and shielding is characterised by the **electron shielding parameter**, σ_e. However, since B_z is undergoing a continuous field sweep in EPR spectroscopy, when Equation (5.27) is combined with (5.26) to give the resonance condition revised to take account of shielding and deshielding the result is

$$\Delta E = h\nu_L = g_e(1 - \sigma_e)\mu_B B_z \tag{5.28}$$

where the term is $g_e(1 - \sigma_e)$ is known as the **g-value**. This is very much the EPR equivalent of chemical shift.

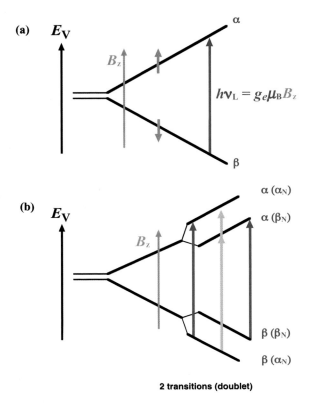

Figure 5.32 Lifting the degeneracy between the two allowed spin states of the spinning electron (I_e 1/2), by application of an external magnetic field, B_z. (a) Two spin states are illustrated by arrows (orange) aligned against (β-**state**) or with (α-**state**) the field direction. A vertical spin state transition is shown (red arrow) along with the resonance condition for inter-conversion of β- to α-state; (b) **formation of spin microstates in response to spin-spin coupling of electron with one neighbouring spinning nucleus (N)** of I 1/2 (*e.g.*, ^1H-nucleus). Two new spin microstates are formed from each main spin state. Nuclear spin must be unchanged during electron spin state transitions hence two spin state transitions are allowed (red arrows) and two transitions disallowed (grey arrows). Note that microstates with antiparallel spins are the more stable. Both diagrams have been drawn assuming constant frequency irradiation and variable strength external magnetic field, B_z. Note that the opposite is true in the case of NMR spectroscopy (**Fig. 5.8**).

5.6.3 Hyperfine splitting

Not only shielding and deshielding but also spin–spin coupling contributes to modulating and perturbing the energies of electron spin states. In the case of EPR, the dominant effect is electron–nucleus spin–spin coupling. This results in **hyperfine splitting** of the EPR signal of interest. There is a general rule that for each spin state of a given resonating electron the number of spin-coupled microstates that result from spin–spin coupling with n identical neighbouring nuclei is 2^n. However, the number of resonance frequency lines that result from coupling with n identical neighbouring nuclei is only $2nI + 1$, where I is the spin quantum number of the neighbouring nuclei, owing to the selection rules, which ensure that there can be no change in coupled nuclear spin state during an electron spin state transition. So for instance, if a resonating electron is coupled with one neighbouring nucleus ($I = 1/2$) then although there are four spin-coupled microstates in total only two resonance frequency lines will result (doublet) (Figure 5.32). Similarly, if two identical neighbouring nuclei ($I = 1/2$) are involved then three resonance frequency lines will result (triplet); if four identical neighbouring nuclei ($I = 1/2$) are involved then five resonance frequency lines will result (quintet) *et cetera*. In EPR, the difference between resonance frequency lines is measured in terms of the **hyperfine coupling constant** (in units of mT). The hyperfine coupling constant is the EPR equivalent of the NMR coupling constant (in units of Hz). The difference in units reflects the fact that in EPR spectroscopy frequency is kept constant and field is varied instead, whilst the reverse is true in a typical NMR experiment.

5.6.4 Biological macromolecule structural information by EPR

In spite of the close theoretical relationship between EPR and NMR spectroscopy, EPR has only very narrow applications. The primary reason for this is that the EPR phenomenon is spectroscopically silent unless there are unpaired electrons. Most biological macromolecules are closed shell molecules and contain no unpaired electrons. Therefore, EPR is of little real value for biological macromolecular structure characterisation. The only exception to this rule is that certain prosthetic groups in proteins may contain redox active metal centres/clusters that have transient or even permanent unpaired electrons (see Chapter 4). These metal centres/clusters can be studied by EPR spectroscopy in order to demonstrate the presence of unpaired electrons. Thereafter, EPR data may then be used to derive the relative structural arrangements of metals within centres or clusters, and to assign putative distributions of redox states should there be any obvious redox heterogeneity. EPR is also useful to detect transient or even metastable radical formation during biocatalysis (see Chapter 8).

6
Diffraction and Microscopy

6.1 Diffraction and microscopy in chemical biology

This chapter is devoted to the contribution that diffraction and microscopy make in deriving and understanding the structures of biological macromolecules. Without doubt, X-ray crystallography is the pre-eminent technique for the structural characterisation of biological macromolecular structure and has been responsible for the derivation of more atomic-level structures of biological macromolecules than all other techniques put together. Hence, X-ray crystallography appears first in this chapter. Thereafter, the attention of the chemical biology reader will be drawn towards electron microscopy and then scanning-probe microscopy. Of these, the technique of cryo-electron microscopy has a realistic potential and capacity to rival X-ray crystallography as the pre-eminent technique for the characterisation of biological macromolecular structures. Scanning probe microscopy is in some ways less developed but shows an impressive diversity in the size and morphology of three-dimensional biological macromolecular structures that may be studied under a variety of conditions. This chapter is intended to provide an explanation of the main theories and ideas that underpin the use of diffraction and microscopy in chemical biology research, then thereafter to provide a bridge from these main theories and ideas to actual examples of successful three-dimensional structure characterisation. In Chapter 5, we illustrated the concepts of multi-dimensional NMR spectroscopy with reference to data derived from the structural characterisation of one main protein, interleukin-1β (IL-1β), a key biological messenger of inflammation (see also Chapter 7). In this chapter, illustrations for successful structural characterisations are taken from the fascinating world of heat shock/stress protein research (see also Chapter 7). There is nothing overstated in saying that much of our current understanding of the molecular workings of biology derives from successful structural characterisations made possible by diffraction and/or microscopy. Therefore, read on!

Essentials of Chemical Biology   Andrew Miller and Julian Tanner
© 2008 John Wiley & Sons, Ltd

6.2 Key principles of X-ray diffraction

When an intense beam of X-rays is directed at a crystal, the result is a dispersal of the beam known as **X-ray diffraction**. If the crystal is sufficiently ordered, then a regular pattern of dispersal or scattering will be generated, known as a **diffraction pattern**. The task now solved of then relating this diffraction pattern back to molecular structure within the crystal has been one of enormous complexity! However, nowadays, provided that biological macromolecules of interest are able to form ordered crystals that diffract X-rays in an ordered and reproducible manner, diffraction patterns of even the most fearsome complexity may be analysed to give accurate predictions of underlying molecular structure in the crystal environment. As a result, **X-ray crystal diffraction** or **X-ray crystallography** has become arguably the most powerful technique available to the chemical biologist for the determination of biological macromolecular structure. Ever more complex structures are being determined, analysed and used to make substantive conclusions about molecular mechanisms in biology. For this reason, it is essential for the chemical biology reader to have a reasonable grasp of the basic principles involved in X-ray crystallography, if for nothing else than to appreciate the advantages and limitations of a technique that has been and remains so pervasive and influential in defining our understanding of biology at a molecular level.

6.2.1 Unit cell

A **crystal** can be described as a three-dimensional periodic arrangement of molecules or a three-dimensional stack of **unit cells** whose edges and vertices form a grid or **direct lattice**. The unit cell is known as the smallest possible unit that maps out the actual crystal structure if translated in any direction, so completely reproducing the three-dimensional environment of electron density present in the crystal structure. The typical unit cell is defined in terms of three dimensions a, b and c together with three inter-dimensional angles α, β and γ (Figure 6.1).

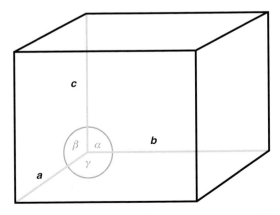

Figure 6.1   Unit Cell: The smallest possible unit which maps out actual crystal reproducing the complete 3D environment of electron density.

These dimensions and angles are important unit cell characteristics that define the seven main **crystal systems**, known as **triclinic**, **monoclinic**, **orthorhombic**, **rhombohedral**, **tetragonal**, **hexagonal** and **cubic**. The unit cell should be thought of as the minimum unit that encapsulates all the main features of the crystal. Accordingly, an X-ray diffraction pattern can be thought of as the result of crystal scattering from a single unit cell. In other words, an X-ray diffraction pattern correlates directly with unit cell electron-density. Just how this takes place will be explained!

6.2.2 Bragg law

The earliest approach to understanding the origins of diffraction patterns was to regard a unit cell as being bisected by stacks of parallel lattice planes defined according to the **Miller indices**, integers h, k and l. Integer h represents the number of parallel lattice planes of a given stack that bisect dimension a in moving from the unit cell origin to the fullest extent of a, k the number of planes of a given stack that cut dimension b in moving from the unit cell origin to the fullest extent of b and l the number of planes of a given stack that cut dimension c in moving from the unit cell origin to the fullest extent of c. Three different sets of hkl-lattice planes are shown to illustrate this point (Figure 6.2). In classical diffraction theory, each lattice plane of a given stack behaves as a mirror that is capable of 'reflecting' X-rays. Assuming that the hkl-lattice planes of a given stack are also a fixed distance apart, d_{hkl}, then wave reflection from this stack will be accompanied by **constructive interference** provided that Equation (6.1) is completely obeyed (Figure 6.3):

$$\lambda = 2d_{hkl}\sin\theta \qquad (6.1)$$

where θ is the **glancing angle** and λ the wavelength of the incident X-ray beam. Equation (6.1) is known as the **Bragg law**. If Equation (6.1) cannot be obeyed then **destructive interference** will result. Only reflections accompanied by constructive interference would be expected to be visible, giving rise to a regular pattern of X-ray dispersal in three-dimensional space that satisfies the Bragg law. This is one of the great fundamental concepts of diffraction. Clearly, unless d_{hkl} distances are uniform, constructive interference will be impossible and no diffraction pattern will be observed. This underlines the importance of well ordered crystals and hence unit cells to derive reproducible diffraction patterns of X-ray dispersal or scattering. Curiously, this classical concept has withstood the development of quantum theories and underpins much of our appreciation of X-ray crystal diffraction even today.

6.2.3 Reciprocal lattice

If an X-ray beam could be reflected from every possible stack of hkl-lattice planes that bisect the unit cell such that every reflection satisfied the Bragg law, then the total ordered pattern of X-ray scattering would represent the complete diffraction pattern. In reality, this is not possible to achieve without rotating the crystal in the path of the X-ray beam and/or using a

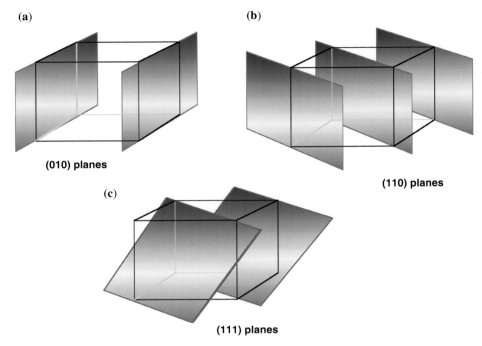

(a)

(010) planes

(b)

(110) planes

(c)

(111) planes

Figure 6.2 *hkl-planes*: Three illustrative sets of atomic planes that bisect the unit cell and from which an incident X-ray beam is said to be reflected giving rise to X-ray scattering or diffraction in three-dimensional space. The (**010**) **planes** (**a**) are only bisected by movement in the *b* axis direction; the (**110**) **planes** (**b**) are bisected by movement in the *a* and *b* axis directions; (**111**) **planes** (**c**) are bisected by movement in all three axis directions.

range of X-ray wavelengths (see Section 6.3.2). A visual/mathematical depiction of complete Bragg law reflection from stacks of *hkl*-lattice planes is the **reciprocal lattice**. The reciprocal lattice has imaginary dimensions a^*, b^* and c^* that are inversions of the *a*, *b* and *c* dimensions of the unit cell. Each reciprocal lattice point corresponds to an *hkl* reflection that satisfies the Bragg law from a given stack of *hkl*-lattice planes that bisect the unit cell. *In effect, a given reciprocal lattice represents a complete theoretical diffraction pattern.*

The **Ewald sphere** was developed as a tool to construct the directions of X-ray scattering. However, it also serves as a means to determine how to sample the vast majority of reciprocal lattice points, or in other words sample the intensity of X-rays scattered by reflection from every possible stack of *hkl*-lattice planes. In order to construct an Ewald sphere, an incident beam of X-rays is considered as being directed towards the origin O of the reciprocal lattice. A sphere is then constructed that cuts the origin O on its surface but whose centre M marks the position of the crystal. The radius MO is $1/\lambda$, where λ is the wavelength of incident X-rays (Figure 6.4). Only reciprocal lattice points that sit on the surface of the sphere correspond to X-ray reflections that may be detected given the orientation of the crystal with respect to the incident X-ray beam and the wavelength of the incident X-rays. If the orientation of

(a)

(b)

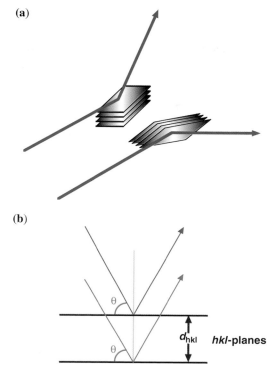

Figure 6.3 Braggs Law: Only reflections (**a**) that obey Bragg's law (**b**) give rise to observed X-ray scattering or diffraction. Hence X-ray scattering is "quantised" in three-dimensional space according to Bragg's law condition.

the crystal changes so does the relative orientation of the reciprocal lattice, allowing other reciprocal lattice points to sit on the surface of the sphere. There is a similar consequence if the X-ray wavelength is varied instead. Hence, the Ewald sphere shows how by varying these two parameters systematically the vast majority of reciprocal lattice points may be sampled and the intensity of the majority of scattered X-ray beams measured.

6.2.4 Structure factors

Another view of X-ray diffraction has grown out of the Bragg law, and this is the consideration of the diffraction phenomenon in terms of vectors. This consideration has led to the following equation, which encapsulates the entire relationship between unit cell electron density and the X-ray diffraction pattern:

$$\rho(xyz) = \frac{1}{V_{cell}} \sum_h \sum_k \sum_l F(hkl) \exp[-2\pi i(hx + ky + lz)] \qquad (6.2)$$

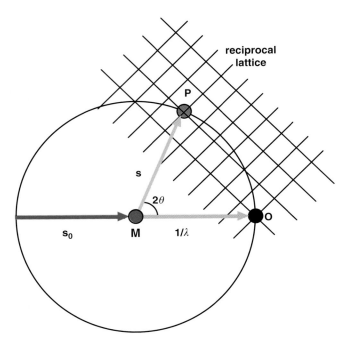

Figure 6.4 Ewald Sphere: Construction that demonstrates how the complete X-ray scattering pattern (all vertices of **reciprocal lattice**) can be visualised by adjusting i) the wavelength (λ) of X-ray beam **s₀** incident upon a crystal mounted at position **M**; ii) the orientation of the crystal relative to beam **s₀**. Each vertex of the reciprocal lattice corresponds with a different **hkl**-reflection. A given **hkl**-reflection may be visualised only when scattered beam **s** cuts the surface of the Ewald sphere at a position **P** coincident with a corresponding reciprocal lattice vertex. In principle, λ and crystal orientation at **M** may be adjusted to visualise the vast majority of vertices of a reciprocal lattice and hence the vast majority if not all of the **hkl**-reflections possible from a given mounted crystal (**Laue Condition**).

where V_{cell} is the **unit cell volume** and $\rho(xyz)$ the **electron density distribution** and $F(hkl)$ is known as the **unit cell structure factor** corresponding to X-ray scattering **from a given stack of parallel hkl-lattice planes**. Each individual unit cell structure factor is a complex number; they collectively represent the ability of any given unit cell to generate X-ray scattering from the complete stack of parallel *hkl*-lattice planes. More generally, the complete set of $F(hkl)$ structure factors represents the ability of the electron density in any given unit cell to interact with and scatter glancing X-ray beams. According to Equation (6.2), the sum over all $F(hkl)$ structure factors is related directly to $\rho(xyz)$ by Fourier series transformation. Hence, if sufficient $F(hkl)$ structure factors can be solved from X-ray diffraction data, then $\rho(xyz)$ can be computed and the crystal structure of the biological macromolecule of interest solved. However, this is not as easy as it sounds!

Any complex number, F, can be represented in a complex plane diagram, as illustrated (Figure 6.5), and so takes on the appearance of a vector with the twin properties of magnitude and direction. Magnitude is defined by the length, $|F|$, and direction by the angle, α, subtended

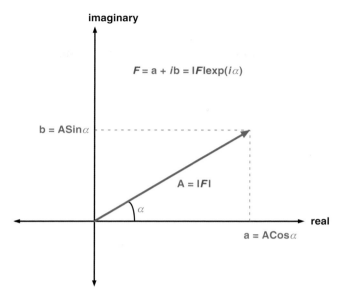

Figure 6.5 Complex plane diagram: Illustration of the two main forms of a complex number **F** and their rendering on a complex plane diagram.

with the real axis. Magnitude $|F|$ is a real number and is known generally as the **modulus** of the complex number. Angle α is known as the **phase** of the complex number. All terms are related to each other according to the following equation:

$$F = |F|\exp[i\alpha] \tag{6.3}$$

Equation (6.2) may now be expanded to the full form as represented by

$$\rho(xyz) = \frac{1}{V_{\text{cell}}} \sum_h \sum_k \sum_l |F(hkl)| \exp[-2\pi i(hx + ky + lz) + i\alpha(hkl)] \tag{6.4}$$

where $|F(hkl)|$ is the **modulus of the structure factor** corresponding to X-ray scattering from a given stack of parallel *hkl*-lattice planes, and $\alpha(hkl)$ is the **phase of the structure factor** corresponding to X-ray scattering from that same stack of parallel *hkl*-lattice planes. Equation (6.4) can be reduced by complex number manipulation to give the 'real' expression

$$\rho(xyz) = \frac{1}{V_{\text{cell}}} \sum_h \sum_k \sum_l |F(hkl)|\cos[2\pi(hx + ky + lz) - \alpha(hkl)] \tag{6.5}$$

6.2.5 The phase problem

An X-ray diffraction pattern can be defined (from Sections 6.2.2 and 6.2.3) as a regular pattern of X-ray dispersal in three-dimensional space that satisfies the Bragg law (**Laue condition**), wherein each unique direction of scatter corresponds to 'reflection' from one unique stack of parallel *hkl*-lattice planes that bisect the unit cell. The discussion in Section 6.2.3 illustrates the possibility of using an Ewald sphere construction to ensure the observation of the maximum number of reflections by varying a few simple parameters. The problem of relating an observed X-ray diffraction pattern to unit cell electron density now rests with the relationship between actual diffraction data and those X-ray parameters and variables that comprise the right-hand side of Expression (6.5). On the one hand, the relationship is surprisingly simple. The intensity of scatter, $I(hkl)$, from a given stack of parallel *hkl*-lattice planes, turns out to be equivalent to $|F(hkl)|^2$, the square of the modulus of the structure factor corresponding to X-ray scattering from that same stack of lattice planes. Fortunately, values of $I(hkl)$ can be measured experimentally with relative ease (see Main Section 6.3), allowing corresponding values of $|F(hkl)|$ to be determined with relative ease too. Unfortunately, no such easy correlation exists between X-ray scattering data and corresponding values of $\alpha(hkl)$ phases. Indeed, this lack of an easy correlation held up the determination of three-dimensional structures of biological macromolecules by X-ray crystallography for several decades until this **phase problem** could be solved. Amazingly, the phase problem now appears in retrospect to be one of the greatest problems for physics and chemistry that was solved during the last century!

The idea of a vector triangle provided the eventual solution to the phase problem. Three associated vectors with appropriately linked properties should be able to form a triangle in vector space (Figure 6.6). Given the fact that each $F(hkl)$ structure factor, corresponding to a given set of *hkl*-lattice planes, is also a vector in the complex plane, then the idea was

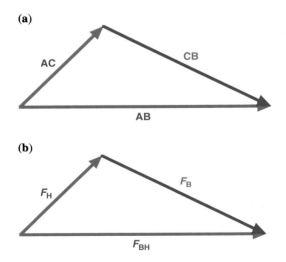

Figure 6.6 **Vector triangle:** Vector summation appears equivalent in real (**a**) or complex (**b**) planes.

advanced that solutions of $F(hkl)$ could be found provided that similar structure-factor-based vector triangle diagrams could be similarly constructed. But how? The most popular approach has been to use the experimental technique of **isomorphous replacement**. The experimental requirements for this will be discussed in Main Section 6.3, so here we only need define isomorphous replacement as the creation of 'heavy atom' derivatives of the biological macromolecule crystal of interest. For the method of isomorphous replacement to work, these heavy atom crystals should be essentially identical with the original biological macromolecule crystal except for the inclusion of heavy atoms (e.g. mercury, Hg; arsenic, As) at reproducibly defined locations within the crystal unit cell.

The heavy atom crystal can generate an X-ray diffraction pattern by X-ray scattering in the same way as the original biological macromolecule crystal. However, this diffraction pattern is dominated by X-ray scattering from the included heavy atoms; heavy atoms are very intense scattering centres because they are also centres of high electron density. Intensity differences between the heavy atom crystal diffraction pattern and that of the original biological macromolecule crystal will be entirely due to the heavy atom scattering provided that the structure of the biological macromolecule and unit cell parameters are essentially unperturbed by the presence of the heavy atom. Hence, the difference between heavy atom and biological macromolecule crystal diffraction patterns represents a new heavy atom diffraction pattern. Accordingly, we can define three discrete sets of interlinked structure factors for three inter-linked diffraction patterns. If $F_B(hkl)$ represents the structure factor corresponding to each set of hkl-lattice planes in the biological macromolecule crystal, then $F_{BH}(hkl)$ represents the same for the heavy atom crystal and $F_H(hkl)$ the same for the heavy atoms alone. The vector triangle relationship between these structure factor terms is illustrated (Figure 6). It turns out that provided one of these vectors can be solved completely, the other two may also be solved, including a complete determination of all the $\alpha_B(hkl)$ phase angles for the original biological macromolecule crystal!

In practice, only $F_H(hkl)$ can be solved completely beginning with a **Patterson function**, $P(uvw)$, that is almost identical in form to Equation (6.5) but for the absence of phase angles (angles are all set to zero) and the involvement of an $|F_H(hkl)|^2$ term, as shown in the following equation:

$$P(uvw) = \frac{1}{V_{cell}} \sum_h \sum_k \sum_l |F_H(hkl)|^2 \cos[2\pi(hu + kv + lw)] \tag{6.6}$$

where u, v and w are relative coordinates in the unit cell. To all intents and purposes u, v and w coordinates should be regarded as being equivalent to the x, y and z coordinates that reference electron density distribution within the unit cell. The Patterson function transforms heavy atom diffraction pattern intensity data into a **Patterson map** that is used to identify the relative positions of all heavy atoms in the unit cell of a given heavy atom crystal. Relative u, v and w coordinates are then transposed into x, y and z coordinates giving a full positional atomic assignment of heavy metal atoms in the unit cell of a heavy atom crystal. Patterson maps will only give positional assignments for very simple systems involving a limited number of atoms and certainly not for complex biological macromolecules! Therefore, there is almost no alternative to the heavy atom approach. However, armed with heavy atom x, y and z

coordinates a complete solution to $F_H(hkl)$ may then be derived, including the $\alpha_H(hkl)$ phase angles! Exactly how this solution is obtained is beyond the scope of this chapter. However, it is enough to know that a complete solution to $F_H(hkl)$ is usually sufficient to solve $F_B(hkl)$ for the original biological macromolecule crystal using the vector triangle associations described in this section and the following vector construction technique.

6.2.6 Harker construction

After isomorphous replacement, the full complement of X-ray diffraction data should include a complete solution to $F_H(hkl)$ and values of $|F_{BH}(hkl)|$ and $|F_B(hkl)|$ from diffraction pattern intensity data. This data may then be analysed with a **Harker construction** (Figure 6.7). For measured diffraction involving each set of hkl-lattice planes in the biological macromolecule crystal, a circle of radius $|F_{BH}(hkl)|$ can be drawn centred upon the origin of a complex plane diagram and then $F_H(hkl)$ is drawn from this origin. Next a second circle of radius $|F_B(hkl)|$ is drawn centred at the end of the $F_H(hkl)$ vector. The two intersection points of the two circles mark the two possible orientations of $F_{BH}(hkl)$ and $F_B(hkl)$ vectors that correctly satisfy the vector triangle relationship that should exist between all three vectors

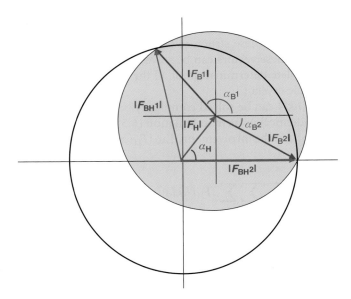

Figure 6.7   Harker Construction: Solution of the X-ray crystallographic phase problem for each *hkl*-reflection by **Harker construction**. Heavy atom structure factor $F_H(hkl)$ is completely solved by **Patterson Function** and plotted on complex plane (white) along with known modulus $|F_{BH}(hkl)|$. The second known modulus $|F_B(hkl)|$ is then included on a second complex plane yellow. Intersection points characterise the two possible solutions for $F_B(hkl)$ and two possible solutions for $\alpha_B(hkl)$ ($\alpha_\beta{}^1$ or $\alpha_\beta{}^2$), one of which is usually eliminated by inspection or with the aid of a second heavy atom derivative.

(Figure 6.6). These two possible orientations simultaneously identify two possible but equally probable $\alpha_B(hkl)$ phase angles, both of which correctly allow the correct vector triangle relationship. With a second heavy atom derivative, the two alternatives may be distinguished easily, although poor isomorphism between the biological macromolecule and heavy atom crystal may mean that additional heavy atom crystals should be prepared for X-ray diffraction studies in order to remove any chance of ambiguity in phase angle assignments. For this reason, isomorphous replacement may become **multiple isomorphous replacement (MIR)**, occasioning the generation and analysis of multiple 'heavy atom' derivatives of the biological macromolecule crystal of interest. Once $\alpha_B(hkl)$ phase angles are established by means of Harker constructions, electron density distribution in the unit cell may be solved directly by means of Equation (6.5), and from this the structure of the biological macromolecule. Obviously, the process is not quite as simple as this and there is plenty of opportunity for error in this entire process. Nevertheless, these basic principles should suffice to allow the interested reader to brave the intricate detail of higher level X-ray diffraction texts.

6.3 Structural information from X-ray diffraction

Main Section 6.2 was compiled as a theoretical introduction to the more practical problems of obtaining X-ray crystal structures of biological macromolecules. In fact, although X-ray diffraction has proved immensely popular as a means of biological macromolecule structure determination, the technique is still quite onerous to implement and the possibility for error surprisingly high. These problems will become clear in this section. The first and still the most difficult problem is that of biological macromolecule crystallisation. If there are no well formed crystals then there can be no X-ray crystal diffraction!

6.3.1 Biological macromolecule crystallisation

Crystallisation is empirical and far from rational. A biological macromolecule crystal is slowly precipitated from solution in the expectation that crystals will begin to form. Very pure biological macromolecule samples are required for this process. Typically, the biological macromolecule of interest is dispersed in a buffer solution, sometimes containing an organic solvent such as **2-methyl-2,4-pentanediol (MPD)**. To this, a **precipitant** such as salt or **polyethyleneglycol (PEG)** is added very slowly until high supersaturation is reached, at which point small aggregates will emerge that may act as the nuclei for future crystal growth. Ideally, a low level of supersaturation is then required in order to allow for sustained crystal growth without the complication of excessive numbers of crystal growth nuclei further appearing. This may be achieved by adjustments in pH and temperature.

The simplest technique for biological macromolecule crystallisation is **batch crystallisation**. This is the simple binary combination of biological macromolecule solution and precipitant to create an instantaneous state of high supersaturation. This minimal process can give diffraction quality crystals under some circumstances but many other techniques

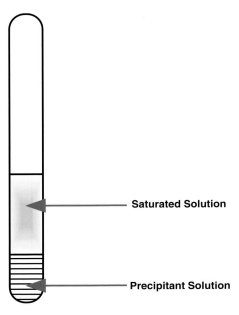

Figure 6.8 Liquid-liquid diffusion: Saturated solution of biological macromolecule (e.g. protein) is placed in a sealed capillary environment in contact with precipitant solution. Slow mixing and liquid diffusion creates sufficient precipitant gradient in the macromolecule solution to "seed" crystallisation.

have needed to be developed. These include the following: **liquid–liquid diffusion, vapour diffusion** and **dialysis**. The liquid–liquid diffusion method (Figure 6.8) uses a narrow bore glass capillary to place a layer of precipitant (approximately 5 μl) in contact with a layer of biological macromolecule solution (approximately 5 μl) over a small surface area. The two layers are intended to gradually diffuse together to bring about crystallisation. There are two alternative vapour diffusion methods, namely the **hanging drop method** (Figure 6.9) and the **sitting drop method** (Figure 6.10). The former method relies upon surface-tension effects to position a combined aliquot of biological macromolecule solution and precipitant (approximately 10 μl) on a glass slide, inverted over a well containing precipitant solution (approximately 1 ml), all in a sealed box. The latter method is an alternative method used if surface-tension effects are insufficient to sustain a hanging drop during the crystallisation process. In both cases, the separated solutions are expected to diffuse together by slow vapour diffusion to bring about crystallisation. Finally, the **dialysis method** (Figure 6.11) separates biological macromolecule solution from precipitant by means of a semipermeable membrane, through which precipitant will diffuse to initiate crystallisation. This technique is quite versatile in that the precipitant may be altered at will and crystallisations may be performed on a range of different scales.

Once crystals have been obtained, they must be isolated and prepared for X-ray crystal diffraction studies. This too is problematic, since biological macromolecule crystals are not the dense packed structures familiar to chemists used to working with small molecules. Rather,

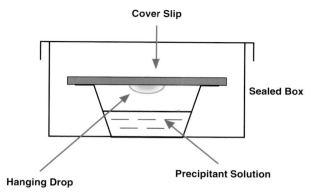

Figure 6.9 Hanging Drop-Vapour Diffusion: Saturated solution of biological macromolecule (e.g. protein) is placed in a sealed environment suspended above precipitant solution. Very slow vapour diffusion leads to very controlled precipitant gradient in the macromolecule solution that "seeds" crystallisation.

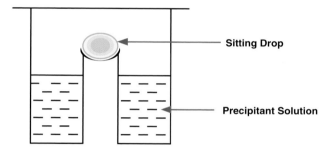

Figure 6.10 Sitting Drop-Vapour Diffusion: Identical principles to the hanging drop method (see **Figure 6.9**).

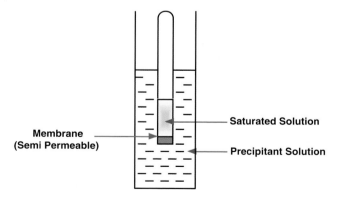

Figure 6.11 Dialysis: Saturated solution of biological macromolecule (e.g. protein) is placed in an environment separated from precipitant solution by semi-permeable membrane. Very slow solute diffusion across the membrane creates precipitant gradient in the macromolecule solution to "seed" crystallisation.

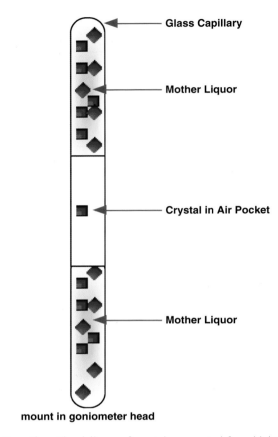

mount in goniometer head

Figure 6.12 Crystal Mounting: The delicacy of crystals generated from biological macromolecule crystallisation requires that individual crystals for X-ray crystallography be mounted in a **sealed capillary** separated from crystal mother liquors by an air pocket. The capillary is mounted in the **goniometer head** of a **four circle diffractometer** (see **Fig. 6.15**).

they are loosely packed, with large solvent-filled holes and channels that may occupy up to 50% of the crystal volume. Therefore, biological macromolecule crystals must always be kept in contact with their mother liquor or in contact with a saturated vapour of the same mother liquor in order to ensure crystal integrity, even during exposure to X-ray beams. Hence, crystals are usually introduced into thin-walled capillaries of borosilicate glass or quartz (Figure 6.12) prior to mounting in an X-ray diffraction instrument, where they will be subjected to sustained X-ray irradiation.

6.3.2 X-ray generation

The traditional image of X-ray generation is that of an evacuated cathode-ray tube in which a cathode is at a high negative potential relative with respect to a metal (usually copper)

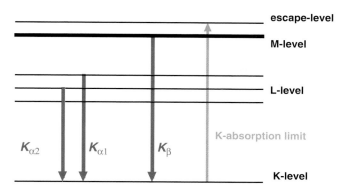

Figure 6.13   K-band transitions: Schematic representation of the orbital energy levels of a Cu-anode mounted in a vaccum-sealed cathode ray tube, also showing the transitions causing characteristic K-band X-ray wavelengths. Electrons bombard the Cu-anode and in the process the high energy electrons reaching the anode "shoot" electrons out of low lying orbitals in the anode atoms. Electrons from higher orbitals occupy the empty positions and in the process emit X-ray radiation of defined wavelength.

anode. Electrons traverse the evacuated tube from cathode (negative) to anode (positive) under the influence of the potential difference and generate X-rays by high energy collision with the anode. Collisions displace low lying electrons, which are then replaced by high lying electrons from within the same atom in a process accompanied by the release of energy in the form of monochromatic X-rays. Copper produces X-rays at three main wavelengths, known as $K_{\alpha1}$, $K_{\alpha2}$ and K_{β} since they originate from so-called **K-band** electronic transitions (Figure 6.13). The respective wavelengths are 1.540 51, 1.544 33 and 1.392 17 Å respectively. However, modern X-ray crystal diffraction prefers to make use of **synchrotron radiation** in preference to the use of cathode-ray tube generated X-rays. Synchrotrons are particle accelerators that circulate injected particles such as electrons in the form of a particle beam at speeds close to the speed of light. These devices are quite simply enormous and the trajectory of any given particle in a beam may be anything up to a few kilometres in path length (Figure 6.14)! Whenever the particle beam is forced to change direction in order to complete its trajectory, electromagnetic radiation is released. This radiation covers a wide range of wavelengths owing to the continuous (non-quantised), broad range of particle momenta in the beam but shows significant intensity even as low as 0.1 Å, a lower limit for X-ray radiation.

Synchrotron X-ray radiation is two orders of magnitude more intense than that from an evacuated cathode-ray tube and tuneable to any desired wavelength in the X-ray spectral range using a monochromator. Hence a given biological macromolecule crystal can be irradiated with high intensity, monochromatic X-rays covering a range of possible X-ray wavelengths (usually around 1 Å) allowing for the sampling of substantial numbers of reciprocal lattice points, or in other words detection of substantial numbers of X-ray scattering events by reflection from a wide range of *hkl*-lattice planes (see Section 6.2.3). Consequently, the diffraction data necessary to construct unit cell electron density distribution may often be collected from just one single biological macromolecule crystal provided that radiation damage to the

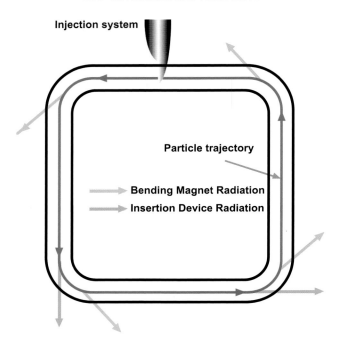

Figure 6.14   Synchrotron: Schematic representation of a particle storage ring with an injector for the charged particles. Radiation can be obtained from the particles while passing the bending magnets. In the straight sections of the ring, devices can be inserted (e.g. **wiggler** or **undulator**) that produce even higher intensity radiation than the bending magnets.

crystal is kept to a minimum. Fortunately, synchrotron-derived X-rays with wavelengths close to 1 Å are inherently less damaging than cathode-ray-tube-derived X-rays close to 1.5 Å in wavelength, owing to the tendency of the shorter wavelength X-rays to be diffracted by a given biological macromolecule crystal rather than to be absorbed causing radiation damage. The general advantages of synchrotron X-ray radiation should now be absolutely clear!

6.3.3 Determination of X-ray diffraction pattern

For a completely accurate crystal structure determination, X-ray scattering must be observed and recorded by reflection from the vast majority of *hkl*-lattice planes associated with a given biological macromolecule crystal. That is to say that an accurate structural determination is only possible if the vast majority of reciprocal lattice points can be sampled. In order to achieve this, the classical approach has been to use a device like a **four-circle diffractometer** (Figure 6.15) in which biological macromolecule crystals are first mounted in a **goniometer head** located at the centre of the diffractometer and then irradiated with an intense beam of X-rays, after which X-ray reflections may be observed sequentially, one at a time, in

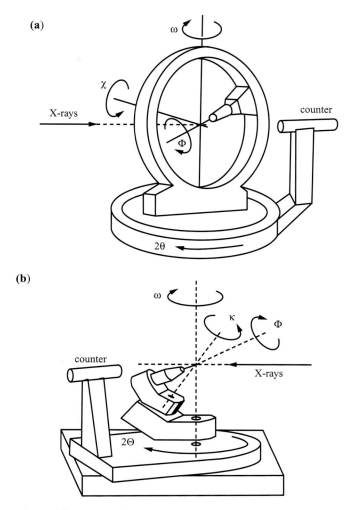

Figure 6.15 **Four Circle Diffractometers**: Two examples (**a**) and (**b**) of **single photon counting devices**. The **goniometer head** positions the diffracting crystal in the path of an incident X-ray beam. The devices allow for rotation of the mounted crystal through at four complete arcs (designated Φ, ω, **2θ** and κ or χ) in order to detect as many **hkl**-reflections (reciprocal lattice points) as possible by diffraction counter prior to crystal destruction by the incident beam (Reproduced from Drenth, 1994, Fig. 2.9).

three-dimensional space around the crystal. X-ray detection is effected using a scintillation counter. Throughout the process of detection, the crystal is made to rotate in small oscillation steps in the goniometer head. As the Ewald sphere concept showed above (see Section 6.2.3), sampling of the reciprocal lattice is maximised with minimal data overlap by a combination of such crystal rotation and the use of a range of possible monochromatic X-ray wavelengths to irradiate the crystal.

Since only one X-ray reflection may be observed at one time, the classical approach to observing an X-ray diffraction pattern is inefficient; typically several weeks are required to collect sufficient scattering data (i.e. 10^4–10^5 X-ray reflections depending upon the size of the biological macromolecule under investigation). Nevertheless, if time is not limiting and the crystal is stable, then the classical approach to X-ray crystal diffraction is still sound and effective. However, even the classical approach is now giving way to the use of four-circle diffractometer-like devices equipped with **image plates** or **electronic area detectors** capable of sampling more X-ray reflections more rapidly and more accurately.

6.3.4 Heavy atom derivatisation

The introduction of heavy atoms into a biological macromolecule crystal, also known as **heavy atom derivatisation**, is a critical part of X-ray crystal structure determination, as indicated in Main Section 6.2. Critically, derivatisation must as far as possible be isomorphous with respect to the original biological macromolecule crystal, otherwise most of the assumptions underpinning the Harker construction break down and the phase problem remains a problem (see Section 6.2.5)! Unfortunately, this is a highly empirical process, like biological macromolecule crystallisation. The biological macromolecule crystal is soaked in a solution containing heavy metal, allowing heavy metal ions or reagents to diffuse through the large solvent-filled holes and channels that make up the crystal. Soaking times will vary from hours to months since the minimum time to reach equilibrium of the reaction is determined by a number of competing factors such as diffusion times through the crystal, ion or reagent accessibility to reactive/combining sites on the biological macromolecule and the nature of the chemical combining process itself. The process of ensuring true isomorphous replacement can be much enhanced through careful attention to biology or through the use of site-selective modification procedures. For instance, where a protein contains Ca^{2+} or Mg^{2+} ions, heavy Sm^{3+} ions are suitable surrogates since they have similar radii. Alternatively, low pH values promote the binding of charged heavy atom reagents such as HgI_4^{2-} or $Au(CN)_2^-$ to biological macromolecules such as proteins or nucleic acids by minimising charge–charge repulsion. Heavy atoms are frequently thiophilic, consequently genetic engineering of proteins to introduce the amino-acid residue cysteine in defined, surface accessible locations in a protein can be a very powerful way of introducing heavy ions such as Hg^{2+} in defined positions with minimal structural distortion to either protein or crystal.

6.3.5 Fitting an electron density map

After a first complete set of $\alpha_B(hkl)$ phase angles has been determined with data obtained from the MIR method, or equivalent, an electron density map may then be calculated. If sufficient X-ray diffraction data has been acquired then this map will fit the known primary sequence of the biological macromolecule reasonably well, giving a preliminary model of biological macromolecule structure. **Structure refinement** will follow to improve the model. If diffraction data is insufficient to define the electron density map unambiguously, then further improvements in $\alpha_B(hkl)$ phase angle data need to be sought. Structure refinement usually requires techniques such as **solvent flattening**. This relies on knowledge that an electron density map is essentially flat in the solvent regions between biological macromolecules due to the 'fluid character' of the solvent molecules in these regions. Ordered solvent molecule structures only occur at interfaces with the biological macromolecule itself or embedded within. Hence by arbitrarily setting all electron density to a low constant value in the identified solvent regions a new electron density map will result, from which new $F_B(hkl)$ structure factors and improved $\alpha_B(hkl)_{imp}$ phase angles may be calculated. These improved $\alpha_B(hkl)_{imp}$ phase angles are then combined with experimental $|F_B(hkl)|$ data determined from experimental X-ray scattering intensities in order to recalculate an electron density map. Several further consecutive rounds of solvent flattening may then take place until convergence is achieved.

Alternatively, if the crystal structure contains several biological macromolecules in defined symmetrical arrays (known as regions of **high non-crystallographic symmetry**), then some form of **multi-fold molecular averaging procedure** may be used to refine even quite poor initial $\alpha_B(hkl)_{imp}$ phase angle data and electron density maps. Ultimately, if the refinement process is sufficient, then the electron density map should closely fit the known primary sequence of the biological macromolecule like 'hand in glove'. Such an example of this close fitting is illustrated in Figure 6.16. In this case the quality of the map is sufficient to allow for detailed structural and functional questions to be asked about the LysU protein structure. The general quality of an electron density map is often given by the **common crystallographic R factor**. This is defined as

$$R = \frac{\sum_h \sum_k \sum_l ||F_{obs}(hkl)| - k|F_{calc}(hkl)||}{\sum_h \sum_k \sum_l |F_{obs}(hkl)|} \tag{6.7}$$

where $|F_{obs}(hkl)|$ is the observed modulus of the structure factor determined from the intensity of X-ray scattering from a given stack of parallel hkl-lattice planes, $|F_{calc}(hkl)|$ the modulus calculated from the a model of the biological macromolecule structure fitted to the refined electron density map and k a scaling factor. For model structures with atoms randomly distributed in the unit cell, the R factor should be 0.59. For well developed, high resolution model structures (<2 Å resolution) the R factor should not generally exceed 0.16. This R factor is an overall number and does not indicate major local errors, but does provide a useful guide to model structure quality.

6.3.6 Biological macromolecule structures by X-ray crystallography

Nowadays, X-ray crystallography has been refined to the point that a sizeable range and diversity of structures have been solved and made available publicly as protein data bank (pdb) files. This is a little confusing, since pdb files also contain structures of other biological

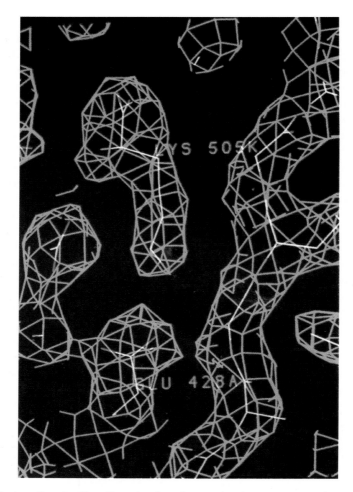

Figure 6.16   Electron Density Map: Example of an electron density map generated computationally from electron density data that has been derived by the application of the equations and principles described in the main text from X-ray crystallographic scattering data. The electron density map corresponds with part of the active site of an enzyme **LysU** (see next **Fig. 6.19**; Chapters 7 and 8) from the organism *Escherichia coli*. This electron density map has been "fitted" with the primary sequence polypeptide chain of LysU (colour code:- carbon: yellow; oxygen: red; nitrogen: blue). Once an electron density map has been determined, fitting of the known primary sequence of the biological macromolecule to the electron density map is the final stage that leads to a defined three-dimensional structure (from Onesti et al., 1995, Fig. 9).

macromolecules in addition to proteins, although the majority are still proteins! These pdb files are basically annotated text files that contain information on the relative coordinates of biological macromolecule atoms in the unit cell, as determined by X-ray diffraction pattern resolutions and electron density fitting. A substantial number of pdb files can be downloaded and visualised using a range of visualisation software programs, also available by download from the internet. Clearly, visualisation requires the use of cartoon depiction methods (see Chapter 1) in order to give clarity, since whole atom representations can be difficult to understand and appreciate. Therefore, relevant software programs specialise in allowing the user to render X-ray crystal structures in a variety of customised cartoon representations suitable for the interest and requirements of the time. The beginning of Chapter 7 documents some truly spectacular X-ray crystal structures, so we shall confine ourselves here to illustrating and discussing structures of three important heat shock/stress proteins from the bacterium *Escherichia coli* (*E. coli*). Typically, many proteins from the bacterium *E. coli* have been studied more extensively than corresponding proteins from other sources, given the predominant use of *E. coli* in genetic engineering, protein overexpression and protein engineering studies (see Chapter 3).

Stress proteins are universal proteins found in all cells of every organism that act to protect proteins in cells from the damaging effects of physiological, environmental and chemical stress. Moreover, stress proteins often play pivotal roles in normal cellular physiology as well. Frequently, stress proteins are some of the most conserved proteins in Nature, and close homologues of stress protein families are found in all cells derived from the very oldest bacteria and protozoans up to the most recent eukaryotes. Chemical biology studies on the structure and function of stress proteins are a fundamental part of a wider investigation into the **chemistry of stress**, but the elucidation of their three-dimensional structures by X-ray crystallography has frequently proven challenging. The majority of stress proteins are molecular chaperones that assist the folding/refolding of other proteins without being involved in the final folded state of these other proteins. Although the three-dimensional structure of a given protein is widely considered to be specified by its sequence of amino-acid residues, the kinetic process of protein folding frequently needs assistance in living cells, hence the requirement for molecular chaperones. Under stress conditions, molecular chaperones are upregulated in order to protect proteins substrates from stressor-induced unfolding and aggregation under stress conditions.

Molecular chaperone GroEL and co-chaperone GroES from *E. coli* (also known as Chaperonin 60 (Cpn60) and Chaperonin 10 (Cpn 10)) are considered to be the archetypal stress protein molecular chaperones. In a wider context, since heat shock is the primary physiological inducer of GroEL and GroES in cells, then GroEL is said to belong to the heat shock protein-60 (Hsp60) family of stress proteins, and GroES to the heat shock protein-10 (Hsp10) family of stress proteins (60 and 10 refer to approximate molecular weights in kDa of GroEL and GroES subunit polypeptides or monomers respectively). Generally, GroEL and GroES operate together as the GroEL/ES molecular chaperone machine, which acts to protect a very wide variety of proteins substrates from stressor-induced unfolding and aggregation under stress conditions in *E. coli* cells (*in vivo*), and otherwise provides assistance for protein folding under normal conditions. Given the complexity of this molecular chaperone machine, the report of the X-ray crystal structure for the GroEL/GroES/(ADP)$_7$ complex in 1997 was regarded as nothing short of a revelation and hailed as a major scientific achievement (Figure 6.17), This structure has since opened the door to an enormous swell of structure/activity studies aimed at understanding everything from molecular recognition (Chapter 7) to the mechanism of GroEL/ES-assisted folding/refolding of model substrate proteins. Starting from this

(a)

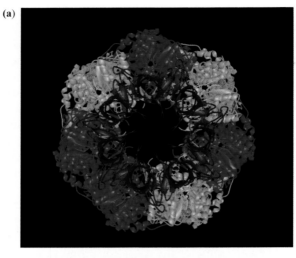

(b)

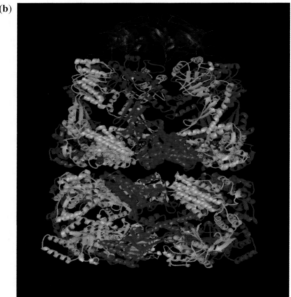

Figure 6.17   Ribbon structure depiction of X-ray crystal structure of the GroEL/GroES/(ADP)$_7$ complex (pdb: **1aon**) Top view (**a**) and side view (**b**) of complex. The X-ray crystal structure shows how GroEL is a homo-oligomer consisting of 14 identical monomers (**red** or **yellow**) (each 57 259Da) that are assembled into 2-stacked rings, each consisting of 7 monomers with a central cavity for the sequestration of protein substrate molecules ("double doughnut" structure). In the case of GroES, the X-ray crystal structure shows how GroES is a homo-oligomer consisting of 7 identical monomers (**blue**) (each 10 368kDa) assembled into a single ring (**blue**). In the presence of ADP, GroES forms a tight complex with GroEL and becomes the "cap" of the same GroEL ring to which the 7 ADP molecules are bound (**space filling representation; blue**). Each ADP molecule is bound to an individual ADP/ATP binding site in each of the GroEL monomers of that ring. GroEL has a total of 14 individual ADP/ATP binding sites (1 ATP/ADP binding site/monomer or 7 ATP/ADP binding sites/7mer GroEL ring) (Reproduced from Jones et al., 2006 Figs. 1a & 1b).

structure, the complete molecular chaperone machine mechanism has now been elucidated in reasonable detail, as shown in Figure 6.18.

If there are stress proteins to assist with the problems of stress, there must be stress proteins able to modulate stress responses and assist the return of cells to normal physiology when appropriate. One such stress protein in *E. coli* is LysU. Unusually for stress proteins, LysU is a homodimeric lysyl tRNA synthetase enzyme that should normally play an essential role in protein biosynthesis in *E. coli* (see Chapters 1 and 3), but is also an excellent synthase for diadenosine-$5',5'''-P^1,P^4$-tetraphosphate (Ap$_4$A) in the presence of Zn^{2+} ions (see Chapters 7 and 8). The X-ray crystal structure of LysU with the amino acid L-lysine bound in both active sites of the dimer was efficiently solved in 1995 (Figure 6.19). Since then other LysU X-ray crystal structures with other ligands bound have also been solved (Figure 6.19). The determination of the first LysU X-ray crystal structure was remarkable in that the protein was able to form excellent crystals within a few weeks of obtaining sufficient protein for studies, but the subsequent determination of the actual X-ray crystal structure from the diffraction pattern then took years. Usually, the reverse is true! The determination of these LysU X-ray crystal structures has since opened up significant enzymic, mechanistic and even molecular modelling studies designed to understand the way the enzyme operates in molecular recognition, binding and catalysis (see Chapters 7 and 8).

Without doubt the X-ray crystal structures illustrated here have proven important starting points for the development of an understanding of GroEL/GroES and LysU protein functions. In fact, the same can be said of the X-ray crystal structures of any number of other biological macromolecules. However, X-ray crystal structures should not be used without question. For one thing, the X-ray crystal structure of any one protein is just that, the structure of the protein in a crystallographic state. Although the crystals of biological macromolecules are very open (see Section 6.3.1), there are still realistic crystal-packing forces involved that can actually distort protein structure and/or suppress conformational changes that might be otherwise highly important for biological macromolecular function in solution. For example, the X-ray crystal structure of the GroEL/GroES/(ADP)$_7$ complex failed completely to demonstrate conformational changes in the double-doughnut structure of GroEL and the 'two-stroke motor' cycle of binding and release of protein substrate (in various states of unfolding) that cooperates together to assist folding/refolding of substrate proteins (Figure 6.18). In fact, the complete picture was only established later by a combination of X-ray crystallography data and structural data from cryo-electron microscopy, with functional data from other dynamic spectroscopic analyses (see Chapter 7). There is a general rule of thumb here. X-ray crystal structures frequently provide a good foundation for understanding in chemical biology, but a proper understanding of dynamic mechanism and function usually requires the application of other techniques building necessarily upon the knowledge of structure gained from X-ray crystal structures (see Chapters 7 and 8). In this respect, NMR spectroscopy (Chapter 5) has a significant advantage over X-ray crystallography in that the structures of biological macromolecules are determined in the solution state. However, it is perhaps gratifying that where X-ray crystal structures are available for comparison with NMR-derived structures then there is frequently close agreement between them.

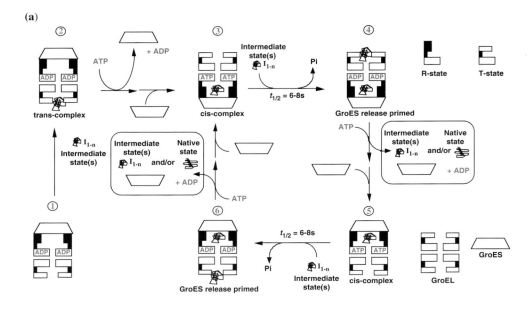

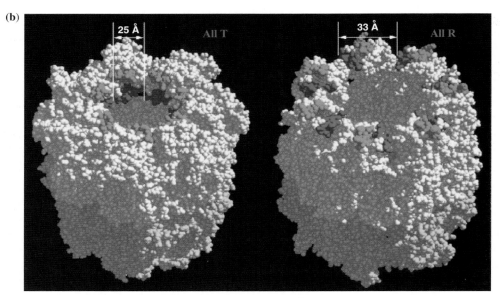

Figure 6.18 Mechanism of GroEL/GroES-assisted refolding of proteins. (a) Complete GroEL/GroES molecular chaperone machine mechanism illustrating the regular cycle of binding and release of protein substrate (in various states of unfolding). This regular process of binding and release of protein substrate has been thought at various times to have catalytic effects on protein folding or else provide a means for the folding of substrate proteins at "infinite dilution" in the GroEL central cavities. However, the cycle is much more consistent with a passive kinetic partitioning mechanism for molecular chaperone machine activity described below (see **c**). The **T**-state and **R**-state nomenclature refer to the conformations of individual GroEL polypeptide subunits in the homo-oligomeric structure. The T-state has a high affinity for substrate protein and the R-state a low affinity (the affinity for ATP is reversed). The term I_{1-n} refers to discrete substrate protein folding intermediates, I, of between 1 and n in number (Reproduced from Jones et al., 2006, Fig. 1c). (*Continued*)

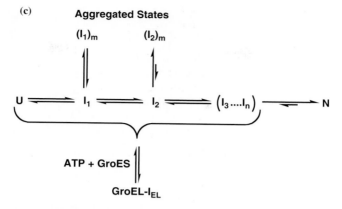

(c)

Aggregated States

$(I_1)_m$ $(I_2)_m$

$$U \rightleftharpoons I_1 \rightleftharpoons I_2 \rightleftharpoons \left(I_3 \cdots I_n \right) \longrightarrow N$$

ATP + GroES

GroEL-I_{EL}

Figure 6.18 (*Continued*) (**b**) **Space filling representation** of GroEL to show the difference between **T** and **R** states. Hydrophobic binding residues (**green & red**) at the mouth of the GroEL cavities drastically change position and move further apart in going from The **T** to **R** states. (**c**) **Passive kinetic partitioning mechanism** of GroEL/GroES molecular chaperone machine. This assumes that protein folding is initiated at an unfolded state, **U**, which folds through a succession of intermediate states I_1, I_2, $(I_3 \ldots I_n)$ before reaching the native state, **N**. States I_1 and I_2 are considered arbitrarily to be unstable to aggregation, forming aggregated states $(I_1)_m$ and $(I_2)_m$ through interaction of their exposed hydrophobic surfaces. GroEL is potentially able to bind to all vulnerable protein folding intermediate states, except **N**, forming a GroEL-bound state **GroEL-I_{EL}**. The nature of this state is a function of the requirement to optimise the free energy of association between GroEL and the given unfolded protein state under the given set of binding conditions. The binding interaction with GroEL is reversed in a controlled manner with the assistance of first ATP and then GroES binding, after which protein substrate is retained by GroEL intra-cavity until ATP hydrolysis is complete ($t_{1/2}$ 6-8s). Thereafter, protein substrate may be released into free solution ready to rebind again if necessary (see **a**). As a result of this cyclical binding and controlled release into a GroEL cavity and then free solution, steady state concentrations of **U**, I_1, I_2 and $(I_3 \ldots I_n)$ are maintained below the critical threshold for aggregation so that these states are free to partition kinetically to **N** (Reproduced from Smith et al., 1999, Scheme 3).

6.4 Neutron diffraction

The basic principles of neutron and X-ray diffraction are quite different, although there is some compatibility in terms of data output. X-ray diffraction or scattering may be considered to be a consequence of interactions between the oscillating electromagnetic fields of X-ray photons and the '**clouds of structural electrons**' surrounding atomic nuclei. In the case of neutron diffraction, neutrons behave as neutral particles that can pass therefore through the clouds of electrons but are then diffracted or scattered by '**nuclear force**' interactions. Hence the phenomenon of neutron scattering is essentially electron independent, but atomic number dependent and invariant with angle. Typically, neutron diffraction data may be processed to a resolution of between 2 and 4 Å in common with X-ray diffraction data.

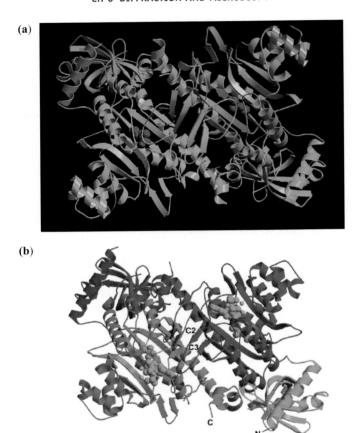

Figure 6.19   X-ray cystallographic images of LysU: (a) Ribbon display representation of the first X-ray crystal structure of *Escherichia coli* (*E. coli*) stress protein lysyl tRNA synthetase **LysU** (pdb: **1lyl**). LysU is known as a potent Ap_4A synthase (See Chapters 7 and 8 for additional details). LysU is a homodimer comprised of two identical polypeptide monomers (**green** & **blue**) each with an active site. Successful crystallisation requires the presence of L-lysine that binds to both active sites (shown in **space filling representation; red**). Ap_4A may be a signal molecule for stress but is more likely to be involved in stress accommodation, helping cells recover from periods of exposure to physiological, environmental or chemical stressors. (**b**) Ribbon display of a later X-ray crystal structure of LysU with substrates L-lysine (**pink**) and β, γ-methylene ATP (AMPPCP) (**cyan**) bound in both active sites together with 3 Mg^{2+} ions (**yellow**), all shown in **space filling respresentation** (pdb: **1e1t**). One complete monomer is shown in **blue**, whereas the other is coloured according to domain structure; *N*-terminal (**orange**), conserved core domain typical to Class II tRNA synthetases (**red**), LysU specific regions (**purple**). In the red domain region, a **motif 2 loop** (**green**) sits over ATP. β-Strands **C2** and **C3** in each monomer interact across the homodimer interface. The loop between strands is positioned above and interacts with the motif 2 loop of the opposite monomer (Reproduced from Hughes et al., 2003, Fig. 1).

Table 6.1 Neutron scattering lengths and atomic scattering
lengths of various elements.

Element	Neutrons $b_{neut} \times 10^{13}$ (cm)	X-rays $b_{X\text{-ray}} \times 10^{13}$ (cm)
H	−3.74	3.8
D	6.67	2.8
C	6.65	16.9
N	9.40	19.7
O	5.80	22.5
P	5.10	42.3
S	2.85	45

The X-ray scattering power of any given atom can be described in terms of the **X-ray scattering length** of that atom, $b_{X\text{-ray}}$, according to the following simple equation:

$$b_{X\text{-ray}} = \text{const.}\, f_{(0)} \tag{6.8}$$

where $f_{(0)}$ is known as the **atomic scattering factor**, a variable that may be used to quantitate the forward scattering of X-rays, while the constant (const.) is equivalent to 2.8×10^{-13} cm. X-ray scattering intensities per atom are related to $b_{X\text{-ray}}^2$. Neutron scattering power may be similarly quantitated but values of $f_{(0)}$ are substantially different, giving rise to a set of **neutron scattering lengths**, b_{neut}, that are often significantly different to X-ray scattering lengths (Table 6.1). Significantly, the neutron scattering lengths for H and D atoms are much more comparable in magnitude to the scattering lengths of other heavier atoms than corresponding X-ray scattering lengths, hence hydrogen atoms are much more clearly visualised by neutron diffraction than by X-ray diffraction. Another significant fact is that b_{neut} values for H and D are negative and positive numbers respectively, indicating that H and D neutron scattering are π out of phase (180°) even though of similar magnitude. Hence neutron diffraction may even be able to identify isotope locations in different positions. In practice, neutron diffraction of biological macromolecules is rarely performed in the absence of a known X-ray crystal structure and should ideally be performed using the same crystals as those used for X-ray diffraction studies. Furthermore, access to neutron sources usually limits the use of neutron diffraction in structural characterisations, but when carried out neutron diffraction studies can reveal a lot of useful information confirming the relative positions of H atoms and the presence of H/D exchange sites, information often poorly revealed by X-ray diffraction data.

6.5 Key principles of electron microscopy

X-ray crystallography is not the only technique that gives detailed information about molecular architecture. The last decade has seen the remarkable rise of electron microscopy, a technique that could soon rival the pre-eminence of X-ray crystallography as the technique of choice for high resolution studies of biological macromolecule structures. There are three main reasons why this might be possible. First, there is no requirement to obtain biological macromolecule crystals, especially given the advent of **cryo-electron microscopy**, which will be discussed primarily here. Second, electron and X-ray wavelengths can be very similar, giving rise to comparable diffraction effects and hence comparable resolutions. Third, unlike X-rays, charged electrons scattered by interaction with a sample may be refocused using electromagnetic lenses, giving rise to a magnified contrast image that may be detected and viewed! This is not to say that the electron equivalent of a structure factor or a reciprocal lattice ceases to be relevant or useful. Indeed, we might even have some uses for the electron diffraction pattern. However, the capacity to create a contrast image post-diffraction places electron microscopy much less in the realms of a diffraction technique and much more like a sophisticated version of the simple light microscope found in the everyday biology classroom. The basic appearance of a modern day electron microscope is illustrated in Figure 6.20. An electron source is mounted upon an evacuated column, in which the electromagnetic condensing, objective and projector lenses are mounted. Two condensing lenses act to focus an intense accelerated beam of electrons upon a sample of interest mounted in a **specimen holder**. Electrons diffracted by interaction with sample molecules are then manipulated by a set of two main objective lenses that are mounted for magnification purposes followed by two main projector lenses that help to project a magnified contrast image onto a viewing screen or into the waiting aperture of a camera set up to capture the images formed.

6.5.1 Duality of matter

The fact that an accelerated beam of electrons can be used to view magnified contrast images in the same way as visible light is used to view magnified images in an ordinary light microscope owes a lot to the famous **duality of matter**. That is, a subatomic particle such as an electron possesses both discrete particle-like and electromagnetic wavelike characteristics. As a negatively charged particle, an electron collides readily with gas molecules in air and as such has no capacity to penetrate air to any significant distance. Therefore, free electron motion requires vacuum conditions equivalent to approximately 10^{-3} N m^{-2} (10^{-3} Pa). Such conditions are created in an electron microscope by high vacuum pumps. Furthermore, as a negatively charged particle, an electron can be accelerated by an electrical potential of the sort generated in the **field emission gun** (**FEM**) of an electron microscope (Figure 6.20). Typically, electrons are released from a tungsten filament crystal wire, not unlike the filament of a light bulb, and accelerated by an electrical potential difference of approximately +200 V. Electrons that have been accelerated through a high vacuum under the influence of such a potential form a focused beam, interact with molecules in the mounted sample and then become scattered as if the beam of electrons were a beam of electromagnetic radiation. Beam refocusing leads to the formation of a magnified contrast image (more about this later!).

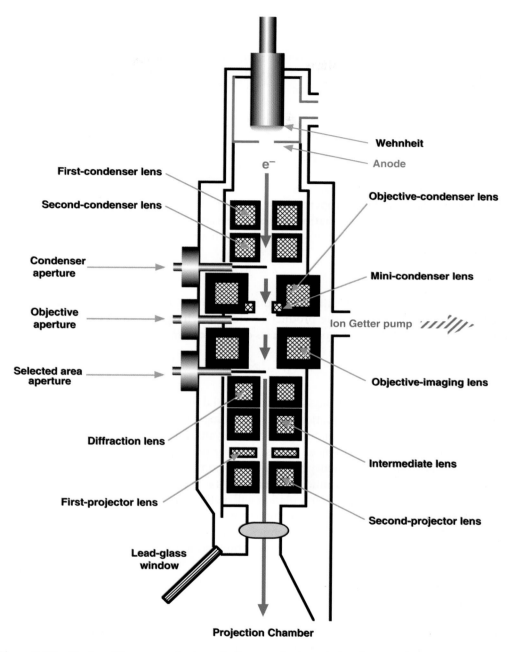

Figure 6.20 Electron Microscope: A schematic diagram of a transmission electron microscope. The sample is placed in the microscope in the path of an **electron beam** generated by the **Field Emission Gun (FEG)** between **condenser** and **objective lenses**.

6.5.2 Electron wavelengths

According to the **Abbé relationship**, which applies to microscopy, resolution or **distance of resolvable separation**, d_R, is related to numerical aperture, NA, and radiation wavelength, λ, according to the following relationship:

$$d_R = 0.61\lambda/\text{NA} \tag{6.9}$$

The value of NA can be set by and is a property of the microscope, hence λ is the critical property for ensuring that d_R is as small as possible. Fortunately, the intrinsic wavelength of a beam of electrons generated as described above is sufficient to give a value of d_R in the Å range. This intrinsic wavelength is a property set by the ultimate equation that relates the duality of matter, namely the **deBroglie equation**, which relates **sub-atomic-particle-like momentum**, p, with concurrent electromagnetic wavelength, λ, where h is Planck's constant:

$$\lambda = h/p \tag{6.10}$$

In the case of an accelerated beam of electrons, p is related to the energy of each accelerated component electron, ϕe (i.e. the product of **electron charge**, e, and **electrical potential difference**, ϕ), and the intrinsic particle **mass of an electron**, m_e, by

$$p = \sqrt{2m_e\phi e} \tag{6.11}$$

which is a reworked version of the standard, classical dynamics equation for kinetic energy. Numerical substitutions into Equation (6.11), assuming ϕ to be $+200$ V, and then substitution of the resulting value of p into Equation (6.10) gives a value for the electromagnetic wavelength λ that translates into a value of d_R as low as 1.4 Å for the most recent electron microscopes. Such a value illustrates that in theory electron microscopy should be able to generate images of biological macromolecules at atomic resolution. In practice, this does not turn out to be so, as the following sections on image manipulation will make plain. However, electron microscopy is a rapidly evolving subject area and this theoretical limit is being rapidly approached, suggesting that some day soon electron microscopy could become the most versatile and significant technique for the characterisation of biological macromolecule structures.

6.5.3 Sample preparation

Nowadays, cryo-electron microscopy, so named for the method of sample preparation and maintenance, is by far the most effective technique of electron microscopy for biological macromolecule characterisation. Therefore, we shall focus on this electron microscopy technique alone from this point onwards. The basis of success in cryo-electron microscopy is very simple though practically quite demanding. A sample of biological macromolecule of interest in water is flash frozen in such a way that individual molecules become embedded in **vitreous ice**. Vitreous ice comprises solid ice that contains little or no formal crystalline structure. Typically, solid ice possesses substantial tetrahedral structure (see Chapter 1) owing to extensive hydrogen bonding relationships between water molecules. However, if liquid water is flash frozen rapidly enough down to a temperature at or below 138 K, then there may be insufficient time for water molecules to orientate and substantially hydrogen bond with each other, leading to a *de facto* solid state without any substantial crystalline structure. In the absence of organised crystalline structural elements, vitreous ice only transmits an incident beam of accelerated electrons without scattering. This creates the ideal situation. When a sample of individual biological macromolecules in vitreous ice is exposed to an incident beam of electrons, only embedded macromolecules are able to scatter electrons and hence produce magnified contrast images after beam refocusing. The vitreous ice should be essentially invisible to the electron beam in theory, and this is substantially true in practice.

Practical realisation of vitreous ice embedded samples of individual biological macromolecules is usually achieved with a **holey carbon grid** (Figure 6.21), which is a thin carbon-based support film (50–200 nm in dimensions) perforated with holes and mounted on a standard electron microscope sample grid. An aqueous sample of a biological macromolecule

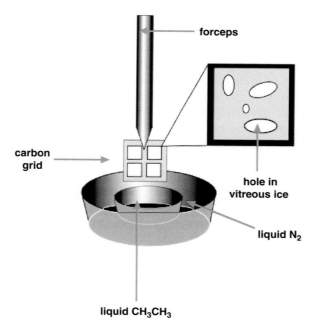

Figure 6.21 Vitreous Ice Freezing Device: A thin (50–200 nm) carbon support film perforated with holes is placed on a standard EM **carbon grid** and then a sample of biological macromolecule is applied and rapidly frozen in liquid ethane (<138 K). After this, the vitrified sample is transferred into a **cryoholder** (under liquid nitrogen conditions) and then transferred to the microscope for visualisation. The holes in the thin film allow for the formation of monolayers of biological macromolecules in a range of orientations embedded within a thin (20–60 μm) layer of vitreous ice. The visualisation of such monolayer regions gives the best possible cryo-EM images of the embedded biological macromolecules.

of interest is applied to the mounted holey carbon grid and flash frozen by virtually instantaneous immersion of the mounted grid in liquid ethane using the illustrated immersion device (Figure 6.21). The result is a thin film of vitreous ice wherein individual biological macromolecules are embedded at semi-regular intervals. This thin film is then mounted in the electron microscope by means of a specially adapted specimen holder known as a **cryo-holder**, which is maintained at 178 K (liquid nitrogen temperature) in order to ensure the continued integrity of the thin film when subjected to a continuous incident beam of accelerated electrons.

6.5.4 Contrast imaging

As described above, electrons diffracted by interaction with individual biological macromolecules embedded in a thin film are manipulated by objective lenses mounted for magnification purposes and afterwards by projector lenses to produce magnified contrast images that are projected onto a viewing screen or into a camera aperture. Such contrast images are generated by direct interactions between accelerated electrons of the incident beam and individual embedded molecules, leading to a variety of **amplitude** and **phase contrast** effects that together create the observed images. Amplitude effects create dark regions within an image that arise from elastic scattering of a proportion of incident beam electrons owing to close atom encounters following thin film penetration. Phase contrast effects create differential shaded regions within an image that arise alternatively from the partial retardation and subsequent re-phasing of a proportion of incident beam electrons owing to longer range encounters that may take place following thin film penetration. As a rule, images generated from biological macromolecules embedded in a thin film are formed primarily from phase contrast effects. Incident electrons automatically experience a $\pi/2$ (90°) phase shift as a result of passing through an embedded biological macromolecule. This effect is then augmented by phase shifts within the focal plane of the objective lenses as well.

6.5.5 Image processing

This is by far the most complex part of the process and is potentially as error prone as the generation and fitting of electron density maps in X-ray crystallography. Typically, several thousand contrast images are generated from the mounted specimen of a given biological macromolecule, each image corresponding to a two-dimensional projection of an individual three-dimensional molecular object. To a first approximation, all these images can be assumed to be perfect projections of the individual molecule concerned onto an image plane (x, y) perpendicular to the incident beam of electrons. Images are **band-pass filtered** to remove high and low frequency noise features and then normalised to a zero-average density. Both processes are designed to remove the effects of heterogeneity in the thickness and structure of the vitreous ice thin film in which molecules are embedded. The normalisation process ensures that all molecular images may be assumed to have the same z positioning. Consequently, we could describe **image density** $P(xy)$ for the image of an individual molecule by the following equation:

$$P(xy) = \sum_X \sum_Y F_{em}(XY)\exp[-2\pi i(Xx + Yy)] \qquad (6.12)$$

where $F_{em}(XY)$ are **electron diffraction structure factors** corresponding to reflections from all possible XY structural planes that bisect the given thin film embedded molecule whose image has been acquired. Equation (6.12) is directly analogous with Equation (6.2), which directly correlates unit cell electron density distribution with unit cell $F(hkl)$ structure factors, which quantify reflections of X-rays from given hkl structural planes. However, the chemical biology reader will probably be relieved to hear that any further similarities between electron microscopy and X-ray crystallography need not be considered here. Instead, we shall need to consider how all the thousands of normalised images are put through extensive image processing procedures in order to derive a complete set of three-dimensional images representative of relevant three-dimensional structure(s) of the specimen biological macromolecule of interest.

Image processing is required owing to the simple fact that three-dimensional biological macromolecules flash frozen and immobilised in a thin film of vitreous ice will be immobilised in completely random orientations. Each distinct, individual orientation should be capable of producing a distinct two-dimensional image. The basis of image processing is to compare, contrast and classify all the individual images obtained and use these as the basis for three-dimensional structure generation. The orientation of any three-dimensional object at a fixed point in time may be characterised by six degrees of freedom, namely **Cartesian coordinates** (x, y, z) and **rotational degrees of freedom** (α, β, γ) (Figure 6.22). Consequently, any two-dimensional image of a three-dimensional object may be similarly characterised, allowing degree of freedom parameters to define the relative relationships between a given set of molecular images under investigation. Since all images can be normalised with respect to their z positioning, only the other five degrees of freedom need be considered in the first instance as image-reference descriptions. However, the first part of the image processing procedure requires that all images be aligned by in-plane translation and/or rotation. Therefore the three in-plane (image-plane) degrees of freedom (x, y, α) are eliminated as image-reference descriptions. All that remains to describe relative image relationships are the two remaining rotational degrees of freedom (β, γ) that correspond to rotations out of the image plane. These two rotational degrees of freedom, subtended about y and x axes, are sufficient to classify all two-dimensional images following initial alignment to eliminate the contribution of the in-plane degrees of freedom. An iterative procedure of **multivariate statistical classifications** and **multi-reference alignment** (**MRA**) processes is then used to sort aligned images into groups of alike images characterised by having similar (β, γ)-defined orientations. Each set of alike images is then segregated and summed as appropriate to form a **classum** (class average), thereby improving signal to noise (signal increases in proportion to number summed per classum; noise in proportion to the square root of number summed per classum). Each classum is uniquely defined and related to another classum by its unique (β, γ)-defined orientation.

The process leading to the generation of a three-dimensional structure now requires that the values of (β, γ) for each classum be identified correctly in order to group classi into related

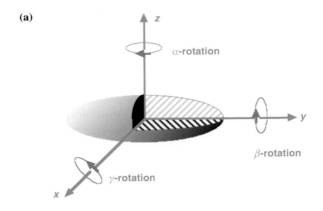

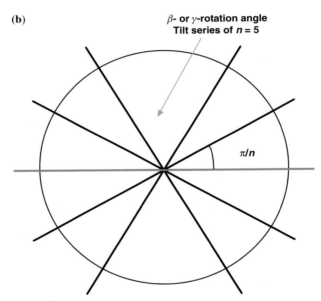

Figure 6.22 **Tilt Series** of EM images: Illustration of the basic degrees of freedom that an embedded biological macromolecule may possess (**a**). (**b**) only variations in β- or γ-rotational degrees of freedom are necessary to classify all images obtained by cryo-EM into β- or γ-rotation angle **tilt series** since variations in α-rotation and (**x, y, z**) coordinates can all be cancelled out during previous image processing and manipulation steps.

(β, γ)-defined **tilt series**. The values of (β, γ) for each classum are also known as the **Euler angles** of a given classum. Euler angles are usually derived using the **common projection line** (**CPL**) theorem. According to the CPL theorem, a common central line projection may be identified in each given pair of two-dimensional images of the same three-dimensional object. In other words, a single, equivalent line (**sinogram**) may be drawn through a given classum pair that traverses equivalent image densities in equivalent distances. The positional matching of sinograms then allows for the relative (β, γ) orientations between each classum to be established. Tilt series may then be built up through the positional matching of sinograms corresponding to every possible classum pair. Thereafter, the three-dimensional structure of the biological macromolecule may now be computer generated directly from these tilt series. The **resolution of the final structure**, d_R, is directly related to the angular distribution of each tilt series (typically <60–$70°$) and the numbers of individual classi, n, that comprise each tilt series. This is summarised by the following equation:

$$d_R = \pi D / n \qquad (6.13)$$

where D is defined as the **maximum particle size**. Given the substantial requirement for alignment, classification and averaging of two-dimensional images in order to derive the three-dimensional structure(s) of biological macromolecules of interest, inherent molecular symmetry is an enormous advantage in obtaining higher resolution structures. For this reason, cryo-electron-microscopy-derived images of virus particles or highly symmetric protein complexes are amongst the best, highest resolution structures so far obtained by this technique.

6.5.6 Biological macromolecule structures from electron microscopy

Compared with X-ray crystallography, cryo-electron microscopy is a technique still in development rather than fully mature. Nevertheless, we have included this technique here because of the inherent potential for atomic-level characterisation with this technique and also because of the impact that this technique has already had on biological macromolecular structure characterisation, even after a relatively short period of time. In fact, many now regard cryo-electron microscopy as a naturally complementary technique to X-ray crystallography. This complementarity with X-ray crystallography has rarely been demonstrated more convincingly than in the characterisation of the *E. coli* GroEL/ES molecular machine (see Section 6.3.6). Cryo-electron microscopy was able to demonstrate ATP/ADP-driven conformational changes not only in the GroEL homo-oligomeric 14-mer (Figure 6.23), not seen by X-ray crystallography, but also in GroEL/GroES/nucleotide complexes, providing structural proof for the changes in molecular shape and topography taking place as part of the 'two-stroke motor' mechanism (Figures 6.17 and 6.18) (see Section 6.3.6). The cryo-electron microscopy and X-ray crystallographic images of GroEL/GroES/ATP$_7$ coincide extraordinarily well, so much so that the cryo-electron image could easily pass as the van der Waals surface description of the X-ray crystallographic structure (Figure 6.24).

Another key success for cryo-electron microscopy has been the visualisation of symmetrical virus structures, owing to the high degree of symmetry in virus structures, ideal for characterisation by the sorts of multifold image reconstruction techniques (described above) required to construct three-dimensional structures of biological macromolecules from cryo-electron microscopy images. As fine recent examples, please note the illustrated symmetrical protein tegument of herpes simplex virus (HSV) and the images of several other virus particles

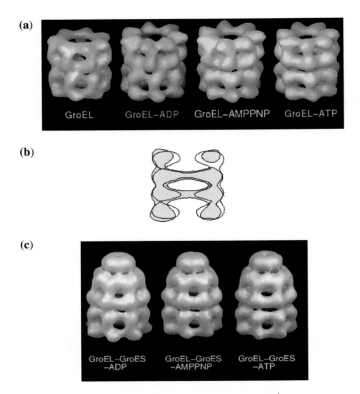

Figure 6.23   EM images of GroEL and GroES: (**a**) Approximately 30 Å resolution images of GroEL (all **T** state), GroEL/ADP (all **R** state), GroEL/β, γ-azido-ATP (AMPPNP) (all **R** state), and GroEL/ATP (all **R** state) (See **Fig. 6.17** for comparison): (**b**) Cross-sectional illustration of GroEL in all **T** state (non-shaded area) and all **R** state (shaded area): (**c**) Approximately 30 Å resolution images of GroEL/GroES/ADP$_7$ (**T** state [**bottom ring**]; **R** state [**top ring**]), GroEL/GroES/AMPPNP$_7$ (**T** state [**bottom ring**]; **R** state [**top ring**]), and GroEL/GroES/ADP$_7$ (**T** state [**bottom ring**]; **R** state [**top ring**]) (See **Figs. 6.17** and **6.18** for comparison). The variety of conformational variations revealed by cryo-electron microscopy is striking and remarkable! (illustrations adapted from Roseman et al., 1996, Figs. 3 & 6).

(Figure 6.25). Critically, cryo-electron microscopy has also been able to provide images of proteins embedded in biological membranes such as the acetylcholine receptor (AchR; see Chapter 7). This technique is here to stay and is sure to improve in resolution and utility. Critically, in comparison with X-ray crystallography, cryo-electron microscopy avoids the need for biological macromolecular crystallisation and so opens the door to structural analysis of biological macromolecules (especially proteins) that are otherwise not amenable to high resolution structural analysis owing to the crystallisation problem. However, cryo-electron microscopy could also be said to have two main drawbacks.

(a) The need for flash freezing of samples, which could be deleterious in some cases.

(b) The need for biological macromolecular symmetry for optimal image processing.

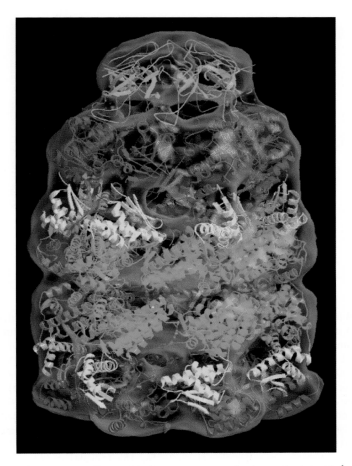

Figure 6.24   EM and X-ray crystallographic images compared:. Approximately 30 Å resolution image of GroEL/GroES/ADP$_7$ (**T** state [bottom ring]; **R** state [top ring]) within which has been incorporated the approximately 2 Å resolution X-ray crystal structure of GroEL/GroES/ADP$_7$ (see **Fig. 6.17** as well). The Cryo-electron microscope image has the appearance of a Van der Waals surface representation of the molecular chaperone machine (illustration adapted from Ranson et al., 2001, Fig. 7).

Point (b) is the more significant since many macromolecular assemblies do not have the fantastic symmetry of a virus particle or of GroEL or GroES. Therefore, the production of high resolution images becomes much more difficult where there is lower molecular symmetry, although far from impossible.

6.6 Key principles of scanning probe microscopy

Scanning probe microscopy will increasingly become another class of imaging technique able to provide equivalent and even complementary structural information to cryo-electron

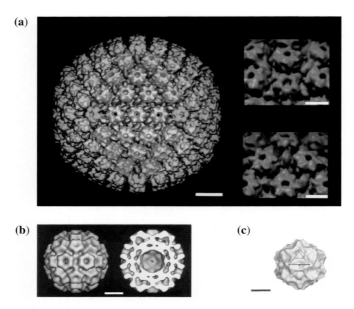

Figure 6.25   EM image of Virus particles: (**a**) Contoured surface at 24 Å resolution of the **Herpes Simplex Virus-1 (HSV-1)** capsid tegument (**left**) rendered visually interesting with **depth cueing, deblobbing** (noise removal) and the addition of **false colour**. This is achieved with **XIMDISP** a visualization tool to aid structure determination. The tegument surface comprises 162 **capsomeres** divided into 12 pentons (**orange**), and 150 hexons (**red**). The hexons homo-oligomers of 6 VP5 (150 kDa) monomers and the pentons, are homo-oligomers of 5 VP5 monomers Additional nodular triplexes (**blue**) reside at sites of threefold symmetry. The capsid encloses **double stranded DNA (dsDNA)**. Bar is 20 nm. Close-ups of hexons and pentons are also illustrated with bar now 30 nm (**top & bottom right**) (illustrations from Conway et al., 1996, Fig. 3). (**b**) Contoured surface at 23 Å resolution of the **Cucumber Mosaic Virus (CMV)** capsid (**left**) and particle in cross-section (**right**) revealing 11 nm inner-cavity. The capsid encloses **RNA**. Bar is 10 nm (illustration from Wikoff et al., 1997, Fig. 1A). (**c**) Contoured surface at 23 Å resolution of the **Canine Parvovirus (CPV)** capsid. The capsid is comprised of 60 VP1, VP2 and VP3 monomers and encloses **single stranded DNA (ssDNA)**. Bar is 20 nm (Reproduced from Agbandje et al., 1995, Fig. 6).

microscopy or X-ray crystallography. There are numerous variations upon the scanning probe theme but two techniques in particular have shown some promise in the imaging of biological macromolecules, namely **scanning tunnelling microscopy (STM)** and **atomic force microscopy (AFM)**.

6.6.1 STM concept

The underlying principles of STM are essentially very simple indeed. If a sharp metal tip is placed within a distance, d_T, of a few Å from a conducting sample surface and a bias voltage, U_z, is applied between tip and surface, a tunnelling current, I_T, will be established between tip and surface due to a quantum mechanical tunnelling effect that is generated under conditions

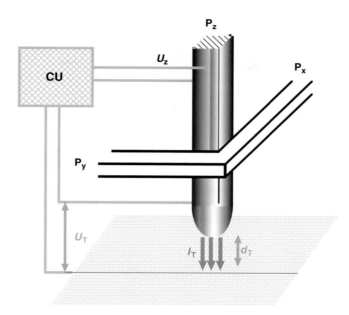

Figure 6.26 **STM** set up: Scanning of the surface takes place in the **near field regime** in which **piezo-electric drives** P_x and P_y raster the **STM tip** across the surface of a sample. Piezo electric drive P_z ensures that the tip remains a short distance d_T (a few Å) from surface encouraging a tunnelling current, I_T, to be established under the influence of a tip to surface potential U_T.

of 'pre-mechanical contact' between tip and sample (Figure 6.26). The current I_T either may be used to probe physical properties locally at the sample surface or may be used to control the distance of separation d_T between tip and sample surface. Typically, the tip is scanned across a sample surface. Exquisite control of lateral and vertical tip motion is performed with subatomic accuracy by **piezo-electric drives** (Figure 6.26). Piezo-drives P_x and P_y scan the tip laterally across the surface, whilst voltage supplied by CU to piezo-drive P_z seeks to adjust vertical tip position as appropriate. The high resolution of STM scanning derives from characteristics of the quantum mechanical tunnelling effect. Since tunnelling only takes place when d_T is a few Å, then STM may be described as a **near-field imaging** technique, whose resolution is neither diffraction nor wavelength limited, in contrast to X-ray crystallography and cryo-electron microscopy. The potential for STM-mediated biological macromolecule structural characterisation should now be clear, especially since STM measurements can be made equally well in air or liquid conditions, in addition to more standard *in vacuo* conditions. This is only possible because free electrons are not part of the imaging process.

6.6.2 Electron tunnelling

In a classical sense, if an electron with total energy E_T meets a potential barrier, V_0, of higher energy, then the electron is unable to pass through. However, in a quantum mechanical

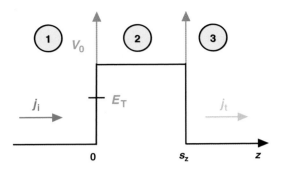

Figure 6.27 1D Tunnelling barrier: Schematic illustration of a tunnelling barrier of length s_z. Incident current density, j_i, is transformed into transmitted current density, j_t, by tunnelling through the barrier which takes place even though electron energy does not exceed E_T, a value less than the classical barrier height V_0.

sense, the electron has anyway a finite probability of location beyond the barrier. This finite relocation probability is **quantum mechanical tunnelling**. Tunnelling is either **elastic** or **inelastic**, depending upon whether energy is preserved or lost as a result of the tunnelling process respectively. The kinetics of tunnelling in relationship to biological electron transfer processes will be discussed in Chapter 8, so only rudimentary concepts relevant to STM will be mentioned here. In STM, the tunnelling barrier is in fact a three-dimensional potential barrier of arbitrary shape; however, the basic principles do not differ substantially from tunnelling through a uniform unidimensional barrier (Figure 6.27). The Schrödinger equation for electron tunnelling through such a simple barrier is given by the following:

$$-\frac{\hbar^2}{2m_e}\frac{d^2\psi_3}{dz^2} = E_T\psi_3 \tag{6.14}$$

where wavefunction ψ_3 has the solution

$$\psi_3 = D_T \exp(-ikz) \tag{6.15}$$

with **integer quantum number**, k, and **barrier tunnelling constant**, D_T. This simple quantum mechanical description allows for the introduction of a number of other important quantum mechanical tunnelling parameters. The first of these is the **barrier transmission coefficient**, T_T, that may be described in terms of **incident current density**, j_i, and **transmitted current density**, j_t, where j_t is equivalent to $|D_T|^2$, as shown:

$$T_T = \frac{j_t}{j_i} = |D_T|^2 \tag{6.16}$$

The squared modulus of D_T is the equivalent of a squared wavefunction, otherwise familiar as the probability density function characteristic of atomic and molecular orbitals. Another important parameter is the **Büttiker–Landauer tunnelling time** τ^{BL} that is expressed in terms of

$$\tau^{BL} = \frac{m_e s_z}{\chi \hbar} \tag{6.17}$$

where s_z is the **variable z-axis barrier dimension** (Figure 6.27) and m_e the electron mass and χ represents a **barrier crossing constant** dependent upon total electron energy E_T and total potential barrier, V_0, according to

$$\chi = [2m_e(V_0 - E_T)]^{1/2}/\hbar \tag{6.18}$$

Hence if the actual energetic barrier height ($V_0 - E_T$) is 4 eV and the z-axis barrier dimension s_z is 5 Å, then time τ^{BL} corresponds to 4×10^{-16} secs. In other words, quantum mechanical tunnelling is an almost instantaneous process. Such a property is almost ideal as the basis for a high resolution imaging technique.

6.6.3 Piezo-electric drives

The heart of control in an STM apparatus is the exquisite sensitivity and fine control of distances exercised by the P_x, P_y and P_z **piezo-electric drives** that control tip motion. These drives are in the form of **bars, tubes** or **bimorphs** all comprised of piezo-electric ceramics in contact with Macor. A **piezo-electric bar changes in length**, Δl_p, as a function of the potential difference, U_p, applied between two opposing bar electrodes according to

$$\Delta l_p = d_{31} \frac{l_p}{h_t} U_p \tag{6.19}$$

where h_t is **bar thickness**, l_p is **bar length** and d_{31} is a **piezo-electric coefficient**. Typically, these three bars are combined together to form a **piezo-electric tripod** (as illustrated in Figure 6.26), that together render simultaneous control of lateral and vertical tip motion. Bars may be replaced by tubes, in which case Equation (6.19) still applies but h_t now corresponds to tube wall thickness and U_p to the potential difference applied between two opposing electrodes mounted inside and outside of the tube respectively (Figure 6.28). The tube is more sensitive than the bar owing to much lower tube wall thickness compared with bar thickness. The piezo-electric bimorph also appears to be a particularly sensitive physical form of piezo-electric drive. To all intents the bimorph is the equivalent of a bimetallic strip. Clamped at both ends, the bimorph comprises two different materials and expands non-uniformly in response to an applied **potential difference**, U_p giving a **displacement**, Δx_p, expressed in terms of

$$\Delta x_p = \frac{3}{8} d_{31} \left(\frac{l_p}{h_t}\right)^2 U_p \tag{6.20}$$

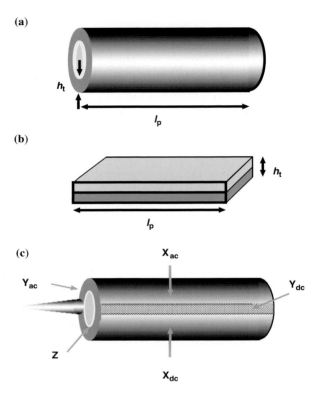

Figure 6.28 **STM tubes and biomorph:** Illustrations of a **piezoelectric tube** (**a**), **biomorph** (**b**) and a complete **single tube** scanner (**c**). The tube and biomorph are explained in the text. In the case of the scanner, **external electrodes** (Y_{ac}, Y_{dc}, X_{ac}, X_{dc}) are applied parallel to the tube axis. As voltage is applied to an external electrode, the tube bends away from that electrode. Otherwise, voltage applied to an inside **Z** electrode causes uniform tube elongation.

where h_t is bimorph thickness and l_p is now bimorph length (Figure 6.28). An ultimate extension of the use of piezo-electric tubes is the realisation of a **single-tube scanner** (Figure 6.28). The piezo-electric tube is fixed at one end and a tip is attached to the other end. Opposing, external electrode pairs (X_{ac}, X_{dc}) and (Y_{ac}, Y_{dc}) are excited by alternating current and direct current sources as indicated so as to induce tube bending motions that bring about lateral tip motion in x or y directions respectively. Tube expansions or contractions along the main tube axis generate vertical tip motion in the z direction. Such single-tube scanners now appear to be some of the most potent STM devices for high speed scanning and low thermal drift.

6.6.4 STM scanning modes

STM imaging modes are either **constant current imaging** (**CCI**) or else **constant height imaging** (**CHI**). The CCI mode is the most commonly used method of imaging. The STM tip is scanned laterally (x, y) across a sample surface by variations in the respective U_x and U_y

potential differences applied to drives P_x and P_y. Vertical (z) tip position is simultaneously adjusted by appropriate changes in the U_z potential applied to drive P_z keeping the tunnelling current I_T constant between tip and surface. Recorded (U_x, U_y) U_z values are then translated into an (x, y)z **topographic image**. To a first approximation, I_T may be kept constant by maintaining a constant distance between tip and sample surface. Therefore, the topographic image is usually assumed to supply an accurate rendition of real surface atomic arrangements and is considered to represent a real surface contour map. However, in reality, the CCI mode contour map is in fact a constant current surface map that does not necessarily have to correspond to the real surface contours. In the CCI mode, tunnelling current I_T is proportional to the following exponential proportionality:

$$I_T \propto \exp(-2\chi s_z) \tag{6.21}$$

The upper limit of CCI mode resolution is determined by the characteristics of the STM tip, assuming that a surface contour map is indeed produced. Where the tip is a semiconductor material, tip-to-surface interactions are presumed to be mediated by a single p_z orbital. Where the tip is a d-band metal then interactions are presumed to be mediated by a single frontier $d_z{}^2$ orbital. In either case, single-orbital-mediated interactions should lead to at least atomic-level resolution of surface features.

The orthogonal CHI mode is a variable I_T mode of scanning well suited to real time data collection. Whilst the more common CCI mode is a typically high surface area technique designed to present a surface contour map after data processing, the CHI mode is better seen as a local flat area technique that monitors local dynamic processes as a function of I_T with time such as a receptor–ligand binding or a chemical transformation event. The vertical (z) tip position is not directly available from CCI mode data unless extracted from a detailed knowledge of absolute I_T plotted as a function of (x, y) location.

6.6.5 Origins of AFM

The origins of AFM, also known as **scanning force microscopy** (**SFM**), are best appreciated by considering the intermolecular forces involved when a tip is scanned across a surface at distances, d_z, of a few Å between tip and surface. If d_z is greater than 10 Å, van der Waals forces dominate. If d_z is less than 10 Å, then meaningful orbital overlaps begin to take place and quantum mechanical exchange–correlation forces apply. Total combined van der Waals interactions between tip and surface primarily obey a distance relationship:

$$F_{VDW}(d_z) = -H\left(\frac{R_z}{6d_z^2}\right) \tag{6.22}$$

where R_z is the **radius of the tip above a surface** and H is a material dependent constant known as a **Hamaker constant**. AFM becomes a practical reality when F_{VDW} can be monitored as a function of lateral (x, y) position while an AFM-specific tip is scanned over a surface of interest. One of the primary advantages of AFM that becomes particularly valuable for the imaging of biological macromolecules is that intermolecular forces can be observed irrespective of the nature of tip or sample surface. There is no requirement for tips and sample surfaces to be of uniformly conducting materials in order for forces to be detected. Hence AFM will apply equally well to insulating and conducting samples. Biological macromolecules are typically insulating materials. Obviously there are other potential surface-to-tip forces that could act upon an AFM-specific tip but F_{VDW} are much the most relevant for the imaging of biological macromolecules.

6.6.6 AFM cantilever

The heart of force detection in an AFM apparatus is a scanning cantilever microfabricated with a tip for force sensing (Figure 6.29). **Forces generated by surface-to-tip interactions,** F_{ST}, lead to **vertical tip displacements,** Δz, that are related to each other in a quasi-static way and to a first approximation by a form of the **Hooke's law equation:**

$$F_{ST} = c_{ST}\Delta z \tag{6.23}$$

where the so-called **spring constant,** c_{ST} (typically $10–10^5$ N m^{-1}), is further described according to the following equation:

$$c_{ST} = \frac{E_M}{4} w_c \frac{h_c^3}{l_c^3} \tag{6.24}$$

The term E_M is known as **Young's modulus,** and w_c, h_c and l_c are the width, thickness and length of the cantilever respectively. The ideal for an AFM apparatus is a cantilever that

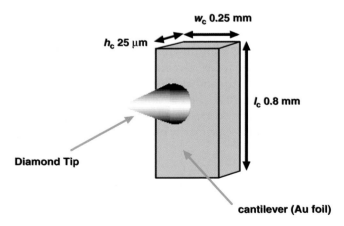

Figure 6.29   AFM cantilever and diamond tip: Schematic illustration to illustrate salient dimensions of an optimal cantilever.

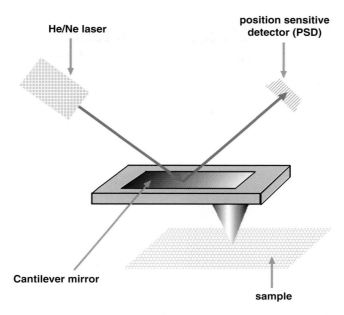

Figure 6.30 **AFM laser beam detection device:** Schematic illustration to show how force evolution between sample and tip may be detected by displacements in the position of a laser beam reflected from a mirror fixed to the rear of the cantilever. Movements in laser position are a very sensitive measure of tip to surface distance changes, Δz, as a result of changes in tip to surface forces, F_{ST}.

possesses the smallest possible spring constant so that any given surface-to-tip force, F_{ST}, results in the largest possible vertical tip displacement, Δz. The best way to accomplish this is to microfabricate a cantilever from Si, SiO$_2$ or (Si)$_3$(N$_3$)$_4$ with substantial length l_c (1–4 mm), modest width w_c (100 μm) and minimal thickness h_c (approximately 1–10 μm). In addition, the sensing tip of the cantilever should be well defined and essentially monatomic. The result is a cantilever with a spring constant of 0.1–1 N m^{-1} whose sensing tip may be displaced by several Å under the influence of surface-to-tip forces as low as 10^{-10} N. Such tip displacements under the influence of surface-to-tip forces may be detected in a number of different ways, of which optical **laser beam deflection** is becoming quite popular and informative (Figure 6.30). Laser light is reflected from a mirror mounted on the back of the cantilever. When a vertical tip displacement takes place causing simultaneous mirror deflection, a **position sensitive detector** (**PSD**) is able to analyse resulting laser beam deflection and hence compute the original vertical tip displacement, Δz. Such a detection system can be sensitive to Δz displacements of less than 1 Å.

6.6.7 AFM scanning modes

AFM force imaging modes are closely related to the STM modes described previously. The modes are either **constant force imaging** (**CFI**) or **variable deflection imaging** (**VDI**) that

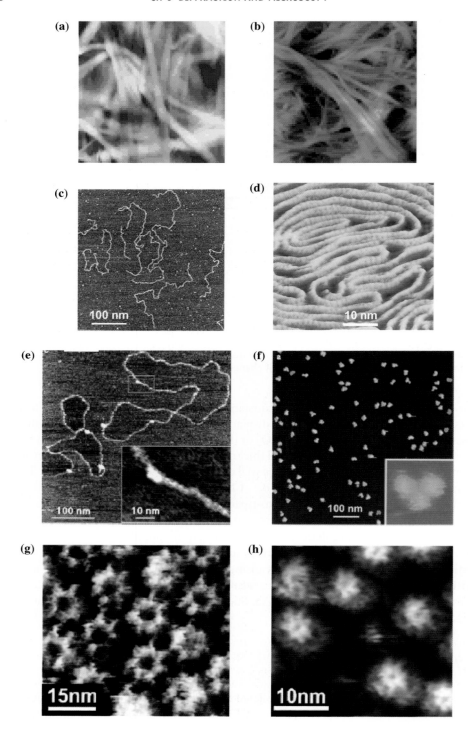

are directly analogous to the CCI and CHI modes respectively used routinely in STM. CFI is the primary scanning mode for AFM analyses and will be discussed first. In STM, a mobile STM tip scans a fixed sample surface of interest. More often than not in AFM the reverse is true and a moving sample surface is scanned against a fixed-position AFM tip. To do this piezo-electric drives scan the sample surface laterally (x, y) against the fixed AFM-tip position by variations in the respective U_x and U_y potential differences applied to drives P_x and P_y. In the CFI mode, vertical (z) adjustments of the sample surface are then made by appropriate changes in U_z potential applied to drive P_z so as to maintain the surface-to-tip force, F_{ST}, constant and the vertical tip displacement, Δz, constant as well. Recorded $(U_x, U_y)U_z$ values may then be translated into a $(x, y)z$ **topographic image**. Once again, to a first approximation a constant surface-to-tip force, F_{ST}, can be considered to result from a constant surface-to-tip distance. Hence this topographic image could be thought of as an accurate rendition of real surface atomic arrangements and should therefore represent a real surface contour map. However, in reality, the CFI mode contour map is in fact a constant force surface that does not necessarily correspond to the real surface. Nevertheless, CFI mode contour maps frequently do provide meaningful and useful images of biological macromolecules (see the next section), in complete contrast with the alternative VDI mode, which appears to provide little information of direct utility for the characterisation of biological macromolecule structure or function. This is in spite of the fact that the VDI mode is directly analogous to the CHI mode used routinely in STM as a local flat area technique for the monitoring of local dynamic processes such as receptor–ligand binding or chemical transformations.

6.6.8 Biological structural information from STM and AFM

STM and AFM are the most direct techniques for structural analysis because image generation does not involve substantial amounts of mathematical processing in order to obtain an image to view. Of these two techniques, AFM now holds the most utility for the visualisation of biological macromolecules and ambient temperatures and even in buffer conditions. Compared with X-ray crystallography, AFM is obviously also a technique still in development rather than fully mature, like cryo-electron microscopy. Nevertheless, we believe that it is necessary

Figure 6.31   AFM Images at different levels of resolution: All images are generated with false colour (**a**) **Collagen fibrils** (Chapter 1); (**b**) **Cellulose fibres** (Chapter 1); (**c**) **plasmid DNA** (Chapter 3); (**d**) DNA attached to cationic surface (Chapter 1); (**e**) DNA adsorbed onto mica and observed in "**humid air**" with RNA polymerase enzyme attached (bright spot) attached: (**f**) **IgG antibody** proteins observed using the fluid "**tapping mode**" in buffer pH 4.0 (see Chapter 7); (**g**) **GroEL** adsorbed onto mica and observed in buffer pH 7.5 (see **Figs. 6.17** and **6.23**; also Chapter 7); (**h**) **GroES** adsorbed onto mica and observed in buffer pH 7.5 (see **Figs. 6.17** and **6.23**; also Chapter 7). Considering the simplicity of the technique, images are impressive, not the least when they are recorded in aqueous buffer! (illustrations a) and b) from www.jpk.com/index.htm; c) from www.spm.phy.bris.ac.uk/research/DNA/dna2.html (A. A. Baker, University of Bristol; e) from Guckenberger et al., 1994, Fig. 3; f) from www.di.com (Digital Instruments, Veeco Metrology Group, Santa Barbara, CA); g) and h) Reproduced from Muller et al., 2002, Fig. 12).

to include this technique here because of the growing improvements in image generation, the inherent potential with this technique for nanometric to atomic-level characterisation of biological macromolecular samples, and the general potential impact that this technique could have on biological macromolecular structure characterisation. The AFM images of GroEL and GroES should suffice to illustrate how close this technique can come in visualisation and resolution power to cryo-electron microscopy (Figure 6.31). Compare these images with the three-dimensionally rendered images of GroEL derived from cryo-electron microscopy previously (Figures 6.23 and 6.24). Moreover, the unique power of AFM to image biological macromolecular samples from nanometric to atomic-level characterisation should also become clear from the two AFM images of collagen and cellulose fibres (see Chapter 1) (Figure 6.31), in comparison to these same high resolution images of GroEL and GroES. Finally, the AFM images of DNA (Figure 6.31), in association with enzymes or a cationic surface, illustrate the power of AFM to render images of biological macromolecules that have no large scale molecular symmetry with minimal effort, owing to the fact that no complex mathematical deconvolutions of data sets are required in producing AFM images in comparison to the situation with X-ray crystallography, or cryo-electron microscopy. Literally, meaningful images can be generated in the time it takes to scan an AFM cantilever over a fixed sample surface of interest to which the biological macromolecule is attached.

7

Molecular Recognition and Binding

7.1 Molecular recognition and binding in chemical biology

Wherever one cares to look in biology, function and activity is founded upon molecular recognition and binding events. These events usually involve interactions between a peptide, protein, nucleic acid, carbohydrate or lipid molecule (**ligand**) and complementary binding sites found in corresponding cognate acceptor molecules (**receptors**), typically proteins, located in lipid membranes or at other key interfaces. Such receptor–ligand interactions are then followed by chemical catalysis if the receptor is a bio-catalyst (see Chapter 8), or else provoke trans-conformational changes in the receptor that then elicit a range of alternate biological responses. Amazingly, the same **non-covalent forces** that create and maintain the structure of biological macromolecules and assemblies (electrostatic forces, van der Waals forces, hydrogen bonds and hydrophobic interactions) are the very same that are involved in molecular recognition and binding events (see Chapter 1). However, the way in which these different forces cooperate together to produce the diversity of molecular recognition and binding events found in biology is breathtaking. Hence the chemical biology reader needs to develop a sound understanding of the principles of molecular recognition and binding events in order to begin properly the journey towards an understanding of the way biology works at the molecular level! Therefore, the objective in this chapter is to map out essential concepts in molecular recognition and binding events, with reference to a few useful biological examples, so that the reader may then have the necessary background to go forward and study other examples of molecular recognition and binding in biology.

Essentials of Chemical Biology   Andrew Miller and Julian Tanner
© 2008 John Wiley & Sons, Ltd

7.1.1 Roles of molecular recognition and binding

Molecular recognition and binding events found in biology are ubiquitous, diverse and pivotal, but there are common themes and principles. In order to impart a flavour of this, we will take a brief look at a number of interlocking but diverse examples of biological molecular recognition and binding events. These examples come from fields as diverse as neurotransmission, bio-catalysis (see Chapter 8), immunity (antibody recognition), autoimmunity, inflammation and chromatin condensation all the way through to the control of gene expression. Truly ubiquitous, diverse and pivotal!

7.1.1.1 *Acetyl choline, receptor and esterase*

Brain tissue is comprised substantially of **neuronal cells** and **glial cells**. The former are the active component of brain tissue responsible for the transmission of sensory, emotional and motor information between brain regions and into the periphery (body) in the form of electrical pulses. The latter are support cells that ensure the metabolic stability and structural integrity of neuronal cells. Neuronal cells communicate with each other through **synaptic junctions** that comprise a narrow intercellular gap (**synaptic cleft**) between membrane regions of two adjacent neuronal cells known as the **presynaptic membrane** and the **postsynaptic membrane** (Figure 7.1). Small molecule messengers known as **neurotransmitters** provide communication across the gap between pre- and postsynaptic membranes. In short, electrical pulses travelling down the presynaptic neuron reach the presynaptic membrane, where they trigger Ca^{2+} influx across the membrane, leading to the migration of **synaptic vesicles** containing neuronal transmitters towards the presynaptic membrane. When they reach the membrane, synaptic vesicles fuse with the presynaptic membrane resulting in the release of substantial neurotransmitter into the synaptic cleft. Neurotransmitter must diffuse across the synaptic junction in order to be recognised by and become bound to binding sites found in **neurotransmitter receptor proteins**. The molecular recognition and binding of the neurotransmitter often facilitates the conversion of the receptor into an ion-channel protein able to re-initiate the propagation of electrical pulses but this time through the postsynaptic neuron. Such a process is critical to the function of all neuronal cells.

One of the main neurotransmitters in the brain is known as **acetylcholine** (**ACh**), which is recognised and bound by the postsynaptic **acetylcholine receptor** (**AChR**) (Figure 7.2). The molecular recognition and binding of ACh by AChR is a seminal event in neurochemistry and as such is archetypical of all binding events between the many known neurotransmitters and their cognate receptor proteins. Neurotransmitters and their interactions with their cognate receptors are central to the chemistry of the brain, and deficiencies (or excesses) of neurotransmitter substances are frequently associated with neurological disease. Indeed, the famous neurodegenerative **Alzheimer disease** has long been associated with deficiencies in neurological levels of ACh, as have various types of clinical depression and memory loss. Whilst the exact details and consequences of the molecular recognition and binding of ACh by AChR have yet to be properly elucidated (in spite of the clear importance), the molecular

(a)

(b)

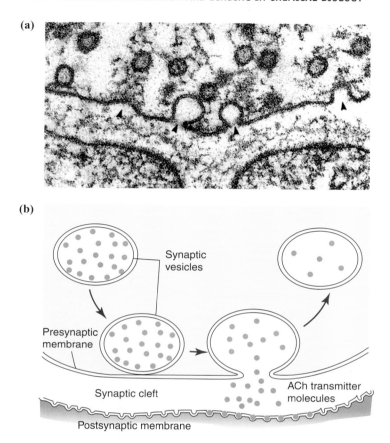

Figure 7.1   Acetyl Choline (ACh) neuronal synapses. (**a**) Electron microscope image. (**b**) Schematic illustration of **synaptic junction** drawn from electron microscope image illustrating the deposition of **ACh transmitter** in the **synaptic cleft** from **synaptic vesicles** (Reproduced from Voet & Voet, 1995 [Wiley], Fig. 34-116).

recognition and binding of ACh by enzyme biocatalyst **acetylcholine esterase (AChE)** is much better known, owing to excellent high resolution X-ray crystallographic data (Figure 7.3), and in many ways is just as significant. AChE will be discussed again (Chapter 8), therefore all that we need to note here is that AChE has a crucial housekeeping function to metabolise excess ACh remaining in the synaptic cleft post-AChR activation, thereby minimising the possibility of neurotransmitter-mediated excitotoxic damage to neighbouring neuronal cells.

7.1.1.2   Adaptive immunity, antibodies and myasthenia gravis

The immune system can seem impossibly complex and indeed the study of the immune system (**immunology**) is without doubt one of the most complex arenas of biology,

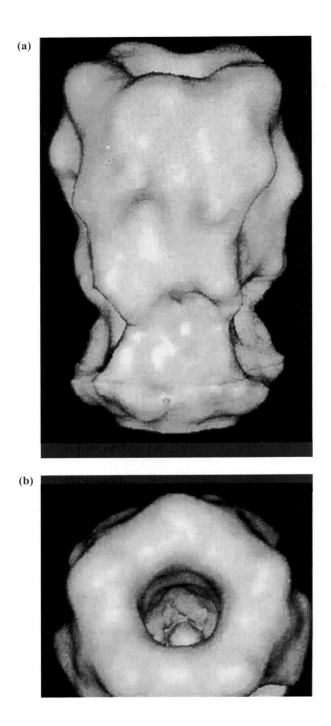

Figure 7.2 Acetyl Choline Receptor (AChR) electron microscopy images of receptor **R** with (**a**) side view-bottom band is the membrane region; (**b**) top-view from the synapse side (Reproduced from Voet & Voet, 1995 [Wiley], Fig. 34-117).

(a)

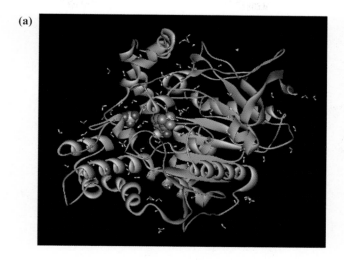

(b)

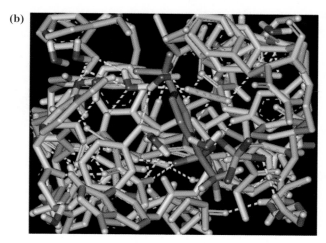

Figure 7.3 AChE X-ray crystallography structures (pdb: **1amn**). (a) **Ribbon display structure** depiction with X-ray crystallographic water molecules illustrated and bound substrate depicted in the **CPK display mode**. Colour coding is as follows: Hydrogen: **White**; Oxygen; **Red**; Nitrogen: **Blue**; Carbon: **Grey**. In this structure, sulphate (Sulphur: **Yellow**) is also included. (b) Close-up of active site to show dense hydrogen-bonding network (**bright yellow**). Bound substrates and water molecules are shown in the **stick display mode**. The protein polypeptide is also shown in **CA display mode**.

comprising a veritable feast of molecular recognition and binding events. In spite of this, there are some useful simplifications once again, in that key components of the immune system such as **antibodies** are amazingly similar in structure. The schematic diagram in Figure 7.4 shows the main architectural features of all antibodies. Four polypeptides, two **heavy chains** and two **light chains**, are linked together covalently by disulphide bonds. Critically, both heavy and both light chains have **constant regions** that differ little between antibodies,

(a)

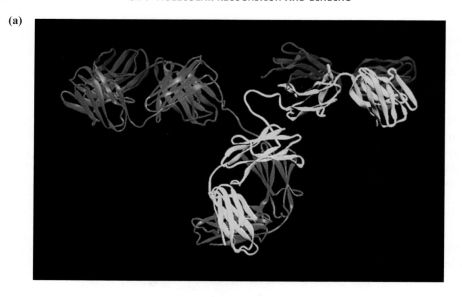

(b)

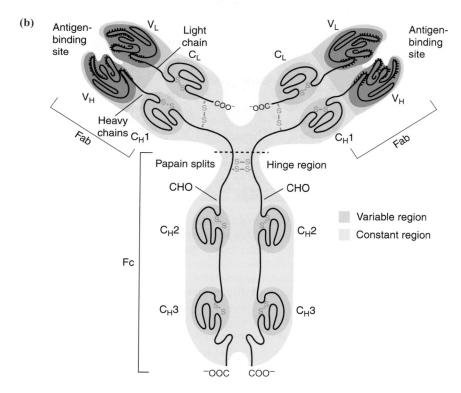

Figure 7.4   Antibody Representations. (a) X-ray crystal structure. (b) **Schematic diagram** drawn from X-ray crystal structure illustrating the conserved structural features of all antibodies (illustrations a) and b) from Voet, Voet & Pratt, 1999 [Wiley], Figs. 7-33 and 7-34 respectively).

irrespective of subclass or type. In addition, both heavy and light chains have also **variable regions** that do vary substantially in amino-acid residue sequence between different types of antibody. Each variable region of a given type of antibody can act as a variable affinity binding site (**antigen binding site**) for the molecular recognition and binding of a complementary protein or peptide known as an **antigen**. Antigens are immune system stimulatory (**immunogenic**) compounds that mobilise the adaptive immune system in response to the formation of antibody–antigen complexes. Immune system diversity is so high in effect that every possible antigen can expect to be matched by a corresponding type of antibody able to recognise and bind to this specific antigen to the exclusion of all others, resulting in a completely specific immune response to this antigen. Such selectivity requires that the antibody type diversity of the immune system must exceed 10^{12}. The chemical biology reader can only marvel that so much diversity in molecular recognition and binding behaviour is possible as a consequence of multiple subtle variations in the amino-acid residue compositions of different antibody variable regions!

Remarkably in the case of the normal functioning of the immune system, self-proteins and peptides do not normally become immune stimulatory antigens, but in autoimmune diseases they do. One such example is myasthenia gravis (**MG**), in which antibodies are generated that target peptide regions (**epitopes**) on the AChR protein, causing destruction of the protein and loss of neuronal cell function (Figure 7.5). If only the process of molecular recognition and binding could be adequately understood in this case, then the ravaging consequences of this

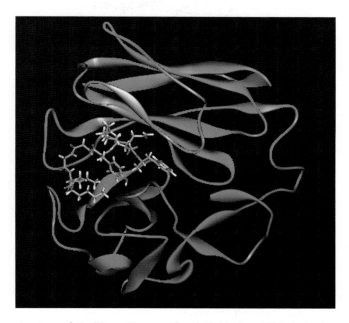

Figure 7.5 X-ray structure of F_V (V_H + V_L; see **Fig. 7.4**) binding AChR-derived peptide (pdb: **1f3r**). This molecular recognition & binding event explains a cascade of events that leads to autoimmunity and self-destruction of the **AChR**.

neurological disorder could be avoided by the design of appropriate inhibitors. An alternative approach might be to study the multi-centre interaction of cytokine **interleukin 1β (IL-1β)** (see Chapter 5) with its **cognate receptor IL-1R**. The molecular recognition and binding of IL-1β to IL-1R is an essential signal for inflammation by stimulating the proliferation of immune system cells as well as other agents of inflammation. As with the immune system, the inflammatory system is equally diverse and complex but underpinned by sequences of molecular recognition and binding events. By studying the interaction between IL-1β and IL-1R (Figure 7.6), there is the promise of being able to identify inhibitors to a molecular

(a)

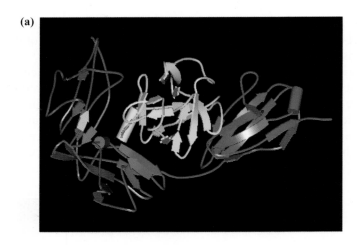

(b)

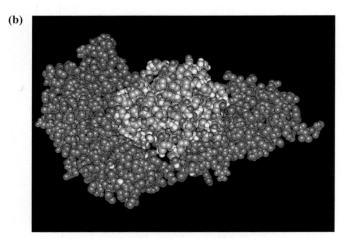

Figure 7.6   Cytokine interleukin-1β (IL-1β) interacting with cognate **IL-1 receptor (IL-1R)** (pdb; **1itb**). **(a)** Side view of IL-1β (**Schematic display; Yellow**) interacting with IL-1R (**Schematic display; Red**). **(b)** Side view of the same but both IL-1β and IL-1R are rendered in **CPK display structure** mode to show density of molecular packing.

interaction that plays a very significant role in generating potentially harmful inflammatory effects during the progress of such neurodegenerative diseases as AD and MG.

7.1.1.3   DNA packaging and expression control

One of the great triumphs of molecular recognition and binding in biology is the controlled packaging for storage and unpackaging for function of DNA in eukaryotic cell nuclei. The secret to this is the phenomenal ordering of DNA into **chromosomes** by means of highly cationic proteins. Chromosomes comprise **chromatin filaments** that themselves comprise myriad **nucleosome core particles** (Figure 7.7). Each nucleosome particle contains four **histone proteins** (**H2A, H2B, H3** and **H4**) that are tightly packed and able to distort DNA double helix to wrap around each set of four proteins twice. Each core particle is then clipped together by a rod of **H1 histone protein**. Four nucleosome core particles in a row form a zigzag arrangement that closes up to form a **solenoid** with six core particles per turn. This solenoid is the basic repeat structure of each chromatin filament. The phenomenal charge–charge recognition by H2A, H2B, H3 and H4 is largely responsible for the extraordinary capacity of these proteins to distort the DNA helical axis from linear to bent with a high degree of curvature. However, little remains known about the molecular processes of assembly and disassembly of chromatin filaments after and before gene expression events.

In DNA terms, the other great triumph of molecular recognition and binding is the control of gene expression through DNA-sequence selective protein binding. Proteins that bind DNA and control expression are known as **transcription factors**. One such is the **GCN4 protein** of yeast that is perhaps the first to be studied in molecular detail (Figure 7.8). The extraordinary fact is that DNA has impressively few genes in the total length, especially where eukaryotes are concerned. In total there are 33 000 human genes as against approximately 30 000 nematode genes and a few thousand in most bacteria. Given the fact that there is relatively little difference between the **human genome** and the **nematode genome** in terms of overall gene number, then the old adage must apply, that is *it is not how many you have but how you use them*. In other words, the high level of expression control (both temporal and cellular) during human development as compared to the situation in nematode development must be the presiding reason that humans are many times more complex as organisms than nematodes. Transcription factors are central to this process of expression control although not the complete reason. The molecular recognition and binding of DNA by GCN4 rests with the remarkable **scissors grip**, where cationic amino-acid residues in the *N*-terminal regions of each extended α-helix charge complement anionic phosphates of the phosphodiester backbone and these residues together with other amino-acid residues make intimate contact with base-pair-specific deoxynucleotide sequences within DNA involving interactions along the DNA major groove. These sequences are non-coding sequences that do not constitute part of any gene but represent control sequences involved in regulating and modulating gene expression through specific interaction with proteins such as transcription factors.

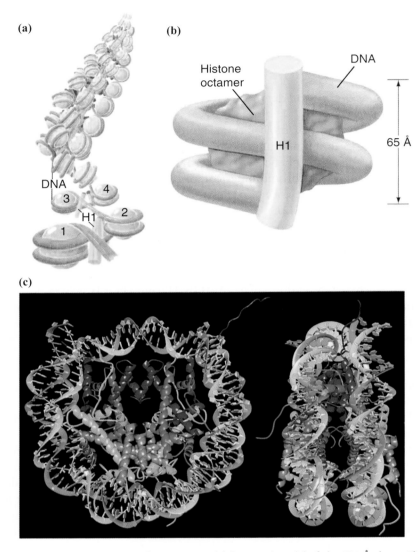

Figure 7.7   Chromatin Filament to Chromosome. (**a**) Proposed model of the 300 Å chromatin filament. The zigzag pattern of **nucleosomes** (1,2,3,4) closes up to form a solenoid with ∼6 nucleosomes per turn. (**b**) Model of histone H1 binding to the DNA of the nucleosome. (**c**) X-ray crystal structure of the **nucleosome core particle**. Two views are illustrated (top-left and side-right) showing **histone octamer** in ribbon structure form (**H2A yellow; H2B red; H3 blue; H4 green**) (illustrations a), b) and c). Reproduced from Voet, Voet & Pratt, 1999 [Wiley], Figs. 23-48, 23-45 and 23-44 respectively).

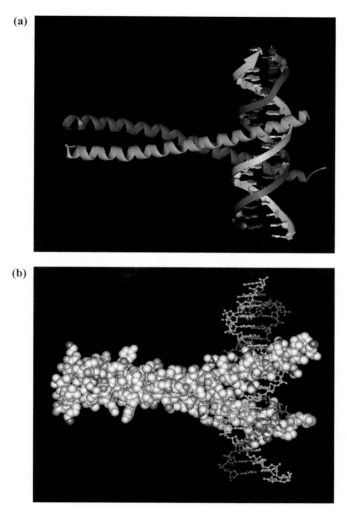

Figure 7.8 X-ray structure of **GCN4 eukaryotic transcription factor** and interactions with double-stranded DNA (pdb: **1ysa**). (**a**) Two helices of protein are shown (red and yellow) in **ribbon display structure**: Two strands of DNA are shown in **rings display**. (**b**) Alternative depiction in which protein is shown in **CPK display mode** (Carbon: **Grey**; Oxygen: **Red**: Nitrogen: **Blue**). Two strands of DNA (blue and yellow) are shown in **ball and stick display structures**.

7.1.2 Theoretical framework for molecular recognition and binding events

From a pharmaceutical point of view, any molecular recognition and binding event such as those mentioned above could represent a critical drug target to alleviate some disease symptoms or even cure the disease, with obvious benefits for patients. Hence a proper molecular-level understanding of recognition and binding events is not just basic knowledge, but may also be a critical prerequisite for successful disease treatment as well. Therefore, the chemical biology reader can surely have no doubts concerning the importance of research in this arena! Unfortunately, we cannot usually study molecular recognition and binding events without a considerable effort in terms of the synthesis/overexpression and purification of the key biological macromolecular components concerned (see Chapters 2 and 3), followed by structural characterisation where possible and desirable (see Chapters 4–6). Only once the appropriate components are available and structurally understood can studies on molecular recognition and binding events truly begin making use of a theoretical framework. This theoretical framework will be covered in this next part of the chapter. Before we begin, however, we make one important point. In any discussion (theoretical or practical) about molecular recognition and binding events, there is often a regrettable tendency to ignore the entire preceding molecular recognition process and concentrate only upon binding. Consequently, most discussions about molecular recognition and binding events barely cover the key issues of molecular motions (translations, rotations, conformational changes) prior to binding and how these are perturbed during long range and then during short range molecular recognition in order to guide a given ligand into making a productive binding encounter with a given cognate receptor. Accordingly, we are presenting a theoretical framework that begins with a short introduction to long range (early) and short range (late) molecular recognition behaviour before continuing on with binding events proper.

7.1.2.1 *Motion in solution*

All biological macromolecules in water medium translate by random or **Brownian motion** in the absence of any applied force. Motion becomes organised the moment an external force is applied by means of an external electric or magnetic field, or as a consequence of gravitational or centrifugal effects. Brownian motion represents the origin and basis of biological macromolecular **diffusion**, a term that represents the combined processes of bulk biological macromolecule movement in a given aqueous buffer medium. The translation and rotation of biological macromolecules also has an inverse effect upon overall water medium properties as well. The primary reason for this is that individual biological macromolecules interact with and bind to substantial numbers of water molecules in aqueous buffer medium. Furthermore, in aqueous buffer medium, counter-ions and biological macromolecules also associate together such that their motions are coupled. As a result, the movement properties of biological macromolecules are an average of small molecule and large macromolecule properties.

Water hydration and counter-ion solvation of biological macromolecules considerably alter the translational and rotational dynamics of biological macromolecules. The effect can be correlated with a number of different solution properties of a given biological macromolecule such as the **hydrated volume** V_h. The term V_h is given by

$$V_h = (M_{MM}/N_0)(\overline{V}_{MM} - \delta \overline{V}_{H_2O}) \qquad (7.1)$$

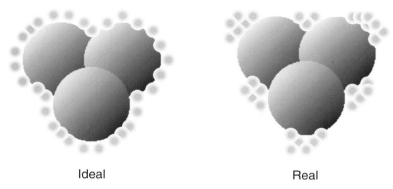

Ideal   Real

Figure 7.9 **Smooth surface hydration** (**ideal**) versus **differential surface hydration by differential affinities** (**real**). Biological macromolecule is represented as summation of grey spheres, water as light blue spheres.

where M_{MM} is the **macromolecule molecular weight**, N_0 is **Avogadro's number**, $\overline{V}_{MM}$ is the **macromolecular partial specific volume** (typically about 0.73 cm^3 g^{-1} for a globular protein and 0.5 for nucleic acids with one Na^+ counter-ion per phosphodiester link) and δ is the **hydration level** (typically 0.3–0.4 for a globular protein). The term $\overline{V}_{H_2O}$ is the **specific volume of bulk water**. Hydration layers are typically 2.8 Å thick at the interfaces between biological macromolecules and the aqueous buffer medium in which they reside. Accordingly, hydration effectively corresponds to a **surface-bound monolayer** of water around the entire accessible surface area of a given biological macromolecule, with other water molecules being bound only transiently beyond the confines of this monolayer. In reality, most biological macromolecules do not have a 'smooth' surface, so a monolayer distribution is not observed save as a surface-average phenomenon. Instead, macromolecules have a certain surface 'roughness', with the result that water molecules of hydration cluster around hydrophilic regions and charges to a greater extent and around hydrophobic regions to a lesser extent (Figure 7.9); for instance, six or seven water molecules will cluster around a charged amino-acid residue in a protein but only one water molecule engages tightly with a hydrophobic amino-acid residue.

Given the highly interactive nature of water molecules and counter-ions with biological macromolecules in aqueous buffer medium, translational or rotational movements of biological macromolecules through buffer medium are significantly impeded. In other words, there are **frictional forces** operating between macromolecules and aqueous buffer medium due to intermolecular interactions that act to retard the rate of macromolecular movement through the aqueous buffer medium and macromolecular rotation. These intermolecular interactions ensure that as each biological macromolecule moves forward then surface-bound and even remote water molecules become displaced. The extent of displacement diminishes with distance from the macromolecule (Figure 7.10). Frictional forces are quantified through the simple definition that *a frictional force equals that force required to maintain velocity or angular velocity constant*. From this simple definition, equations may be derived.

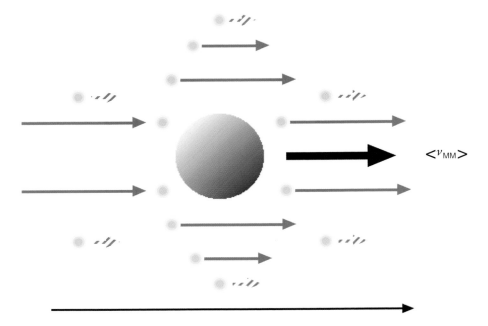

Figure 7.10 Illustration of **Stick Boundary Condition**. Solute biological macromolecule shown as single grey sphere moves with an average velocity $<v_{MM}>$ through water (shown as light blue spheres). Water molecules in immediate hydration layer move at the same average velocity due to tight hydration interactions. Under **Slip Boundary Conditions**, water molecules do not possess hydration interactions and therefore do not move with the biological macromolecule at all.

In the case of the translational frictional forces opposing translational motion, there are two extremes known as the **stick boundary condition (strong intermolecular interactions)** and the **slip boundary condition (negligible intermolecular interactions)** that are characterised by the following two basic equations ((7.2) and (7.3) respectively):

$$f_{\text{trans,sph}} = 6\pi \eta r_{\text{sph}} \tag{7.2}$$

$$f_{\text{trans,sph}} = 4\pi \eta r_{\text{sph}} \tag{7.3}$$

where $f_{\text{trans,sph}}$ is the **coefficient of translational frictional force** acting on a spherical macromolecule, r_{sph} is the **spherical macromolecular radius** and η is the **viscosity** of the aqueous buffer medium. Equation (7.2) is known as **Stokes' law**. Under stick boundary conditions, the water molecules that comprise the immediate hydration layer interact so well with a given biological macromolecule that they move at the same pace as that macromolecule. Under slip boundary conditions, the water molecules that comprise the immediate hydration layer interact to a negligible extent and so have no forward velocity imparted from any given macromolecule (Figure 7.10). In the case of the rotational friction forces that oppose rotational motion, the **coefficient of rotational friction force**, $f_{\text{rot,sph}}$, acting on a spherical molecule tends to zero under slip boundary conditions. Therefore, we only need consider the situation under stick boundary conditions. In this instance, Equation (7.4) applies:

$$f_{rot,sph} = 6\eta\, V_{sph} \tag{7.4}$$

where V_{sph} is the **spherical macromolecular volume.**

However, it should be obvious that a smooth, perfect sphere makes for a poor approximation of biological macromolecule shape. As a result Equations (7.2)–(7.4) do not account very accurately for the frictional forces acting upon a given biological macromolecule in motion. Fortunately, this situation may be resolved to a first approximation for globular proteins by introducing a monolayer of hydration to the sphere and then applying the stick boundary conditions without reservation. In this instance, translational and rotational frictional forces acting on a given biological macromolecule in motion in aqueous buffer medium are then defined by the revised equations

$$f_{trans} = 6\pi\, \eta (3\, V_h/4\pi)^{1/3} \tag{7.5}$$

$$f_{rot} = 6\eta\, V_h \tag{7.6}$$

Unfortunately, a uniformly hydrated sphere provides a rather poor approximation of many other biological macromolecules in solution. Instead, an **oblate ellipsoid** or a **prolate ellipsoid** give a much closer approximation to the shape of many biological macromolecules in solution that are not spherical but are compact, globular or irregular rigid bodies (Figure 7.11)! In this event, there is a further need to modify the equations that define translational and rotational friction forces. Hence Equation (7.5) becomes

$$f_{trans} = 6\pi\, \eta\, F_{trans}(3\, V_h/4\pi)^{1/3} \tag{7.7}$$

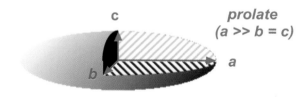

Figure 7.11   Two **non-spheroidal representations** of biological macromolecules in solution.

where F_{trans} is known as the translational **shape factor** or **Perrin factor**. In a similar way Equation (7.6) becomes either

$$f_{rot,a} = 6\eta\, F_{rot,a}\, V_h \tag{7.8}$$

or

$$f_{rot,b} = 6\eta\, F_{rot,b}\, V_h \tag{7.9}$$

respectively depending upon whether there is primary rotation about the a-axis or the b-axis of the ellipsoid in solution. In all cases, shape factors are greater than zero. In the event that the biological macromolecule takes on an extended linear form in aqueous buffer solution, then the translational friction forces can be defined on the assumption that the linear form is comprised of linked spherical but non-interacting segments by a simple variation of Equation (7.5):

$$f_{trans} = N\zeta = N6\pi\eta(3\,V_{seg,h}/4\pi)^{1/3} \tag{7.10}$$

where N is the segment number and $V_{seg,h}$ is the **hydrated segment volume**.

Having now discussed hydrated volume, molecular shape and the frictional forces that oppose rotational and translational motion, we are now ready to discuss **diffusion**, the complete set of processes (including Brownian motion) that together bring about the bulk movement of biological macromolecules from one place to another in aqueous buffer solution. The processes that comprise diffusion are quantified by means of the concept of **flux**. Flux is defined as

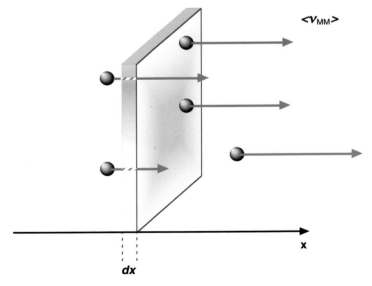

Figure 7.12 Diagrammatic illustration of biological macromolecular diffusion through an area of depth *dx*.

the *rate of mass transport across a unit surface area* (Figure 7.12). Hence for a two-component system of biological macromolecule in water, the **flux of macromolecular solute**, J_{MM}, in water traversing a unit surface area (1 m² or 1 cm² as appropriate) can be defined by

$$J_{MM} = C_{MM} \langle v_{MM} \rangle \tag{7.11}$$

where C_{MM} is **biological macromolecule concentration** and $\langle v_{MM} \rangle$ is **average macromolecule velocity**. Whilst this view of flux gives the correct dimensions and value for J_{MM}, there is a regrettable lack of directionality in this expression. Therefore, flux is often redefined in terms of time-dependent changes in the macromolecular concentration gradient along a defined axis (by convention the *x*-axis) (Figure 7.12). Since we have selected one from a possible three Cartesian axes, then the concentration gradient must be described in the form of a partial differential proportionality expression:

$$J_{MM} \propto - (\partial C_{MM}/\partial x)_t \tag{7.12}$$

Converting this into an equation, the result is

$$J_{MM} = - D_{MM} (\partial C_{MM}/\partial x)_t \tag{7.13}$$

where D_{MM} is known as a **diffusion coefficient**. Equation (7.13) is known as **Fick's first law of diffusion**. For biological macromolecules, D_{MM} is usually 10^{-7} to 10^{-6} cm² s^{-1} for macromolecules moving according to Brownian motion. This is a lower limit for macromolecule diffusion that is undeniably slow! However, macromolecular diffusion is much enhanced when an external force is applied and also when a molecular recognition and binding event takes place, in which case molecular motion leading to binding is accelerated as described in the following section. Before such perturbations to Brownian motion are discussed, it is worth noting that there is an attractively simple relationship between those coefficients of translational friction force f_{trans}, expressed according to molecular shape by Equations (7.5), (7.7) or (7.10), and the corresponding **diffusion coefficient at infinite macromolecular dilution**, $D_{0,MM}$. This relationship is given by

$$D_{0,MM} = \frac{kT}{f_{trans}} \tag{7.14}$$

where k is the Boltzmann constant. Equation (7.14) is known as the **Einstein–Sutherland equation** and shows that $D_{0,MM}$ is dependent on both temperature T and viscosity η. Therefore, values of $D_{0,MM}$ are usually standardised to measurements made with biological macromolecules dispersed in pure water at 20 °C and not aqueous buffer medium.

7.1.2.2 Long range molecular recognition

Biological macromolecules in translation by Brownian motion alone are inevitably very slow and infrequent. The expression that governs the **encounter rate**, k_a, between two types of biological macromolecule A and B in aqueous buffer medium is given as follows:

$$k_a = 4\pi N_0\, r_{AB}(D_A + D_B)10^3 (M^{-1}s^{-1}) \tag{7.15}$$

where N_0 is Avogadro's number and r_{AB} the **sum of the two macromolecule radii**, while D_A and D_B are **diffusion constants** for A and B respectively (Figure 7.13). Note that both r_{AB} and the diffusion constants are expressed in centimetre units, therefore the 10^3 term is included in Equation (7.15) in order that the encounter rate can be expressed in units of M^{-1} s^{-1} (i.e. l mol^{-1} s^{-1}; where $1\,l = 10^3$ cm^3). Typically, values of k_a emerge at between 10^8 and 10^9 M^{-1} s^{-1}. While this number of molecular encounters per unit concentration per unit time may seem large, there is no certainty that these will be productive binding encounters without additional interventions from long range molecular recognition processes.

In the case of biological molecular recognition and binding events, recognition is often promoted significantly by the complementary electrostatic surface properties of biological ligands and their cognate receptors. The surfaces of biological macromolecules can be treated as systems of point charges and electrostatic dipoles that interact with each other. Point charges in particular provide for especially long range attractive electrostatic interactions ($1/r$ dependency; where r is the intermolecular distance) (see Chapter 1 for the expression for the potential energy of monopole–monopole interactions) and are likely to play key roles in mediating the long range molecular recognition between biological ligands and their cognate receptors. Attractive electrostatic effects not only enhance encounter rates by increasing effective values of diffusion constants but may also 'steer' ligands and cognate receptors to make productive binding encounters with each other owing to the presence of

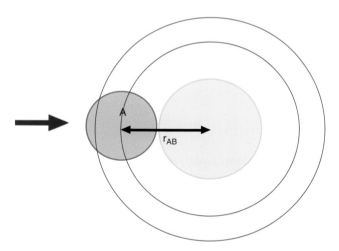

Figure 7.13 Ligand **A** collides with the biological macromolecular **receptor B** by traversing through a spherical surface of area $4\pi r_{AB}^2$ that is concentric about **B**. The total flux of **A** through this spherical surface, taking into account that **B** is also moving leads to a derivation of the encounter rate k_a (**equation 7.15**).

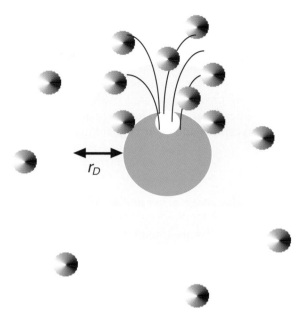

Figure 7.14   Late molecular recognition. Electrostatic field lines radiate from systems of point charges and dipoles that are located over the entire surface of the biological macromolecule receptor (red). Influence of charge/dipole systems diminish to insignificance beyond the **Debye Length r_D** from the macromolecular surface. Charge/dipole systems are extensive in the vicinity of the binding site (white region) and radiate electrostatic lines of force (blue) that assist the close range navigation of ligand molecules (grey) into binding interactions within the receptor binding site by means of close-range and contact forces.

uneven but complementary distributions of surface point charges and electrostatic dipoles (Figure 7.14).

These attractive electrostatic interactions are attenuated in aqueous buffer medium due to ionic screening effects from buffer salts. Any biological macromolecule associates with counter-ions and also attracts a cloud of more weakly associated ions and counter-ions at greater distance from the macromolecule surface. The presence of these weakly associated ions and counter-ions alters the **permittivity** ε of the aqueous buffer medium and in so doing reduces the magnitude of electrostatic attractions (see Equation (1.2)). The attenuating effect of ions and counter-ions on electrostatic interactions in aqueous buffer medium can be viewed another way through the **Debye–Hückel theory**, which gives us

$$r_D = \left(\frac{\varepsilon k T}{2 N_0 e^2 I} \right)^{1/2} \tag{7.16}$$

where r_D is known as the **Debye length** and I is the **ionic strength** of the buffer medium in question. The Debye length represents the upper distance limit of separation between two point charges beyond which electrostatic interactions become negligible owing to the decline in electrostatic potential V that takes place as charges separate to greater and greater distances from each other (see Equation (1.2)). Equation (7.16) includes several terms relating to the nature of the aqueous buffer medium in which the point charges may be located, of which ionic strength is especially influential upon the value of r_D. Critically, r_D varies between 5 and 10 Å in aqueous buffer media as values of I vary from 0.4 to 0.1 M. Such values of I are typical of many physiological aqueous buffer media and therefore 5–10 Å represents an approximate upper distance limit for long range molecular recognition between biological macromolecular receptors and their cognate ligands in aqueous buffer medium (Figure 7.14).

7.1.2.3 Short range molecular recognition and binding

Once ligands and their cognate receptors come into close proximity, there are a number of factors that come into play in order to maximise the opportunities for productive binding encounters. First and foremost, complementary attractive long range electrostatic interactions are replaced by complementary attractive short range electrostatic and van der Waals interactions that also act to 'steer' ligands and cognate receptors to make productive binding encounters. This is made all the more possible because macromolecule collisions in aqueous buffer medium usually result in the formation of long lived, non-covalent encounter complexes (in contrast with small molecules), owing to the extensive disruption of water of hydration at the time of collision, followed by the reinstatement of water of hydration in such a way as to make a new solvent cage around the entire encounter complex, locking ligands and cognate receptors into extended proximity (Figure 7.14). The two macromolecules may then explore one another through numerous short range collisions and surface diffusion until attractive intermolecular interactions are optimised through docking of ligands into appropriate binding sites in their cognate receptors. Binding strength (see below) is then further optimised during docking by the formation of strong contact interactions such as hydrogen bonds, and by careful adaptation between ligands and receptor binding sites so as to maximise both attractive short range interactions and also contributions to binding strength from the hydrophobic effect through the wholesale exclusion of water molecules of hydration from the binding interface (Figure 7.14) (see Chapter 1).

7.2 Theoretical models of binding

Having considered something of the theories of biological macromolecular motion, collisions and encounters in an aqueous buffer medium, we now require a framework with which to be able to study and measure the effectiveness of final binding events themselves. Fundamentally, 'everything can be said to bind to everything else' to a greater or lesser extent. Molecules in a biological milieu are continuously associating with and dissociating from neighbouring molecules. The vast majority of these binding events are too weak and transient to measure effectively. These are known as **non-specific binding events** (or **non-specific interactions**). Studies of molecular recognition are primarily concerned with the tiny minority of strong,

$$R \quad + \quad L \quad \rightleftharpoons \quad RL$$

Scheme 7.1

stable interactions otherwise known as **specific binding events** (or **specific interactions**). These stand 'head and shoulders' above the non-specific background, a bit like spectral peaks projecting above background noise. Specific binding events are the cornerstone of chemical biology.

7.2.1 Single-site, single-affinity binding

In order to study binding, theoretical models, analytical equations and appropriate constants are needed to characterise the strength of a given binding event. Single-site, single-affinity binding is the easiest form of binding to model. In this case the binding equilibrium is represented by the binding scheme in Scheme 7.1, where R is receptor (enzyme, protein etc.) and L is ligand. For this simple binding equilibrium, we can define two **equilibrium binding constants** that give a measure of the equilibrium position, either to the right-hand side of the equation or to the left-hand side. These two constants are the **association constant**, K_a, given by

$$K_a = \frac{[RL]}{[R][L]} (M^{-1}) \tag{7.17}$$

or the **dissociation constant**, K_d, given by

$$K_d = \frac{[R][L]}{[RL]} (M) \tag{7.18}$$

Either constant will do but they are reciprocals of each other. The principal units of K_a can be defined as per molar (M^{-1}) and the units of K_d as molar (M) (NB M = mol l^{-1} or mol dm^{-3}). These constants define the strength and integrity of molecular recognition at the single binding site under the equilibrium conditions being investigated. Generally speaking, K_a values of 10^5–10^6 M^{-1} or higher correspond to tight, specific binding equilibria. In other words, K_d values of 10^{-5}–10^{-6} M (or 10^{-1} μM, where $\mu M = \mu mol\ dm^{-3}$). Much of our understanding and appreciation of molecular recognition events derives from our being able to measure and interpret the magnitude of these constants. Therefore, a good deal of this chapter will be concerned with equilibrium binding constants and how we measure them.

In order to measure any constant, we need an equation that relates this constant to variables that may be determined by experiment. For a single-site, single-affinity binding model, there is a relatively simple way of deriving such an equation. If we define total concentration of receptor $[R]_0$ according to

$$[R]_0 = [RL] + [R] \tag{7.19}$$

so that total receptor concentration is a sum of the concentrations of ligand bound and ligand free states. If we now substitute for [R] from Equation (7.17) then we achieve the following:

$$[R]_0 = [RL] + \frac{[RL]}{K_a[L]} \tag{7.20}$$

which rearranges to

$$[RL] = [R]_0 \left(\frac{K_a[L]}{1 + K_a[L]} \right) \tag{7.21}$$

Finally, let us introduce B, which represents the number of moles of ligand L bound per mole of receptor R (B may also be defined as the combined mole fraction of ligand L bound to receptor). This is given mathematically by the simple ratio represented by

$$B = \frac{[RL]}{[R]_0} \tag{7.22}$$

Substituting for [RL] from Equation (7.21) then gives us the following expression that happily relates K_a to experimental variables:

$$B = \frac{K_a[L]}{1 + K_a[L]} \tag{7.23}$$

Equation (7.23) is a classical rectangular hyperbola as shown by a typical plot of B versus [L] (Figure 7.15). This plot is sometimes known as a **binding isotherm**. A similar rectangular hyperbola is also seen in biocatalyst studies, reflecting the fact that if sufficient ligand is present then all the active sites in a receptor should be effectively occupied or saturated with ligand on a continuous basis with time. *The binding isotherm and related functions is absolutely fundamental to biological molecular recognition and binding.* Very commonly, Equation (7.23) is transposed into a linear form:

$$B = 1 - \frac{1}{K_a} \frac{B}{[L]} \tag{7.24}$$

which is known as a **Scatchard equation**. This linear form is also illustrated (Figure 7.16). It is impressive how often this very simple equation surfaces in the analysis of equilibrium binding constants, as we shall see. This equation also has the necessary virtue that the two variables B and [L] may be measured with relative ease by a wide range of possible techniques as described later on in this chapter.

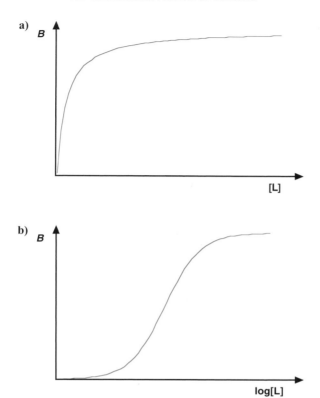

Figure 7.15 Ideal binding isotherms. (**a**) Classical hyperbolic binding isotherm obtained by plotting values of **B** against **[L]**. (**b**) Classical semi-log plot obtained by plotting values of **B** against **log[L]**. Appearance of sigmoidal shape implies that binding interactions between ligand and receptor are $>70\%$ saturated and binding data are therefore appropriate to derive accurate **association constant** K_a or **dissociation constant** K_d values.

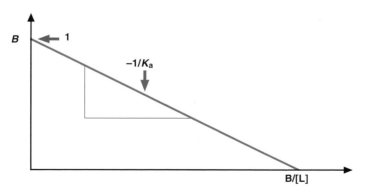

Figure 7.16   Ideal single-site, single-affinity binding **Scatchard Plot**.

7.2.2 Independent multiple-site, equal affinity binding

The Scatchard equation can be very simply adapted for a multiple-site, single-affinity binding model as well. In this case, the binding equilibrium equation can be represented by the binding scheme in Scheme 7.2, where n corresponds to the total number of independent binding sites located on the receptor R. Equal site affinity is critical. If the affinity of each binding site were different for each ligand L, then we would be forced to use a **multiple-site, variable affinity binding model** which is a great deal more complicated (see Section 7.2.3)! However, where independent binding sites are involved of approximately equal affinity then the combined mole fraction for binding can be simply expressed as

$$B = \frac{\sum_{i=1}^{i=n} [RL]_i}{[R]_0} \tag{7.25}$$

By analogy to the derivation of Equation (7.23), we can then substitute for the sum of $[RL]_i$ terms with a sum of rectangular hyperbolic expressions as follows:

$$B = \sum_{1}^{n} \frac{K_a[L]}{1 + K_a[L]} \tag{7.26}$$

where K_a is now the **site association constant** for *each* individual ith binding site. K_a is identical for each individual binding site, hence the simple sum expression can be converted into the simple product expression

$$B = n\frac{K_a[L]}{1 + K_a[L]} \tag{7.27}$$

Equation (7.27) can then be transposed into the linear form

$$B = n - \frac{1}{K_a}\frac{B}{[L]} \tag{7.28}$$

This linear form, Equation (7.28), is also illustrated (Figure 7.17). Note that B becomes equal to n at complete saturation binding when $[L]$ is in large excess and all receptor binding sites are occupied.

7.2.3 Independent multiple-site, variable affinity binding

Multiple-site, variable affinity binding models are necessarily much more complicated and demand some quite fearsome mathematics to model correctly. For this reason, we would try

$$\mathbf{R} \quad + \quad n\mathbf{L} \quad \rightleftharpoons \quad \mathbf{RL}_n$$

Scheme 7.2

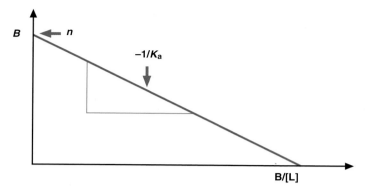

Figure 7.17 Ideal independent multiple-site, equal affinity binding **Scatchard Plot**.

and apply simpler binding models wherever possible. In the case of multiple-site, variable affinity binding models, binding behaviour cannot be reduced to a single equilibrium binding event but is comprised of a series of binding equilibria that each fit the general scheme (Scheme 7.3), where the total number of independent binding sites of variable affinity located on receptor R is n and the final saturating binding equilibrium corresponds with the situation when i equals n. Each binding equilibrium for a given site has independent **stoichiometric equilibrium binding constants**. By analogy to Equation (7.17), the equation for each **stoichiometric association constant**, $K_{a,i}$, is as follows:

$$K_{a,i} = \frac{[RL_i]}{[RL_{i-1}][L]} \tag{7.29}$$

In comparison with the previous section, the relationship between B and the complete set of $K_{a,i}$ constants does not involve a simple sum converting through into a simple product expression, but is instead a complex polynomial expression of degree n:

$$B = \frac{K_{a,1}[L] + 2K_{a,1}K_{a,2}[L]^2 + \cdots i(K_{a,1}K_{a,2}\ldots K_{a,i})[L]^i + \cdots n(K_{a,1}K_{a,2}\cdots K_{a,n})[L]^n}{1 + K_{a,1}[L] + K_{a,1}K_{a,2}[L]^2 + \cdots (K_{a,1}K_{a,2}\ldots K_{a,i})[L]^i + \cdots (K_{a,1}K_{a,2}\cdots K_{a,n})[L]^n} \tag{7.30}$$

undeniably a complex expression! There are n terms in this equation corresponding to the n roots of the polynomial representing the number of independent binding sites in the receptor R. This is known as a **real sites equation**, with good reason as we shall see. In order to solve such an equation, the polynomial needs to be equated with another algebraic expression. This new expression is known as a **ghost sites equation** that has all the appearance of Equation (7.26), except comprised of **stoichiometric ghost site association constants** that are all different

$$RL_{i\text{-}1} \quad + \quad L \; \rightleftharpoons \; RL_i$$

Scheme 7.3

from each other:

$$B = \frac{K_\alpha[\mathrm{L}]}{1 + K_\alpha[\mathrm{L}]} + \frac{K_\beta[\mathrm{L}]}{1 + K_\beta[\mathrm{L}]} + \cdots \frac{K_\mathrm{v}[\mathrm{L}]}{1 + K_\mathrm{v}[\mathrm{L}]} = \sum_\alpha^\mathrm{v} \frac{K_\omega[\mathrm{L}]}{1 + K_\omega[\mathrm{L}]} \tag{7.31}$$

Do not confuse K_α–K_ω with the **stoichiometric real site association constants** in Equation (7.30). The ghost site constants are not real numbers but are in fact imaginary numbers, pure mathematical conveniences that allow us to write Equation (7.31) in a form that is more amenable to solution and then equate this to the polynomial expression (7.30)!

A simple example should serve to illustrate how equations of the form of (7.30) and (7.31) can be used in combination to solve for stoichiometric real site association constants. Imagine we have a receptor R with two independent binding sites of two different affinities. In a real scenario, four equilibria and two stoichiometric association constants account for the interaction between two separate ligands L and this receptor (Figure 7.18). Two independent equilibria then make up a parallel imaginary scenario (Figure 7.18). A real sites equation

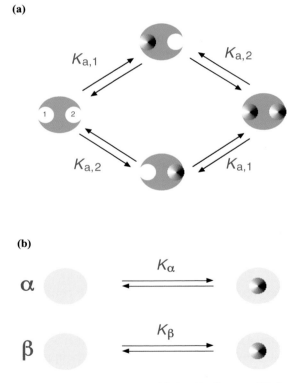

Figure 7.18 Independent multiple-site variable affinity binding equilibria. (**a**) Diagram illustrates the emergence of four different equilibrium constants to describe the binding interactions between ligands (grey) and two independent binding sites of significantly different affinities found in a biological macromolecular receptor (red). (**b**) Imaginary "parallel" single-site, single-affinity ghost sites equilibria used to help derive a unique solution for equilibrium constants applicable to situation shown in (**a**).

(polynomial of degree 2) may be written to account for the real scenario and then directly equated with a ghost sites equation containing two summed terms harbouring two different imaginary numbers K_α and K_β as shown:

$$\frac{K_{a,1}[L] + 2K_{a,1}K_{a,2}[L]^2}{1 + K_{a,1}[L] + K_{a,1}K_{a,2}[L]^2} = B = \frac{K_\alpha[L]}{1 + K_\alpha[L]} + \frac{K_\beta[L]}{1 + K_\beta[L]} \tag{7.32}$$

Experimental values of B and $[L]$ may then be used to solve for K_α and K_β in the right-hand equality, which are in turn used to extract values of $K_{a,1}$ and $K_{a,2}$ from the left-hand equality. Hopefully, it is clear how this approach can be expanded in general to include receptors with more than two independent binding sites of different affinities using additional roots of the polynomial on the left and additional imaginary terms on the right.

7.2.4 Dependent multiple-site cooperative binding and Hill equation

The moment that we lift the constraint of independent binding sites, the number of possible interlinked equilibria, each with its own stoichiometric equilibrium binding constants, might be expected to jump alarmingly together with the complexity of the analysis. However perhaps surprisingly, when there is a tendency for ligand binding at any one receptor binding site to enhance persistently ligand binding at neighbouring binding sites (**positive cooperativity**), then binding behaviour can be accounted for in terms of a considerably reduced form of Equation (7.30) as shown:

$$B = \frac{n(K_{a,1}K_{a,2}\cdots K_{a,n})[L]^n}{1 + (K_{a,1}K_{a,2}\cdots K_{a,n})[L]^n} \tag{7.33}$$

Such a simplification is possible because positive cooperativity ensures that only end point saturation binding equilibria can dominate ligand binding behaviour and hence only the highest power terms are relevant in an expression for B. Equation (7.33) can be simplified even further to give the following equation:

$$\frac{B}{n} = \frac{[L]^n}{K' + [L]^n} \tag{7.34}$$

which is in the form of a sigmoid (Figure 7.19). The linearised form of this equation is

$$\log\left(\frac{B}{n - B}\right) = n\log[L] - \log K' \tag{7.35}$$

This is the **Hill equation** for cooperative binding of ligands by a receptor (see Chapter 8 for the Hill equation equivalent for cooperative biocatalysis). The term n represents the maximum value of B at saturation as well as the effective number of binding sites involved in cooperative binding activity (Figure 7.19). For the sake of completeness, when there is a tendency for ligand

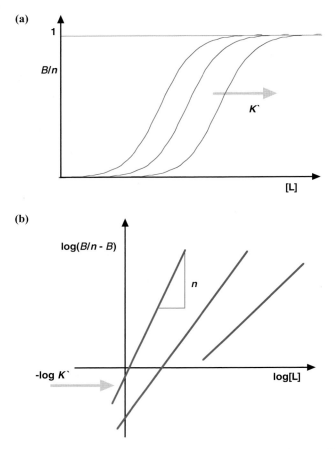

Figure 7.19   Dependent multiple-site variable affinity cooperative binding equilibria. (a) Classical sigmoidal binding isotherms indicative of ligand-receptor interactions that involve strong **positive cooperativity**. Curves move to right as composite equilibrium constant K' increases. (b) Linear **Hill plots** derived from sigmoidal data illustrated in (a). Gradients and intercepts define values of n and K' respectively.

binding at any one receptor binding site to reduce persistently ligand binding at neighbouring binding sites (**negative cooperativity**) then binding behaviour can also be accounted for in terms of a considerably reduced form of Equation (7.30), that is equivalent to Equation (7.23)!

7.3 Analysing molecular recognition and binding

Now that we have covered the main theoretical models of binding and molecular recognition events, including their analytical equations and equilibrium binding constants, we must show that equilibrium binding constants can be derived from the experimental equivalents of B and [L].

7.3.1 Equilibrium dialysis

This is the most ideal method for determining accurate experiment evaluation of B and $[L]$ and hence equilibrium dissociation and association constants. In brief, receptor R and ligand L are combined on one side of a semi-permeable membrane in a dialysis device. Ligand L is able to traverse the membrane but not the receptor R. Therefore, when the system is allowed to reach equilibrium, then the receptor/ligand binding equilibrium on the one side of the membrane is matched by an equilibrated pool of free ligand L on the other side of the membrane (Figure 7.20). The concentrations of free ligand $[L]$ on either side of the semi-permeable membrane are equivalent. Given this, very accurate values of B may be determined as follows. First, free ligand concentration $[L]$ is measured, after which the **total molar quantity of ligand bound to receptor**, m_{RL}, is measured, knowing the **total volume**, V_{tot}, of the system and the **total molar quantity of ligand added initially**, m_{L_0}, as follows:

$$m_{L_0} - V_{tot}[L] = m_{RL} \tag{7.36}$$

From this, the corresponding value of B may be determined according to the following relationship:

$$B = \frac{[RL]}{[R]_0} \equiv \frac{m_{RL}}{m_{R_0}} \tag{7.37}$$

provided that **the total molar quantity of receptor** m_{R_0} present is known accurately as well. By combining Expressions (7.36) and (7.37) we obtain the following:

$$B = \frac{(m_{L_0} - V_{tot}[L])}{m_{R_0}} \tag{7.38}$$

Provided that values of B are then determined under identical experimental conditions but with different values of m_{L_0}, an accurate binding isotherm will be generated that obeys

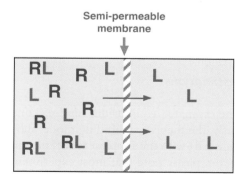

Figure 7.20 Diagrammatic representation of experimental arrangement for **equilibrium dialysis**.

the usual hyperbolic binding curve given by Equations (7.23) or (7.27), or alternatively the sigmoidal curve associated with positive cooperativity (given by Equation (7.34)). However, whilst equilibrium dialysis is optimal for the determination of equilibrium binding constants, this technique is frequently impracticable for studying the interaction of ligands with most biological macromolecules since these are usually too unstable and usually unavailable in the quantities required to effect a complete set of equilibrium dialysis experiments.

7.3.2 Titration methodologies

There are many ways in which to achieve a titration binding experiment, but the underlying principles are quite similar to each other. Frequently, a fixed concentration of receptor R is titrated with ligand L until approximately all the receptor binding sites are occupied, a state known as **saturation** (sometimes, it may be more appropriate to do the reverse, titrating a fixed concentration of ligand L with receptor R until saturation is achieved). Progress towards saturation is monitored using any one of a number of physical or spectroscopic techniques. In each case, we are looking for a progressive change, Δx, in a selected physical property or spectroscopic signature. At each stage of the titration, Δx is identifiable with B provided that the change is a direct consequence of ligand binding alone and equilibrium has been properly established. In this case, Δx at each stage in the titration is the **sum of the physical property/spectroscopic signature of bound ligand**, x_b, and that of **free ligand**, x_f, in the presence of receptor. This is illustrated by

$$\Delta x = \alpha x_b + (1 - \alpha)x_f - x_{back} \qquad (7.39)$$

where α corresponds to the **fraction of ligand bound** at a given stage in the titration and x_{back} to **background contribution from free ligand** (in the absence of receptor) and free receptor (in the absence of ligand). When Δx is plotted as a function of **total ligand concentration** $[L]_0$ an experimental binding isotherm will result (Figure 7.21), or else a sigmoidal isotherm, depending upon whether or not positive cooperativity is involved in binding (Figure 7.21). At this point, a decision needs to be taken about which theoretical binding model is most appropriate for the receptor R and ligand L under investigation, after which data is fitted with the most appropriate analytical equation to extract equilibrium binding constants.

7.3.2.1   Titration data estimations

How good the values of the estimated equilibrium binding constants are depends upon a number of factors. Obviously, the theoretical binding model should be as close to reality as possible. We would normally start with the simplest model first and make things more complicated if necessary. However, please note that most experimental binding data is plotted using $[L]_0$ whereas the actual analytical equations involve only **free ligand concentration** $[L]$. Most experimental methods for observing binding events do not explicitly involve a

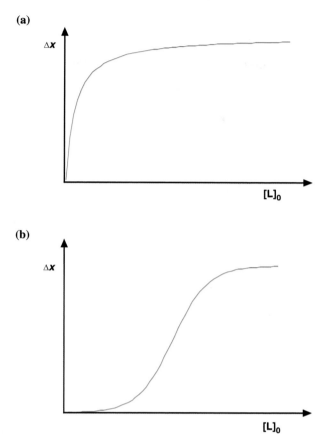

Figure 7.21 Experimental titration binding isotherms. (a) **Hyperbolic titration binding isotherm** obtained by titrating fixed **[R]** with increasing values of **[L]$_0$**, and then plotting observed Δx against **[L]$_0$**. Hyperbolic binding isotherm is observed characteristically when **single/independent multiple site, single affinity** binding interactions occur. (b) Sigmoidal titration binding isotherm is characteristic of **dependent multiple site, variable affinity** binding interactions taking place between ligand and receptor with strong **positive cooperativity**.

precise determination of [L] but instead assume that [L] and [L]$_0$ are approximately the same. Obviously they are not, especially at concentrations of [L]$_0$ less than any K_d values. Fortunately, we can avoid problems with using this approximation provided that the experimental data set converges to saturation as closely as possible. The best way to verify this is to plot Δx versus log[L]$_0$ (**semi-log plot**). If the experimental data plots out in the form of a sigmoid approaching an asymptotic plateau at high values of log[L]$_0$ (see Figure 7.15, where Δx is equivalent to B), then we can be sure that receptor R binding sites are approaching saturation and that the experimental data set is adequate for the determination of binding constants. Obviously, this semi-log plot diagnostic approach only applies when strong positive cooperativity is *not* involved in binding. Alternatively, performing titrations at concentrations of receptor equivalent to approximate K_d values increases the chance for saturation too.

7.3.2.2   *Physical properties versus spectroscopic signatures*

Typical physical properties that can change with receptor–ligand binding interactions are for example (1) **enthalpy (heat)**, (2) **overall charge** and (3) **solution refractive index changes**. These changes in physical property can be observed from low to saturating concentrations of ligand by means of techniques such as **isothermal titration calorimetry (ITC)**, **capillary electrophoresis** and **resonant mirror biosensing** respectively (see below). Spectroscopic signatures that change with receptor–ligand binding interactions are numerous but the most frequently used are **fluorescence, nuclear magnetic resonance, circular dichroism** and **UV–visible** spectroscopic signatures in this context. The corresponding spectroscopic techniques have been described previously (Chapters 4 and 5) so will not be covered significantly here except where they feature in worked examples of studies on molecular recognition and binding events. When physical properties are used to study receptor–ligand binding interactions then observed changes are typically in the physical state of the whole system of interacting molecules. When spectroscopic signatures are used to study receptor–ligand binding interactions then observed changes are typically caused only by changes in the spectroscopic behaviour of selected spectroscopically active functional group(s) as a consequence of local environment changes experienced upon binding. Having said this, there are otherwise no fundamental differences in approach between studies on molecular recognition and binding events conducted using changes in physical properties or changes in spectroscopic signatures to report on receptor–ligand binding interactions.

7.3.3 Isothermal titration calorimetry and binding thermodynamics

Isothermal titration calorimetry (ITC) is almost the ultimate titration methodology in that this technique is based entirely upon titration of heat energy and then deconvolution of this information into equilibrium binding constant information. However, the real beauty of this technique is that it engages directly with the thermodynamics of receptor–ligand binding interactions.

7.3.3.1   *Equilibrium thermodynamics of molecular recognition and binding*

Every species i in aqueous solution is credited with a **chemical potential** $\mu_i(aq)$ at a given concentration c_i that is defined according to

$$\mu_i(aq) = \mu_i^0(aq) + RT\ln(\gamma_i c_i / c_r) \tag{7.40}$$

where μ_i^0 (aq) is the **standard chemical potential** at a **standard concentration** c_r of 1 M
(1 mol l^{-1}), and γ_i is an **interaction parameter**. An **ideal solution** is defined as one in which
there are no solute–solute interactions and for which the interaction parameter is therefore
equivalent to unity. Clearly, solute–solute interactions must exist in reality for molecular
recognition and binding events to take place, so there is not such thing as a completely ideal
solution involving biological macromolecules. Essentially, μ_i^0(aq) is a function of solute–
solvent interactions while γ_i is a function of solute–solute interactions that tend to a value of
unity as interactions decline to zero.

Consider the original binding equilibrium (Scheme 7.1). By definition, equilibrium is
reached when there is no chemical potential difference between the two sides of the equilibrium. That is,

$$\mu_R^{eq} + \mu_L^{eq} = \mu_{RL}^{eq} \tag{7.41}$$

By substitution into Equation (7.41) from Equation (7.40) and the reorganisation of terms we
arrive at the following containing a left-hand side expression that is a difference of standard
chemical potentials:

$$\mu_{RL}^0 - \mu_R^0 - \mu_L^0 = RT\ln\left(\frac{[R]_{eq}[L]_{eq}}{[RL]_{eq}c_r}\right) \tag{7.42}$$

By definition, the left-hand side of the equation is equivalent to the **standard free energy
change of binding** $\Delta G^0(T)_{bind}$, therefore Equation (7.42) can be further adapted to give

$$\Delta G^0(T)_{bind} = -RT\ln\left(\frac{[RL]_{eq}c_r}{[R]_{eq}[L]_{eq}}\right) \tag{7.43}$$

In the brackets is the **absolute association constant** K_a^0, which is related directly to the
experimental association constant introduced in Equation (7.17) according to the following
simple equation:

$$K_a = K_a^0/c_r \tag{7.44}$$

Hence the key thermodynamic equation for binding is

$$\Delta G^0(T)_{bind} = -RT\ln(K_a c_r) \tag{7.45}$$

By means of this equation, measured association constant values can be converted directly into
a key thermodynamic parameter. Other binding thermodynamic parameters may be obtained
through thermodynamic equations or preferentially measured by ITC. The key parameters
are **standard enthalpy change of binding** ΔH_{bind}^0 and **standard entropy change of binding**
ΔS_{bind}^0. These quantities relate directly to $\Delta G^0(T)_{bind}$ according to the well known and central

thermodynamic relationship

$$\Delta G^0(T)_{\text{bind}} = \Delta H^0_{\text{bind}} - T\Delta S^0_{\text{bind}} \tag{7.46}$$

7.3.3.2   Enthalpy of binding and ITC

By definition, a **change in enthalpy** of a given system dH equates to **total heat energy** q added (or subtracted), provided that this heat energy is transferred under conditions of constant temperature and pressure, and that the system is **thermodynamically closed** (meaning that no chemical matter is added or subtracted). The fundamental equation that defines this situation is

$$dH = q + V_c dp \tag{7.47}$$

where V_c is **constant closed system volume** and dp is **change in pressure**, which should be zero for most situations involving biological macromolecule interactions. In other words, enthalpy change corresponds directly to heat energy added to or subtracted from a closed system of interest such as the mixture of a given ligand and its cognate biological macromolecule receptor interacting with each other in solution.

An ITC titration experiment seeks to measure the total heat energy q exchanged (i.e. either taken up or released) each time an aliquot of ligand L ($dn_0(\text{L})$) is injected into a stirred and equilibrated solution of cognate receptor R in a calorimeter vessel (Figure 7.22). The total heat energy exchanged per injection is then given by

$$q/dn^0(\text{L}) = \Delta H^0_{\text{bind}} \frac{[1/2 + \{[1 - (1/2)(1 + K_d) - [\text{RL}]/2]\}]}{\{[\text{RL}]^2 - 2[\text{RL}](1 - K_d) + (1 + K_d)^2\}^{1/2}} \tag{7.48}$$

The derivation of this equation is well beyond the scope of this book! However, this equation does show that the primary experimental output from an ITC heat titration experiment is ΔH^0_{bind} and the experimental dissociation constant K_d. The total heat energy exchanged as a function of ligand–receptor interactions is at its greatest at the beginning of a given titration since most of the molecules in each injected aliquot of ligand bind to receptor and either take up or release heat energy, as appropriate (Figure 7.23). As the titration proceeds, the total heat energy exchanged must decline, since more of the ligand binding sites become occupied and are prevented from participating in heat exchanges. The total heat energy exchanged will tend to zero as the titration reaches completion, provided that there is no significant contribution to total heat energy q exchanged from other concomitant effects with each injection such as dilution effects (dilution effects can be very significant depending upon the biological macromolecular ligands and/or receptors that are being diluted during the titration process).

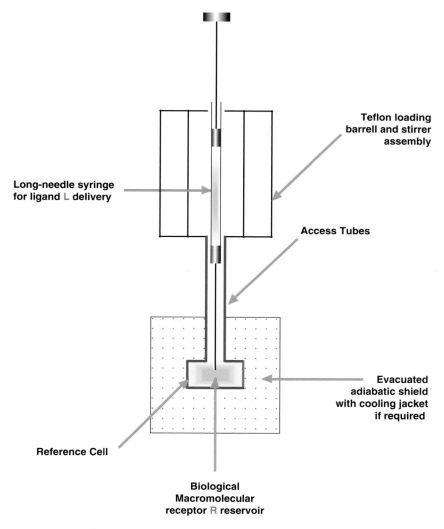

Figure 7.22 Schematic diagram of **Isothermal titration calorimeter** (**ITC**) device showing how a solution of receptor **R** is maintained in an ITC cell within an adiabatic shield and ligand **L** is injected in with stirring from above.

7.3.3.3 Van't Hoff relationships

A key thermodynamic equation for the characterisation of binding events is the **Van't Hoff relationship**, which is a partial derivative equation as shown:

$$\left(\frac{\partial \ln K_a}{\partial T} \right)_{p,V} = \frac{\Delta H_{bind}}{RT^2} \tag{7.49}$$

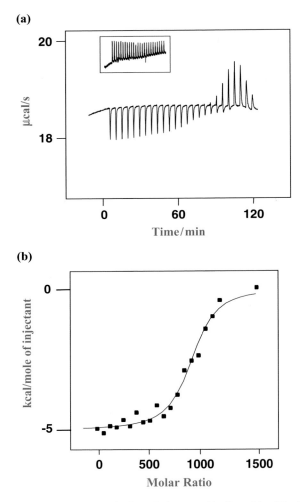

Figure 7.23 ITC output from interaction of adenoviral μ peptide ligand **L** with plasmid DNA receptor **R**. (**a**) Heat exchange data obtained in real time. Negative peak implies that combination of **L** with **R** causes heat evolution from cell (exothermic); positive peak implies that the combination of **L** with **R** causes heat absorbtion by the cell (endothermic); (**b**) ITC software analysis output. Data is fit with **equation 7.48** (adapted from Keller et al., 2002, Fig. 4).

Equation (7.49) integrates in a number of ways, of which the most commonly used is

$$\ln K_a = -\frac{\Delta H_{bind}}{RT} + \frac{\Delta S_{bind}}{R} \tag{7.50}$$

Equation (7.50) relates equilibrium association constant with **enthalpy change of binding** ΔH_{bind} and **entropy change of binding** ΔS_{bind}. Provided that both are temperature

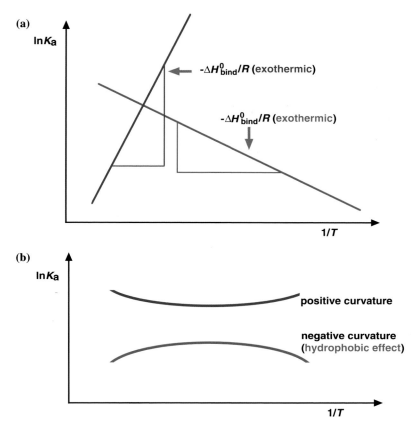

Figure 7.24   Van't Hoff Relationship Plots. (a) Classical linear plots obtained in the event that ΔH_{bind} is temperature independent over the temperature range studied. **(b)** Curved plots that characterise the situation when ΔH_{bind} is temperature dependent. Negative curvature is characteristic of the involvement of hydrophobic effect in receptor-ligand binding interactions.

independent properties, a linear relationship will be observed when experimental association constant data are plotted against absolute temperature using Equation (7.50) (Figure 7.24). The gradient and intercept of this linear Van't Hoff plot then gives us the equivalent of $\Delta H_{\text{bind}}^{0}$ and $\Delta S_{\text{bind}}^{0}$ values. Such a linear Van't Hoff plot is an essential tool for the derivation of thermodynamic parameters from equilibrium association constant data obtained by experimental methods other than ITC, such as those described in the following sections. Obviously, if we calculate $\Delta H_{\text{bind}}^{0}$ and $\Delta S_{\text{bind}}^{0}$ values first using Equation (7.50), then $\Delta G^{0}(T)_{\text{bind}}$ may be calculated in turn using Equation (7.46).

Quite frequently, however, the Van't Hoff plot is not linear but has a curvature. In this case, data must be fitted by means of the series integration shown:

$$\ln K_{\text{a}} = a + b(1/T) + c\ln T \qquad (7.51)$$

where a, b and c are variable series constants. The constant c then relates onwards to the **heat capacity change on binding** $\Delta C_{p\,bind}$ according to

$$\Delta C_{p\,bind} = Rc \qquad (7.52)$$

When the Van't Hoff plot is *linear*, then c becomes zero and $\Delta C_{p\,bind}$ is also zero. In other words, when ΔH_{bind} is independent of absolute temperature then there is no change in heat capacity of the combined ligand and receptor system after ligands bind to receptors. Critically, when the Van't Hoff plot has a negative curvature, then c becomes negative and also $\Delta C_{p\,bind}$ becomes negative (Figure 7.24). In other words, there is a loss in system heat capacity after ligands bind to receptors. Such a thermodynamic signature usually suggests that the hydrophobic effect is making a significant contribution towards ligand–receptor binding interactions. In fact, this thermodynamic signature is perhaps the only major way to prove that the hydrophobic effect is involved in mediating binding interactions! The reason for this loss of system heat capacity upon binding is the main requirement of the hydrophobic effect that highly ordered solvation cages of water that surround hydrophobic functional groups should be displaced into free solution in order for these hydrophobic functional groups to make intimate contact with each other (see Chapter 1).

7.3.4 Capillary electrophoresis

Capillary Electrophoresis (CE) is one of the most developed examples of emerging 'lab-on-a-chip' technologies that have direct applications to chemical biology owing to their capacity to give meaningful information generated from only the smallest quantities of biological macromolecule material (microgram levels). The basis of the technique is the very high resolution of charged species of different overall charge owing to the unique flow properties of buffer solutions in **micro-bore capillaries** (**micro-capillaries**) fashioned from silicon oxide/hydroxide and charge–charge interactions that take place between charged solutes and the inner bore of a given micro-capillary. A micro-capillary is shown diagrammatically (Figure 7.25). When an electrical potential difference is applied across such a micro-capillary, then there is a bulk movement of buffer solution from anode (positive) to cathode (negative) effected by **electro-osmotic flow** (**EOF**). This bulk movement of liquid in the micro-capillary is driven by the negative surface charge on the interior of the capillary bore due to ionisation of silicon hydroxide functional groups ($SiO^-/SiOH$), an effect that increases with increasing pH. This surface charge is compensated for by a complementary cationic **Stern layer**, which acts to repel other cationic species towards the cathode and retard the motion of anionic counter-ion species in the same direction owing to partial attraction. The repulsion of cationic species towards the cathode dominates and they 'drag' the buffer solution in a concerted manner toward the cathode as a result of interactions between cation water-solvation cages and water molecules in the bulk solution. EOF has a characteristic flat flow profile compared with typical non-linear laminar flow (Figure 7.25).

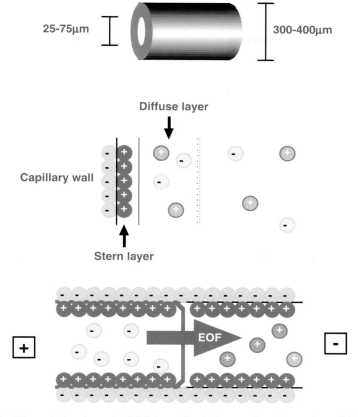

Figure 7.25 **Capillary electrophoresis.** (**a**) Schematic of microcapillary dimensions. (**b**) Ion-solute structure at the capillary wall. (**c**) Schematic illustration of **electro-osmotic flow (EOF)** created in the **microcapillary** as a result of capillary bore surface charges.

Overlaid on top of EOF is the effect of **electrophoretic mobility**. Electrophoresis can be defined as the differential movement of charged species (ions) by attraction or repulsion in an **electric field** of strength E_e according to

$$v_e = \mu_e E_e \tag{7.53}$$

where v_e is **electrophoretic velocity** and μ_e is **electrophoretic mobility**. Hence, any ionic species moving in a micro-bore capillary under the influence of an applied electrical potential difference will in fact move with an **apparent electrophoretic mobility** μ_a given by

$$\mu_a = \mu_e + \mu_{EOF} \tag{7.54}$$

where μ_{EOF} is **EOF electrophoretic mobility**. Typically, EOF mobility is greater (approximately 10 times) than electrophoretic mobility. In the case of cationic species that anyway migrate faster then anionic species in a micro-bore capillary, EOF mobility and electrophoretic mobility may coincide more closely. The **time to detector** t_e that it takes for a given charged (anionic or cationic) species to migrate from the anode (positive) end of a micro-bore capillary to a detector positioned at the cathode (negative) end of the capillary is given by

$$t_e = \frac{1}{\mu_a} l_e \frac{L_e}{V_e} \qquad (7.55)$$

where l_e is the **effective length of the capillary** from anode to detector, L_e is **total length** and V_e is the **applied potential difference from anode to cathode** along the length of the capillary.

The basis for using CE to determine association constants for receptor–ligand interactions is a change in overall charge following the binding of ligand L to receptor R due to the formation of complementary ionic associations and hydrogen bonds. Such a change in overall charge should be reflected by a change in apparent electrophoretic mobility μ_a of the receptor–ligand RL complex compared with the mobility of the free receptor R in the absence of ligand L, and an inverse change in the time to detector t_e, according to Equation 7.55. Therefore, when a fixed concentration of receptor R is titrated with ligand L until approximately all the receptor binding sites are occupied, the progress towards saturation may be observed by progressive change in the magnitude of the physical property time to detector, Δt_e (selected physical property) as a function of total ligand concentration, $[L]_0$. Hence when Δt_e is plotted as a function of total ligand concentration $[L]_0$ at fixed receptor concentration $[R]$ a hyperbolic or sigmoidal binding isotherm will result, as this can be analysed in the most appropriate way (Figure 7.26). Obviously, if required, the titration experiment may be performed in reverse using a fixed concentration of ligand L titrated with an increasing concentration of receptor R. In this case, the change in apparent electrophoretic mobility μ_a of the receptor–ligand RL complex compared with the mobility of the free ligand L in the absence of receptor R is what matters.

7.3.5 Resonant mirror biosensing (surface plasmon resonance)

Resonant mirror biosensing is a superb technique for the analysis of receptor–ligand interactions in real time. Therefore, association constants may be determined directly from kinetic constants! This may sound a little strange, but let us consider the binding equilibrium shown in Scheme 7.4. By definition, equilibrium is reached when the **rate of association** k_{ass} (M^{-1} s^{-1}) of receptor with ligand is equalled by the **rate of** receptor–ligand complex **dissociation** k_{diss} (s^{-1}). Hence

$$k_{ass}[R][L] = k_{diss}[RL] \qquad (7.56)$$

$$R \;+\; L \;\; \underset{k_{diss}}{\overset{k_{ass}}{\rightleftharpoons}} \;\; RL$$

Scheme 7.4

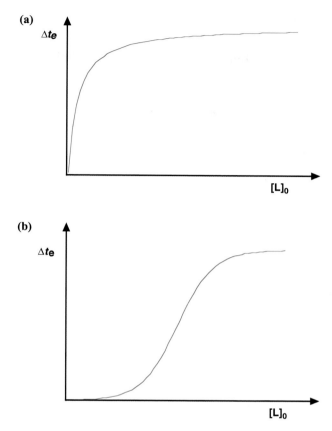

Figure 7.26 Experimental titration binding isotherms. (a) Hyperbolic titration binding isotherm obtained by titrating fixed **[R]** with increasing values of **[L]$_0$**, and then plotting observed Δt_e against **[L]$_0$**. Hyperbolic binding isotherm occurs with **single/independent multiple-site, single/equal affinity binding** interactions. (b) Sigmoidal titration binding isotherm is characteristic of **dependent multiple-site, variable affinity binding** interactions with strong positive cooperativity.

This simple relationship rearranges to give

$$\frac{k_{\mathrm{ass}}}{k_{\mathrm{diss}}} = \frac{[\mathrm{RL}]}{[\mathrm{R}][\mathrm{L}]} = K_{\mathrm{a}} \tag{7.57}$$

Therefore, equilibrium binding constants such as K_{a} or indeed K_{d} can be determined from a simple ratio of rate constants. Equations such as (7.57) are a form of **Haldane relationship**, although the term Haldane relationship is more usually applied to expressions in reaction kinetics that link rate constants with an equilibrium constant (see Chapter 8). If the receptor R is immobilised (imm) for any reason by covalent attachment to a solid phase, then the relationship in Equation (7.57) becomes slightly modified:

$$\frac{k_{ass}}{k_{diss}} = \frac{[RL]_{imm}}{[R]_{imm}[L]} = K_a \tag{7.58}$$

Obviously, an equivalent expression could be written for the reverse situation when the ligand L is **immobilised** (**imm**) instead. In either case, to a first approximation the association constant written in Equation (7.57) is said to be essentially identical to the constant defined in Equation (7.58). This is important, since immobilisation of receptor R (or ligand L) to a solid phase resin is central to resonant mirror biosensing.

The principle of resonant mirror biosensing is as follows. This is a two-phase technique that involves laser light refracted through a prism block over a range of angles (Figure 7.27). For the most part, incident light is refracted through a prism block and exits without loss of intensity due to **total internal reflection**. However, at one unique angle (**resonant angle**), an **evanescent wave** is propagated (quantum mechanical tunnelling effect) into a **resonant layer** attached to the prism block, such that the exit light intensity is significantly reduced. The exact resonant angle is a function of the refractive index of the resonant layer. In fact the resonant angle is extremely sensitive to the refractive index so that even only modest changes to the refractive index (10^{-3}) of the resonant layer will result in measurable changes in the resonant angle! The resonant layer comprises a **hydrogel** that is functionalised for the covalent coupling of a biological macromolecule, such as a receptor R molecule of interest. After R has been immobilised at a certain concentration, an aliquot of ligand L may be added that diffuses into the hydrogel and consequently causes some immediate perturbation to the refractive index of the resonant layer. However, subsequent molecular recognition and binding events often result in an even more substantial perturbation to the refractive index of the resonant layer, an effect that can be monitored in **real time** (s) by observing corresponding changes in resonant angle over a period of seconds–minutes (Figure 7.28). Such a plot of resonant angle change as a function of time represents a receptor–ligand association phase that obeys the following exponential:

$$Y_t = (Y_\infty - Y_0)[1 - \exp(-k_{on}t)] + Y_0 \tag{7.59}$$

where Y_t is the **resonant angle** at time t, Y_∞ the **final angle** and Y_0 the **initial angle**. The term k_{on} is a **first order**, **total ligand concentration** $[L]_0$ **dependent**, **on-rate** for receptor–ligand association.

Once a given receptor–ligand association phase is complete, the hydrogel is washed with buffer to promote dissociation of ligand L, causing relaxation of the refractive index of the resonant layer back towards its initial receptor immobilised value. Relaxation of the refractive index is monitored in real time by observing the corresponding relaxation of the resonant angle over a similar period of seconds–minutes (Figure 7.28). In this case, a plot of resonance angle change as a function of time represents a receptor–ligand dissociation phase that obeys the following exponential:

$$Y_t = Y_\infty \exp(-k_{diss}t) + Y_0 \tag{7.60}$$

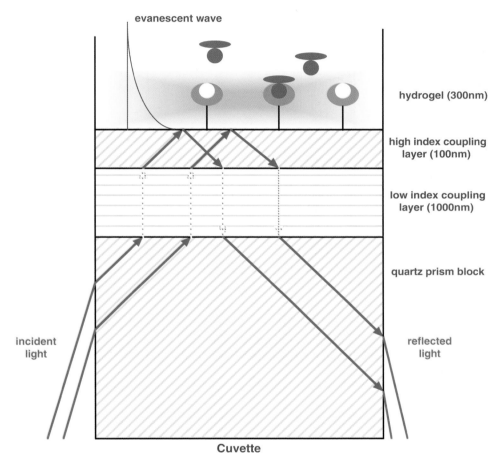

Figure 7.27 Schematic illustration of **Surface Plasmon Resonance** (**SPR**). Incident light is normally subject to total internal reflection in the prism block except for losses due to evanescent wave penetration of the **hydrogel layer** at the **resonant angle**. Changes in resonant angle due to receptor-ligand interactions are the basis for the real time observation of molecular recognition and association/dissociation events.

For a given total ligand concentration $[L]_0$ the complete plot of resonant angle change data against time is known as a **sensogram**. Sensograms are obtained usually using a wide range of different total ligand concentrations $[L]_0$ in order to derive accurate values of k_{ass} and k_{on} and hence K_a as follows. A definitive value of k_{ass} may be determined from the association phases of as many sensograms as possible, making use of Equation (7.59) to derive k_{on} values,

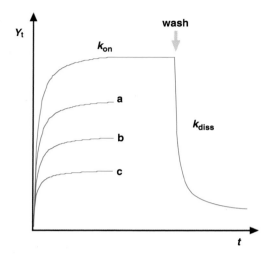

Figure 7.28 Schematic illustration of **sensograms**. Real time observations of change in **resonant angle** Y_t with receptor-ligand association (**a, b, c** etc) are used to determine values of unimolecular rate constant k_{on} as a function of **total ligand concentration [L]$_0$**. A wash step is then introduced to promote real time dissociation of ligand from receptor. Subsequent real time changes in Y_t with dissociation are used to determine values of unimolecular rate constant k_{diss}.

and then these data are plotted versus $[L]_0$ according to

$$k_{on} = k_{diss} + k_{ass}[L]_0 \qquad (7.61)$$

The gradient of this plot represents a definitive value for k_{ass} ($M^{-1}S^{-1}$), assuming that the plot is linear (Figure 7.29). By contrast, a definitive value of k_{diss} may be obtained either from

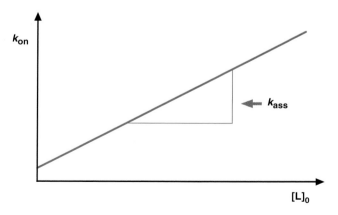

Figure 7.29 Schematic illustration of plot of k_{on} as a function of **total ligand concentration [L]$_0$**. The gradient gives a value for the bimolecular rate constant k_{ass}.

the intercept of the k_{on} versus $[L]_0$ plot (Figure 7.29) or more accurately as an average of individual values obtained from the dissociation phases of as many sensograms as possible, making use of Equation (7.60). Finally, definitive values of kinetic constants can then be processed using Equation (7.58) to give meaningful values of K_a generated once again from only the smallest quantities of biological macromolecule material (microgram levels). The ability of resonant mirror biosensing to give both kinetic and thermodynamic information about biological molecular recognition and binding events is currently almost unique and so is correspondingly very important!

7.4 Biological molecular recognition studies

In this concluding section, we shall look at a small number of molecular recognition events in order to exemplify the theoretical discussions above. Nowadays, there are myriad studies that could be given, but we have chosen to focus on a few examples interesting for their contrasting demonstrations of molecular recognition and binding events.

7.4.1 LysU enzyme substrate recognition

Many enzymes (protein bio-catalysts) are well characterised as biocatalysts but quite often key molecular recognition and binding events that precede biocatalysis are overlooked. This cannot be said to be true of LysU. LysU is a homodimeric lysyl tRNA synthetase enzyme, and one of the primary enzymes involved in Ap_4A synthesis in the bacterium *E. coli* (see Chapter 6, Figure 6.17). The enzymic surface mechanism of LysU-catalysed Ap_4A synthesis is well known and is illustrated in Figure 7.30. The first step (Step 1) is very specific and apparently only ATP or deoxy-ATP analogues are able to act as first nucleotide substrates to form a lysyl-adenylate intermediate. The second step step (Step 2) is unusual in requiring the use of the Zn^{2+} ion (see Chapter 8). The X-ray crystal structures of LysU demonstrate a host of hydrogen bonding interactions responsible for determining the strength and specificity of binding between substrates and enzyme active site in Step 1 (Figure 7.31). Also, cationic amino-acid residues are present in the vicinity of the polyphosphate chain for electrostatic (long and short range) interactions; similarly, anionic amino-acid residues are present in the vicinity of L-lysine for equivalent electrostatic interactions. Complementarities between enzyme active sites and substrates are usually extensive at the level of charge and hydrogen bonding in order to ensure optimal specificity of molecular recognition and binding.

The molecular recognition and binding behaviour of the first step has now been studied in some detail and is proving very interesting. Catalysis requires a precise order of substrate binding that was demonstrated by a combination of fluorescence binding titration experiments and ITC binding titration experiments. Initially, the presence of Mg^{2+} ions was found to be essential for L-lysine binding to either active site of the LysU dimer. Thereafter, the binding of L-lysine at both sites was found to be responsible for a substantial structural rearrangement of the *C*-terminal active site domain of each monomer, as observed by CD spectroscopy (Figure 7.32). The change in LysU conformation elicited by L-lysine binding

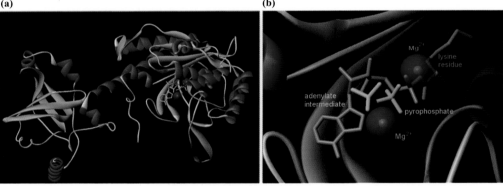

Step 1

Step 2

Figure 7.30 Illustration of **Step 1** and **Step 2** of enzymic surface mechanism of LysU catalyzed diadenosine-5′, 5‴-P^1,P^4-tetraphosphate (Ap$_4$A) **4** formation (see Chapters 6 and 8). (**a**) **Ribbon display structure** illustration of LysU monomer with bound lysyladenylate intermediate **3** and pyrophosphate rendered in **stick display mode** (**orange**: AMP residue; **green**: lysyl residue; **light blue**: pyrophosphate). Mg^{+2} ions are rendered as Van der Waals spheres (**purple**). (**b**) Active site close-up of LysU monomer structure shown in (**a**) (pdb: **1e1t**).

was also sufficient to induce a significant change in intrinsic tryptophan fluorescence upon L-lysine binding. Therefore, intrinsic tryptophan fluorescence binding titration experiments were used successfully to determine the site dissociation constant K_d for L-lysine and the binding stoichiometry (K_d 7.96 ± 1.40 μM; 0.95 ± 0.1 L-lysine/monomer) (Figure 7.32). ITC binding experiments revealed a similar value for K_d and binding stoichiometry (K_d 4.95 ± 2.54 μM; 0.87 ± 0.14 L-lysine/monomer) (Figure 7.33). Critically, ATP was unable to bind to LysU until after the association of L-lysine and Mg^{2+} ions. Note how binding stoichiometry is determined either by curve fitting with the appropriate binding equation or else directly from plots (Figure 7.32).

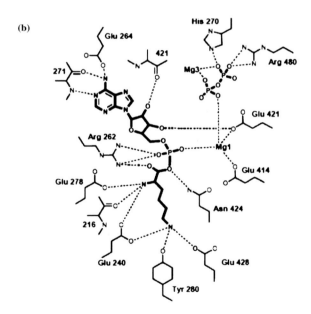

Figure 7.31 Two dimensional schematic representation of the active site of LysU. H-bond interactions are shown for the ternary complex between L-lysine **1**, ATP **2** and LysU (**a**), and for the complex between the lysyladenylate intermediate **3** and LysU (**b**) (see **Fig. 7.30**). The **motif 2** residue Arg262 is critical for the molecular recognition and binding of both L-lysine **1** and ATP **2** α-phosphate to LysU. A number of conserved residues in the motif 2 loop (residues 264–271) assume an ordered conformation only upon ATP binding. Positions of the Mg^{2+} binding sites are also shown. There are 3 Mg^{2+} ions **Mg1**, **Mg2** and **Mg3** in (**a**) and 2 Mg^{2+} ions **Mg1** and **Mg3** in (**b**) (Reproduced from Desogus et al., 2000, Fig. 4).

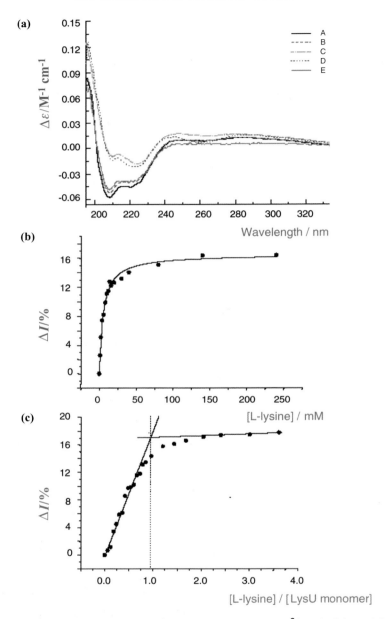

Figure 7.32   Affects of L-lysine binding to LysU in the presence of Mg²⁺ and K⁺ ions. (a) CD spectra of LysU (2 μM) in neutral buffer in the presence of no substrates (**A**, black); 10 mM MgCl$_2$ (**B**, red); 1 mM L-lysine, 10 mM MgCl$_2$ (**C**, green); 1mM L-lysine, 10 mM MgCl$_2$, 250μM β,γ-methylene ATP (AMPPCP) (**D**, blue); 10 mM MgCl$_2$, 250 μM AMPPCP (**E**, yellow-green). (**b**) Fluorescence binding titration of LysU (0.5 μM) with L-lysine in buffer pH 8.0 in the presence of 10mM MgCl$_2$. (**c**) High concentration fluorescence binding titration of LysU (17 μM) with L-lysine in buffer pH 8.0 in the presence of 10 mM MgCl$_2$. Linear regions of data are extrapolated to intercept (**Klotz transition**) that defines saturation binding stoichiometry (adapted from Hughes et al., 2003, Fig. 2).

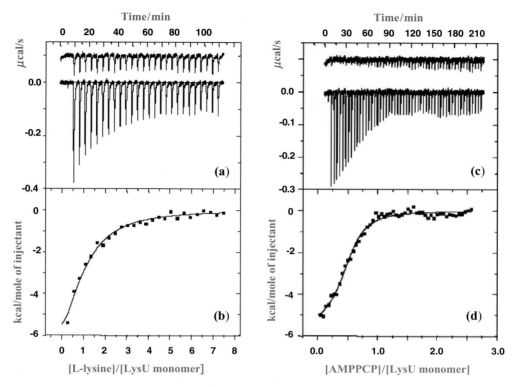

Figure 7.33 **ITC binding experiments** showing the affects of L-lysine and AMPPCP binding to LysU in the presence of Mg^{2+} and K^+ ions. (**a**) Calorimetric titration profile deriving from the titration of LysU ($6 \mu M$ monomer) with injected aliquots of L-lysine in buffer pH 8.0 at $20°C$ in the presence of 10 mM $MgCl_2$ (upper trace; control titration in absence of LysU). (**b**) Heat absorbed per mole of L-lysine titrant versus [L-lysine]/[LysU monomer]. (**c**) Calorimetric titration profile deriving from the titration of LysU (20 μM monomer) with injected aliquots of β,γ-methylene ATP (AMPPCP) in buffer pH 8.0 at $20°C$ in the presence of 1mM L-lysine, 10 mM $MgCl_2$ (**d**) Heat absorbed per mole of L-lysine titrant versus [AMPPCP]/[LysU monomer] (adapted from Hughes et al., 2003, Fig. 3).

ATP binding was studied by an ITC binding experiment in the absence of any other spectroscopic signature that could be titrated to saturation. ITC studies were performed using hydrolysis resistant β,γ-methylene-ATP (AMPCP) in place of ATP in order to avoid complications in ITC measurements from ATP hydrolysis (Figure 7.33). In this case the value for K_d was found to be $1.22 \pm 0.15 \mu M$ and the stoichiometry 0.51 ± 0.01 AMPPCP/monomer. Only one ATP molecule was found to bind per LysU dimer, suggesting that ATP binding was accompanied by strong negative cooperativity leading to half-of-sites binding. Consequently, the ordered process of LysU molecular recognition and binding of substrates requires that half-of-sites catalysis takes place subsequently. In order to understand the basis of half-of-sites binding, theoretical molecular modelling studies were performed using the X-ray crystal structures of LysU as a starting point. Molecular modelling is largely beyond our scope here, but it is worth noting that **molecular mechanics Poisson–Boltzmann surface area** (**MM-PBSA**) modelling experiments were able to demonstrate that the two LysU active sites are not structurally and functionally equivalent to each other even before the above experiments were performed. In the event, ATP was calculated to bind to one site (Site 2) about 25 kcal mol^{-1} more tightly than to the other (Site 1). This difference is more than adequate to account for the negative cooperativity and half-of-sites binding observed experimentally. Moreover, molecular dynamics simulations (see Chapter 5) were able to indicate that binding of ATP to one active site (Site 2) was capable of inducing Arginine 269 (Arg 269) closure of the same site, thereby causing an opening up of the other active site (Site 1) via a trans-conformational relay system operating through the dimer interface by means of physical contacts between the C2–C3 loops of each monomer and corresponding Motif 2 loops in the corresponding monomer, proximal to each active site (Figure 7.34). Such a conformational opening of Site 1 would be sufficient explanation for impaired ATP binding affinity and half-of-sites reactivity!

Clearly, the results of modelling studies should always be correlated where possible with experimental observations. However, the combination of experimental techniques with molecular modelling represents an important chemical biology case study for the investigation of the molecular recognition and binding events that precede catalysis in an enzyme biocatalyst mechanism. Not only has a clear substrate order of addition been established for LysU, but also a half-of-sites binding mechanism. Obviously, the precise combination of experimental techniques and modelling studies will vary according to the biocatalyst under investigation, but the outcomes should be illustrative of the need to combine as many techniques as possible in order to understand. Now, not only does conformational opening of LysU Site 1 appear to be an important reason that Site 1 has a lower affinity for ATP than Site 2 and does not experimentally bind ATP, but also lysyl-adenylate formation and pyrophosphate release in Site 2 appears likely to trigger a subsequent reverse set of trans-conformational changes across the dimer interface allowing Site 1 to bind ATP, close up and initiate Step 1 catalysis of lysyl-adenylate formation in turn. We appear to be making significant progress in understanding the molecular recognition and binding behaviour of LysU!

7.4.2 Stress protein molecular chaperones

Stress protein molecular chaperones have already been introduced (see Chapter 6). Such proteins have a rich and varied molecular recognition and binding behaviour. Important examples include GroEL and the procollagen/collagen molecular chaperone protein known as heat shock protein 47 (Hsp47).

7.4.2.1   GroEL

GroEL is a paradox in molecular recognition and binding. A wide range of different unfolded protein substrates binds to GroEL with K_d values in the micromolar–nanomolar range. Such

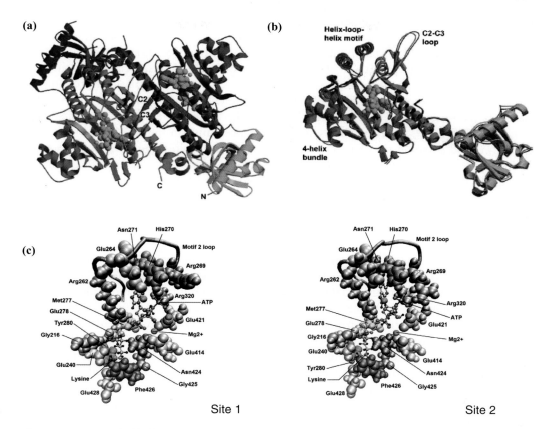

Site 1   Site 2

Figure 7.34   LysU half-of-sites binding of ATP and half-of-sites reactivity: (a) **Ribbon display** of X-ray crystal structure of LysU with substrates L-lysine (**pink**) and β,γ-methylene ATP (AMPPCP) (**cyan**) bound in both active sites together with 3 Mg^{2+} ions (**yellow**), all shown in **space filling representation. Monomer 1** is shown in **blue, monomer 2** is coloured according to domain structure; N -terminal (**orange**), conserved core domain typical to Class II tRNA synthetases (**red**), LysU specific regions (**purple**). In the central domain region, a **motif 2 loop** (**green**) sits over ATP. β-Strands **C2** and **C3** in each monomer interact across the homodimer interface. The intervening **C2-C3** loop is positioned above and interacts with the **motif 2** loop of the opposite monomer. (**b**) Superposition of **monomer 1** and **monomer 2** post molecular mechanics simulation (1ns). Colour code is as in (a) monomer 2. Superposition involves fitting the conserved core domain. There is a relative movement of several loops and domains, resulting in asymmetry. (**c**) **Assymetry observed in active sites.** In **site 1** (monomer 1), the active site is "open", in **site 2** (monomer 2), the active site is "closed" (Arg 269 of **motif 2** loop closes the binding pocket) and binds nucleotide more tightly than the "open" site. Active site closure in monomer 2 appears to result in the displacement of attached motif 2 loop leading to coupled displacements in the **C2-C3 loop**, the **C2** β-strand, and hence the motif 2 loop of monomer 1. As a result, site 1 (monomer 1) is opened. Such structural and binding asymmetry seen in molecular simulation accounts for **experimental half-of-sites binding** of nucleotide (**Fig. 7.33**) and suggests a mechanism for **half-of-sites reactivity**, where only one active site at a time is involved in the binding of ATP and catalysis of Step 1 (**Fig. 7.30**) (illustrations a) and b) Reproduced from Hughes et al., 2003, Fig. 1; c) and d) from Boonyalai et al., 2008, in preparation).

binding strength should clearly be characterised as specific, and yet GroEL has a promiscuous capacity with GroES to assist the folding/refolding of a diverse range of protein substrates. How is this possible? How is it possible to investigate this? In order to simplify the investigation but at the same time retain valuable information, extrinsic fluorescence binding titration experiments were performed using a series of peptide surrogates for unfolded protein substrates. Peptide binding interactions with GroEL were reported in each case by means of a dansyl (Dns) group (see Chapter 4) covalently attached to each peptide. Dns groups show a marked shift in I_{max} and an increase in fluorescence emission intensity with increase in quantum yield ϕ_F upon transfer from a free, aqueous hydrophilic environment to a more hydrophobic ligand-bound environment.

Initially, GroEL was found to have a preference for interaction with peptides comprising sequences or arrays of amino-acid residues that are amphiphilic, comprising hydrophobic and polar neutral/cationic residues. Sequences or arrays exclusively polar in character or else harbouring an excess of anionic residues were not recognised or bound at all (Figure 7.35). Following this, the role of secondary structure in molecular recognition and binding was investigated by the systematic preparation of a series of six peptides divisible into two groups known as the *AMPH series*, designed with a graded ability to form a cationic amphiphilic α-helical structure in solution, and the *NON-AMPH series*, designed with the graded ability to form a non-amphiphilic α-helical structure in solution (Figure 7.35). Extrinsic fluorescence titration experiments were performed using all six peptides. Owing to the molecular weight size difference between GroEL and peptides, and the potential number of peptide binding sites, fluorescence titration experiments were actually performed in reverse, keeping peptide concentrations fixed and titrating with increasing GroEL until fluorescence saturation was achieved (Figure 7.36). From such experiments values of K_d were determined, with the discovery that the most α-helical AMPH series peptide (AMPH$^+$) was much the most effective GroEL 'substrate', with a binding interaction affinity (K_d 5 nM) as strong as if not stronger than known binding interactions between GroEL and other protein 'substrates'. Extrinsic fluorescence binding titration experiments under a range of different conditions were also able to show the importance of the hydrophobic effect in peptide–GroEL association (Figure 7.37). Similar titration experiments were used to show that peptides and GroES compete for the same binding sites on GroEL, in accordance with the known GroEL/GroES mechanism (Figure 7.37) (see Figures 6.17 and 6.18). Finally, the sum total of all these experiments was the main conclusion that GroEL has a preference to bind regions or subdomains in an unfolded protein substrate that have a propensity to form polar neutral and/or cationic, amphiphilic secondary structural elements in solution. This robust conclusion appears to provide the required explanation for the general–specific molecular recognition and binding behaviour of GroEL.

GroEL has an almost predatory enthusiasm for the binding and hydrolysis of ATP as part of the known GroEL/GroES mechanism (Figures 6.17 and 6.18). Indeed, ATP binding sites reside in each subunit polypeptide of the GroEL 14-mer and binding of ATP at a given site invokes considerable positive cooperativity in the binding of ATP by the remaining six subunits within the corresponding ring of seven. Cooperativity is boosted by a T to R state transition in the conformation of each subunit in response to binding of increasing amounts of ATP, where the R state has a higher affinity for ATP binding than the T state (Figure 6.18).

(a)

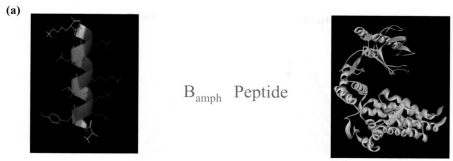

B_{amph} Peptide

NH_2-A L Y K K I I K K L L E S K-OH

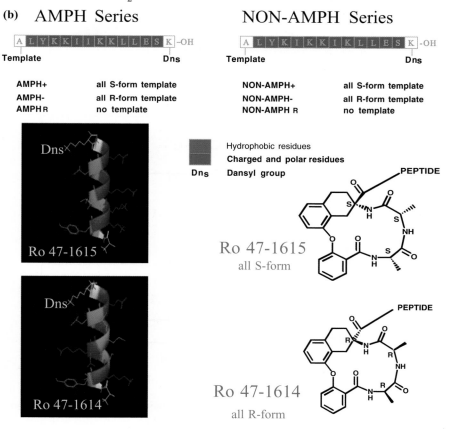

Figure 7.35 GroEL peptide substrates: (a) Basic Amphiphilic (B_{amph}) peptide, the optimal first round substrate peptide. Hydrophilic residues (**red**) and hydrophobic residues (**green**) are disposed for B_{amph} to have the ability to form an amphiphilic α-helix in solution (**left**), considered to be potentially optimal to interact with exposed hydrophobic residue "patches" in GroEL (coloured regions in GroEL monomer, **right**). (**b**) Summary of AMPH and NON-AMPH series peptides with helix forming template (Ro 47-1615) and control template (Ro 47-1614) (**right**) and proposed amphiphilic (**AMPH**) (**upper left**) and non-amphiphilic (**NON-AMPH**) helical structures (**lower left**) illustrated (peptide structure illustrations in a) and b) are adapted from Preuss et al., 1999, Fig. 3).

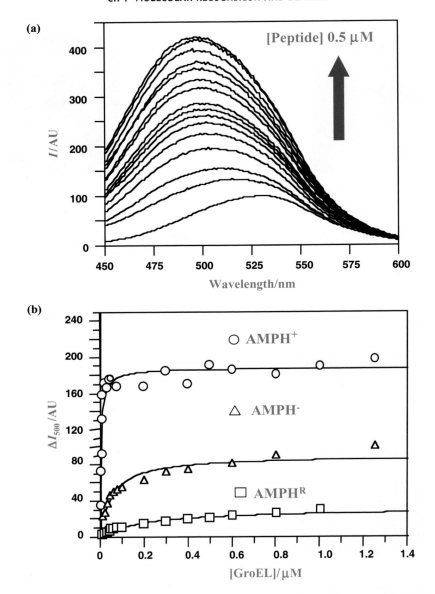

Figure 7.36 Peptide association with GroEL: (**a**) Fluorescence emission spectra from fluorescence binding titration experiment with fixed concentration of AMPH$^+$ peptide(0.5 μM) titrated with GroEL until saturation in buffer pH 7.5 at 20°C. Note I_{max} blue shift and increase in emission intensity as titration progresses. (**b**) Three binding isotherms from three fluorescence binding titration experiments involving the indicated peptides under conditions described in (a) (Reproduced from Preuss et al., 1999, Fig. 6).

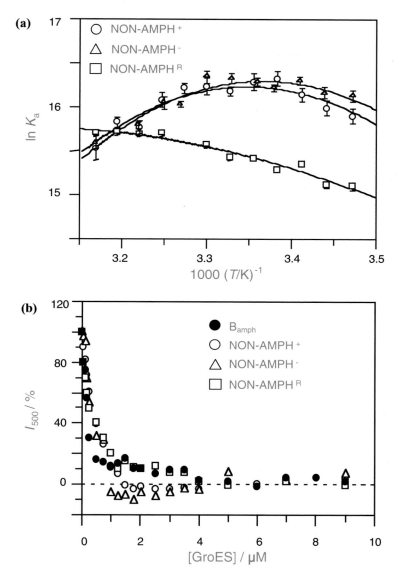

Figure 7.37 Forces and competition involved in binding GroEL peptide substrates: (**a**) Standard **Van't Hoff plots** prepared from data obtained through fluorescence binding titration experiments. Negative curvature suggests that the hydrophobic effect plays an important part in NON-AMPH series peptide binding to GroEL, and by implication AMPH series peptides too. (**b**) **Competition binding experiments** in which interaction of fixed concentration of peptides with GroEL (0.5 μM) is studied in the presence of increasing GroES. Fixed concentrations of ATP, MgCl$_2$ and KCl are also present. GroES competes very effectively for binding to GroEL consistent with shared GroEL binding sites (see **Fig. 6.18**). Competition experiments give important validation that peptides are realistic alternate substrates for proteins in molecular recognition and binding studies involving GroEL (a) and b) adapted from Preuss et al., 1999, Figs. 8 and 9c respectively).

This positive cooperativity in binding ATP is highly analogous to another famous example of positive cooperativity, namely the binding of oxygen to haem iron in the hetero-tetramer haemoglobin, the oxygen carrying protein found in red blood cells (see Chapter 1). In both cases, cooperativity in binding can be demonstrated by binding isotherms and Hill equations (see Section 7.2.4).

7.4.2.2 Hsp47

Hsp47 is a molecular chaperone specific to procollagen biogenesis and so is almost the exact opposite of GroEL. Furthermore, Hsp47 performs molecular chaperone functions either as a monomeric protein (47 kDa) or as a trimer (141 kDa) (Figure 7.38). However, Hsp47 is also a paradox in molecular recognition and binding. The protein is actually a member of the serine protease inhibitor (serpin) superfamily, one of the most widely studied and structurally characterised protein families. The main function of the serpin superfamily is clearly completely different to that of a procollagen/collagen molecular chaperone! Therefore, how is this possible? How do we investigate? Almost from the start, molecular recognition and binding studies were seen to be a key way to reach an understanding about the function and role of Hsp47 in procollagen biogenesis. Such studies were enabled by intrinsic fluorescence and CD binding titration experiments to probe the interactions between Hsp47 and procollagen-like model peptide (PPG)$_{10}$ (Figure 7.38). From such experiments, values of K_d were determined that were surprisingly strong (approximately 800 nM). Moreover, CD binding titration experiments also demonstrated that peptide binding resulted in an increase in P_{II} helix character, actually helping procollagen triple helix (molecular rope, see Chapter 1) to form (Figure 7.39)!

Intrinsic fluorescence titration experiments were also of value in demonstrating the effect of pH upon peptide–Hsp47 interactions; measured binding affinities were found to drop by over 10^3 in moving from neutral–mildly alkali to mildly acidic conditions (pH $\leq$ 6.3) (Figure 7.39). Careful CD and fluorescence pH-titration experiments were found to be useful in understanding this behaviour. By means of these experiments, Hsp47 was observed to undergo reversible pH-driven trans-conformational changes from one main conformational state (*alkali state*) at neutral–mildly alkali pH to an alternative main conformational state (*acid state*)

Figure 7.38 **Procollagen-like mimic peptide (PPG)$_{10}$ in interaction with Hsp47: (a) Ribbon display** model structure of monomeric Heat Shock Protein 47 (Hsp47) with classical serpin fold. View is from bottom illustrating the reactive centre loop (RCL) (**red**) and the 5-strand A β-sheet shown (**green**). (**b**) Ribbon display model of Hsp47 homo-oligomeric trimer (monomers in red, yellow and green) formed by the insertion of the RCL of one Hsp47 monomer into the 5-strand A β-sheet of another Hsp47 monomer (head-to-tail interactions). (**c**) Intrinsic tryptophan fluorescence binding isotherm from fluorescence titration binding experiment using fixed concentration of Hsp47 titrated with (PPG)$_{10}$ until saturation in buffer pH 7.5 at 20°C. (**d**) CD binding isotherm from CD titration binding experiment using fixed concentration of Hsp47 titrated with (PPG)$_{10}$ until saturation in buffer pH 7.5 at 20°C (illustrations a) and b) are from Dafforn et al., 2001, Figs. 1a and 6c respectively; c) and d) are adapted from Dafforn et al., 2001, Fig. 4a).

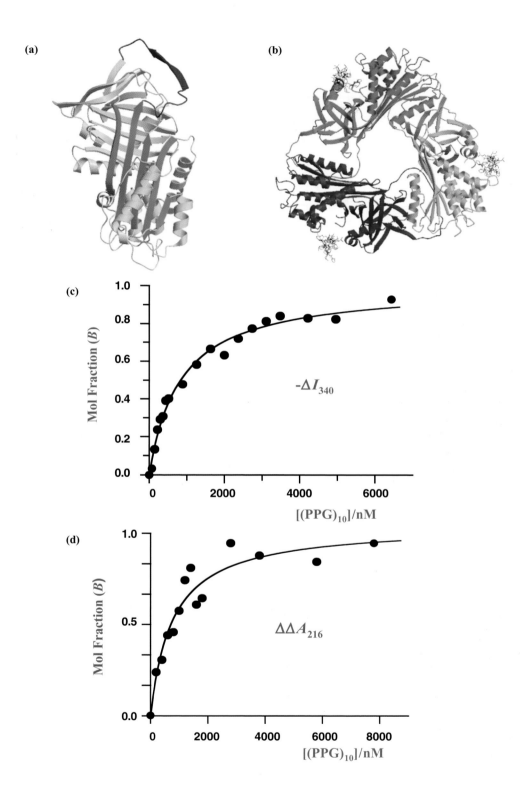

(a)

(b)

(c)

$-\Delta I_{340}$

(d)

$\Delta\Delta A_{216}$

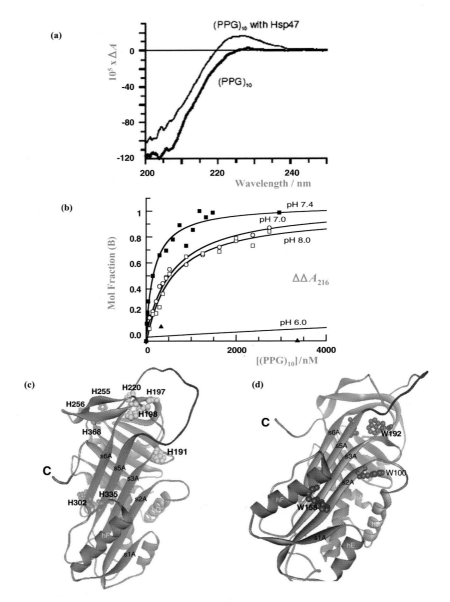

Figure 7.39 Implications of (PPG)$_{10}$ interaction with Hsp47: (**a**) Endpoint of CD titration binding experiment (see Figure 7.38d) illustrating the change in (PPG)$_{10}$ CD spectrum in the presence and absence of Hsp47. (**b**) Repeat of CD titration binding experiment (see **Fig. 7.38d**) in buffer at different pH. (**c**) Ribbon display of Hsp47 to show histidine residue clusters (**ball and stick** representation) for protein engineering. These are breach (**yellow**), gate (**green**) and shutter (**pink**) clusters. (**d**) Ribbon display of Hsp47 to show tryptophan residues (**ball and stick** surface representation, purple) for protein engineering (illustrations a) and b) are adapted from Dafforn et al., 2001, Figs. 4b and 4d respectively; c) and d) are from Homma et al., 2008).

at pH 6 and below, in a process mediated *via* a putative transitional state (*intermediate state*) (see Figures 4.8 and 4.13 Chapter 4). The close correlation between binding affinity and conformational data suggested the important conclusion that pH-driven trans-conformational changes are the reason for the changes in binding affinity with pH (**conformational pH switch mechanism**), implying that only the alkali state of Hsp47 is competent to bind procollagen-like model peptide (PPG)$_{10}$ and by implication procollagen/collagen. Importantly, the results of all these titration experiments and the conformational pH switch mechanism actually appear to make sense biologically. Hsp47 is known to bind to and assist procollagen assembly in the endoplasmic reticulum (neutral–mildly alkali pH) (a major site of protein synthesis is eukaryotic cells) and then remain bound to assist protein trafficking to the *cis*-Golgi (approximately pH 6.4) (a major site of protein storage before export from eukaryotic cells), where procollagen molecules then dissociate from Hsp47 to begin the process of fibrilisation prior to export from cells. Hsp47 is then apparently returned to the endoplasmic reticulum in order to repeat the process.

Since the conformational pH-switch mechanism is central to the biological activity of Hsp47, further understanding is essential. Detailed site-directed mutagenesis (protein engineering) studies are a powerful way forward (see Chapter 3). In the case of Hsp47, histidine amino-acid residues found in histidine clusters (*breach*, *shutter* and *gate* regions) were systematically mutated in turn to alanine residues. Results demonstrated that *breach* and *gate* histidines appeared to control and modulate the conformational pH switch, with H191 acting as a potential *trigger residue* to initiate the correct pH-driven conformational change process (Figure 7.39). Selective mutations of tryptophan residues to phenylalanine residues were then used to determine those sub-domains of Hsp47 most susceptible to conformational change with pH. In the event, the A β-sheet region around W100, centred close to H191, was found to be the most influenced by conformational change as a function of pH (Figure 7.39). Importantly, this region underpins the anticipated binding site region of Hsp47 for collagen/procollagen and procollagen-like model peptide (PPG)$_{10}$! Therefore, the results all seem to interlock to give a complete understanding. So why should a serpin superfamily member become a molecular chaperone involved in procollagen biogenesis? In fact, all serpin superfamily members studied to date have a remarkable conformational plasticity. According to the data describe above, this plasticity also seems to be ideally suited to molecular chaperone duties as well!

7.4.3 Complementary peptides

By definition, a sense peptide is one whose sequence is coded for by the nucleotide sequence (read 5' $\rightarrow$ 3') of sense mRNA, whose sequence contains the same coding information as the sense strand of DNA. Conversely, a complementary peptide is coded for by the nucleotide sequence (read 5' $\rightarrow$ 3') of complementary mRNA, with the same sequence information as the complementary strand of DNA. Frequently, sense and complementary peptides are capable of specific interactions, in a process that may involve an amino-acid interaction code embedded within the genetic code and its complement (Figure 7.40). One application of sense–complementary peptide interactions may be in the design of complementary

(a)

(b)

(c)

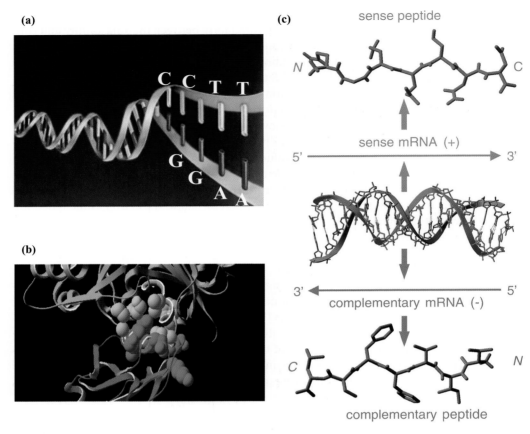

Figure 7.40 Sense-complementary peptide concepts; (**a**) DNA double helix is maintained throughout by Watson-Crick base pairs. (**b**) Protein-protein interactions may be driven in part by a peptide/protein equivalent of Watson-Crick base pairs. (**c**) Specific sense-complementary peptide interactions may provide the basis for understanding. A sense peptide is coded for by the nucleotide sequence in sense mRNA that has the same sequence information as the sense strand of DNA. A corresponding complementary peptide is coded from by the nucleotide sequence in complementary mRNA that has the same sequence information as the complementary strand of DNA. Sense and corresponding complementary peptides are capable of specific interactions suggesting that there may be a peptide/protein binding interaction code associated with the genetic code and its complement.

(antisense) peptide mini-receptor inhibitors of proteins binding to receptors. At its simplest level, a complementary peptide inhibitor is designed first by looking at the mRNA (or DNA sense strand) sequence coding for a target region of interest in a given target protein. From this, the complementary sequence can then be deduced by Watson–Crick base pair rules and the corresponding peptide sequence determined from the complementary mRNA (or DNA complementary strand) sequence according to the genetic code. Successful complementary peptide mini-receptor inhibitors have been designed against a variety of proteins including the cytokine interleukin-1β (IL-1β) involved in mediating inflammation (see Chapters 5 and 7).

(a)

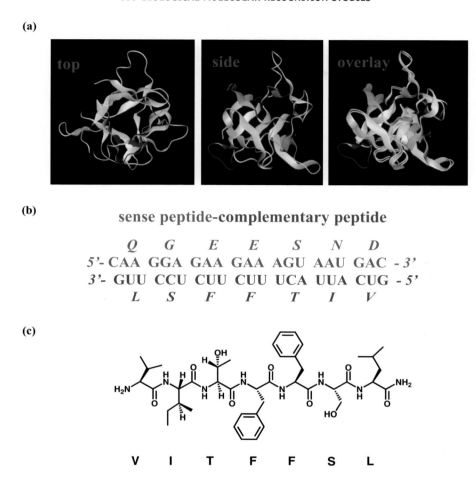

(b)

sense peptide-complementary peptide

Q   G   E   E   S   N   D
5'- CAA GGA GAA GAA AGU AAU GAC - 3'
3'- GUU CCU CUU CUU UCA UUA CUG - 5'
L   S   F   F   T   I   V

(c)

V   I   T   F   F   S   L

Figure 7.41 Complementary peptide derivation: (a) Three **ribbon structure** views of interleukin-1β (IL-1β) X-ray structure (pdb: **1i1b**), showing (**top & side**) key receptor binding residue regions (**yellow**) and the **Boraschi loop** (**red**). **Overlay** structure involves superposition of Interleukin-1 receptor antagonist (IL-1ra) X-ray structure (pdb: **1ilt**) upon IL-1β (side view) to demonstrate the general structural similarity between these protein family member proteins, but also the absence of Boraschi loop in IL-1ra. IL-1ra is the only known natural inhibitor of IL-1β. (**b**) mRNA sequence of Boraschi loop and decoded amino acid residue sequence (**red**) set alongside deduced mRNA sequence of complementary peptide and decoded amino acid residue sequence (**blue**). (**c**) Structure of complementary peptide corresponding with the Boraschi loop; a potential complementary (antisense) peptide mini-receptor inhibitor of IL-1β.

In the case of IL-1β, the complementary peptide inhibitor was designed against an exposed, functional surface loop (β-bulge) known as the Boraschi loop (Figure 7.41). Although biological activity of the complementary peptide and close relatives could be shown with some ease, evidence of specific binding of peptide to IL-1β was essential. How to do this? Given difficulties in obtaining adequate quantities of IL-1β, an analysis technique was required able

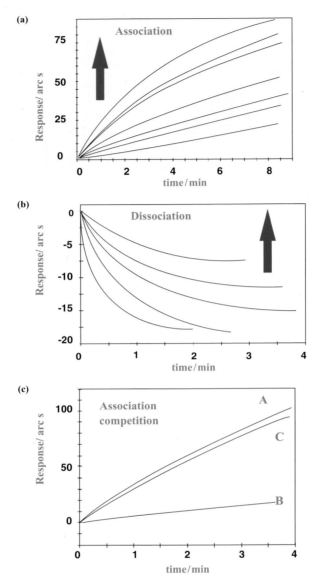

Figure 7.42 Resonant mirror binding assays: (a) Set of **association curves** for the association of complementary peptide **VITFFSL** with immobilised IL-1β (0.39 μM). **(b)** Set of **dissociation curves** for the dissociation of complementary peptide **VITFFSL** from immobilised IL-1β (0.39 μM) at neutral pH and 37°C. **(c)** Competition binding experiment showing association curves for complementary peptide with immobilised IL-1β (0.39 μM) at neutral pH and 37°C either alone (**A**), in the presence of a peptide with the Boraschi loop sequence (**B**) or with a peptide with a reordered Boraschi loop sequence (**C**). Experiment demonstrates specific interactions between complementary peptide and Boraschi loop competed with by a peptide with the Boraschi loop sequence. Complementary peptide will also not associate with a variety of control proteins including IL-1ra, further demonstrating peptide binding specificity for immobilised IL-1β (adapted from Heal et al., 2002, Fig. 4).

to yield data with minimal sample quantity, hence resonant mirror biosensing was used. The interactions of immobilised IL-1β with increasing quantities of complementary peptide inhibitor were analysed in real time (Figure 7.42), and values of K_d were determined that were reasonably strong (approximately 5 μM). A re-ordered version of the complementary peptide (same amino-acid composition; different residue order) was shown not to bind to immobilised IL-1β. Furthermore, the complementary peptide itself was shown not to bind to other proteins, including interleukin-1 receptor antagonist (IL-1ra), which has the same fold as IL-1β but without a corresponding Boraschi loop (Figure 7.41). Finally, a peptide with the sequence of the Boraschi loop was shown to compete with immobilised IL-1β for binding to the complementary peptide, providing proof of specific complementary peptide binding to the Boraschi surface loop (Figure 7.42). Complementary peptides still attract significant controversy, given the current absence of an unambiguous mechanism of interaction between a sense and corresponding complementary peptide. However, resonant mirror biosensing has enabled huge progress to be made in understanding. A wider role for sense–complementary peptide interactions in biology remains to be identified.

8

Kinetics and catalysis

8.1 Catalysis in chemical biology

According to some theories about the origins of life, the key to the creation of organisms is molecular complexity that is sufficient to give self-organisation (see Chapter 10). However, self-organisation alone is insufficient to give life. Instead, self-organisation needs to be partnered with the capacity to accelerate or catalyse chemical inter-conversions as well. This capacity to catalyse chemical inter-conversions is known as **catalysis**. Catalysis is frequently performed by a **catalyst**, which is usually defined as an entity that enhances the rate of a given chemical reaction in both forward and reverse directions without being itself permanently changed in the process. Therefore, a **biocatalyst** is a biologically relevant catalyst. Typically, biocatalysts accelerate biological chemical reactions with relative rate enhancements of between 10^5 and 10^{10} relative to the non-catalysed reactions. Catalysis is universal to all cells of all organisms and the range and diversity of known biocatalysts is simply staggering! Biocatalysts are clearly an absolute fundamental for both the origin of life and the promulgation of life.

Biocatalysts are overwhelmingly proteins (**enzymes**) and sometimes RNA nucleic acids (**ribozymes**). They catalyse an amazing diversity of reactions for myriads of different important reasons. Enzymes take centre stage in **metabolism**, which is the process by which chemical potential is generated and stored by coupling the synthesis of adenosine 5′-triphosphate (ATP) (the preferred 'form' of stored chemical energy in all cells) with the stepwise degradation and/or reorganisation of covalent bonds of **primary metabolites** such as glucose (Chapter 1). For instance, **triose phosphate isomerase** (**TIM**) (see Chapter 1) catalyses the seemingly innocuous interconversion between dihydroxyacetone phosphate and glyceraldehyde-3-phosphate in the catabolic pathway known as **glycolysis** (Figure 8.1). Yet surprisingly, TIM is now considered to be a 'perfect enzyme' (see Section 8.4.8), which makes the interconversion

Essentials of Chemical Biology   Andrew Miller and Julian Tanner
© 2008 John Wiley & Sons, Ltd

possible at a rate that is literally as fast as substrate reaches the enzyme active site. Indeed, without TIM the glycolysis pathway would be unable to deliver on a net gain of two ATP molecules for each glucose molecule consumed (see Figure 8.1). In a similar vein, the dimeric enzyme **malate dehydrogenase (MDH)** catalyses the mere reduction of a carbonyl functional group in **oxalic acid** to give **malic acid**, making use of the cofactor **nicotinamide adenine din-ucleotide hydride, reduced form (NADH)** (Figure 8.2), yet this interconversion establishes closure of the **tricarboxylic acid (TCA) cycle**, which takes metabolites from glycolysis and delivers on a net gain of reducing cofactor molecules for each complete rotation through the TCA cycle. There are other types of catabolic enzyme, such as **chymotrypsin**, which within the gut digests polypeptides into oligopeptides (Figure 8.3), for absorption across the gut wall into the blood stream. Alternatively, **ribonuclease A (RNAse A)** does for RNA polynu-cleotide what chymotrypsin does for polypeptides, albeit by a very different mechanism

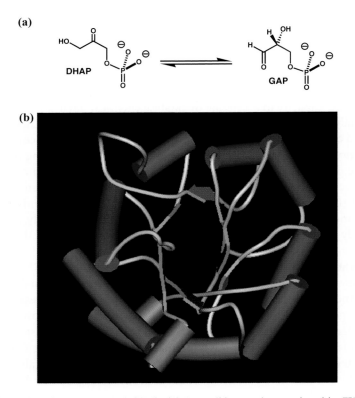

Figure 8.1 Triose Phosphate Isomerase (TIM). (a) Reversible reaction catalyzed by TIM where DHAP is dihydroxy acetone phosphate, and GAP is glyceraldehyde-3-phosphate; (b) **schematic display structure** of TIM (chicken muscle) (top view) (pdb: **1tim**); (c) chemical illustration of **glycolysis** - a primary catabolic pathway able to yield two molecules of ATP/glucose consumed, made possible only through the catalytic activity of TIM. Enzyme abbreviations are as follows; **HK**, hexokinase; **PGI**, phosphoglucose ismerase; **PFK**, phosphofructokinase; **GAPDH**, glyceraldehyde-3-phosphate dehydrogenase; **PGK**, phosphoglycerate kinase; **PGM**, phosphoglycerate mutase; **PK**, pyruvate kinase.

(c)

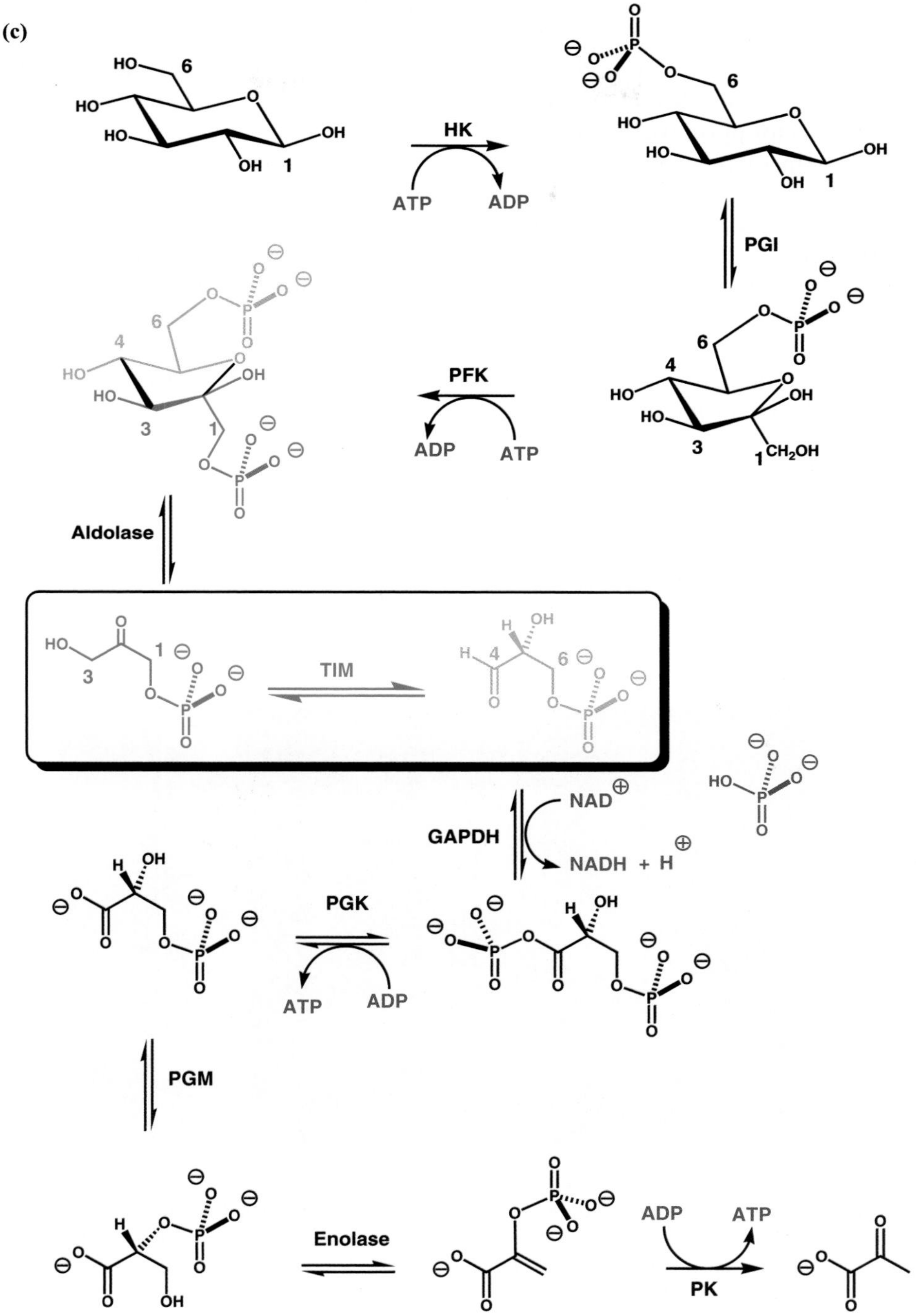

Figure 8.1 (*Continued*)

(Figure 8.4). Enzymes are not only involved in **catabolism** (i.e. breaking down), but also play a role in **anabolism** (i.e. building up) of monomeric building blocks required for biological macromolecular assembly. In this respect, examples include **alanine α-racemase (AlaR)**, **glutamate α-decarboxylase** and **aspartate transaminase (aspAT)** enzymes, which all make use of the cofactor **pyridoxal phosphate (PLP)** (Figure 8.5).

Many enzymes have protective functions frequently outside cells. For instance, **lysozyme** (see Chapter 1), which is produced externally in tears, functions to catalyse the hydrolysis of *O*-glycosidic links in complex polysaccharides of bacterial cell walls, in order to weaken and destroy those cell walls, kill the bacteria and protect the surface of the eye from infection (Figure 8.6). **Chloramphenicol acetyl transferase (CAT)** is an example of a bacterial enzyme evolved to inactivate the antibiotic chloramphenicol by controlled acetylation (Figure 8.7). Then there is **superoxide dismutase (SOD)**, which is an astonishing di-metal enzyme family that catalyses the disproportionation of **superoxide radicals** into **oxygen** and **hydrogen peroxide** with extraordinary efficiency (Figure 8.8). Superoxide radicals are generated when

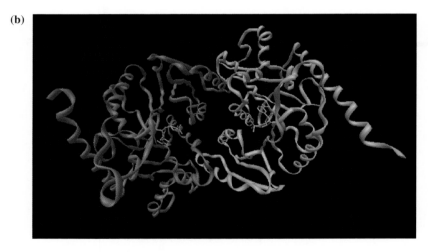

Figure 8.2 Malate Dehydrogenase (MDH). (a) Reversible reaction catalyzed by MDH where NADH is nicotinamide adenine dinucleotide, reduced form; **(b) ribbon display structure** of MDH (porcine heart) (side view) (pdb:**4mdh**). The homo-dimeric protein consists of two polypeptides chains (**yellow** and **red**), with nicotinamide adenine dinudeotide (NAD$^+$) in both independent catalytic sites illustrated in a **ball and stick (blue)** representation; **(c)** chemical illustration of the **tricarboxylic acid cycle (TCA)** to demonstrate the importance of MDH catalysis in cycle closure. Enzyme abbreviations are: **PDH**, pyruvate dehyrogensase; **CS**, citrate synthase.

(c)

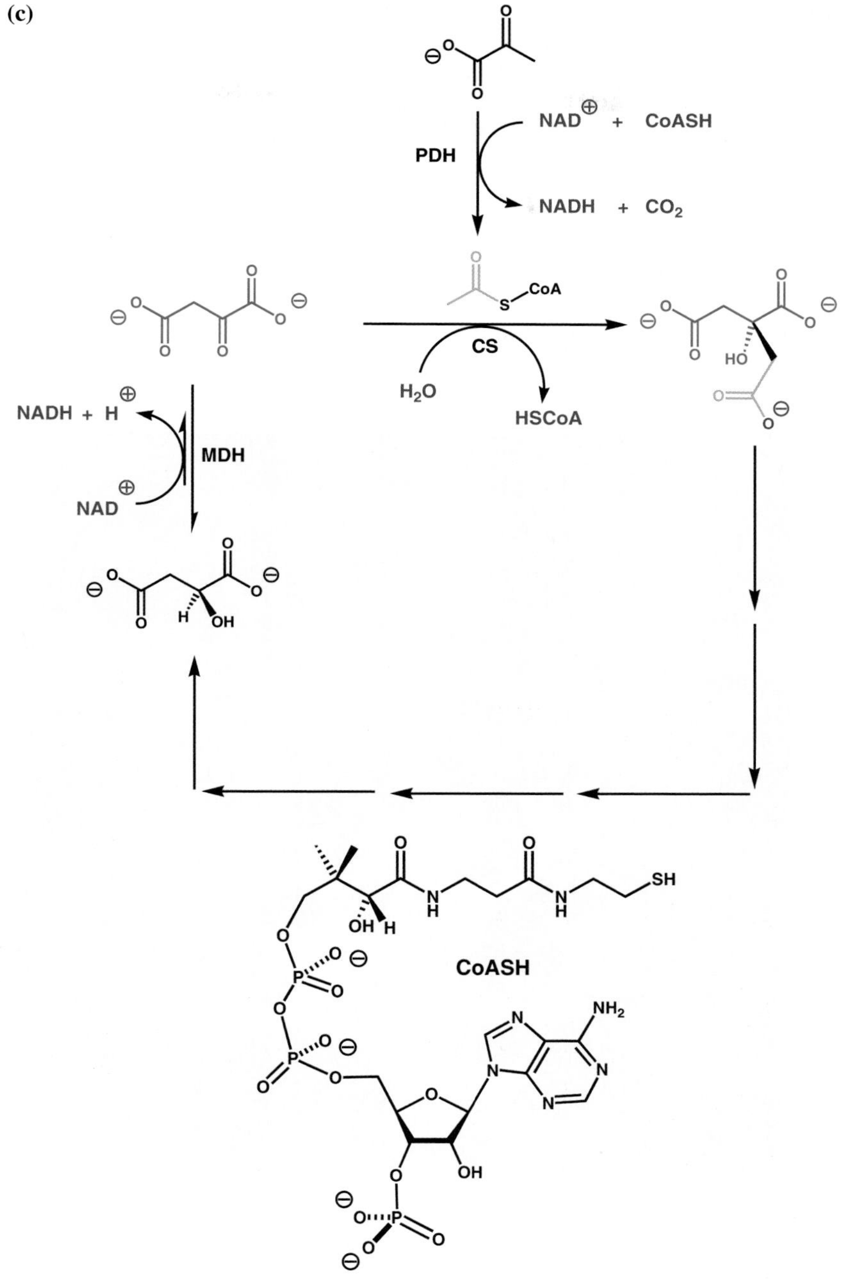

Figure 8.2 (*Continued*)

(a)

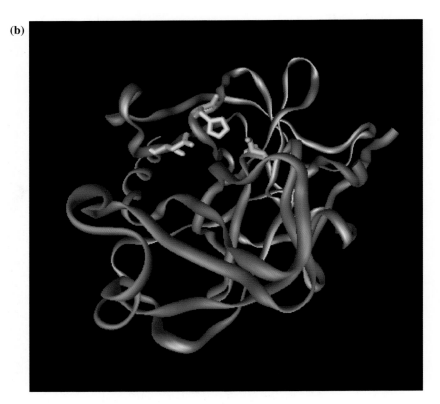

(b)

Figure 8.3 *α*-**Chymotrypsin.** (a) Hydrolytic reaction catalyzed by *α*-chymotrypsin, where amino acid residue side chain R_2 is hydrophobic or aromatic in character; (b) **ribbon display structure** of *α*-chymotrypsin (bovine pancreatic) (pdb: **4cha**) in which key active site residues **D102, H57** and **S195** (left to right) involved in biocatalysis are shown (yellow) rendered in a tube display style (See **Fig. 8.50** **(b)**).

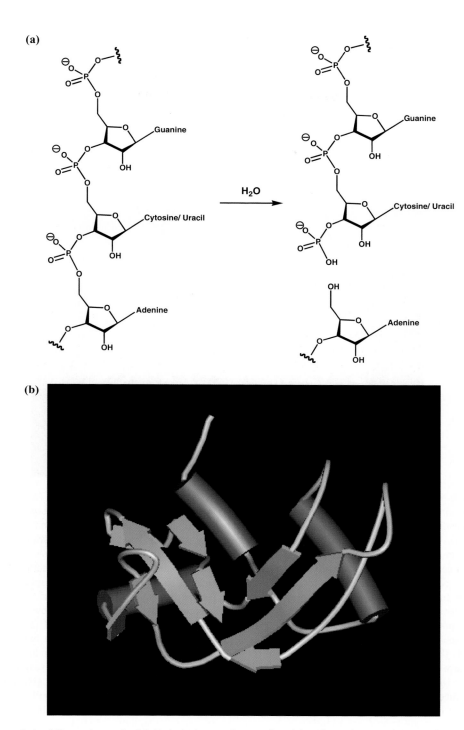

Figure 8.4 Ribonuclease A. (a) Hydrolytic reaction catalyzed by ribonuclease A (RNAse A), note that hydrolytic cleavage occurs at the 3′-side of a pyrimidine nucleoside; **(b) cartoon display structure** of RNAse A (bovine pancreatic) (side view) (pdb: **7rsa**).

(a)

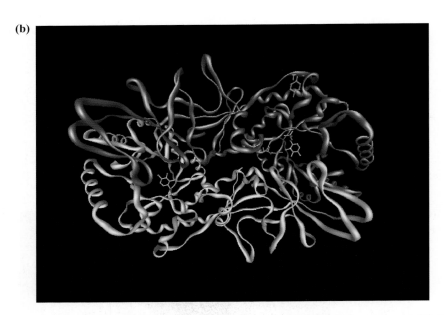

(b)

Figure 8.5   Alanine racemase. (a) Racemisation reaction catalyzed by alanine racemase (AlaR), note that requires the cofactor **pyridoxal phosphate (PLP)** in order to take place; **(b) ribbon display structure** of homo-dimeric **AlaR** (*Bacillus Stearothermophilus*) (pdb: **2sfp**) showing both polypeptide chains (yellow and red). PLP appears bound in both independent catalytic sites rendered by **ball and stick display** (blue); in one catalytic site, key catalytic residues **Y265** and **K39** (top to bottom) are shown (**green**), also rendered by **ball and stick display** (**green**). **Glutamate** α-**decarboxylase. (c)** α-decarboxylation reaction catalyzed by glutamate α- decarboxylase that requires the cofactor pyridoxal phosphate (PLP) in order to take place; **(d) ribbon display structure** of **T-state** (neutral pH) homo-hexameric glutamate α-decarboxylase (**GadB**) (*Escherichia coli*) showing all polypeptide chains (two in **green, yellow** and **blue**) (pdb: **1pmo**); **(e) ribbon display structure** of **R-state** (acidic pH) homo-hexameric GadB (*Escherichia coli*) showing all polypeptide chains (two in **green, yellow** and **blue**) and six *N*-terminal α-helices, (1–14, **red**) that are key sites for protonation and chloride-ion binding induced cooperativity (pdb: **1pmm**). **Aspartate transaminase. (f)** Transamination reaction catalyzed by aspartate transaminase (**aspAT**) that requires the cofactor pyridoxal phosphate (PLP) in order to take place; **(g) ribbon display structure** of homo-dimeric aspAT (*Escherichia coli*) (pdb: **2aat**) showing one of two polypeptide chains. **PLP** appears bound in independent catalytic site rendered by **ball and stick display** (**yellow**); key substrate binding residues R386 and R292 (right to left) are shown (**red**), also rendered by **ball and stick display.**

(c)

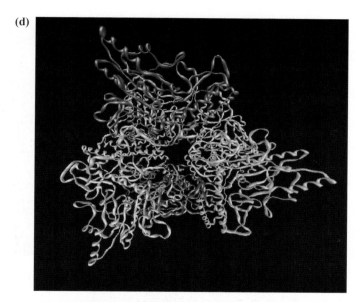

L-glutamate   **GABA**

(d)

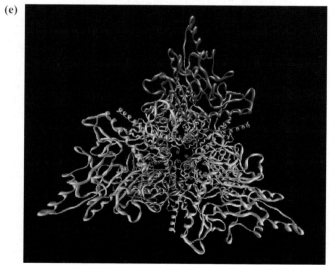

(e)

Figure 8.5 *(Continued)*

(f)

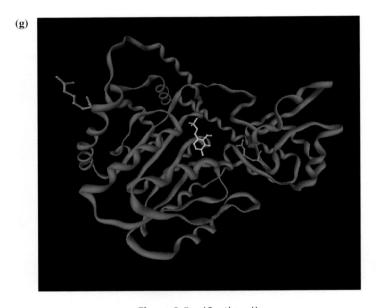

L-aspartate   α-ketoglutarate   PLP   L-glutamate   oxalate

(g)

Figure 8.5   *(Continued)*

the reduction of oxygen to water during **respiration** is incomplete, which is surprisingly frequent. These radicals are lethal to all the biological macromolecules and macromolecular lipid assemblies in a cell unless they are dealt with promptly by SOD. In fact, certain cells of the immune system actually use superoxide radicals deliberately in a controlled fashion to destroy invading microorganisms! Now let us consider **carbonic anhydrase** (**CA**) (see Chapter 1), which has been described as one of the most efficient biocatalysts of all; it catalyses the simple interconversion of carbonic acid into water and carbon dioxide (Figure 8.9). Why is this enzyme protective? Quite simply, CA acts to preserve the pH of blood at around pH 7, avoiding the problem of acidification that would otherwise take place as dissolved carbon dioxide levels rise in blood following glucose metabolism and TCA cycle activity in cells. Blood acidification or acidosis is spectacularly lethal! Finally, in Chapter 7, we have already met **acetyl choline esterase** (**AChE**), without which excess of the neurotransmitter acetyl choline would not be removed by hydrolysis from relevant synaptic clefts (Figure 8.10), leading to uncontrolled neurotransmission associated with such neurological conditions as seizures and epilepsy.

The chemical biology reader should also be aware that there are numbers of enzymes that can have multiple functions and that there are also biocatalysts that are not enzymes. In the first class, the enzyme **LysU** makes for an interesting case in point (see Chapter 7).

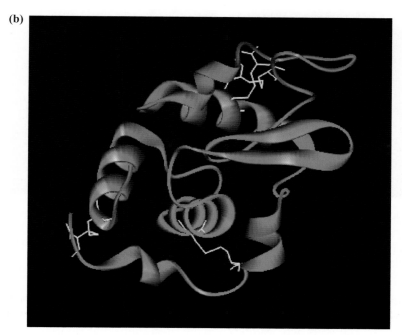

Figure 8.6 **Lysozyme**. (a) Hydrolysis reaction catalyzed by lysozyme: (b) **ribbon display structure** of lysozyme (hen-egg white) (pdb: **6lyz**) wherein the four disulphide bonds and their corresponding cysteine residues are rendered in a **stick display style (yellow)**. The catalytic site is a broad cleft through the polypeptide.

This is a **lysyl tRNA synthetase** enzyme in the first instance that should have the expected capacity to couple the naturally available amino acid L-lysine to appropriate cognate tRNAs bearing anti-codon sequences complementary to lysine codons (see Section 1.6.1). However in the presence of zinc ions, Zn^{2+}, the function of this enzyme becomes altered to catalyse the biosynthesis of diadenosine-$5',5'''$-P^1,P^4-tetraphosphate (Ap_4A) followed by

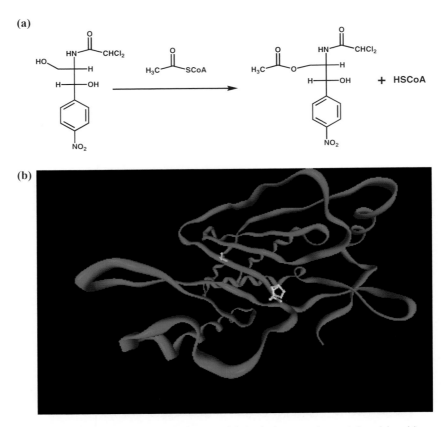

Figure 8.7 Chloramphenicol acetyl transferase. (a) Acylation reaction catalyzed by chloramphenicol acetyl transferease (**CAT**); (**b**) **ribbon display structure** of CAT (Type III, *Escherichia coli*) (pdb: **1cla**) wherein two key catalytic residues **H195** and **S148** (right to left) are displayed (**yellow**), in **ball and stick representation.**

diadenosine-5′,5′′′-P^1,P^3-tetraphosphate (Ap$_3$A) in a sequential fashion (Figure 8.11) (see Chapter 7). Finally, the discovery that RNA itself can act as a biocatalyst (**ribozyme**) was a huge revelation several years ago, leading to many suggestions that ribozymes may be the first biocatalysts, formed in advance of enzymes (Figure 8.12). Accordingly, there has been much discussion about an RNA-world that precedes the protein-world in a molecular theory of evolution (see Chapter 10).

8.1.1 Simple principles in biocatalysis

The **active** or **catalytic site** of any biocatalyst represents the region of structure devoted to biocatalysis in any given biocatalyst. Catalytic sites are usually surprisingly small and frequently occupy a very small area/volume of the overall structure. During the first stage

(a)

$$2O_2^{\cdot -} + 2H^{\oplus} \longrightarrow H_2O_2 + O_2$$

(b)

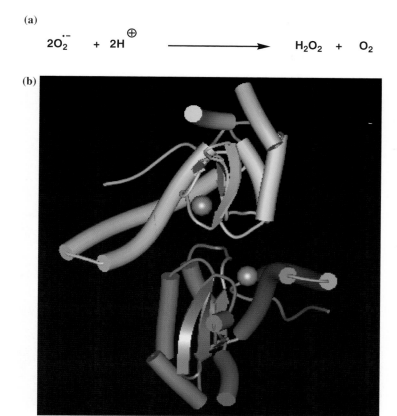

Figure 8.8 Super Oxide Dismutase. (a) Disproportionation reaction catalyzed by super oxide dismutase (**SOD**); (b) **cartoon display structure** of homo-tetrameric **MnSOD** (manganese containing human mitochondrial) (pdb:**1n0j**) illustrating two out of the four identical polypeptide chains (orange, yellow) and manganese ions ($Mn^{2+/3+}$) (**purple**) rendered as **van der Waals spheres** for complete clarity.

of biocatalysis, a **substrate** molecule must be recognised and bound to a catalytic site in a process of **molecular recognition and binding** that is completely equivalent to those processes described and discussed in detail in Chapter 7. Therefore, Chapter 7 is sufficient to appreciate the first stage of biocatalysis. During the second stage of biocatalysis, a bound substrate must be transformed into a bound **product** by biocatalysis and then released into the bulk solution. The ways and means of biocatalysis will form the principal subject matter of this chapter.

But first, in order to study biocatalysis, there needs to be a ready supply of a biocatalyst of interest made available through techniques such as those described in Chapter 3. Structure is always very helpful to interpret function (Chapters 4–6). After this, there need to be techniques of analysis and a sound theoretical framework with which to interpret biocatalysis data and elaborate those key mechanisms of biocatalyts that make biocatalysis possible. For this reason, we will begin this chapter with a detailed discussion of ways to acquire and analyse biocatalytic data using various models of biocatalysis. Following this, we will take a look at those theories

(a)

$$CO_2 + H_2O \rightleftharpoons HCO_3^{\ominus} + H^{\oplus}$$

(b)

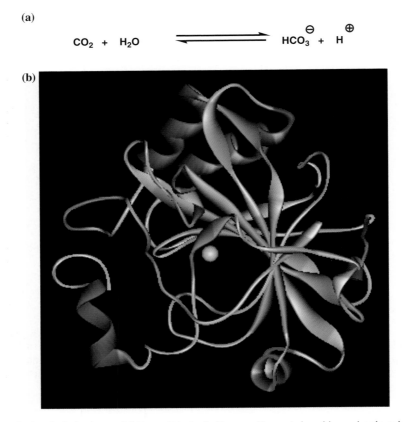

Figure 8.9   Carbonic Anhydrase. (a) Reversible hydration reaction catalyzed by carbonic anhydrase (**CA**): **(b) ribbon display structure** of monomeric CA (Type I, human erythrocyte) (pdb: **2cab**) illustrating α-helices (**red**) and β-sheet (**blue**) plus a central zinc ion (Zn^{2+}) (**yellow**) rendered as **van der Waals sphere** for complete clarity.

of biocatalysis that help explain how biocatalysts are able to be such effective catalysts of those chemical reactions required for life. Throughout this chapter, we will make reference to the examples of biocatalysts introduced to the chemical biology reader already, as an aid to understanding. In reality, the route to real understanding in biocatalysis is long and involved for each and every biocatalyst under investigation. Little wonder that there remains much to do before we can eventually arrive at a complete understanding of known biocatalysts, let alone all those yet unknown!

8.1.2 Steady state kinetics in biocatalysis

The study of reaction rates and catalysis is known as **kinetics**. Typically, the catalytic effect of any one biocatalyst is evaluated under **steady state** and/or **pre-steady-state** conditions (see

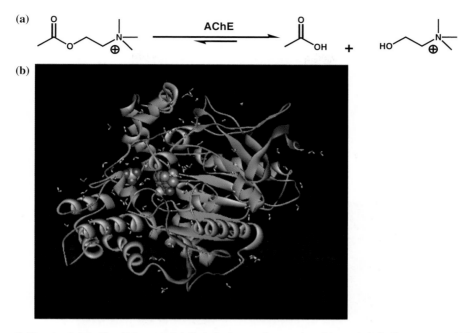

Figure 8.10   Acetylcholine Esterase. (a) Hydrolysis reaction catalyzed by acetyl choline esterase (**AChE**): (**b**) **ribbon display structure** of AChE (*Torpedo californica*) (pdb: **1amn**) illustrating crystallographic water molecules (oxygen: red; hydrogen: white) plus sulphate ion and substrate analogue bound in catalytic site. Both these are rendered as **CPK structures** (**red:** oxygen; **yellow:** sulphur; **grey:** carbon: **blue:** nitrogen).

main Section 8.3). Steady state kinetic analyses are used to understand the surface mechanistic behaviour of a given biocatalyst that is operating at **stasis** and capable of performing multiple catalytic turnovers. Stasis implies that rate measurements (i.e. data describing rates of conversion of a given substrate into product) are restricted to short time intervals, over which the concentrations of substrates and reactants do not change significantly. Therefore, stasis also implies that kinetic analysis takes place while there is metastable equilibrium between substrate(s), product(s) and/or various biocatalyst species. Steady state analysis is very representative of biocatalyst behaviour under conditions of normal metabolism, although a rather blunt tool for the investigation of detailed mechanistic steps associated with a given biocatalytic process taking place in the catalytic site of a given biocatalyst. Nonetheless, steady state kinetic analyses usually require relatively simple apparatus and simple procedures to implement and so are performed routinely.

8.1.3 Steady state bioassays

Steady state kinetic analyses can be as diverse as the range of biocatalysts themselves. Rate enhancements brought about by any one biocatalyst are usually assessed by means of a **bioassay**.

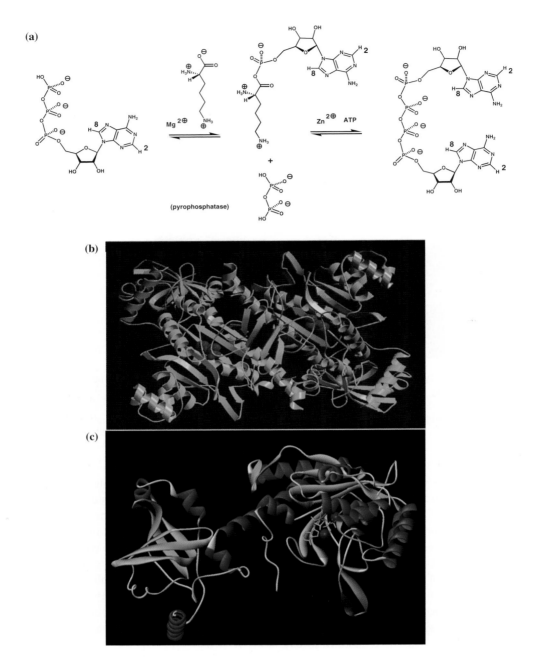

Figure 8.11 Lysyl tRNA synthetase. (a) Ap_4A synthesis reaction catalyzed by lysyl tRNA synthetase isozyme (LysU): (b) **ribbon display structure** of homo-dimeric LysU (*Escherichia coli*) (pdb: **1lyl**) showing both polypeptides (blue and green) and catalytic site bound L-lysine (red) rendered as **CPK structures**: (c) cartoon display structure of LysU monomer illustrating α-helices (**red**) and β-sheets (**blue**) with ATP (**orange**) and L-lysine (**green**) bound in the catalytic site with two Mg^{2+} ions (**purple**). The Mg^{2+} ions are rendered as **van der Waals spheres** while ATP and L-lysine are rendered as **ball and stick structures** (pdb: **1e1t**).

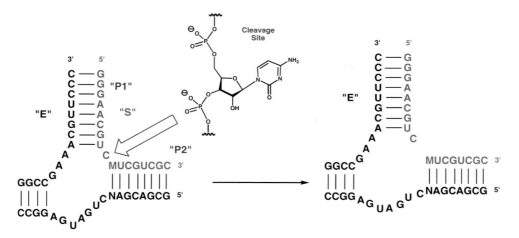

Figure 8.12 Ribozyme. Hydrolysis reaction catalyzed by ribozyme that consists of an enzyme "E" strand and a substrate "S" strand. Hydrolysis takes place below a cytidine nucleotide, converting "S" into two product strands "P1" and "P2" that dissociate from the "E" strand.

There is at least one unique bioassay for each biocatalyst. A bioassay is used to generate rate data, namely the variation in **initial rate** v of substrate to product conversion as a function of **initial substrate concentration** [S] while keeping the biocatalyst concentration constant throughout (Figure 8.13). Rate data may itself be determined as a function of temperature, pH, ionic strength and even other fixed concentrations of second, third or even fourth substrates. This rate data is then processed by means of any number of appropriate **steady state kinetics equations** to give standard biocatalytic parameters (that will be described below) and an indication of the surface mechanism by which the biocatalyst brings about biocatalysis. These standard parameters allow for simple comparisons between biocatalyst performances.

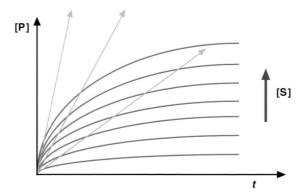

Figure 8.13 Schematic diagram to illustrate the concept of **initial rates.** In the presence of a fixed concentration of biocatalyst, variable concentrations of substrate **S** are converted into product **P** over a **time t**. Steady state analyses require initial concentrations of substrate, [S] and initial rates of product formation, v, that derive from the slopes of tangents (blue arrows) to initial slopes as illustrated.

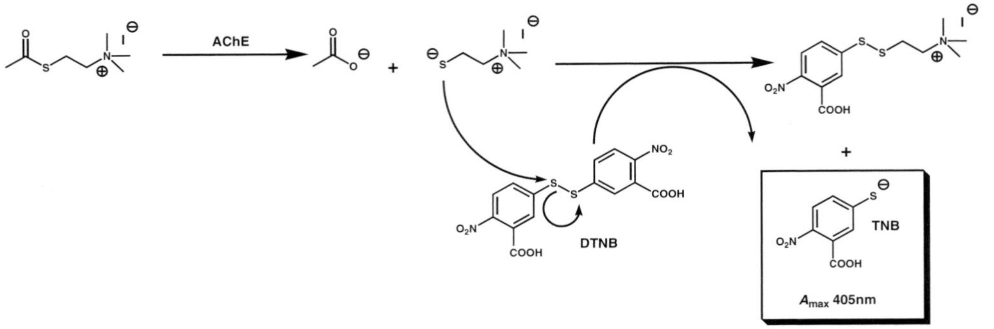

Figure 8.14 Colourimetric assay. Acetyl Choline Esterase (AChE) assay system involving **thio-acetylcholine** that is hydrolyzed to thio-choline. This in turn combines with colourless reagent **5,5′-dithio-bis(nitrobenzoic acid) (DTNB)** to form yellow coloured **5-thio-2-nitro-benzoic acid (TNB)**.

The majority of steady state bioassays tend to be **photometric assays**, but many other **steady state bioassays** including ^1H-NMR assays, **HPLC assays**, **radiometric assays**, **oxygen electrode assays** and **gel assays** may be used. In all cases, the main principle is to determine how values of v (directly or indirectly) vary as a function of [S] while keeping the biocatalyst concentration constant throughout. Photometric steady state bioassays make use of some form of **chromogenic substrate** or **reagent** that becomes chemically altered into a chromophore during biocatalysis and as a result absorbs significantly at a particular wavelength of absorption. The initial rate of formation of product is usually said to correlate with the initial rate of formation of the chromophore as determined by **UV–visible spectroscopy**. Steady state bioassays of AChE and CA both make use of chromogenic reagents (Figures 8.14 and 8.15).

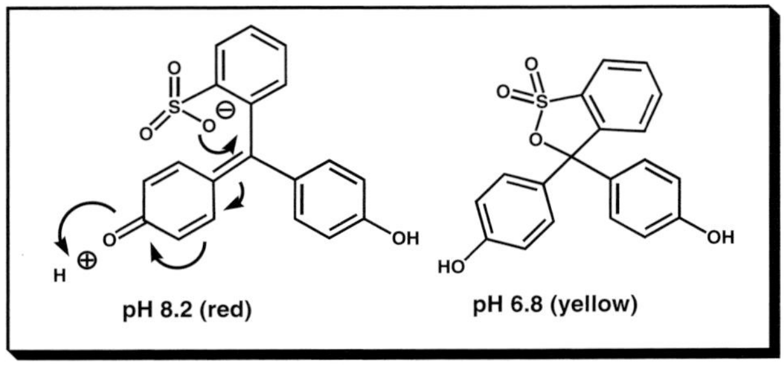

Figure 8.15 Colourimetric assay. Carbonic Anhydrase (CA) assay system. Changes in pH with enzyme catalysis are followed with great precision and accuracy by **pH-sensitive dye** that changes absorbance profile with pH-change.

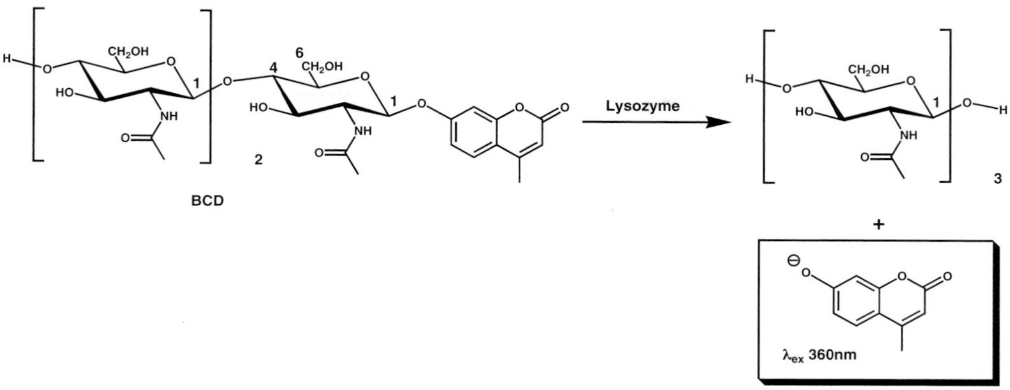

Figure 8.16 Fluorimetric assay. Lysozyme assay system. Assay is performed under mildly acidic conditions but appearance of **charged fluorophore** requires pH- quenching to pH 9.

A steady state bioassay of lysozyme instead makes use of a chromogenic substrate that may also be detected by fluorescence as well. Hence, the initial rate of product formation then correlates with the initial rate of formation of the fluorophore as determined by **fluorescence spectroscopy** (Figure 8.16). In the case of TIM the actual reaction catalysed is impossible to observe with a chromogenic substrate or reagent directly, but a **coupled assay system** can be used in which one product is irreversibly transformed into a follow-on product through biocatalytic reduction using the cofactor NADH, a **reverse-chromogenic reagent** (Figure 8.17). The initial loss of NADH by oxidation to NAD^+ is

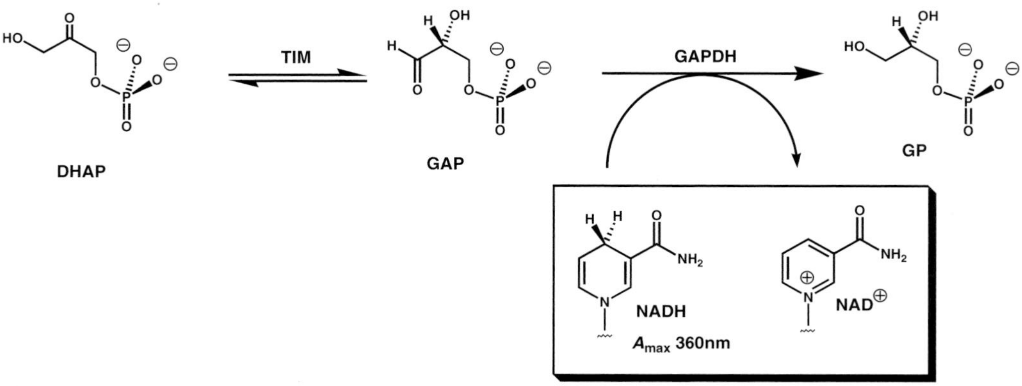

Figure 8.17 Enzyme coupled assay. Triose Phosphate Isomerase (TIM) assay system with glyceraldehyde 3-phosphate dehydrogenase (GAPDH) **colourimetric coupled assay** for detection purposes. In this version of the TIM assay, dihydroxyacetone phosphate (DHAP) is converted enzymically to glyceraldehyde 3-phosphate (GAP) that is onward converted to **glycerol phosphate (GP)** by means of the coupled enzyme GAPDH enzyme that uses the **reverse-colourimetric reductant** NADH.

said to correlate inversely with the initial rate of TIM-catalysed dihydroxyacetone phosphate (DHAP) product formation. Where the enzyme is concerned, NADH is an intrinsic part of the direct catalytic mechanism and so initial loss of NADH with time correlates inversely but directly with the initial rate of MDH-catalysed oxalic acid product formation (Figure 8.18).

HPLC steady state bioassays make use of a change in physical elution time when substrate is converted to product. For instance, a steady state bioassay for the enzyme LysU (see Chapters 6 and 7) makes use of the fact that substrate adenosine 5′-triphosphate (ATP) and product Ap_4A elute at different times from an HPLC column. Hence, the initial rate of formation of Ap_4A correlates either to the initial rate of Ap_4A peak formation or inversely to the initial rate of ATP peak disappearance (Figure 8.19). The LysU-catalysed conversion of Ap_4A to Ap_3A can also be observed by means of the same HPLC bioassay. A similar principle applies to the ^1H-NMR steady state bioassay, in which the initial rate of formation of Ap_4A correlates either to the initial rate of appearance of Ap_4A-purine signals observed by 1D ^1H-NMR spectroscopy or inversely to the initial rate of disappearance of ATP-purine signals (Figure 8.20). An oxygen electrode steady state bioassay is usually required where biocatalysts that evolve or consume oxygen are involved. Where the enzyme SOD is concerned, the appropriate steady state bioassay requires the use of a calibrated **oxygen electrode** to measure the initial rate of oxygen produced as a function of initial superoxide concentration (Figure 8.21). Radiometric steady state bioassays normally involve the transformation of a radioactive substrate into product and the clean isolation of the latter from the former. In the case of the bioassay for CAT, the product is much more hydrophobic than the substrate and may be extracted cleanly into

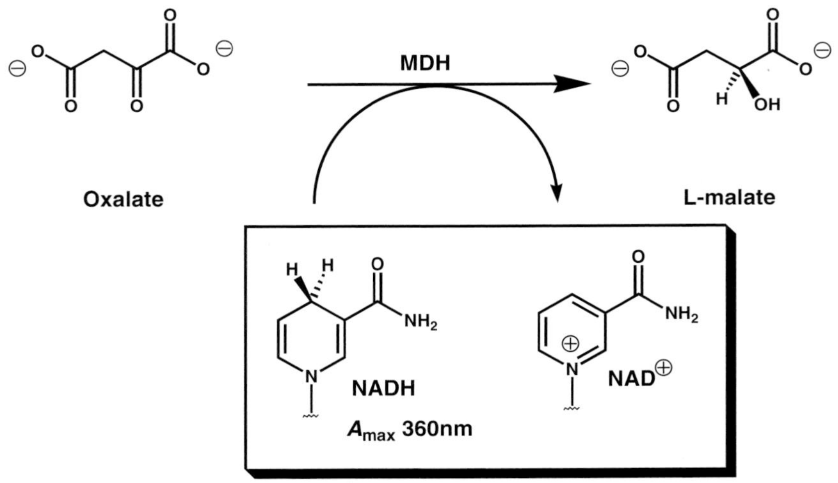

Figure 8.18 Colourimetric assay. Malate dehydrogenase (MDH) assay system. Oxalate is onward converted to L-malate by means of enzyme MDH that uses the reverse-colourimetric reductant NADH to effect catalytic reduction.

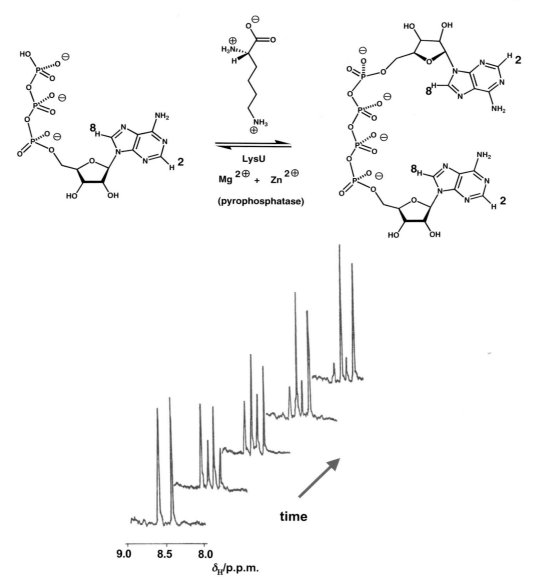

Figure 8.19 ¹*H*-NMR assay. Lysyl tRNA synthetase (LysU) assay system. Conversion of ATP into Ap₄A is observed by ¹*H*-NMR spectroscopy when reaction is run in a 5mm NMR tube. ¹*H* signals of adenine ring are shifted *upfield* with conversion of ATP (δ_H 8.55 [*H*-2] and 8.29 [*H*-8] p.p.m.) to Ap₄A (δ_H 8.40 [*H*-2] and 8.18 [*H*-8] p.p.m.). Rates of conversion are followed by changes in appropriate ¹*H*-NMR signal peak areas as a function of time (illustration adapted from Theoclitou et al., 1996, Fig. 2).

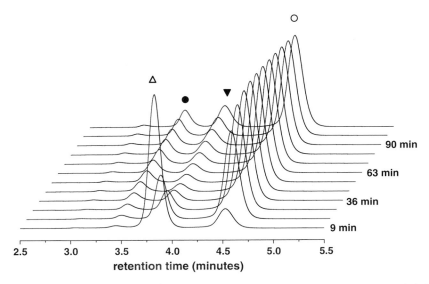

Figure 8.20 HPLC assay. Lysyl tRNA synthetase (LysU) assay system. LysU converts ATP ($\triangle$) into Ap$_4$A ($\circ$) (see Fig. 8.8). Rates of conversion are followed by changes in appropriate HPLC peak area as a function of time. LysU has recently been shown to further catalyze the onwards formation of Ap$_3$A ($\blacktriangledown$) from Ap$_4$A ($\circ$) via an ADP ($\bullet$) intermediate. This second stage reaction is clearly visible by HPLC assay.

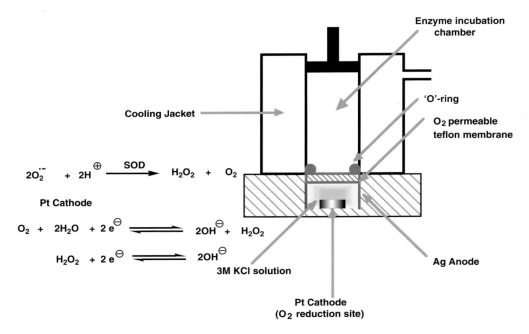

Figure 8.21 Oxygen electrode assay. Superoxide dismutase (SOD) assay in which enzyme generates H_2O_2 that is further reduced at the Pt-cathode to the expense of oxygen. Current generated through reduction is calibrated with respect to oxygen produced by SOD.

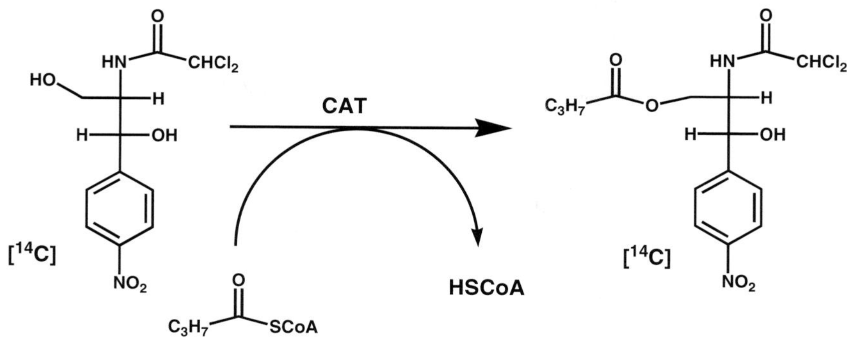

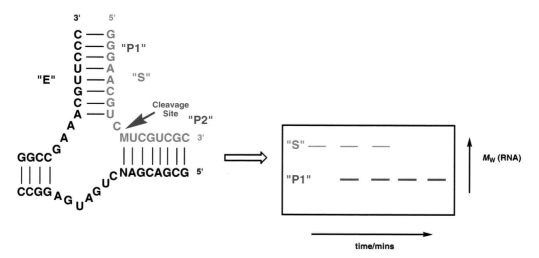

Figure 8.22 Radiographic assay. Chloramphenicol Acetyl Transferase (CAT) assay system. Butyrylation of Chloramphenicol generates a more hydrophobic product that is separated from substrate by extraction into organic solvent.

organic solvents (Figure 8.22). Hence the initial accumulation of [^{14}C] in the organic extract is said to correlate with the initial formation of product. Finally, gel steady state bioassays form the basis of ribozyme analyses, owing to the difference in molecular weight between substrate and product polynucleotides. In this case the initial formation of product is determined by the initial increase in product band intensities or inversely to the initial decrease in substrate band intensities (Figure 8.23).

Figure 8.23 Gel assay. Ribozyme assay system. One strand of the ribozyme acts as the biocatalyst **E** and the other strand acts as the substrate **S**. **S** is specifically cleaved at the indicated site generating two product oligonucleotides **P1** and **P2**. The conversion of **S** into larger molecular weight product **P1** can be followed by **gel electrophoresis** with time.

8.2 Steady state kinetic schemes

All steady state kinetics equations are derived by careful analyses from different steady state kinetic schemes that seek to define the likely surface mechanism by which any one biocatalyst may bring about biocatalysis. In all cases, final steady state kinetics equations seek to define a graphical relationship between v and [S] that varies depending upon differences in the surface mechanism of biocatalysis. Therefore, a steady state equation that most closely accounts for the observed relationship between v and [S] data not only allows for the most accurate determination of biocatalytic parameters, but also informs us of the most probable surface mechanism. There can be as many steady state kinetics equations as there are kinetic schemes but there comes a point when greater complexity brings diminishing returns in understanding. For this reason, we shall only present the chemical biology reader with those schemes and equations that are still prevalent and which we consider the most important in general. Wherever possible, reference will be made to the most appropriate kinetic scheme and steady state equations for the analysis of the steady state kinetic behaviour of those biocatalyst examples introduced earlier in the chapter (Section 8.1).

8.2.1 Simple steady state kinetics and Michaelis–Menten equation

The simplest possible kinetic scheme is the **Uni Uni kinetic scheme** (Scheme 8.1), where Uni indicates one substrate and the second Uni indicates the evolution of only a single product. The main feature of this highly simplified kinetic scheme is the presence of an intermediate chemical species designated ES that is a complex (essentially non-covalent) between biocatalyst E and substrate molecule S. This is sometimes referred to as the **Michaelis complex** for reasons that will become apparent shortly! Given such a simple mechanistic scheme, v can be expressed as

$$v = k_2[\text{ES}] \tag{8.1}$$

For the purposes of the following analysis, biocatalysis is assumed to be irreversible and each biocatalyst E possesses only a single catalytic site. Hence, if the **total concentration of biocatalyst** is $[\text{E}]_0$, then this must be the sum of **free enzyme**, [E], and **Michaelis complex**, [ES], **concentrations** as indicated in

$$[\text{E}]_0 = [\text{E}] + [\text{ES}] \tag{8.2}$$

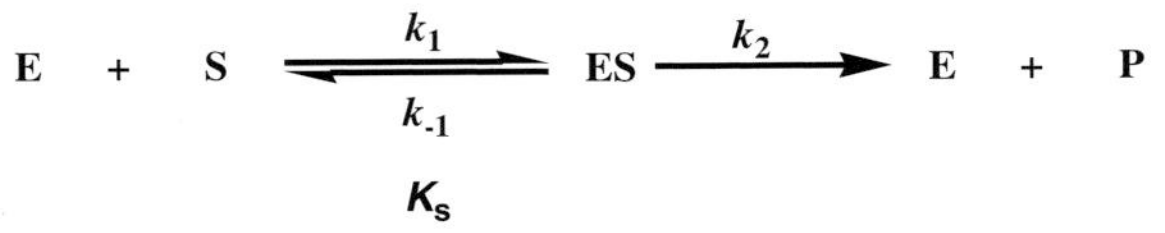

$$\text{E} \ + \ \text{S} \ \underset{k_{-1}}{\overset{k_1}{\rightleftharpoons}} \ \text{ES} \ \overset{k_2}{\longrightarrow} \ \text{E} \ + \ \text{P}$$

$$\textit{K}_\textbf{s}$$

Scheme 8.1

If Equation (8.1) is then divided through by Equation (8.2) we arrive at

$$\frac{v}{[E]_0} = \frac{k_2[ES]}{[E] + [ES]} \tag{8.3}$$

In order to solve Equation (8.3), expressions for [E] and [ES] are required that are obtained by applying Briggs–Haldane steady state principles. According to these principles, biocatalysis rapidly attains a condition of stasis under which all biocatalyst species are at a constant equilibrium concentration. In other words [E] and [ES] are constant with time. Stasis is reflected by

$$k_1[E][S] = k_{-1}[ES] + k_2[ES] \tag{8.4}$$

which rearranges to give the steady state expression

$$[ES] = \frac{k_1}{k_{-1} + k_2}[E][S] \tag{8.5}$$

Hence, substituting for [ES] in Equation (8.3) followed by rationalisation of terms, we arrive at

$$v = \frac{k_2[E]_0[S]}{\left(k_2 + k_{-1}/k_1\right) + [S]} \tag{8.6}$$

This equation may be further simplified by substituting for the bracketed aggregate of rate constants by the constant K_m where

$$K_m = \left(k_2 + k_{-1}/k_1\right) = k_2/k_1 + K_s \tag{8.7}$$

The result is

$$v = \frac{k_{cat}[E]_0[S]}{K_m + [S]} \tag{8.8}$$

where K_m is known as the **Michaelis constant**. Compared with Equation (8.6), there is one further change in that rate constant k_2 has been relabelled as k_{cat}, which is known as the **catalytic constant** or **turnover number**. Equation (8.8) is known as the **Michaelis–Menten** or **Henri–Michaelis–Menten** equation after the pioneers of biocatalysis who originally derived this equation.

The Michaelis–Menten equation classically describes a rectangular hyperbola and has the form shown in Figure 8.24. In this graphical form K_m can be described in simple terms as

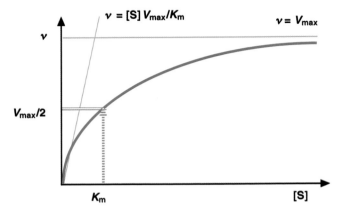

Figure 8.24 Basic steady state biocatalyst kinetic profile

the value of [S] corresponding to an initial rate of catalysis equivalent to $V_{max}/2$, where V_{max} is the maximum initial rate of catalysis that is possible. A similar rectangular hyperbola is also seen in molecular recognition studies, reflecting the fact that if sufficient substrate is present then all the active sites in a biocatalyst should be effectively occupied or saturated with reacting substrate on a continuous basis with time. *The Michaelis–Menten equation and associated rectangular hyperbolic graphical depiction are absolutely fundamental to steady state biocatalysis.* Although this equation has been derived above by a steady state analysis of the simplest possible kinetic model for biocatalyst action, the form of this equation is frequently retained irrespective of the complexity of the kinetic model, as we shall see. The reason for this is simple: biocatalysis always involves saturation at high values of [S], hence some form of saturating function is essential to describe the catalytic behaviour of a given biocatalyst, and the Michaelis–Menten equation is almost the simplest possible description of a saturating function!

There are two important limits to Equation (8.8). In the first instance, when $[S] \gg K_m$, then Equation (8.8) reduces to

$$v = k_{cat}[E]_0 = V_{max} \tag{8.9}$$

Alternatively, when $K_m \gg [S]$ then Equation (8.8) reduces to

$$v = \left(\frac{k_{cat}}{K_m}\right)[E]_0[S] \tag{8.10}$$

However, at low [S] almost all the biological catalyst is free of bound substrate. Therefore, $[E]_0$ may be substituted for by [E], the concentration of free catalyst in solution. This results in the following equation

$$v = \left(\frac{k_{cat}}{K_m}\right)[E][S] \tag{8.11}$$

where (k_{cat}/K_m) represents the **specificity constant** for a given substrate of a given biological catalyst. In practice, Equation (8.11) applies over a wider range of [S] values than those obeying the inequality that $K_m \gg [S]$, which is extremely useful for reaction kinetic analyses.

8.2.2 Interpretation of k_{cat} and K_m

In the preceding section, the term K_m has been defined in terms of the value of [S] corresponding to an initial rate of catalysis equivalent to $V_{max}/2$, or in terms of an aggregate of rate constants. However, we can give a much more subtle, all embracing definition of K_m with reference to Equation (8.7). At the limit where $k_{-1} \gg k_2$, the K_m reduces to K_s, an ES complex equilibrium dissociation constant. Therefore, in general terms K_m can be considered as either a real or apparent equilibrium dissociation constant (a K_d equivalent—see Chapter 7) that provides a direct measure of the amount of biocatalyst 'locked up' in binding to a substrate, reaction intermediate and even the product during a catalytic process.

As to k_{cat}, this has been called the catalytic constant or turnover number, and as Equation (8.9) makes clear k_{cat} is also a first order rate constant that defines maximum catalytic rate at saturating concentrations of substrate per catalytic binding site in a biocatalyst per unit time. However, with reference to Equation (8.1), k_{cat} is more precisely identified as the first order rate constant for the decomposition of an ES complex. Therefore, in general terms k_{cat} can be considered as a first order rate constant that is a function of the first order rate constants for decomposition or transformation of all complexes formed between the biocatalyst and a substrate, reaction intermediate or even product during a catalytic process.

8.2.3 Determination of k_{cat} and K_m

Parameters k_{cat}, V_{max} and K_m may be determined from real catalytic rate data by means of a **single** or **double reciprocal plot**. The single reciprocal plot or **Hanes plot** is based upon the following algebraically rearranged version of Equation (8.8):

$$\frac{[S]}{v} = \frac{K_m}{V_{max}} + \frac{[S]}{V_{max}} \tag{8.12}$$

When initial rate data, v, and initial substrate concentration data, [S], are plotted with Equation (8.12), data should fit to a straight line (Figure 8.25). Typical error distortion associated with this plot is encountered at very low values of v and [S] only. The double-reciprocal plot

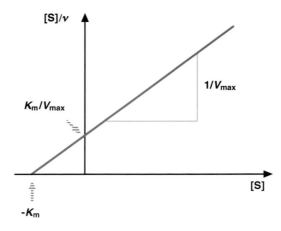

Figure 8.25   Linear, single-reciprocal **Hanes** plot.

or **Lineweaver–Burk plot** has tended to be used more widely than the Hanes plot. However, this popularity is a little misplaced. A Lineweaver–Burk plot is based upon this alternative rearranged version of Equation (8.8):

$$\frac{1}{v} = \frac{K_m}{V_{max}} \frac{1}{[S]} + \frac{1}{V_{max}} \tag{8.13}$$

In this case, initial rate and concentration data also give a straight line plot, but one suffering from gross systematic error distortion with increasingly low values of v and $[S]$ (Figure 8.26). For this reason, we would not recommend the use of Lineweaver–Burk plots as a rule unless for

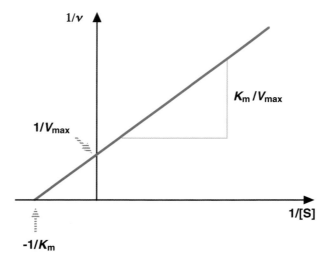

Figure 8.26   Linear, double-reciprocal **Lineweaver-Burk** plot.

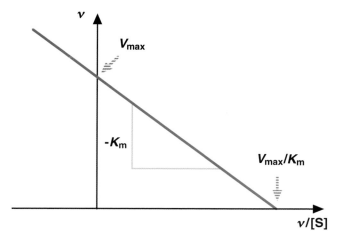

Figure 8.27 Linear, single-reciprocal **Eadie-Hofstee** plot.

multisubstrate kinetics experiments. Another version of kinetic data presentation is the **Eadie–Hofstee plot**, which is a single-reciprocal plot that is based upon the following rearranged version of Equation (8.8):

$$v = V_{max} - K_m \frac{v}{[S]} \tag{8.14}$$

In this case, initial rate and concentration data also give a straight line plot, but one also suffering from gross systematic error distortion with increasingly low values of v and $[S]$ (Figure 8.27).

8.2.4 Effect of steady state inhibitors

Biocatalyst **inhibitors** I are 'substrate-like' molecules that interact with a given biocatalyst and interfere with the progress of biocatalysis. Inhibitors usually act in one of three ways, either by **competitive inhibition**, **non-competitive inhibition** or **uncompetitive inhibition**. The mode of inhibition is different in each case and as a result a different steady state kinetic scheme is required to account for each mode of inhibition. Consequently, each mode of inhibition is characterised by a different steady state kinetic equation that gives rise to a different graphical output of v versus $[S]$ data, as we will show below. These substantial differences in graphical output can be used to diagnose the type of inhibition if unknown.

8.2.4.1 *Competitive inhibition*

When inhibitor I acts as a **competitive inhibitor** of the biocatalyst, then the inhibitor acts by binding to the active site of the biocatalyst in direct competition with the substrate. If we look

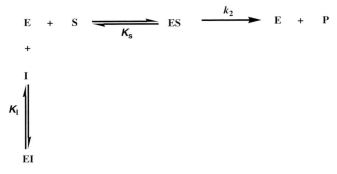

Scheme 8.2

at inhibition through the lens of the Uni Uni kinetic scheme used to derive the Michaelis–Menten equation (8.8), then the presence of the competitive inhibitor modifies the kinetic scheme in the way shown in Scheme 8.2. Applying a Briggs–Haldane steady state approach to this kinetic scheme yields the following steady state kinetic equation:

$$v = \frac{k_2[E]_0[S]}{K_m\left(1 + \dfrac{[I]}{K_I}\right) + [S]} \tag{8.15}$$

where K_I is an **equilibrium dissociation constant for the biocatalyst–inhibitor complex**, EI, that defines the strength of interaction between biocatalyst and inhibitor. Equation (8.15) can be rearranged into a double-reciprocal form as follows:

$$\frac{1}{v} = \frac{K_m\left(1 + \dfrac{[I]}{K_I}\right)}{V_{max}}\frac{1}{[S]} + \frac{1}{V_{max}} \tag{8.16}$$

In the event that a particular inhibitor I acts by competitive inhibition, then plots of $1/v$ versus $1/[S]$ data obtained at different fixed concentrations of $[I]$ should obey Equation (8.16) and take on the visual appearance shown in Figure 8.28. This graphical depiction of $1/v$ versus $1/[S]$ data not only confirms the existence of competitive inhibition but allows for the determination of K_I as well.

8.2.4.2 Non-competitive inhibition

If I acts as a **non-competitive inhibitor** of the biocatalyst, then the inhibitor acts by binding not to the active site but to an **allosteric site** (i.e., alternative, non-overlapping, non-active-site-binding region) present in both the free biocatalyst and the biocatalyst–substrate complex. The classical non-competitive inhibitor has no direct effect upon substrate binding and vice versa; however, the resulting ESI complex is catalytically inactive. Hence, if we repeat the analysis outlined in 8.2.4.1 then the appropriate kinetic scheme becomes as in Scheme 8.3,

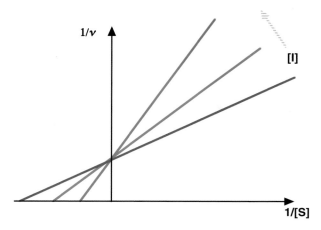

Figure 8.28 Successive Lineweaver-Burke plots typical of **competitive inhibition** of a bio-catalyst that operates mechanistically through the simplest **Uni Uni Kinetic Scheme (Scheme 8.1)**

and the modified steady state equation becomes

$$v = \frac{\left[k_2[\mathrm{E}]_0 \Big/ \left(1 + \frac{[\mathrm{I}]}{K_\mathrm{I}}\right)\right][\mathrm{S}]}{K_\mathrm{m} + [\mathrm{S}]} \tag{8.17}$$

Once again, Equation (8.17) can be rearranged into a double-reciprocal form as follows:

$$\frac{1}{v} = \frac{K_\mathrm{m}}{V_{\max}}\left(1 + \frac{[\mathrm{I}]}{K_\mathrm{I}}\right)\frac{1}{[\mathrm{S}]} + \frac{1}{V_{\max}}\left(1 + \frac{[\mathrm{I}]}{K_\mathrm{I}}\right) \tag{8.18}$$

In the event that a particular inhibitor I acts by non-competitive inhibition, plots of $1/v$ versus $1/[\mathrm{S}]$ data obtained at different fixed concentrations of [I] should obey Equation (8.18) and

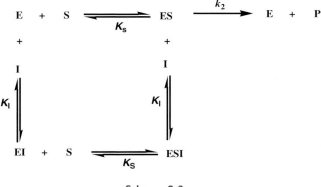

Scheme 8.3

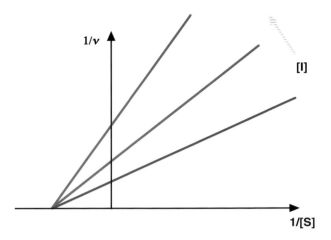

Figure 8.29   Successive Lineweaver-Burke plots typical of **non-competitive inhibition** of a bio-catalyst that operates mechanistically through the simplest **Uni Uni Kinetic Scheme (Scheme 8.1)**

take on the visual appearance shown in Figure 8.29. Clearly, when I acts as a non-competitive inhibitor then the only practical effect is to reduce the maximal effective rate of catalysis, V_{max}.

8.2.4.3   Uncompetitive inhibition

If I acts as an **uncompetitive inhibitor** of the biocatalyst, then the inhibitor acts by binding to an allosteric site revealed only in the biocatalyst–substrate complex. In this case the kinetic scheme becomes modified again (Scheme 8.4), and the modified steady-state equation becomes

$$v = \frac{\left[k_2 [\mathrm{E}]_0 \Big/ \left(1 + \frac{[\mathrm{I}]}{K_\mathrm{I}} \right) \right] [\mathrm{S}]}{\left[K_\mathrm{m} \Big/ \left(1 + \frac{[\mathrm{I}]}{K_\mathrm{I}} \right) \right] + [\mathrm{S}]} \tag{8.19}$$

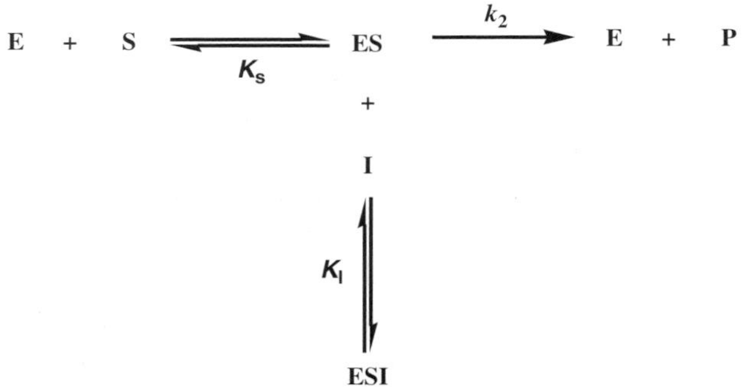

$$\mathrm{E} \;+\; \mathrm{S} \underset{K_\mathbf{s}}{\rightleftharpoons} \mathrm{ES} \xrightarrow{k_2} \mathrm{E} \;+\; \mathrm{P}$$

$$+$$

$$\mathrm{I}$$

$$K_\mathrm{I} \updownarrow$$

$$\mathrm{ESI}$$

Scheme 8.4

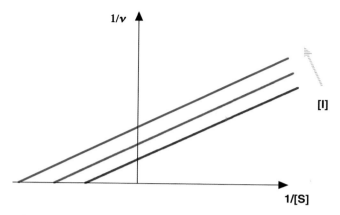

Figure 8.30 Successive Lineweaver-Burke plots typical of **un-competitive inhibition** of a bio-catalyst that operates mechanistically through the simplest **Uni Uni Kinetic Scheme (Scheme 8.1)**

which rearranges to double-reciprocal form:

$$\frac{1}{v} = \frac{K_m}{V_{max}} \frac{1}{[S]} + \frac{1}{V_{max}}\left(1 + \frac{[I]}{K_I}\right)$$

(8.20)

When a particular inhibitor I acts by uncompetitive inhibition, then plots of $1/v$ versus $1/[S]$ data obtained at different fixed concentrations of [I] should obey Equation (8.20) and take on the visual appearance shown in Figure 8.30. In this case, when I acts as a non-competitive inhibitor, there are practical reductions in both the maximal effective rate of catalysis V_{max} and K_m in equal proportion.

8.2.5 Applicability of Michaelis–Menten equation

The Michaelis–Menten equation (8.8) and the irreversible Uni Uni kinetic scheme (Scheme 8.1) are only really applicable to an **irreversible** biocatalytic process involving a **single substrate** interacting with a biocatalyst that comprises a single catalytic site. Hence with reference to the biocatalyst examples given in Section 8.1, Equation (8.8), the Uni Uni kinetic scheme is only really directly applicable to the steady state kinetic analysis of TIM biocatalysis (Figure 8.1, Table 8.1). Furthermore, even this statement is only valid with the proviso that all biocatalytic initial rate values are determined in the absence of product. Similarly, the Uni Uni kinetic schemes for competitive, uncompetitive and non-competitive inhibition are only really applicable directly for the steady state kinetic analysis for the inhibition of TIM (Table 8.1). Therefore, why are Equation (8.8) and the irreversible Uni Uni kinetic scheme apparently used so widely for the steady state analysis of many different biocatalytic processes? A main reason for this is that Equation (8.8) is simple to use and measured k_{cat} and K_M parameters can be easily interpreted. There is only a necessity to adapt catalysis conditions such that

Table 8.1 Summary of kinetic constants for the enzymes featured in Section 8.1 of Chapter 8. All the data are obtained from the enzyme database – BRENDA (http://www.brenda-enzymes.info/) except where indicated: (a) value of k_{cat}/K_M estimated assuming all substrate added in buffer is available to enzyme (i.e., has not been sequestered as acetal or ketal derivatives, as appropriate) (b) k_{cat} data from Fields et al., 2006; (c) k_{cat} data from rat source; (d) kinetic data from Masaki et al., 2001; (e) k_{cat} data from Day and Shaw, 1992; (f) kinetic data from bovine source; (g) kinetic data from human source; (h) all kinetic data from Wright et al., 2006. Abbreviations: **GAP**: 3-glyceraldehyde 3-phosphate; **DHAP**: dihydroxyacetone phosphate; **OAA**: oxaloacetate; **NADH**: reduced nicotinamide adenine dinucleotide; **chloramp**: chloramphenicol; **thio-ACh**: thio acetylcholine. Roman numeral denote compounds illustrated in the set of structures accompanying this table.

Enzyme	Substrate	k_{cat} (s^{-1})	K_M (M)	k_{cat}/K_M (M^{-1} s^{-1})	Inhibitor	K_I (M)
I. TIM (chicken) E.C. 5.3.1.1 1tim (pdb)	GAP	4300 (pH 7.6)	0.47 × 10^{-3} (pH 7.6)	9.0 × 10^6	AsO$_4$$^{3-}$	11 × 10^{-3}
	DHAP	430 (pH 7.6)	0.47 × 10^{-3} (pH 7.6)	4.4 × 10^5	Ia	—
				1 × 10^8 (a)	Ib	—
II. MDH (porcine) E.C. 1.1.1.37 4mdh (pdb)	OAA	—	0.03 × 10^{-3} (pH 7.5)	—	ADP	1.34 × 10^{-3}
	NADH	400 (pH 7.2) (b)	0.02 × 10^{-3} (pH 7.5)	2 × 10^7	AMP	0.95 × 10^{-3}
					cAMP	0.56 × 10^{-3}
III. α-chymotrypsin (bovine pancreas) E.C. 3.4.21.1 4cha (pdb)	IIIa	110 (pH 8.3)	7.4 × 10^{-6} (pH 8.3)	1.5 × 10^7	IIIb	2.5 × 10^{-8}
					IIIc	irrev.
IV. RNAse A (bovine pancreas) E.C. 3.1.27.5 7rsa (pdb)	poly(pC)	—	0.46 × 10^{-3}	—	IVa	—
	2',3'-cCMP	2.5 (c)	0.46 × 10^{-3} (pH 5.5)	5.4 × 10^3	IVb	—
V. AlaR (B. stearothermophilus) E.C. 5.1.1.1 2sfp (pdb)	L-ala	1.1	2.7 × 10^{-3}	4 × 10^2	Va	6 × 10^{-3}
					Vb	
VI. GadB (E. coli) E.C. 4.1.1.15 1pmo & 1pmm (pdb)	L-glu	9.5	0.5 × 10^{-3} (pH 4.6)	1.9 × 10^4	NO?	—
					O$_2$?	—

Enzyme	Substrate					
VII. aspAT (E. coli) E.C. 2.6.1.1 2aat (pdb)	L-asp	259 (pH 8.4)	1.3×10^{-3} (pH 8.0)	2.0×10^5	VIIa? VIIb?	— —
VIII. lysozyme (hen egg) E.C. 3.2.1.17 6lyz (pdb)	VIIIa	0.05 (d)	2.4×10^{-5} (d)	2×10^3	VIIIb	8×10^{-8}
IX. CAT III (E. coli) E.C. 2.3.1.28 1cla (pdb)	Acetyl-CoA Chloramp	600 (e) —	0.093×10^{-3} 0.012×10^{-3}	6.4×10^6 —	IXa	irrev.
X. Mn-SOD (human) E.C. 1.15.1.1 1n0j (pdb)	$O_2^{\cdot -}$	100000 (f)	0.355×10^{-3} (f)	2.8×10^8	ClO_4^- Xa	—
XI. CA-I (human) E.C. 4.2.1.1 2cab (pdb)	CO_2	800 (pH 7.2)	3.6×10^{-3} (pH 7.2)	2.2×10^5	XIa XIb XIc XId	0.40×10^{-6} 0.01×10^{-6} 0.09×10^{-6} 0.003×10^{-6}
XII. AChE (T. californica) E.C. 3.1.1.7 1amn (pdb)	thio-ACh	6500 (g)	0.046×10^{-3} (g)	1.4×10^8	XIIa XIIb XIIc	0.175×10^{-3} 0.003×10^{-6} irrev.
XIII. LysU (h) (E. coli) E.C. 6.1.1.6 1lyl (pdb)	ATP L-lys	2.7 1.8	7×10^{-3} 23×10^{-6}	3.8×10^2 7.8×10^4	GTP ITP	— —

steady state kinetic measurements of initial rates are made under pseudo-irreversible Uni Uni kinetic conditions where all but one substrate are in substantial excess and no product is present. Furthermore, where a biocatalyst has more then one catalytic site, steady state analyses should be performed under conditions where only one of the sites is active at any one time, or else where the catalytic sites are at least able to operate completely independently of each other. In the latter case, measured values of k_{cat} should then be divided through by the number of catalytic sites to provide a value per catalytic site, otherwise known as the turnover number per catalytic site.

Hence steady state kinetic analyses of RNAse A, lysozyme and CA (Figures 8.4, 8.6 and 8.9) can easily be accommodated within Equation (8.8) and the irreversible Uni Uni kinetic scheme to a reasonable approximation, since water is obviously an abundant substrate. The same could be said to be true of steady state kinetic analyses of bovine-pancreatic-α-chymotrypsin-catalysed polypeptide hydrolysis and AChE-catalysed acetylcholine hydrolysis (Figures 8.3 and 8.10). Even reactions catalysed by PLP-dependent AlaR, GadB and aspAT (Figure 8.5), or those assisted by CAT and LysU (Figures 8.7 and 8.11), may be accommodated within Equation (8.8) and the Uni Uni kinetic scheme given appropriate steady state kinetic conditions. However, while such an approach may have the virtue of simplicity, more careful and intensive steady state kinetic analyses with more complex kinetic schemes have the power to demonstrate and/or confirm mechanisms in biocatalysis and should be performed. So let us take a more detailed look at more complex kinetic schemes.

8.2.6 Multiple-substrate/product steady state kinetics

In this section, we shall begin to see how the Briggs–Haldane steady state approach can be enlarged to derive steady state kinetics equations appropriate to more complex kinetic schemes. In doing this, there will be some pleasant surprises in that the form of these new steady state kinetic equations will follow the form of Michaelis–Menten equation (8.8) with a few adaptations not unlike those seen in the Uni Uni steady state kinetic scheme adapted to fit the presence of inhibitors (see Section 8.2.4).

8.2.6.1 *Multiple catalytic sites, non-cooperative Uni Uni kinetic scheme*

Initially, let us look at the situation of a single-substrate biocatalyst with two independent catalytic sites where each site is capable of binding substrate and catalysing the formation of product. This scenario can be analysed by means of the Briggs–Haldane steady state approach with reference to the illustrated Uni Uni kinetic scheme, once again assuming irreversibility (Scheme 8.5). By analogy to the treatment in Section 8.2.1, we can generate by inspection two important equations from the scheme:

$$v = k_2[ES] + k_2[SE] + 2k_2[SES] \tag{8.21}$$

$$[E]_0 = [E] + [ES] + [SE] + [SES] \tag{8.22}$$

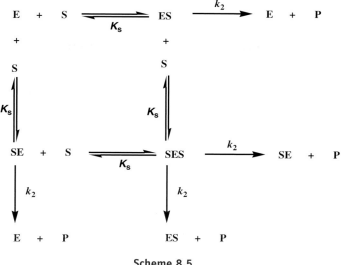

Scheme 8.5

Dividing Equation (8.21) through by (8.22) gives

$$\frac{v}{[E]_0} = \frac{k_2[ES] + k_2[SE] + 2k_2[SES]}{[E] + [ES] + [SE] + [SES]} \tag{8.23}$$

Alternative equilibrium dissociation equations (see Chapter 7) can then be derived on the basis of stasis for constant K_S such as Equation (8.24) for example, which defines K_S as

$$K_S = \frac{[E][S]}{[ES]} = \frac{[SE][S]}{[SES]} \tag{8.24}$$

Thereafter, these equations can be rearranged to give solutions for [ES], [SE] and [SES] that may be substituted into Equation (8.23) to give us the complete steady state kinetic equation after algebraic manipulation:

$$v = \frac{2k_2[E]_0[S]}{K_S + [S]} \tag{8.25}$$

This is essentially identical with the form of the Michaelis–Menten equation (8.8), although the meaning of the corresponding biocatalytic parameters is slightly modified. The kinetic scheme upon which this derivation is based is clearly limited to a single-substrate biocatalyst that operates with two independent catalytic sites. Such a biocatalyst could be monomeric with two catalytic sites, or else homodimeric with one catalytic site per subunit. With reference to the biocatalyst examples described in Section 8.1, the chemical biology reader should be able to see that Equation (8.25) and the Uni Uni kinetic scheme for two catalytic sites seems appropriate for the steady state kinetic analysis of homo-dimeric *B. stearothermophilus* AlaR biocatalysis (Figure 8.5, Table 8.1). Furthermore, we might easily extrapolate from Equation (8.25) to a four-independent-catalytic-site equation

$$v = \frac{4k_2[E]_0[S]}{K_S + [S]} \tag{8.26}$$

In this case, Equation (8.26) and the irreversible Uni Uni kinetic scheme for four catalytic sites is appropriate for the steady state kinetic analysis of homo-tetrameric, human mitochondrial MnSOD biocatalysis (Figure 8.8, Table 8.1) with one catalytic site containing one manganese ion per subunit. These sites are not only independent, but each turnover of a catalytic site involves one substrate superoxide radical being transformed to only one of two possible redox products depending upon the oxidation state of the manganese ion involved.

8.2.6.2 Multiple catalytic sites, cooperative Uni Uni kinetic scheme and Hill equation

Where biocatalysts possess more than one catalytic site and these sites are distributed over several associated subunits, then the catalysis at one catalytic site is much more likely to be dependent upon catalysis taking place at the other sites as well. Dependency can either be positive or negative. If positive, then catalysis at the one catalytic site should boost catalysis at the other sites in the biocatalyst. If negative, then catalysis at the one catalytic site should attenuate catalysis at the other sites, even to the limit at which none of the other sites are able to function at all. The positive effect is known as **positive cooperativity** and the negative effect as **negative cooperativity**. The same concept has been discussed in Chapter 7 with respect to ligand binding to receptors with multiple binding sites.

Now we shall consider explicitly the situation of a single-substrate biocatalyst with two catalytic sites each capable of binding substrate and catalysing the formation of product, but where the efficiency of substrate binding at the one site is dependent upon substrate binding at the other. The relevant Uni Uni kinetic scheme is as shown in Scheme 8.6, assuming irreversibility again. In fact, the overall rate derived in the previous section still applies as before, but for convenience this will be restated here as

$$\frac{v}{[E]_0} = \frac{k_2[ES] + k_2[SE] + 2k_2[SES]}{[E] + [ES] + [SE] + [SES]} \tag{8.27}$$

However, owing to the presence of αK_S the substitutions for [ES], [SE] and [SES] are different as shown. Equations can be derived for equilibrium dissociation constants K_S and αK_S (assuming that $\alpha > 1$) such as Equation (8.28) for example, defining αK_S:

$$\alpha K_S = \frac{[ES][S]}{[SES]} = \frac{[SE][S]}{[SES]} \tag{8.28}$$

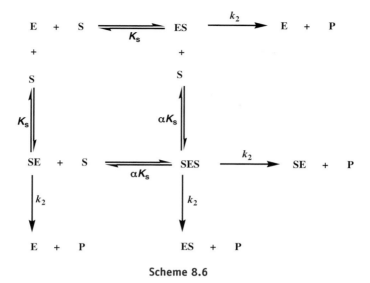

Scheme 8.6

Thereafter, these equations can be rearranged to give solutions for [ES], [SE] and [SES] such as Equation (8.29) for example, defining [SES]:

$$[SES] = \frac{[E][S]^2}{\alpha K_S^2} \tag{8.29}$$

all of which are substituted into Equation (8.27) to give the following complete equation after some arithmetic manipulation:

$$\frac{v}{[E]_0} = \frac{2k_2 \left(\dfrac{[S]}{K_S} + \dfrac{[S]^2}{\alpha K_S^2} \right)}{1 + \dfrac{2[S]}{K_S} + \dfrac{[S]^2}{\alpha K_S^2}} \tag{8.30}$$

This equation embodies all the features of positive cooperative binding of substrate and the effect of this upon biocatalytic rate. Given the power terms, this equation is decidedly *not* identical with the Michaelis–Menten equation (8.8)! However, an alternative and equally important biocatalytic equation can be derived from Equation (8.30) with a little more work and a few simple assumptions. First, let us assume that cooperative binding is sufficiently positive that terms in [S] are eliminated from Equation (8.30). Second, let us define V_{max} according to

$$V_{max} = 2k_2[E]_0 \tag{8.31}$$

Hence, if we simplify Equation (8.30) with the assumption and substitute in from Equation (8.31), then the result is the power equation

$$\frac{v}{V_{max}} = \frac{[S]^2/\alpha K_S^2}{1 + \left([S]^2/\alpha K_S^2\right)} = \frac{[S]^2}{\alpha K_S^2 + [S]^2} \tag{8.32}$$

Equation (8.32) is applicable only to a biocatalyst with two distinct but strongly binding-dependent active sites. A more general form can be deduced from (8.32) that applies to any biocatalyst with n distinct but strongly binding-dependent active sites (where $n \geq 2$). This general form is given by

$$\frac{v}{V_{max}} = \frac{[S]^n}{K' + [S]^n} \tag{8.33}$$

Equation (8.33) is known as the **Hill equation**. This equation is almost the same in form as the original Michaelis–Menten equation except for the presence of power terms. These power terms ensure that a plot of v against [S] no longer fits a rectangular hyperbolic function but instead fits a **sigmoidal function** whose dimensions are influenced strongly by the value of n and also K' (Figure 8.31). *The Hill equation and associated sigmoidal graphical depictions are fundamental to cooperative biocatalysis.* Note that although the saturating hyperbolic function of non-cooperative biocatalysis has been abolished in cooperative biocatalysis, the alternative sigmoidal functions must still tend to saturation since biocatalysis must always involve saturation at high values of [S].

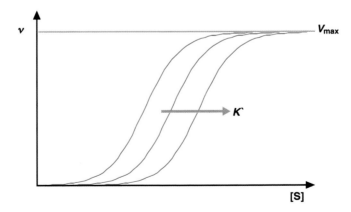

Figure 8.31 Classical sigmoidal rate curves indicative of bio-catalysis with strong **positive cooperativity** involved in the catalytic mechanism. Curves move to the right as constant K' increases.

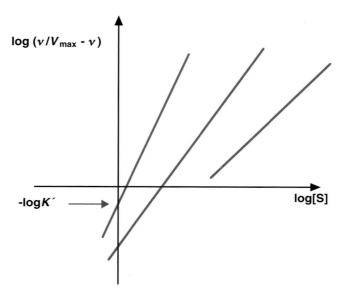

Figure 8.32 Linear kinetic **Hill plots** derived from sigmoidal data illustrated (**Fig. 8.31**). Gradients and intercepts define values of **n** and **K′** respectively.

In common with the Michaelis–Menten equation, there are linearised forms of the Hill equation, of which the most widely used form is given by

$$\log\left(\frac{v}{V_{\max} - v}\right) = n \log[S] - \log K' \tag{8.34}$$

which is derived by simple arithmetic manipulation from Equation (8.33). Where unambiguous cooperative biocatalysis is taking place, then a plot of values of $\log(v/V_{\max} - v)$ versus $\log[S]$ should render a straight line of slope n (Figure 8.32).

In principle, all single-substrate multi-subunit/multi-catalytic-site biocatalysts may be subject to positive cooperativity in catalysis under certain conditions according to Equation (8.34). The single-substrate multi-subunit/multi-catalytic-site biocatalyst is almost designed for this opportunity. However, as we have seen already this opportunity need not be taken advantage of for a given single-substrate biocatalyst operating in a given catalytic niche. Also, positive cooperativity does not necessarily have to be a subject to substrate binding. For instance, pH changes may induce cooperative shifts in catalytic behaviour of a single-substrate biocatalyst such as the homo-hexameric E. coli GadB enzyme responsible for α-decarboxylation of glutamate to give carbon dioxide and γ-amino butyric acid (GABA) (Figure 8.5, Table 8.1). In this case, Equation (8.34) needs to be modified so that $[H^+]$ replaces $[S]$ to reflect the actual single participant in this positive cooperative process. The effect of increasing $[H^+]$ is to promote a rapid and substantial conformational change within the homohexameric enzyme structure, leading to transition from the inactive form (T state) of the enzyme at neutral pH to the highly active form (R state) at lower pH (<5.2). Clearly, Equation (8.33) does not hold strictly for multiple-substrate multi-subunit/multi-catalytic-site biocatalysts. However, catalysis conditions might be adapted such that steady state kinetic measurements of initial rates are made under pseudo-irreversible Uni Uni kinetic conditions where all but one substrate are in substantial excess and no product is present. In this way, positive cooperativity involving multiple-substrate binding at multiple-dependent catalytic sites may still be analysed to a reasonable approximation using Equation (8.33).

Please note that, in general, cooperativity in catalysis may just as well be negative as positive. For instance, homodimeric *E. coli* LysU has two catalytic sites (one per monomer), but only one is involved in catalysis at any one time since multiple-substrate binding at the one binding site suppresses multiple-substrate binding at the other in a process of negative cooperativity. The catalytic mechanism of LysU is still complex, involving as it does multiple substrates (see below), but at least only one catalytic site need be considered (Figure 8.11, Table 8.1). In addition, the chemical biology reader should also be aware that whether single or multiple substrate, multi-subunit/multi-catalytic-site biocatalysts may be subject to the binding of **allosteric activators** or **allosteric modulators** as well, namely molecules that bind in discrete binding sites separate from catalytic sites, thereby stimulating or reducing catalytic activity. In the case of GadB enzyme, Cl^- and other halide ions act as allosteric activators that not only stimulate GadB catalysis but also promote the positive cooperative effect of $[H^+]$ on GadB conformational change and catalysis by encouraging the transition from T to R state to take place at higher pH (6.0–5.5).

8.2.6.3 Uni Bi kinetic scheme

The next level of complexity is to review the situation of a single-substrate biocatalyst with a single catalytic site that is responsible for more than one product-forming/release step (a **multiple-product** situation). This scenario will be analysed by means of the Briggs–Haldane steady state approach with reference to the indicated **Uni Bi kinetic scheme**, where Uni refers to one substrate and Bi to the evolution of two products. Irreversibility is also assumed (Scheme 8.7). By analogy with the previous treatments above, we may derive two equations:

$$\nu = k_2[ES] \tag{8.1}$$

$$[E]_0 = [E] + [ES] + [ES'] \tag{8.35}$$

$$E + S \underset{k_{-1}}{\overset{k_1}{\rightleftharpoons}} ES \xrightarrow{k_2} ES' + P_A \xrightarrow{k_3} E + P_B$$

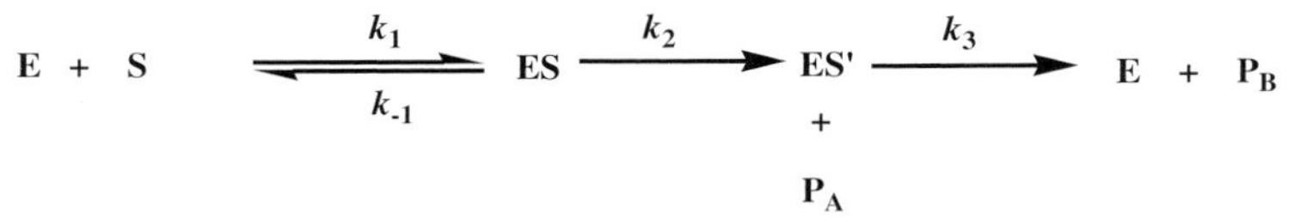

Scheme 8.7

As before, the upper equation is divided through by the lower equation to give

$$\frac{v}{[E]_0} = \frac{k_2[ES]}{[E] + [ES] + [ES']} \tag{8.36}$$

Finding solutions to $[E]$ and $[ES']$ requires that stasis exists, that their concentrations are constant with time and accordingly that the rates of formation and decomposition of ES and ES' are equal, giving rise to the following two equations:

$$k_1[E][S] = (k_{-1} + k_2)[ES] \tag{8.37}$$

$$[ES'] = (k_2/k_3)[ES] \tag{8.38}$$

By using Equation (8.37) and rearranging Equation (8.38) to give an expression for $[E]$, we can then substitute for $[E]$ and $[ES']$ in Equation (8.36) and cancel out $[ES]$ terms, thereby giving the intermediate equation

$$\frac{v}{[E]_0} = \frac{k_2}{\left(\dfrac{k_{-1} + k_2}{k_1[S]}\right) + \left(\dfrac{k_3 + k_2}{k_3}\right)} \tag{8.39}$$

With further algebraic manipulation to convert this into the form of the Michaelis–Menten equation (8.8), we arrive at

$$v = \frac{\left(\dfrac{k_2 k_3}{k_2 + k_3}\right)[E]_0[S]}{\left(\dfrac{k_3[k_{-1} + k_2]}{k_1[k_2 + k_3]}\right) + [S]} \tag{8.40}$$

where the collection of rate constants in the numerator is equivalent to the Michaelis–Menten k_{cat} and the collection of rate constants in the denominator is the equivalent of K_m! Once again, Equation (8.40) is essentially identical with the form of the Michaelis–Menten equation (8.8). The kinetic scheme upon which this derivation is based is clearly limited to a single-substrate biocatalyst that generates two products from a single active site. With reference to the biocatalyst examples described in main Section 8.1, the chemical biology reader should be able to surmise that Equation (8.40) and the Uni Bi kinetic scheme should be applicable to the steady state kinetic analysis for bicarbonate heterolysis into carbon dioxide and hydroxide catalysed by monomeric CA I from human erythrocytes (Figure 8.9, Table 8.1) under conditions where initial rates can be measured with no product present.

8.2.6.4 Ordered Bi Uni kinetic scheme

Now we shift from a multiple-product to a **multiple-substrate** scenario involving a biocatalyst with a single catalytic site that binds a leading substrate, S_A, and then a following substrate, S_B. Any such **bisubstrate reaction** is usually known as a having a **sequential** or **single-displacement** reaction mechanism, on the basis that substrates bind first, react and then release product in a consistent manner as part of the standard catalytic cycle. This particular scenario may be analysed by means of the Briggs–Haldane steady state approach with reference to an **ordered Bi Uni kinetic scheme**, where Bi refers to the involvement of two substrates and Uni to the evolution of only a single product by an irreversible catalytic process (Scheme 8.8). Hence, once again by analogy to the treatment in Section 8.2.1, we can generate equations

$$v = k_3[ES_AS_B] \tag{8.41}$$

$$[E]_0 = [E] + [ES_A] + [ES_AS_B] \tag{8.42}$$

which combine easily to produce

$$\frac{v}{[E]_0} = \frac{k_3[ES_AS_B]}{[E] + [ES_A] + [ES_AS_B]} \tag{8.43}$$

As before, equilibrium equations can then be derived for constants K_A and K_B. Thereafter, these equations can be rearranged to give solutions for $[ES_A]$ and $[ES_AS_B]$ that may be substituted into Equation (8.43) giving us the complete steady state kinetics

$$v = \frac{k_3[E]_0[S_A][S_B]}{[S_A][S_B] + K_B[S_A] + K_A K_B} \tag{8.44}$$

At constant $[S_A]$ Equation (8.44) reduces to Equation (8.45) after dividing the right-hand

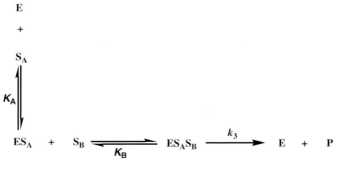

Scheme 8.8

side by $[S_A]$ and gathering terms:

$$v = \frac{k_3[E]_0[S_B]}{K_B\left(1 + K_A/[S_A]\right) + [S_B]} \tag{8.45}$$

which the chemical biology reader should recognise is the classic form of the Michaelis–Menten equation (8.8)! If we now substitute in for V_{max} according to

$$V_{max} = k_3[E]_0 \tag{8.46}$$

and rearrange the resulting equation into a double-reciprocal form, then we end up with

$$\frac{1}{v} = \frac{K_B\left(1 + \dfrac{K_A}{[S_A]}\right)}{V_{max}}\frac{1}{[S_B]} + \frac{1}{V_{max}} \tag{8.47}$$

In the event that the kinetic mechanism of a given biocatalyst of interest obeys the irreversible, single-catalytic-site, ordered Bi Uni mechanism, then plots of actual $1/v$ versus $1/[S]$ data obtained at different fixed initial concentrations of $[S_A]$ will also obey Equation (8.47) and take on the visual appearance shown (Figure 8.33). Clearly, such linear graphical data would be sufficient to allow all constants to be determined. Hopefully, the chemical biology reader can recognise the relationship between Equations (8.47) and (8.13) that defines the simple Lineweaver–Burk plot derived from the original Michaelis–Menten equation for the linear analysis of kinetic data. With reference to the biocatalyst examples described in main Section 8.1, the chemical biology reader may be able to guess that Equation (8.47) and the ordered Bi Uni kinetic scheme should be applicable to the steady state kinetic analysis for bicarbonate synthesis from carbon dioxide and hydroxide catalysed by monomeric CA I from human erythrocytes (Figure 8.9, Table 8.1) when initial rates are measured with no prod-

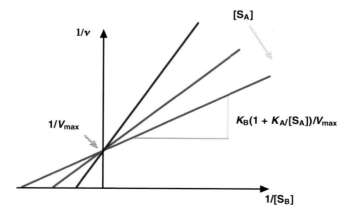

Figure 8.33 Successive Lineweaver-Burke plots typical of **ordered Bi Uni Kinetic Scheme (Scheme 8.8)**.

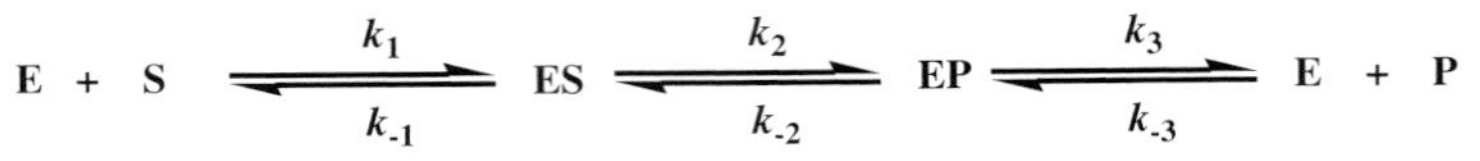

$$E + S \underset{k_{-1}}{\overset{k_1}{\rightleftharpoons}} ES \underset{k_{-2}}{\overset{k_2}{\rightleftharpoons}} EP \underset{k_{-3}}{\overset{k_3}{\rightleftharpoons}} E + P$$

Scheme 8.9

uct present. In this situation, hydroxide is the leading substrate, S_A, and carbon dioxide the following substrate, S_B.

8.2.7 Multiple-substrate/product King–Altman kinetics

A more generally applicable way of providing steady state kinetics equations for multiple-substrate/product kinetic schemes is to use the **King–Altman derivation approach.** We shall examine the principles behind this with reference to the simplest single-catalytic-site, **reversible Uni Uni kinetic scheme** that is shown in Scheme 8.9. This reversible scheme is actually most appropriate for the complete steady state kinetic analysis of chicken TIM (Figure 8.1, Table 8.1). According to the King–Altman treatment, we must begin as usual by stating equations that represent the rate of product formation v. In this case, they are essentially modified versions of equations (8.1) and (8.36) as follows:

$$v = k_2[ES] - k_{-2}[EP] \tag{8.48}$$

$$\frac{v}{[E]_0} = \frac{k_2[ES] - k_{-2}[EP]}{[E] + [ES] + [EP]} \tag{8.49}$$

However, instead of trying to derive explicit expressions for [E], [ES] and [EP] and then substituting these back into Equation (8.49), the King–Altman approach seeks first to construct a vector equivalent diagram linking all the biocatalyst species together (Figure 8.34). Expressions for [E], [ES] and [EP] are then derived by considering all the alternative pathways to any given species starting from one or other or both of the other biocatalyst species (Figure 8.34). The result is

$$[E] \equiv k_{-2}k_{-1} + k_{-1}k_3 + k_2k_3 \tag{8.50}$$

$$[ES] \equiv k_{-2}k_1[S] + k_3k_1[S] + k_{-3}[P]k_{-2} \tag{8.51}$$

$$[EP] \equiv k_1[S]k_2 + k_{-1}k_{-3}[P] + k_2k_{-3}[P] \tag{8.52}$$

These can all be substituted back into Equation (8.49), and after the gathering (extensive!) and subtracting of terms where relevant we end up with a relatively simple result

$$\frac{v}{[E]_0} = \frac{k_1k_2k_3[S] - k_{-1}k_{-2}k_{-3}[P]}{(k_{-2}k_{-1} + k_{-1}k_3 + k_2k_3) + k_1(k_{-2} + k_2 + k_3)[S] + k_{-3}(k_{-1} + k_{-2} + k_2)[P]} \tag{8.53}$$

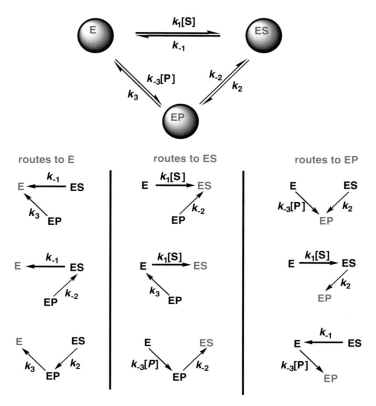

Figure 8.34 Full set of **King-Altmann** diagrams for the **reversible Uni Uni Kinetic Scheme** (**Scheme 8.9**).

8.2.7.1 *Reversible Uni Uni kinetic scheme*

Unfortunately, the form of Equation (8.53) is a little way off the form of the Michaelis–Menten equation. For this reason, the King–Altman approach is usually supplemented by an approach developed by **Cleland**. The **Cleland approach** seeks to group kinetic rate constants together into **numbers** (*num*), **coefficients** (*Coef*) and **constants** (*const*) that themselves can be collectively defined as experimental steady-state kinetic parameters equivalent to k_{cat}, V_{max} and K_m of the original Michaelis–Menten equation. After such substitutions, the result is that equations may be algebraically manipulated to reproduce the form of the Michaelis–Menten equation (8.8). Use of the Cleland approach is illustrated as follows.

First, we will need to rewrite Equation (8.53) in the so-called Cleland form, giving

$$v = \frac{num_1[\mathrm{S}] - num_2[\mathrm{P}]}{const + Coef_\mathrm{S}[\mathrm{S}] + Coef_\mathrm{P}[\mathrm{P}]} \tag{8.54}$$

Second, we will need to define steady state kinetic parameters as follows:

$$K_{eq} = \frac{num_1}{num_2} = \frac{k_1 k_2 k_3}{k_{-1} k_{-2} k_{-3}} \tag{8.55}$$

$$V_{max\,f} = \frac{num_1}{Coef_S} \tag{8.56}$$

$$V_{max\,b} = \frac{num_2}{Coef_P} \tag{8.57}$$

$$K_{m\,S} = \frac{const}{Coef_S} \tag{8.58}$$

$$K_{m\,P} = \frac{const}{Coef_P} \tag{8.59}$$

then substitute all these into Equation (8.54) after algebraic manipulation of the right-hand side by multiplication with the term ($num_2/[Coef_S \times Coef_P]$) in order to facilitate the in-substitution of all the steady state kinetic parameters given by Equations (8.55)–(8.59). The initial result is that Equation (8.54) is now transformed into

$$v = \frac{V_{max\,f} V_{max\,b} \left([S] - [P]/K_{eq} \right)}{K_{m\,S} V_{max\,b} + V_{max\,b}[S] + V_{max\,f}[P]/K_{eq}} \tag{8.60}$$

However, algebraic manipulation of Equations (8.55) to (8.59) results in the following equation for K_{eq}:

$$K_{eq} = \frac{V_{max\,f} K_{m\,P}}{V_{max\,b} K_{m\,S}} \tag{8.61}$$

This can be substituted into the denominator of Equation (8.60), allowing us to transform (8.60) substantially to give a properly useful steady state kinetic equation:

$$\frac{v}{V_{max\,f}} = \frac{[S] - [P]/K_{eq}}{K_{m\,S} \left(1 + [P]/K_{m\,P} \right) + [S]} \tag{8.62}$$

This equation now expresses initial net forward rate for the conversion of substrate into product in the presence of significant concentrations of both [S] and [P]. Any relationship that relates any equilibrium constant to kinetic rate constants is known as a **Haldane relationship**. Equation (8.61) is a typical Haldane relationship. Therefore, the operation using Equation (8.61) to simplify Equation (8.60) to give (8.62) is known as a **Haldane simplification** – owing to the use of a Haldane relationship to effect the simplification. Clearly, if there is no significant [P] then Equation (8.62) reduces to the following:

$$\frac{v}{V_{\max f}} = \frac{[S]}{K_{mS} + [S]} \qquad (8.63)$$

which now possesses the simple form of the Michaelis–Menten equation (8.8) once again, although the meanings of the corresponding biocatalytic parameters are obviously different. Equations (8.56) and (8.58) define $V_{\max f}$ and K_{mS} respectively such that by in-substitution from Equation (8.53) we end up with

$$V_{\max f} = \frac{k_1 k_2 k_3 [E]_0}{k_1 (k_{-2} + k_2 + k_3)} \qquad (8.64)$$

$$K_{mS} = \frac{(k_{-1}k_{-2} + k_{-1}k_3 + k_2 k_3)}{k_1 (k_{-2} + k_2 + k_3)} \qquad (8.65)$$

Provided that the kinetic mechanism of a given biocatalyst of interest follows the reversible Uni Uni mechanism, then plots of actual $1/v$ versus $1/[S]$ data obtained in the presence of negligible [P] will be fitted by the double-reciprocal version of Equation (8.63)

$$\frac{1}{v} = \frac{K_{mS}}{V_{\max f}} \frac{1}{[S]} + \frac{1}{V_{\max f}} \qquad (8.66)$$

and take on the visual appearance shown in Figure 8.35. However, there is little likelihood of being able to determine individual microscopic rate constants from this graphical representation

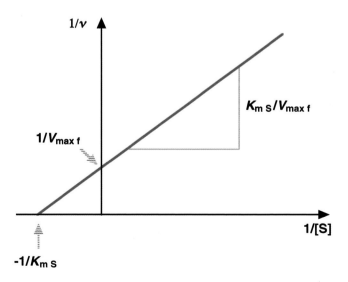

Figure 8.35 Lineweaver-Burke plot for the **reversible Uni Uni Kinetic Scheme (Scheme 8.9)**.

of rate data even with Equations (8.64) and (8.65) to help. Instead, assistance from pre-steady-state kinetic analyses are essential to identify some or all of the microscopic rate constants that make up the steady state kinetic parameters $V_{\max f}$ and $K_{m\,S}$. Equation (8.66) is almost indistinguishable from Equation (8.13), but for the identities of the kinetic components. *This equivalence proves that, whether biocatalyst reactions are irreversible or reversible, provided that steady state analyses are performed in which initial rates are determined in the absence of product, then irreversible kinetic schemes are really quite adequate for almost all steady state kinetic analyses of biocatalysis.*

The King–Altman approach described here can be summarised as a process in which an 'original rate equation' (such as Equation (8.53)) is customarily developed, converted into a coefficient form (such as Equation (8.54)) and from there simplified to 'steady state kinetic forms' (for example Equations (8.62) and (8.63)) by algebraic manipulation and Haldane simplification. This King–Altman approach is an approach that can be generalised for the derivation of most steady state kinetic equations based upon most complex kinetic schemes. Clearly these derivations can be substantial, but we shall not bother to reproduce these here except to cover a few important examples of particular relevance to the biocatalyst examples described in Section 8.1.

8.2.7.2 *Ordered Bi Bi kinetic scheme*

The first of these important examples is another multiple-substrate/multiple-product scenario. In this instance a biocatalyst with a single catalytic site binds a leading substrate, S_A, then a following substrate, S_B, thereby setting up a process of chemical transformation. Upon completion of the transformation, a leading product, P_P, is then released succeeded by a following product, P_Q. Steady state kinetic equations are derived by means of the King–Altman approach with reference to the **ordered Bi Bi kinetic scheme**, which also assumes catalytic irreversibility (Scheme 8.10). This scheme corresponds to a typical bisubstrate reaction with a sequential or single-displacement mechanism. The corresponding King–Altman diagram

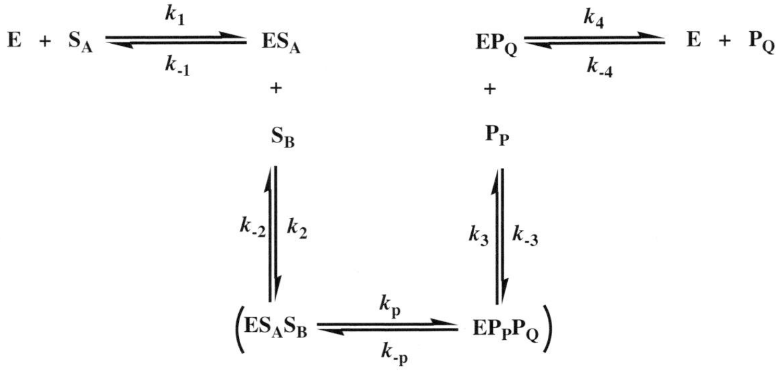

Scheme 8.10

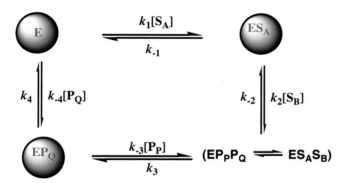

Figure 8.36 King-Altmann diagram for the **ordered Bi Bi Kinetic Scheme (Scheme 8.10)**.

is illustrated in Figure 8.36. From this diagram, a rate equation may be derived that accounts for the initial net forward rate for the conversion of substrates into products under conditions where product concentrations are negligible:

$$\frac{v}{V_{\text{max f}}} = \frac{[S_A][S_B]}{K_{iS_A}K_{mS_B} + K_{mS_B}[S_A] + K_{mS_A}[S_B] + [S_A][S_B]} \tag{8.67}$$

When $[S_B]$ is constant, Equation (8.67) reduces to

$$\frac{v}{V_{\text{max f}}} = \frac{[S_A]}{K_{mS_A}\left(1 + \left[K_{iS_A}K_{mS_B}\big/K_{mS_A}[S_B]\right]\right) + [S_A]\left(1 + \left[K_{mS_B}\big/[S_B]\right]\right)} \tag{8.68}$$

which is then rearranged into a double-reciprocal form as follows:

$$\frac{1}{v} = \frac{K_{mS_A}}{V_{\text{max f}}}\left(1 + \left[K_{iS_A}K_{mS_B}/K_{mS_A}[S_B]\right]\right)\frac{1}{[S_A]} + \frac{1}{V_{\text{max f}}}\left(1 + \left[K_{mS_B}/[S_B]\right]\right) \tag{8.69}$$

Provided that the kinetic mechanism of a biocatalyst of interest obeys the irreversible, single-catalytic-site, ordered Bi Bi kinetic scheme, then plots of actual $1/v$ versus $1/[S_A]$ data obtained in the presence of various fixed concentrations of the S_B substrate, $[S_B]$, should obey the double-reciprocal equation (8.69) giving the putative graphical output shown in Figure 8.37.

Equation (8.69) and this ordered Bi Bi kinetic scheme are applicable for the steady state kinetic analyses of several of the biocatalysts outlined in Section 8.1. These include porcine mitochondrial MDH and *E. coli* CAT (Figures 8.2 and 8.7, Table 8.1). In the case of MDH, the leading substrate, S_A, is NAD^+ and the following substrate, S_B, is oxalate. MDH is homodimeric but both catalytic sites are completely independent. Clearly, $V_{\text{max f}}$ values derived from Equation (8.69) can be converted into k_{cat} values for MDH that must be divided through by two in order to derive the correct turnover number per catalytic site. With respect to CAT, only one catalytic site binds both substrates but the mechanism may be random, in which

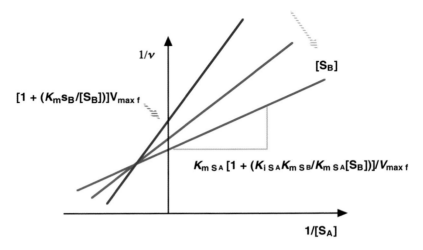

Figure 8.37 Set of Lineweaver-Burk plots for the **ordered Bi Bi Kinetic Scheme** (**Scheme 8.10**). Plot gradient decreases with increasing initial levels of substrate **[S$_B$]**.

case either chloramphenicol or acetylCoA bind first. Finally, under appropriate conditions, the ordered Bi Bi kinetic scheme is also applicable for steady state kinetic analysis of the first catalytic step (Step 1) of homo-dimeric LysU catalysed Ap$_4$A formation (Figure 8.11, Table 8.1). LysU Step 1 is highly ordered since the leading substrate, lysine-Mg^{2+}, must bind to both catalytic sites first in order to organise the catalytic domains of LysU prior to the binding of the following substrate, ATP, to only one out of the two available catalytic sites, hence leading to the catalysis of lysyl adenylate intermediate formation in only one of the two catalytic sites at any one time.

8.2.7.3 Ping-pong Bi Bi kinetic scheme

A bisubstrate reaction that invokes a situation in which one or more products are released before all substrates have been bound to catalytic site(s) is said to have a double-displacement or ping-pong reaction mechanism. The corresponding **ping-pong Bi Bi kinetic scheme**, assuming catalytic irreversibility (Scheme 8.11), is the simplest summary of this scenario. In such a ping-pong kinetic scheme, the biocatalyst itself with a single catalytic site is also

$$\text{E} + \text{S}_A \underset{k_{-1}}{\overset{k_1}{\rightleftharpoons}} \text{ES}_A \underset{k_{-p}}{\overset{k_p}{\rightleftharpoons}} \text{FP}_P \underset{k_{-2}}{\overset{k_2}{\rightleftharpoons}} \text{P}_P$$

$$+$$

$$\text{P}_Q + \text{E} \underset{k_4}{\overset{k_{-4}}{\rightleftharpoons}} \text{EP}_Q \underset{k_{p'}}{\overset{k_{-p'}}{\rightleftharpoons}} \text{FS}_B \underset{k_3}{\overset{k_{-3}}{\rightleftharpoons}} \text{S}_B + \text{F}$$

Scheme 8.11

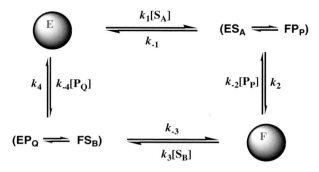

Figure 8.38 King-Altmann diagram for the **Ping Pong Bi Bi Kinetic Scheme (Scheme 8.11).**

temporarily altered (usually covalently) as part of the biocatalytic mechanism from a standard state represented by E to an altered state defined by F, prior to return to the E state. Once again, the King–Altman diagram is illustrated (Figure 8.38), and we derive from this the rate equation that expresses the initial net forward rate for the conversion of substrates into products in the presence of negligible concentrations of products:

$$\frac{v}{V_{\max f}} = \frac{[S_A][S_B]}{K_{m S_B}[S_A] + K_{m S_A}[S_B] + [S_A][S_B]} \tag{8.70}$$

When $[S_B]$ is constant, Equation (8.70) reduces to

$$\frac{v}{V_{\max f}} = \frac{[S_A]}{K_{m S_A} + [S_A]\left(1 + \left[\dfrac{K_{m S_B}}{[S_B]}\right]\right)} \tag{8.71}$$

which relates to the double-reciprocal form

$$\frac{1}{v} = \frac{K_{m S_A}}{V_{\max f}} \frac{1}{[S_A]} + \frac{1}{V_{\max}}\left(1 + \left[\dfrac{K_{m S_B}}{[S_B]}\right]\right) \tag{8.72}$$

As before, provided that the kinetic mechanism of the given biocatalyst of interest brings about biocatalysis through the ping-pong Bi Bi mechanism, then plots of actual $1/v$ versus $1/[S_A]$ data obtained in the presence of various fixed concentrations of the S_B substrate, $[S_B]$, should be fitted closely by Equation (8.72), resulting in the parallel graphical output shown in Figure 8.39. Equation (8.72) and this ping-pong Bi Bi kinetic scheme are applicable for the steady state kinetic analyses of many of our example biocatalysts, including homo-dimeric *E. coli* AspAT (Figure 8.5, Table 8.1), together with the monomeric hydrolytic enzymes bovine pancreatic α-chymotrypsin (Figure 8.3, Table 8.1) and *T. californica* AChE (Figure 8.10, Table 8.1), which both require an acyl-enzyme covalent intermediate (F state) as an essential part of their catalytic cycles. Similarly, Equation (8.72) and this ping-pong Bi Bi kinetic scheme are also applicable for the steady state kinetic analyses of monomeric hydrolytic enzymes bovine pancreatic RNAse A (Figure 8.4, Table 8.1) and hen egg-white lysozyme (Figure 8.6, Table 8.1)

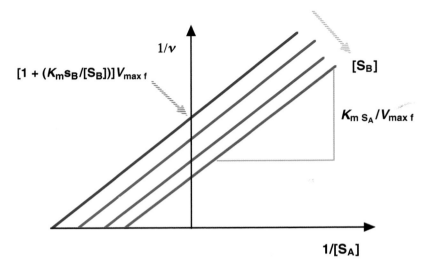

Figure 8.39 Lineweaver-Burk Plots for the **Ping Pong Bi Bi Kinetic Scheme (Scheme 8.11)**.

since they both involve a non-covalent enzyme–intermediate complex (F state) as an integral part of their catalytic cycles. Please note that although *E. coli* AspAT is homodimeric and there are substantial conformational changes taking place in subunits during the catalytic cycle, evidence for catalytic site dependence and cooperativity in catalysis has not been observed so far even though the two active sites do not appear to be exactly equivalent. Hence the two catalytic sites are essentially independent of each other, making this ping-pong Bi Bi kinetic scheme applicable for each individual AspAT catalytic site.

8.2.7.4   Ordered Ter Bi and Ter Ter kinetic schemes

The kinetic scheme corresponding with the **ordered Ter Bi kinetic scheme** is illustrated in Scheme 8.12, which gives the following initial net forward rate for the conversion of substrates into products in the presence of negligible concentrations of products:

$$\frac{v}{V_{\max f}} = \frac{[S_A][S_B][S_C]}{K_{iS_A}K_{iS_B}K_{mS_C} + K_{iS_B}K_{mS_C}[S_A] + K_{iS_A}K_{mS_B}[S_C] + K_{mS_C}[S_A][S_B] +}$$

$$K_{mS_B}[S_A][S_C] + K_{mS_A}[S_B][S_C] + [S_A][S_B][S_C] \tag{8.73}$$

When $[S_B]$ and $[S_C]$ are constant, Equation (8.73) rearranges to

$$\frac{v}{V_{\max f}} = \frac{[S_A]}{K_{mS_A}\left(1 + \frac{K_{iS_A}K_{iS_B}K_{mS_C}}{K_{mS_A}[S_B][S_C]} + \frac{K_{iS_A}K_{mS_B}}{K_{mS_A}[S_B]}\right) + [S_A]\left(1 + \frac{K_{iS_B}K_{mS_C}}{[S_B][S_C]} + \frac{K_{mS_B}}{[S_B]} + \frac{K_{mS_C}}{[S_C]}\right)}$$

$$\tag{8.74}$$

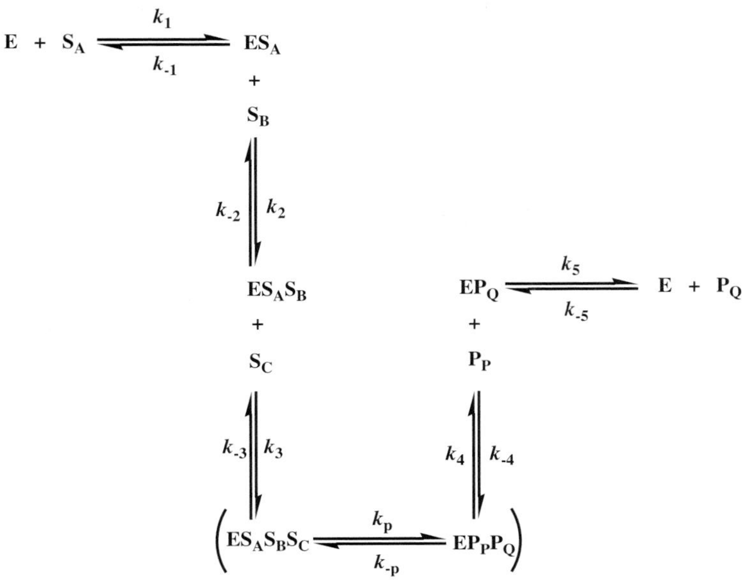

Scheme 8.12

which relates to the following double reciprocal:

$$
\frac{1}{v} = \frac{K_{m\,S_A}}{V_{max\,f}} \left(1 + \frac{K_{i\,S_A} K_{i\,S_B} K_{m\,S_C}}{K_{m\,S_A}[S_B][S_C]} + \frac{K_{i\,S_A} K_{m\,S_B}}{K_{m\,S_A}[S_B]} \right) \frac{1}{[S_A]}
$$

$$
+ \frac{1}{V_{max}} \left(1 + \frac{K_{i\,S_B} K_{m\,S_C}}{[S_B][S_C]} + \frac{K_{m\,S_B}}{[S_B]} + \frac{K_{m\,S_C}}{[S_C]} \right) \tag{8.75}
$$

Assuming that the ordered Ter Bi mechanism applies, plots of actual $1/v$ versus $1/[S_A]$ data obtained in the presence of various fixed concentrations of the S_B and S_C substrates, $[S_B]$ and $[S_C]$, should be fitted by Equation (8.75) resulting in the off-axis graphical output shown in Figure 8.40. The scheme corresponding to the **ordered Ter Ter kinetic scheme** is also shown (Scheme 8.13). Fortunately, the initial net forward rate for the conversion of substrates into products in the presence of negligible concentrations of products obeys the same steady state rate equations as the Ter Bi kinetic scheme.

Interestingly, Equation (8.75) and the irreversible, single catalytic site, Ter Ter kinetic scheme may also be applicable for the steady state kinetic analysis of the overall conversion of two molecules of ATP to Ap_4A and pyrophosphate, catalysed by LysU with the assistance of the third substrate lysine-Mg^{2+} (Figure 8.11, Table 8.1). The combination of ATP, the first nucleotide substrate, with lysine-Mg^2 to give intermediate lysyl adenylate represents the formation of a transient non-covalent enzyme–intermediate complex. Pyrophosphate product now dissociates from the catalytic site allowing for ATP, the second nucleotide substrate, to enter in its place and form Ap_4A by in-line displacement of lysine from the adenylate

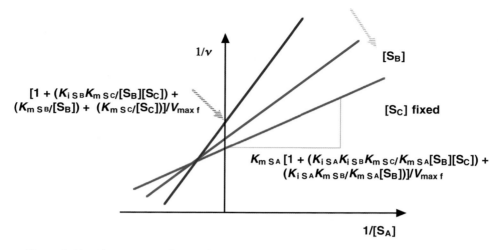

Figure 8.40   Lineweaver-Burk Plots for the **ordered Ter Bi Kinetic Scheme (Scheme 8.12)**.

intermediate. This is not a perfect fit with the ordered Ter Ter kinetic scheme since there are some elements of ping-pong kinetics but the Ter Ter kinetic scheme is workable on the assumption that enzyme-associated adenylate intermediate is indeed transient.

Unsurprisingly, the complexity of steady state kinetics equations starts to tell above the Ter Ter kinetic scheme level. Moreover, this complexity is probably superfluous to further

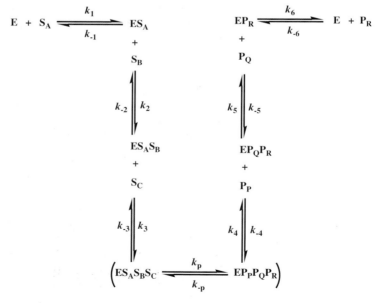

Scheme 8.13

understanding of biocatalysis. Essentially, the equations and kinetic schemes described in Chapter 8 thus far are more than adequate for the steady state analysis of most biological catalytic events. Moreover, as already stated steady state kinetics, whilst being a useful measure of 'surface' biocatalyst activity, is unable to penetrate the realities of biocatalyst-associated chemical transformations, the rapid binding of substrate and then the release of product. For a more detailed analysis of chemical events on a given biocatalyst, other faster techniques are required: in particular, pre-steady-state kinetics!

8.3 Pre-steady-state kinetics

The arena of **pre-steady-state kinetics**, also known as **single-turnover kinetics**, begins under conditions where biocatalysis is observed in the presence of a large amount of biocatalyst under rapid mixing ($\ll$sec), non-equilibrium conditions. This is no longer steady state kinetics. Therefore, complex kinetic schemes and complex steady state kinetics equations derived from steady state analyses are no longer required. In fact, kinetic schemes become very simple, since we are usually only observing state-to-state changes (either in the biocatalyst itself or in substrate/product bound to the biocatalyst under investigation), which all obey first order or pseudo-first-order kinetics. For this reason, an appreciation of first order kinetics is an essential prerequisite for understanding pre-steady-state kinetics. Pre-steady-state analyses are used primarily to reach a much more detailed understanding surrounding the mechanistic behaviour of a given biocatalysis. In order to achieve this, such analyses are always performed under non-equilibrium rapid mixing conditions and involve only a single catalytic turnover. **Relaxation** towards equilibrium is then observed by continuous monitoring of an appropriate physical property or spectroscopic signal (usually fluorescence intensity) over a time interval sufficient for a change in state (either in the biocatalyst itself or in substrate/product bound to the biocatalyst) to take place. Relaxation data allows catalytic effects to be correlated with actual physical and chemical properties of the biocatalyst or substrate/product. Therefore, pre-steady-state kinetic analyses can open up the precise process by which a given biocatalyst promotes inter-conversions between substrate(s) and product(s), including substrate binding and product release steps, with precise microscopic rate constants. However, in spite of this utility such analyses require large amounts of biocatalyst with some relatively sophisticated fast kinetics apparatus and so are not performed routinely without a great deal of background preparation.

8.3.1 Pre-steady-state bioassays

Pre-steady-state bioassays are performed by linking up some form of **rapid mixing device** to a spectrometer, which is usually a spectrofluorimeter calibrated to detect changes in fluorescence signal intensity at a defined wavelength over a fixed time period (approximately 4–200 ms). There are three main types of rapid mixing device, namely **rapid mixing continuous flow**, **stopped flow** and **rapid quench**. In the first (Figure 8.41), two syringes are individually loaded with samples of biocatalyst, substrate, product or even biocatalyst–substrate species

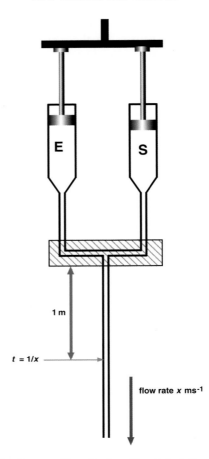

Figure 8.41   Rapid Mixing Continuous Flow Device. Biocatalyst **E** and substrate **S** are combined in a mixing zone (hatched area) and the mixture ejected along a common outlet tube. Distance from the mixing zone determines **time *t*** from mixing. Spectroscopic monitoring of mixture as a function of distance generates first order **relaxation curves** for analysis.

that are 'fired' together into a mixing chamber and then expelled down a flow-tube at constant flow rate (approximately 10 m s^{-1}) such that the distance along the tube is proportional to 'age' (i.e. time). For instance, given the indicated flow rate, at 1 cm from the mixing chamber the solution is 1 ms 'old'. The power of this method is that the output from rapid mixing may be observed even at an age as recent as 10 µs.

In the case of the stopped flow device (Figure 8.42), two compressed syringes are set up to express small volumes (50–200 µl) at any one time. These syringes are individually loaded with samples as above and small volumes of these samples are then fired together into a mixing chamber and expelled down a flow-tube at constant flow rate (approximately 10 m s^{-1}) prior to a mechanical stop. A fixed detector at a distance of 1 cm from the mixing chamber is then positioned to observe solution that is initially 1 ms 'old' at the end of continuous flow. Compression converts continuous into static flow, so spectroscopic and/or physical changes

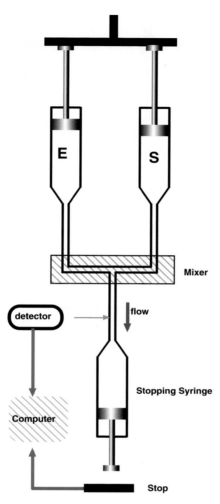

Figure 8.42 Stopped Flow Device. Biocatalyst **E** and substrate **S** are combined in a mixing zone (hatched area) and the mixture ejected along a common outlet tube activating a stopping syringe that provokes detection by the detector. Spectroscopic monitoring of mixture as a function of **time *t*** then generates first order **relaxation curves** for analysis.

in solution are then monitored normally *in situ* in full view of the fixed detector. Note that the first 1 ms is lost and represents the **dead time of mixing** of the apparatus, before which nothing can be observed. Finally, the rapid quench device (Figure 8.43) consists similarly of two compressed syringes set up to express small volumes into a mixing chamber that links through a flow-tube into a second mixing chamber, where a third syringe is on hand to introduce an agent such as strong acid that prevents any further reaction from taking place by acting as a chemical quenching agent. Such a device has a dead time of mixing of 4–5 ms and a window of observation extending from 100 to 150 ms only. Ultimately, stopped flow devices are much the most popular and versatile devices for pre-steady-state analyses.

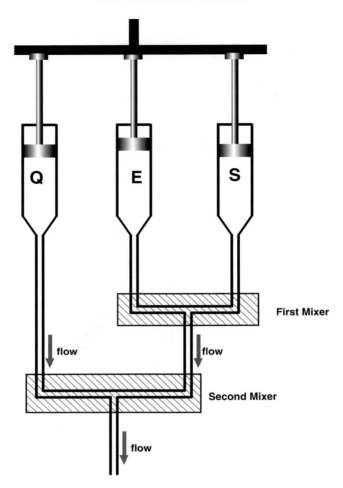

Figure 8.43   Rapid Quench Device. Biocatalyst **E** and substrate **S** are combined in a mixing zone (hatched area) and the mixture ejected along a common outlet tube in order to be combined with quencher **Q** in another mixing zone. Different mixing times correlate with different reaction **times *t*** pre-quenching. Spectroscopic monitoring as a function of ***t*** gives first order **relaxation curves** for analysis.

8.3.2 First order pre-steady-state kinetics

When there is an irreversible conversion of a species A to B that follows the given kinetic scheme (Scheme 8.14(a)), then the rate of disappearance of A follows

$$-\mathrm{d}[A]/\mathrm{d}t = k_1[A] \tag{8.76}$$

The reaction rate depends cleanly on the concentration of only one chemical species and so is said to obey **first order kinetics**. In a similar way, if a reaction does depend upon

(a)   A $\xrightarrow{k_1}$ B

(b) A $\underset{k_{-1}}{\overset{k_1}{\rightleftharpoons}}$ B

Scheme 8.14

the concentration of two chemical species but one species is in such large excess that its concentration is effectively constant during the course of the reaction, then the reaction rate will depend effectively on the concentration of only one species again and is said to obey **pseudo-first-order kinetics.** Equation (8.76) integrates to give

$$[A]_t = [A]_0 \exp(-k_1 t) \tag{8.77}$$

where $[A]_0$ is the initial concentration of species A at the beginning of reaction, and $[A]_t$ is the concentration of species A at time t. Note the exponential dependence of $[A]_t$ on time. Given the fact that $[B]_t$, the concentration of species B at time t, is related simply to $[A]_t$ by the relationship

$$[A]_t = [A]_0 - [B]_t \tag{8.78}$$

then Equation (8.77) can be rewritten for $[B]_t$ as shown:

$$[B]_t = [A]_0 [1 - \exp(-k_1 t)] \tag{8.79}$$

which represents an inverted exponential dependence. In the case of both Equations (8.77) and (8.79) the term k_1 is the **first order rate constant** for the conversion of species A to B, and the term $[A]_0$ behaves as an **amplitude** that scales the dimensions of the exponential together with k_1 (Figure 8.44).

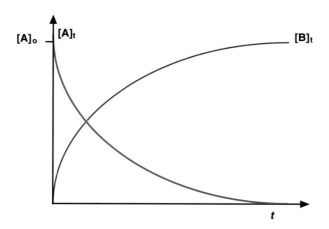

Figure 8.44 Variation of concentration of species **A** and **B** with time where the conversion from **A** to **B** obeys first order kinetics and is irreversible.

Now for the reversible conversion of a species A to B that follows an alternative kinetic scheme (Scheme 8.14(b)). In this instance, matters could become more complicated. However, if we just consider the situation in which pure A is allowed to convert to B until equilibrium is established, then the rate of approach to equilibrium will still involve an exponential dependence, although modified with respect to Equations (8.77) and (8.79). A complete derivation of these modified equations is not necessary here, but the student should be aware that there must be differences in the way rate constants appear and also differences in the amplitude to accommodate the existence of equilibrium. Hence the equilibrium version of Equation (8.77) is as follows:

$$[A]_t = \Delta[A]_0 \exp\left[-\left(k_1 + k_{-1}\right)t\right] + [A]_{eq} \tag{8.80}$$

where $\Delta[A]_0$ is the total change in concentration as species A is converted to B starting from initial concentration $[A]_0$ and converging at final equilibrium concentration $[A]_{eq}$. $\Delta[A]_0$ represents the correct amplitude in this case (Figure 8.45), and is given explicitly by the following equation

$$\Delta[A]_0 = [A]_0 \left(\frac{k_1}{k_1 + k_{-1}}\right) \tag{8.81}$$

We can rewrite Equations (8.80) and (8.81) in terms of product B as follows:

$$[B]_t = \Delta[B]_0 \exp\left[-\left(k_1 + k_{-1}\right)t\right] + [B]_{eq} \tag{8.82}$$

$$\Delta[B]_0 = [B]_0 \left(\frac{k_{-1}}{k_1 + k_{-1}}\right) \tag{8.83}$$

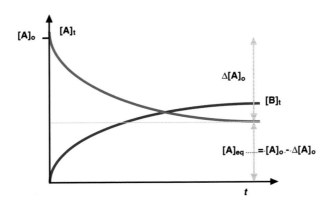

Figure 8.45 Variation of concentration of species **A** and **B** with time where the conversion from **A** to **B** obeys first order kinetics but is reversible and as such converges to equilibrium.

Obviously Equations (8.82) and (8.83) apply to the reverse scenario in which pure B is allowed to convert to A starting from initial concentration $[B]_0$ and converging at final equilibrium concentration $[B]_{eq}$, in other words the exact opposite of the scenario to which Equations (8.80) and (8.81) apply. Now let us return to pre-steady-state kinetic analysis!

8.3.3 Further pre-steady-state equations

Consider the following Uni Uni biocatalysis kinetic scheme that involves two biocatalyst–substrate species intermediates that are generated prior to product formation and release (Scheme 8.15). Most of the steps involve the inter-conversions of biocatalyst–substrate or biocatalyst–product species and hence microscopic inter-conversion rates will depend only upon single-species concentrations. In other words, these inter-conversions must obey first order kinetics. Similarly, if S and E are combined under conditions where $[S] \gg [E]$, such that $[S]$ is effectively unchanged during reaction, then the microscopic inter-conversion rate from E to ES will once again depend effectively only upon $[E]$ such that this inter-conversion obeys pseudo-first-order kinetics. Accordingly, every step/inter-conversion shown in the biocatalysis reaction scheme above obeys and could be analysed by appropriate variations of Equation (8.80).

In practice, if we are to analyse biocatalysis under conditions in which pure substrate and/or product are followed to chemical equilibrium in the presence of pure biocatalyst, then rapid mixing devices are essential (see Section 8.3.1). Using such devices, a large quantity of biocatalyst ($[E] \cong$ mM level) may be combined (ms time scale) with a significant excess of substrate(s) and/or product(s) ($[S]$ and/or $[P] \gg$ mM) and the relaxation to chemical equilibrium followed over the ms–s timescale. Relaxation to equilibrium is followed through changes with time in an appropriate physical property or spectroscopic signature (frequently fluorescence output) that is linked with mechanistic activity involving the biocatalyst. The plot of signal S_t against time results in a **relaxation curve**. This is typically analysed using a multi-exponential equation (8.84), derived in form from Equation (8.80):

$$S_t = at + b \sum_i C_i \exp\left(-k_i t\right) \tag{8.84}$$

where a is the slope of the signal base line, b the value of the base line at time t, C_i the amplitude for the ith mechanistic step and k_i the corresponding rate constant. In effect, one rapid mixing experiment could provide sufficient information from the evolution of S_t with time t to determine the microscopic rate constants and amplitude factors for each mechanistic step of a biocatalyst pathway. Values of k_i are not true microscopic rate constant

$$E + S \underset{k_{-1}\,(k_{off})}{\overset{k_1\,(k_{on})}{\rightleftharpoons}} ES \underset{k_{-2}}{\overset{k_2}{\rightleftharpoons}} ES' \underset{k_{-3}}{\overset{k_3}{\rightleftharpoons}} EP \overset{k_4}{\longrightarrow} E + P$$

Scheme 8.15

values since each k_i term corresponds to a sum of rate constants (see Equations (8.80) and (8.82)). However, actual microscopic rate constant values may be assigned given knowledge of corresponding values of C_i since amplitudes also contain rate constant terms (see Equations (8.81) and (8.83)).

In practice, one rapid mixing experiment is rarely if ever sufficient to obtain all the information required on steps in a pathway including microscopic rate constants. Instead, a range of relaxation curves must usually be acquired over a substantial range of $[E]_0$, $[S]$ and/or $[P]$ values to confirm measured values of C_i and k_i. Furthermore, individual steps in the biocatalyst pathway may need to be isolated for more extensive steady state analysis by careful choice of pre-steady-state conditions, the use of substrate and/or product analogues and changes in the physical property or spectroscopic signature used to monitor relaxation. For instance, the selection of a substrate analogue able to bind to biocatalyst E but not able to proceed to the ES′ state would allow for precise pre-steady-state analysis of the first binding equilibrium step without interference from the later steps. Experiments of this type ensure that a significant range of pre-steady-state kinetic experiments may be devised to tease out the mechanistic detail of different steps in a biocatalyst pathway and/or determine individual microscopic rate constants in this pathway.

8.4 Theories of biocatalysis

So far in this chapter, the chemical biology reader has been introduced to examples of biocatalysts, kinetics assays, steady state kinetic analysis as a means to probe basic mechanisms and pre-steady-state kinetic analysis as a means to measure rates of on-catalyst events. In order to complete this survey of biocatalysis, we now need to consider those factors that make biocatalysis possible. In other words, how do biocatalysts achieve the catalytic rate enhancements that they do? This is a simple question but in reality needs to be answered in many different ways according to the biocatalyst concerned. For certain, there are general principles that underpin the operation of all biocatalysts, but there again other principles are employed more selectively. Several classical theories of catalysis have been developed over time, which include the concepts of **intramolecular catalysis**, **'orbital steering'**, **general acid–base catalysis**, **electrophilic catalysis** and **nucleophilic catalysis**. Such classical theories are useful starting points in our quest to understand how biocatalysts are able to effect biocatalysis with such efficiency.

8.4.1 Intramolecular catalysis and stereo-control in catalysis

Intramolecular catalysis is a very fundamental concept in biocatalysis. In essence, some catalysis is made possible just by binding substrates in close proximity to each other in the catalytic site(s). The same is true of binding substrates in close proximity to active site functional groups that participate in the catalytic process (Figure 8.46). Binding in proximity within catalytic

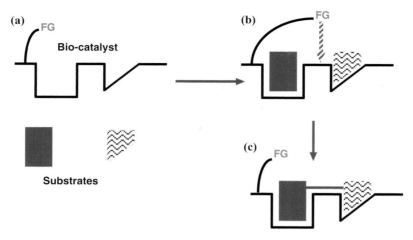

Figure 8.46 Schematic illustration to show the principle of **intramolecular catalysis**. Rate of reaction between the two substrates is enabled by binding and close proximity in the active site region (**a**). **Neighbouring group participation** involving neighbouring functional group assistance provides additional rate enhancement (**anchimeric assistance**) (**b**) for bond construction (**c**).

site(s) enhances the contact frequency between substrates and/or functional groups to a level significantly in excess of that possible in free solution. The physical consequence of this is enhanced reaction rates. This effect is known as **intramolecular catalysis**. Intramolecular catalysis can be quantified by saying that the binding of substrates and/or functional groups in close proximity enhances contact frequencies in a manner equivalent to increasing the **effective concentration** of each substrate and/or functional group in free solution, to the point that identical contact frequencies would be made possible. The consequence of such simple binding for reaction rates is impressive. Intramolecular catalysis can account for between 10^2- and 10^3-fold of the total rate enhancement in biocatalysis, which typically varies anywhere from 10^5- to 10^9-fold, depending upon the nature of the chemical reactions involved and the biocatalyst.

Another consequence of the simple binding of substrates to catalytic site(s) is that biocatalysts can exert strong effects on chirality during reactions. Biocatalysts such as enzymes are themselves chiral and so too are their catalytic site(s). Consequently, where substrates are chiral ES complexes binding different enantiomers are themselves diastereomeric with respect to each other, involving different binding modes and different binding energies. Frequently, this effect ensures that biocatalysts chose only certain select substrate enantiomers for biocatalysis. Where substrates are achiral, then the ES complex is still chiral and reactions involving achiral substrates frequently give rise to new chiral centres. In addition, since substrates typically remain in association with the biocatalyst during catalytic conversion into products, then the transfer of chiral functional groups frequently takes place with either retention or inversion of absolute configuration, depending upon the nature of the chemical reactions involved and the biocatalyst (Figure 8.47).

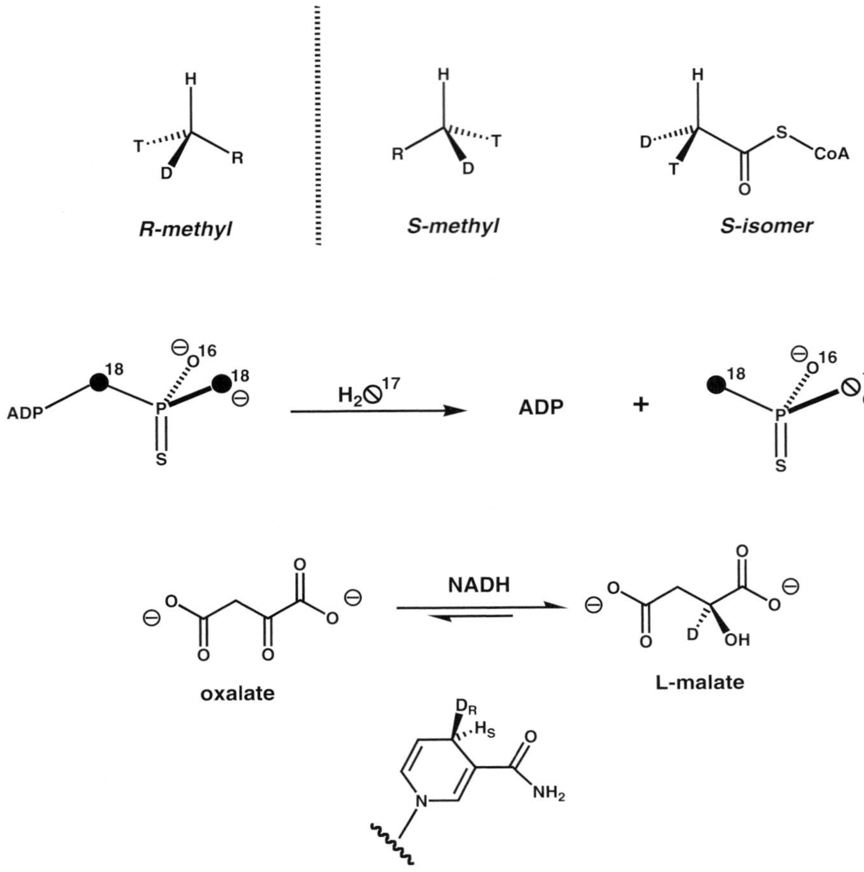

Figure 8.47 Stereochemistry in Catalysis. Biocatalyst stereochemistry may be followed with **chiral substrates** to reveal stereochemical changes during catalysis. Substrates include, chiral acetylCoA and phosphate (that undergo inversion or retention of configuration with reaction), and chiral NADH(D) designed to demonstrate whether **prochiral** (**proR** or **proS**) are employed in reduction. mMDH uses the proR hydrogen as illustrated by deuterium (D) transfer to the product (bottom). **D**, deuterium; **T**, tritium.

8.4.2 'Orbital steering'

The concept of 'orbital steering' is a direct successor to intramolecular catalysis. According this concept, rate enhancements conferred by simple binding can be significantly enhanced if the frontier orbitals responsible for reactivity can also be orientated and brought into optimal alignment. Such optimal alignments would then enhance reaction rates by increasing the frequency of productive contacts between substrates and/or functional groups. Both intramolecular catalysis and 'orbital steering' effects provide a general background to biocatalysis and may make contributions towards the rate enhancement of most biocatalytic processes.

8.4.3 Induced fit and strain

Strain is an old concept that has been used in organic chemistry since the beginning of stereo-electronic explanations for reactivity. Strain is connected with the consequences of introducing unnatural bond angles and dihedral angles into small molecules, either by design or by coercion that leads to an increase in molecular potential energy and hence chemical potential for reactivity. According to one theory of biocatalysis, a biocatalyst structure is rigid and the substrate must undergo a process of **induced fit** to the relevant active site for optimal binding. Induced fit implies the introduction of strain into the substrate molecule, thereby preparing the bound substrate in the biocatalyst-ground state ES complex to enter the biocatalyst–transition-state complex, $ES^{\ddagger}$. The active site of the rigid biocatalyst structure is envisaged to be completely complementary to the reaction transition state, hence biocatalyst–transition-state interactions are said to be strain free. However, evidence is accumulating to show that biocatalyst structure should not be regarded as rigid at all. Rather, substrate–biocatalyst interactions are just as likely to involve induced fit of the biocatalyst structure to accommodate optimal binding of a 'rigid substrate' within a catalytic site. Therefore, strain may play a role to promote rate enhancements of some reactions under the influence of a biocatalyst but the role should be subtle at best.

8.4.4 General acid–base catalysis

General acid–base catalysis is an essential part of biocatalysis. In order to appreciate the principles of rate enhancement through general acid–base catalysis, we need to begin with the two **Brønsted equations** that separately describe general base and general acid catalysis. These equations relate rate of reaction to the equilibrium that exists between a given base B and its conjugate acid BH^+ as defined by the **base equilibrium ionisation constant**, K_d^B:

$$K_d^B = \frac{[B][H^+]}{[BH^+]} \tag{8.85}$$

By definition,

$$pK_d^B = -\log K_d^B \tag{8.86}$$

General base catalysis is said to occur when the measured rate k_B of a given chemical reaction changes according to the nature of the base B used to catalyse the reaction. Quite frequently, the measured rate k_B varies systematically with the strength of the various bases used to catalyse the reaction according to the first Brønsted equation

$$\log k_B = C + \beta \, pK_d^B \tag{8.87}$$

where C is a reaction constant and β is the **Brønsted β-value**. β provides a measure of the sensitivity of reaction rate to pK_d^B values, which in turn define the relative basic strengths of the different bases used to catalyse the reaction. The higher is the pK_d^B value, the greater is the basic strength of the corresponding base B and the faster the reaction. Brønsted β-values vary from 0 to 1 but are typically measured in the 0.3–0.6 region.

In a similar way, general acid catalysis is said to occur when the measured rate k_A of a given chemical reaction changes according to the nature of the acid HA used to catalyse the reaction. Quite frequently, the measured rate k_A varies systematically with the strength of the various acids used to catalyse the reaction according to the second Brønsted equation

$$\log k_A = C - \alpha\, p K_d^A \tag{8.88}$$

where C is a reaction constant once again and α is the **Brønsted α-value**. α provides a measure of the sensitivity of reaction rate to pK_d^A values that in turn define the relative acid strengths of the different acids used to catalyse the reaction. The lower is the pK_d^A value, the greater is the acid strength of the corresponding acid HA and the faster the reaction. Brønsted α-values vary within a similar range to Brønsted β-values. For the sake of completeness, note that the equilibrium that exists between a given acid HA and its conjugate base A^- is defined by the **acid equilibrium ionisation constant**, K_d^A:

$$K_d^A = \frac{[A^-][H^+]}{[HA]} \tag{8.89}$$

8.4.4.1   Dixon–Webb log plots

Clearly, the effect of pH upon biocatalytic rates can be indirect or direct. In indirect terms, conformational and other structural changes (e.g. changes in oligomerisation state) induced by changes in solution pH can indirectly perturb biocatalysis rates. However, if the ionisation state of (a) given functional group(s) is in fact critical to efficient biocatalysis, then the effect of pH on biocatalysis rates will be direct. In this case, the concepts introduced in the previous section can be used to quantify the effect of pH as follows. Almost the simplest case is to consider a scenario in which the ionisation state of two functional groups (one acidic, designated **group 1**, and one basic, designated **group 2**) is critical to efficient catalysis by the simplest irreversible, single-catalytic-site, Uni Uni kinetic scheme (see Section 8.2.1). Hence, assuming that biocatalysis is not possible unless the ionisation state is completely correct, the Uni Uni kinetic scheme may be integrated with a series of protonation/deprotonation ionisation equilibria as shown in Scheme 8.16. Now we can use the same kinetic treatment as was used previously in this chapter to derive a meaningful kinetic equation or two! By analogy to the treatment in Section 8.2.1, we can generate two initial equations

$$v = k_2[E^nS] \tag{8.90}$$

$$[E]_0 = [E^n] + [E^{n+1}] + [E^{n-1}] + [E^nS] + [E^{n+1}S] + [E^{n-1}S] \tag{8.91}$$

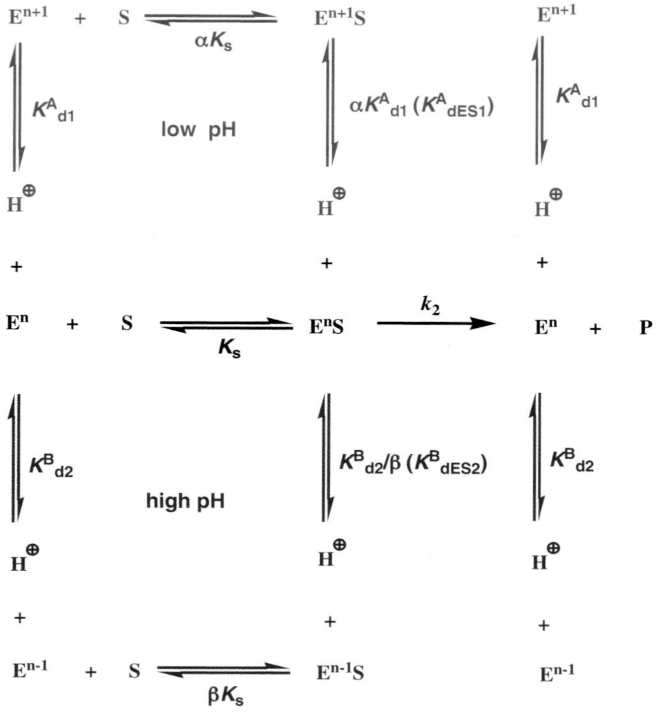

$$E^{n+1} + S \xrightleftharpoons[\alpha K_S]{} E^{n+1}S \qquad E^{n+1}$$

$$\qquad K^A_{d1} \qquad\qquad \text{low pH} \qquad \alpha K^A_{d1}\,(K^A_{dES1}) \qquad K^A_{d1}$$

$$H^{\oplus} \qquad\qquad\qquad H^{\oplus} \qquad\qquad\qquad H^{\oplus}$$

$$+ \qquad\qquad\qquad\quad + \qquad\qquad\qquad\quad +$$

$$E^n + S \xrightleftharpoons[K_S]{} E^nS \xrightarrow{k_2} E^n + P$$

$$\qquad K^B_{d2} \qquad\qquad \text{high pH} \qquad K^B_{d2}/\beta\,(K^B_{dES2}) \qquad K^B_{d2}$$

$$H^{\oplus} \qquad\qquad\qquad H^{\oplus} \qquad\qquad\qquad H^{\oplus}$$

$$+ \qquad\qquad\qquad\quad + \qquad\qquad\qquad\quad +$$

$$E^{n-1} + S \xrightleftharpoons[\beta K_S]{} E^{n-1}S \qquad E^{n-1}$$

Scheme 8.16

that combine smoothly to produce

$$\frac{v}{[E]_0} = \frac{k_2[E^nS]}{[E^n] + [E^{n+1}] + [E^{n-1}] + [E^nS] + [E^{n+1}S] + [E^{n-1}S]} \tag{8.92}$$

Different equilibrium dissociation constant and equilibrium ionisation constant equations may then be derived with reference to the kinetic scheme (Scheme 8.16) on the basis of stasis, such as Equation (8.93), which defines an equilibrium dissociation constant αK_S, or Equation (8.94), which defines the equilibrium ionisation constant K^A_{d1} for acidic functional group 1, or 8.95 that defines the equilibrium ionisation constant K^B_{d2} for basic functional group 2:

$$\alpha K_S = \frac{[E^{n+1}][S]}{[E^{n+1}S]} \tag{8.93}$$

$$K^A_{d1} = \frac{[E^n][H^+]}{[E^{n+1}]} \tag{8.94}$$

$$K^B_{d2} = \frac{[E^{n-1}][H^+]}{[E^n]} \tag{8.95}$$

Thereafter, these equations and others can be rearranged to give solutions for all the enzyme species including $[E^{n+1}]$ and $[E^{n+1}S]$ for instance. These solutions are then substituted back into Equation (8.92) giving us a complete steady state kinetics/ionisation equilibrium:

$$\frac{v}{k_2[E]_0} = \frac{[S]}{K_S\left(1 + \dfrac{[H^+]}{K_{d1}^A} + \dfrac{K_{d2}^B}{[H^+]}\right) + [S]\left(1 + \dfrac{[H^+]}{\alpha K_{d1}^A} + \dfrac{K_{d2}^B}{\beta[H^+]}\right)} \tag{8.96}$$

This equation is still relatively complicated if concise. Therefore, we will have to apply some 'boundary conditions' to reduce this further in order to obtain useful information. Let us assume that $[S] \gg [K_S]$ (i.e. k_{cat} conditions), then making the usual substitution for V_{max} (see above) we arrive at

$$\frac{V_{max,app[H+]}}{V_{max}} = \frac{1}{\left(1 + \dfrac{[H^+]}{K_{dES1}^A} + \dfrac{K_{dES2}^B}{[H^+]}\right)} \tag{8.97}$$

where v is now defined and substituted for by $V_{max,app[H+]}$, the optimal catalytic rate at a given pH, and αK_{d1}^A and K_{d2}^B/β are substituted for by K_{dES1}^A and K_{dES2}^B respectively, corresponding to the ionisation equilibrium constants for functional group 1 and group 2 respectively modified by the presence of substrate bound to the biocatalyst active site (see Scheme 8.16). The logarithmic form of (8.97) is now given by

$$\log\frac{V_{max,app[H+]}}{V_{max}} = -\log\left(1 + \frac{[H^+]}{K_{dES1}^A} + \frac{K_{dES2}^B}{[H^+]}\right) \tag{8.98}$$

This is the famous **Dixon-Webb equation**. Further simplification is now possible if we take the two extremes of low pH (high $[H^+]$), and high pH (low $[H^+]$). The low pH form of Equation (8.98) is Equation (8.99) and the high pH form is Equation (8.100):

$$\log\frac{V_{max,app[H+]}}{V_{max}} = -\log[H^+] + \log K_{dES1}^A = pH - pK_{dES1}^A \tag{8.99}$$

$$\log\frac{V_{max,app[H+]}}{V_{max}} = \log[H^+] - \log K_{dES2}^B = -pH + pK_{dES2}^B \tag{8.100}$$

Both equations link catalytic rate to general pH ($-\log[H^+]$) and the specific pK_{dES1}^A ($-\log K_{dES1}^A$) of the acidic functional group 1 or the specific pK_{dES2}^B ($-\log K_{dES2}^B$) of the basic functional group 2. Both equations plotted together produce a classic bell-shaped curve (Figure 8.48), where optimal rate is set to fall at a value of pH that is a compromise between the joint requirements for acidic functional group 1 to be *unprotonated* and for basic functional group 2 to be *protonated* in order for optimal biocatalysis to take place! The classic bell-shaped curve is a fusion of two **Dixon–Webb log plots** and is the classical representation for the dependence of biocatalytic rate on pH for a **diprotic mechanism**.

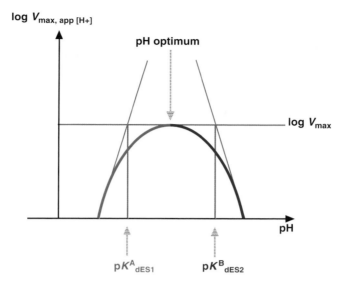

Figure 8.48 Schematic illustration to show the principle of **Dixon Webb Log Plots.** Plot due to low pH **equation 8.99** is shown (**red**), and the plot due to high pH **equation 8.100** is also shown (**blue**). On the combined plot, optimal pH position is shown along with log values of **ES** equilibrium ionization constants, $\mathbf{p}K_{\mathrm{dES1}}^{\mathrm{A}}$ and $\mathbf{p}K_{\mathrm{dES2}}^{\mathrm{B}}$.

8.4.5 Electrophilic and nucleophilic catalysis

Both electrophilic and nucleophilic catalysis are exceedingly common components of bio-catalytic mechanisms, involving as they do the formation of reactive, metastable covalent intermediates. For instance, metal ions are frequently used by biocatalysts to enhance reaction rates by coordinating to reactive functional groups in substrates and then stabilising those anionic charges formed post-reaction. Other examples of electrophilic catalysis at work in biocatalytic mechanisms involve the covalent use of non-peptidic cofactors that promote enzyme catalysed reaction pathways by acting as electrophilic reactants (electron sinks) that trap substrates covalently in the form of high energy reactive intermediates, which themselves then react before releasing the cofactor for a following round of catalytic activity.

Nucleophilic catalysis is also an exceedingly common component of biocatalytic mecha-nisms. In addition to substrate coordination, metals may also ionise water and in the process provide a source of extremely nucleophilic hydroxyl ions that are considerably more reactive than water. Alternatively, enzyme active sites have a particularly rich source of nucleophilic functional groups donated by such residues as **serine, threonine, cysteine, aspartic acid, glutamic acid, lysine, histidine** and **tyrosine** (see Chapter 1). These groups all have the propensity to trap appropriate substrates covalently under the right conditions in order to form high energy reactive intermediates, which themselves then react before releasing the functional group for a following round of catalytic activity.

8.4.6 Mechanisms of biocatalysis by selected biocatalysts

With reference to the examples of biocatalysts in main Section 8.1, this is a good moment to pause and consider the known mechanisms of these biocatalysts. Intramolecular catalysis and to some extent 'orbital steering' almost certainly make mechanistic contributions to rate enhancements brought about by all the biocatalyst examples mentioned in this chapter. Contributions from induced fit and strain are harder to assess. By contrast, general acid and general base catalysis appear to be employed in a highly selective manner by some biocatalysts to bring about catalytic rate enhancements. The same is true of electrophilic and nucleophilic catalysis. Bovine pancreatic RNAse A and hen egg-white lysozyme are almost archetypical biocatalysts, which employ general acid/general base catalysis with a classical diprotic mechanism that may be analysed by Dixon plots (Figure 8.49). Chicken TIM too makes use of general acid/general base catalysis for rate acceleration (Figure 8.49). Both bovine pancreatic α-chymotrypsin and *T. californica* AChE make use of general acid/general base catalysis and nucleophilic catalysis involving the formation of reactive acyl–enzyme intermediates (Figure 8.50). By contrast, *E. coli* AspAT, *E. coli* GadB and *B. stearothermophilus* AlaR all employ general acid/general base catalysis used in combination with electrophilic catalysis made possible through the provision of the cofactor pyridoxal phosphate (PLP) (Figure 8.51). Finally, ribozymes, human mitochondrial MnSOD, human erythrocyte CA I and even *E. coli* LysU make substantial use of metal-ion-centred electrophilic catalysis to make mechanistic contributions to rate enhancements (Figure 8.52). Having said this, the role of Zn^{2+} in *E. coli* LysU catalysis remains a little controversial. In the illustrated mechanism, the contribution of Zn^{2+} is in N^7–N^7 chelation, increasing the effective concentration of incoming ATP with respect to the lysyl adenylate intermediate. Such a chelate contribution could be considered electrophilic catalysis in one sense, although Zn^{2+} may also have a role to coordinate oxygen attached to the α-phosphate of the lysyl adenylate intermediate in order to encourage nucleophilic attack by incoming ATP as well as or instead of N^7–N^7 chelation (Figure 8.52).

8.4.7 Transition state stabilisation and biocatalysis

A Chapter on biocatalysis is not really complete without introducing the idea of transition state theory and the concept of transition state stabilisation as the most fundamental means in biocatalysis for biocatalysts to effect rate enhancements.

8.4.7.1 Basic transition state concepts

In order for a reaction to take place between two species A and B, both reactants need to meet in a productive collision as a result of which mutual orientations are appropriate for a reaction to occur. Frequently, collisions will be unproductive, leaving the reactants to separate and await the opportunity for a future productive collision. Collisions both productive and unproductive

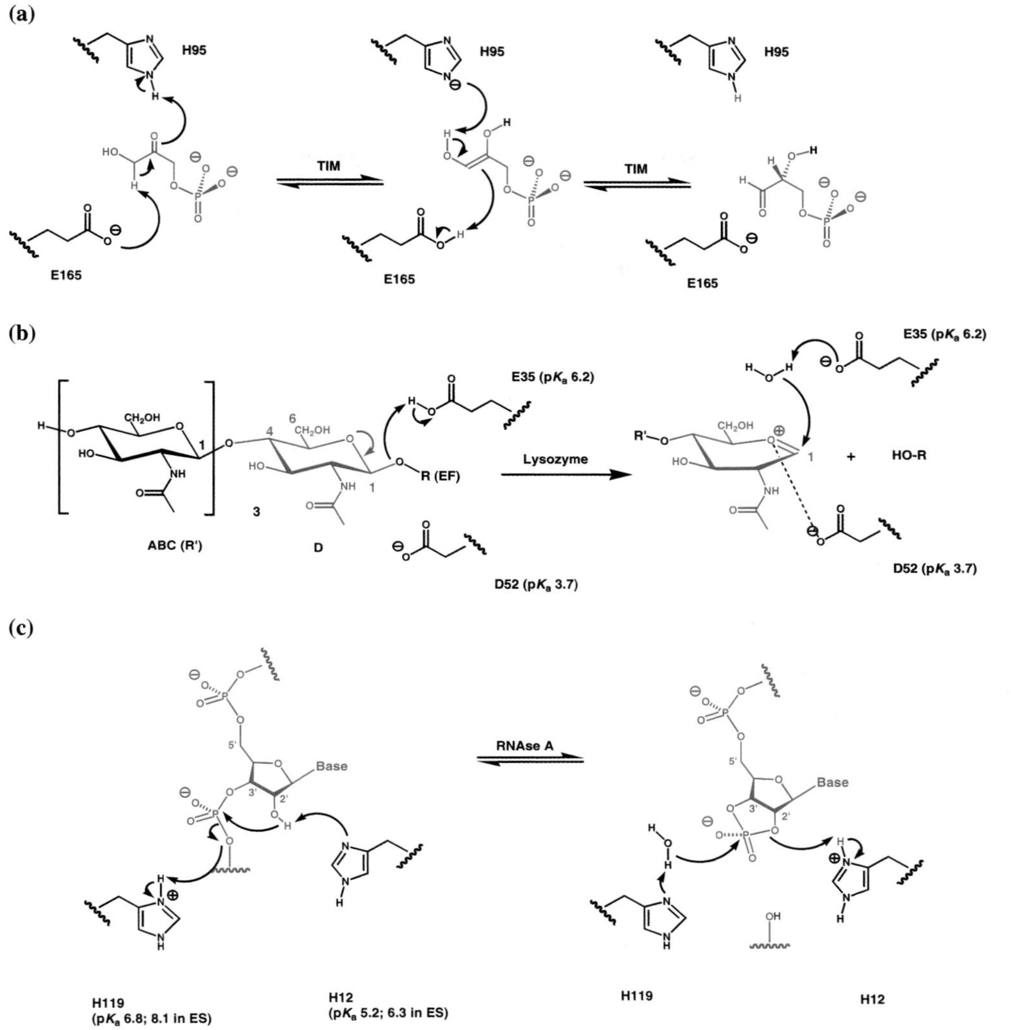

Figure 8.49 Mechanisms of three enzymes that utilise **general acid-base catalysis** as part of their mechanistic paths to successful bio-catalysis. (**a**) triose phosphate isomerase (TIM). (**b**) lysozyme. (**c**) RNAse A. In all cases substrates are shown in red. Lone pair donor amino acid residues are general bases, lone pair acceptor amino acid residues are general acids. Note that pK_a (a commonly used term) is the equivalent of pK_d^A or pK_d^B (as written in this text book) as appropriate for an acidic or basic functional group.

can be appreciated by means of a three-dimensional **potential energy surface** that depicts the mutual potential energy of two reactants as a function of all possible trajectories of approach and separation (Figure 8.53). As a rule, productive collisions are associated with the trajectory, or pathway of minimum potential energy, on the potential energy surface. This is known as the **reaction coordinate**. The point of highest potential energy along a reaction

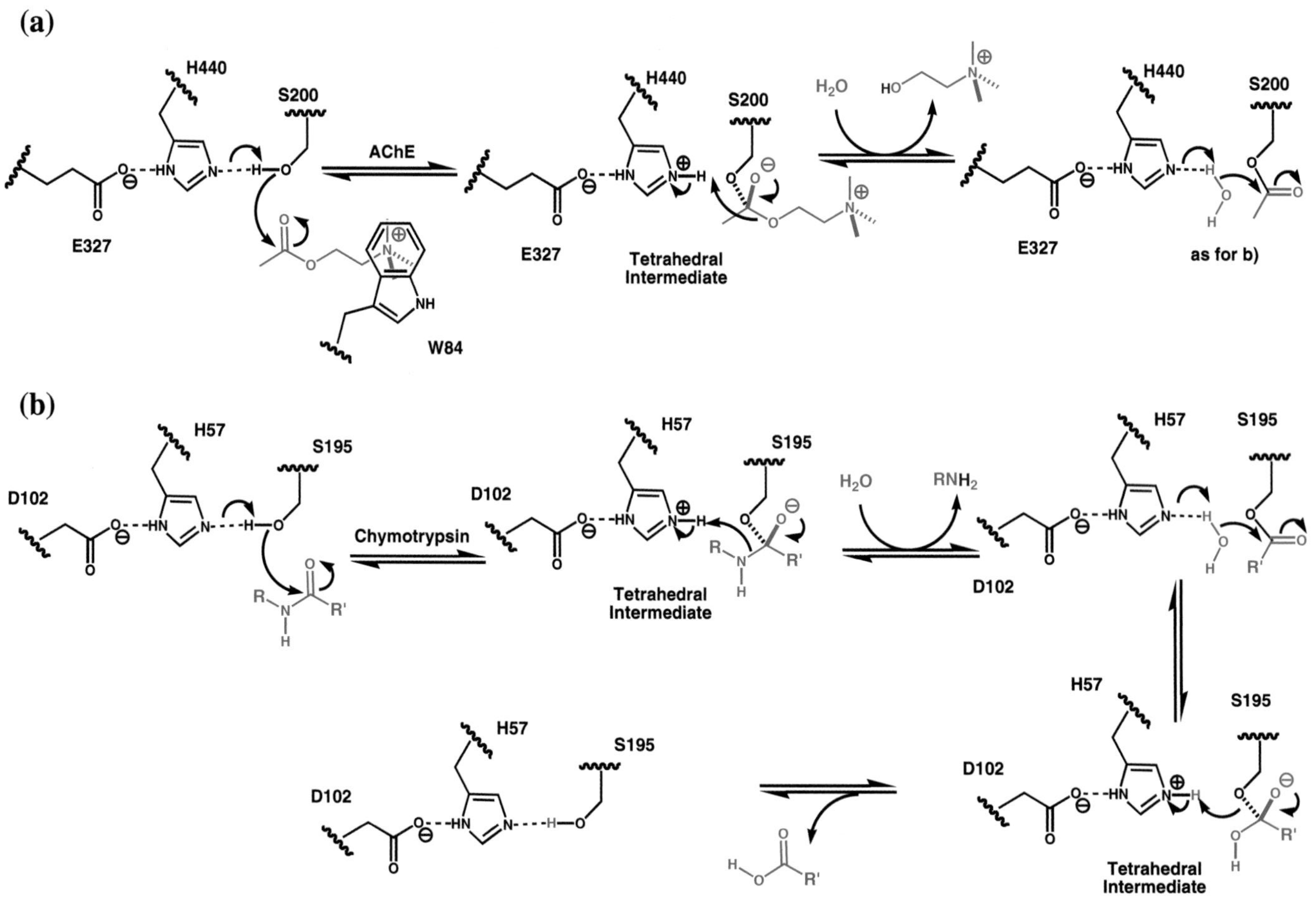

Figure 8.50 Mechanisms for two bio-catalysts that employ **nucleophilic catalysis** as part of their mechanistic paths to successful bio-catalysis. **(a)** acetyl choline esterasase. **(b)** serine protease chymotrypsin. All substrates are shown in red. Nucleophilic catalysis is brought about by appropriate amino acid residues that possess nucleophilic side chains for routine nucleophilic catalysis operations.

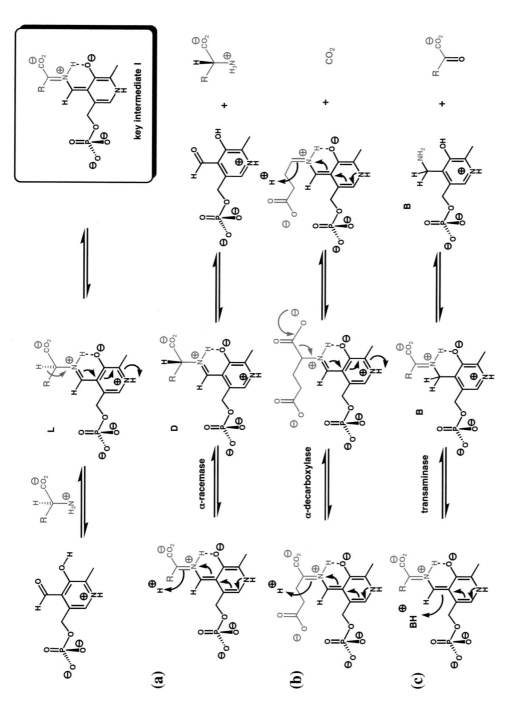

Figure 8.51 Mechanisms of three types of bio-catalyst that employ **electrophilic catalysis** as part of their mechanistic paths to successful bio-catalysis. All substrates are shown in red. Electrophilic catalysis is brought about by the use of **pyridoxal phosphate**, a natural cofactor for electrophilic catalysis operations.

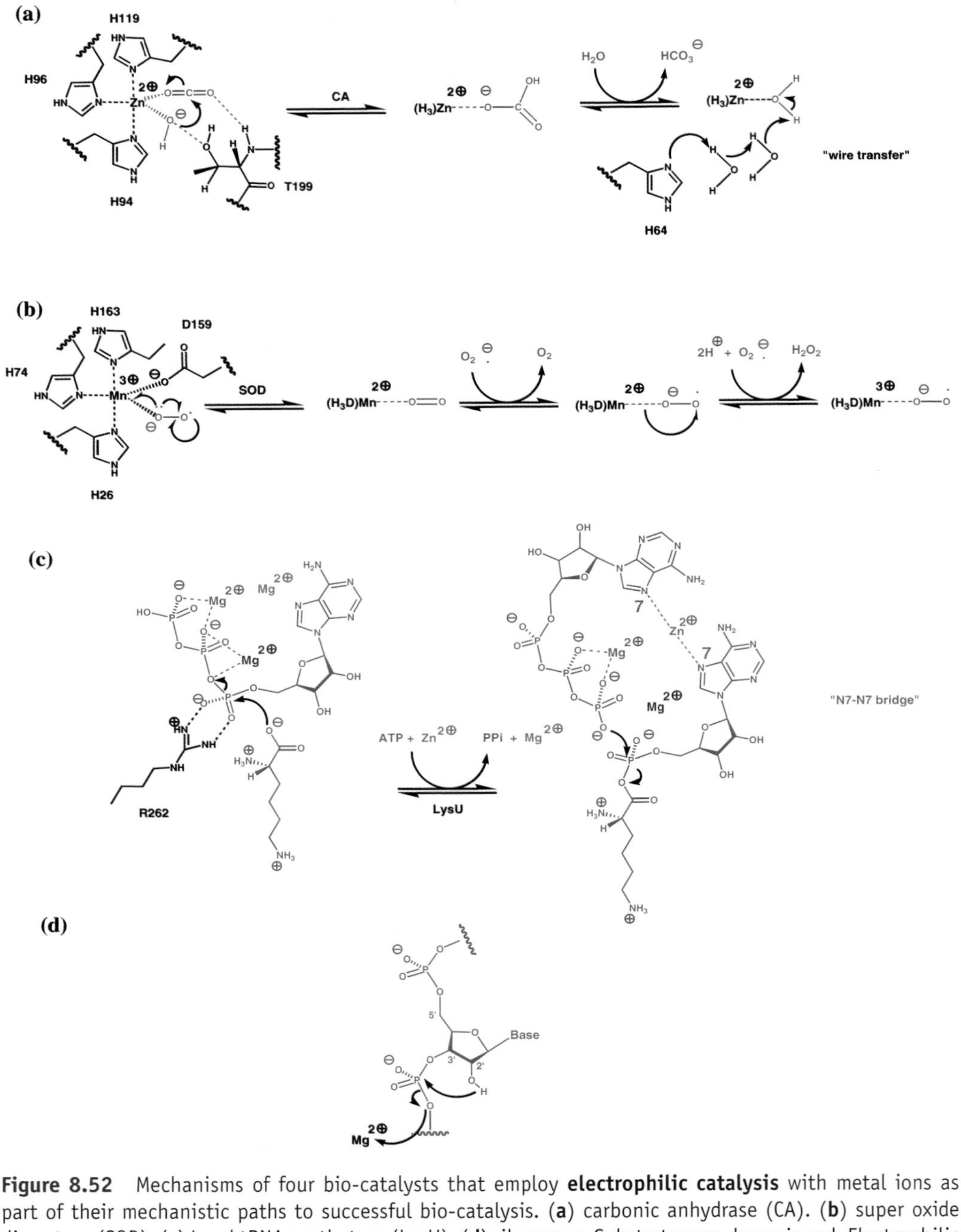

Figure 8.52 Mechanisms of four bio-catalysts that employ **electrophilic catalysis** with metal ions as part of their mechanistic paths to successful bio-catalysis. (**a**) carbonic anhydrase (CA). (**b**) super oxide dismutase (SOD). (**c**) Lysyl tRNA synthetase (LysU). (**d**) ribozymes. Substrates are shown in red. Electrophilic catalysis is brought about in all cases by the use of a critical metal ion such as Zn^{2+}, Mn^{2+} and/or Mg^{2+}.

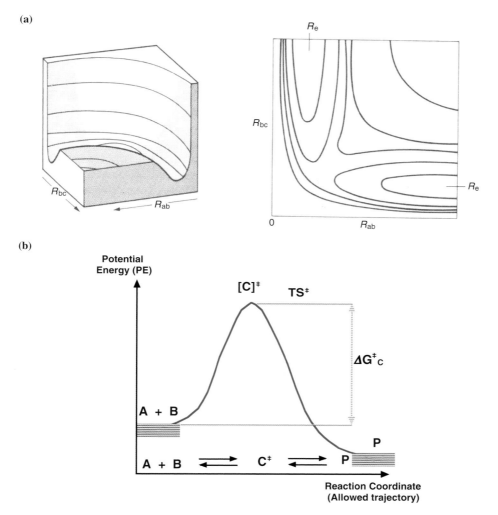

Figure 8.53 Schematic illustrations of **potential energy surface, reaction coordinate** and **transition state**. (**a**) 3D depiction of **potential energy surface-left** and **contour depiction**-right. (**b**) Conversion of species **A** and **B** to **P**, illustrating the **transition state C‡** and **free energy of activation** $\Delta G_c^{\ddagger}$ (illustrations a) and b) Reproduced from Atkins, 1995, Figs. 27.15 & 27.16 respectively).

coordinate is typically a **saddle-point** or **col** in the potential energy surface. This represents the point of highest potential energy in a productive collision between two reactants, and corresponds to the point of maximum molecular reorganisation appropriate for product formation.

Transition state theory or **absolute reaction rate theory** is built upon these ideas of a potential energy surface and reaction coordinate to account for reactivity. The theory seeks to understand and appreciate reactivity in terms of the structure and behaviour of reaction transition states. A **transition state** is defined as a transient, unstable species that is found

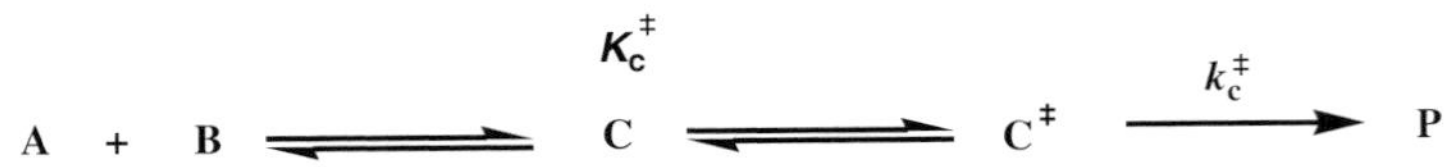

$$K_c^{\ddagger}$$

$$A \;+\; B \; \rightleftharpoons \; C \; \rightleftharpoons \; C^{\ddagger} \; \xrightarrow{\; k_c^{\ddagger} \;} \; P$$

Scheme 8.17

at the energy maximum along a given reaction coordinate (i.e. at the saddle-point in a given potential energy surface) through which reactants must pass for successful conversion to product (Figure 8.53). Given this definition, a transition state can only be formed by reactants if they approach each other along the reaction coordinate. Any other trajectory will not do. In other words, we can redefine a productive collision as one able to generate a transition state and an unproductive collision as one that is unable to generate a transition state. The structure of a given transition state is typically thought to comprise a number of fragile, purely transient high energy bonds that vibrate through the saddle-point at a frequency ν_{TS} in a manner unconstrained by the usual restoring forces found in ground state covalent bonds (see Chapter 4). While the existence of transition states is still the subject of some debate, the idea that there is some form of 'activated complex' formed between reactants that represents a 'gateway to product formation' has been very appealing to chemists for some time and is certainly a powerful aid to understanding biocatalysis as well, as we shall see!

In relating transition state structure and behaviour to reactivity, transition state theory relies on two key assumptions. These are that the absolute rate of reaction depends upon the rate of decomposition of the transition state, and that any transition state is in quasi-equilibrium with its corresponding reactants. Hence, if we consider the most rudimentary of reaction schemes (Figure 8.53, Scheme 8.17), then a simple rate equation may be devised in which rate of formation of product P obeys

$$\mathrm{d}[P]/\mathrm{d}t = k_c^{\ddagger}[C^{\ddagger}] \tag{8.101}$$

The **transition state forward decomposition rate constant** $k_c^{\ddagger}$ can be further defined as the product of two terms:

$$k_c^{\ddagger} = \kappa \nu_{TS} \tag{8.102}$$

where κ is the **transmission coefficient** that represents the mole fraction of transition states formed that progress towards product instead of reverting to reactants. This constant of proportionality acts as a correction for factors such as quantum mechanical tunnelling (see Chapter 6) and solvent friction effects (see Chapter 7). According to transition state theory, k_P the **forward rate constant** of reaction (from reactants A and B) is then defined as the product of $k_c^{\ddagger}$ and the **quasi-equilibrium association constant** $K_c^{\ddagger}$ as shown:

$$k_P = \kappa \nu_{TS} K_c^{\ddagger} \tag{8.103}$$

Customarily, an equilibrium concentration is defined as a ratio of bulk concentrations; however, according to statistical thermodynamics, an equilibrium constant can also be written in terms of **partition functions** that quantify the relative populations of molecules in different states. Hence, the term $K_c^{\ddagger}$ is usually written out as

$$K_c^{\ddagger} = \frac{q^{\ddagger}}{q^A q^B} N_0 \exp\left(-E_0/kT\right)$$

(8.104)

where the q terms are the relevant partition functions, N_0 is Avogadro's number, E_0 is the difference between transition state and reactant ground state zero-point energies and k is the standard Boltzmann constant. The partition function $q^{\ddagger}$ is usually replaced by a product term in which the vibrational motion of the transition state along the reaction coordinate that promotes product formation is separately factored out, giving

$$q^{\ddagger} = q^{\ddagger} \frac{kT}{h\nu_{\text{TS}}}$$

(8.105)

Hence, substituting Equation (8.105) back into (8.104) gives

$$K_c^{\ddagger} = \frac{kT}{h\nu_{\text{TS}}} \frac{q^{\ddagger}}{q^A q^B} N_0 \exp\left(-E_0/kT\right)$$

(8.106)

Further, substituting Equation (8.106) back into Equation (8.103) results in

$$k_{\text{P}} = \kappa \frac{kT}{h} \frac{q^{\ddagger}}{q^A q^B} N_0 \exp\left(-E_0/kT\right)$$

(8.107)

Finally, the quasi-equilibrium statistical thermodynamics part of Equation (8.107) may be substituted for by the standard expression relating equilibrium constant to a standard Gibbs free energy change for the equilibrium (see Chapter 7), with the result that Equation (8.107) may be rewritten as

$$k_{\text{P}} = \kappa \frac{kT}{h} \frac{\exp\left(-\Delta G_0^{\ddagger}/RT\right)}{C_r}$$

(8.108)

where the term $\Delta G_0^{\ddagger}$ is actually a quasi-Gibbs free energy term that is known as the standard **free energy of activation** and represents the quasi-thermodynamic barrier to reaction term C_r is the standard concentration typically 1 M.

8.4.7.2 *Binding energy in biocatalysis*

The concepts of reaction coordinate, transition state and free energy of activation are central to reaching a fundamental understanding of chemical reactivity and also the effects of biocatalysis upon chemical reactivity. Haldane was first to propose that biocatalysts use the energy released from substrate binding to increase reaction rates by *distorting the structures of their substrates towards those of their products*, and in so doing allowing transition states to make more

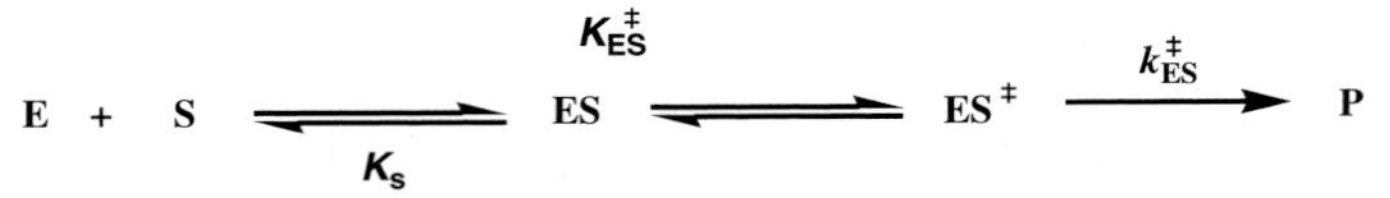

$$E + S \xrightleftharpoons[K_S]{} ES \xrightleftharpoons[]{K_{ES}^\ddagger} ES^\ddagger \xrightarrow{k_{ES}^\ddagger} P$$

Scheme 8.18

favourable contacts with the biocatalyst than substrates. Pauling went on to suggest that the structure of a biocatalyst should be more properly complementary to a transition state rather than a substrate in order to optimise the use of binding energy for catalysis. In any event, both suggestions have at their heart the central idea that the biocatalyst principally acts to catalyse a given reaction by using binding energy to reduce free energy of activation, leading to increases in reaction rate (see Equation (8.108)).

Nowadays, we can be even more explicit! Let us return to a simple kinetic scheme (Scheme 8.18). If the rate of conversion of ES to P is slow, then K_m reduces to K_S, the equilibrium dissociation constant for ES complex. Assuming also that $[S] \gg K_m$, then the binding equilibrium is very much in favour of ES formation (i.e., ES formation is energetically favoured). Together, this allows us to draw a simple reaction coordinate diagram representing the minimum energy pathway for the combination of substrate with biocatalyst followed by the formation of a biocatalyst–transition-state complex, $ES^\ddagger$, from the ground state ES complex (Figure 8.54). Note that the free energy of activation for the biocatalyst-assisted reaction from free E and S is denoted $\Delta G_{ES}^\ddagger$. $\Delta G_{ES}^\ddagger$ is involved in the following sum:

$$\Delta G_T^\ddagger = \Delta G_{ES}^\ddagger - \Delta G_S \tag{8.109}$$

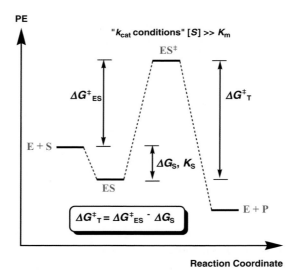

Figure 8.54 Schematic illustration of **reaction coordinate diagram** for the simplest **Uni Uni Kinetic Scheme (Scheme 8.1)** for bio-catalysis. The reaction coordinate profile is drawn under the assumption that excess substrate is present so that k_{cat} **conditions** prevail. Two types of free energy of activation exist, from **E + S** ($\Delta G_{ES}^\ddagger$) and from **ES** ($\Delta G_T^\ddagger$).

where ΔG_S is the **free energy change of substrate binding** associated with the corresponding equilibrium association constant ($1/K_S$; N.B., K_S is an equilibrium dissociation constant) and $\Delta G^{\ddagger}_T$ is the **free energy of activation for the direct conversion of ground state ES into ES‡**.

Conditions where $[S] \gg K_m$ are often known as the 'k_{cat} conditions' of catalysis. When $[S] \gg K_m$ there is no free biocatalyst E at all, hence the first equilibrium effectively disappears and the measured rate constant of reaction, k_P in Equation (8.107), becomes identified directly with the first order Michaelis–Menten term k_{cat} according to Equations (8.1) and (8.9). In a similar way, $\Delta G_0^{\ddagger}$ in Equation (8.108) becomes identified directly with $\Delta G^{\ddagger}_T$ by definition. If both ES and ES‡ are bound equally more effectively by a uniform value ΔG_R (Figure 8.55), then K_S and by implication K_m are reduced, but there is no change in k_{cat}. If ES is bound to

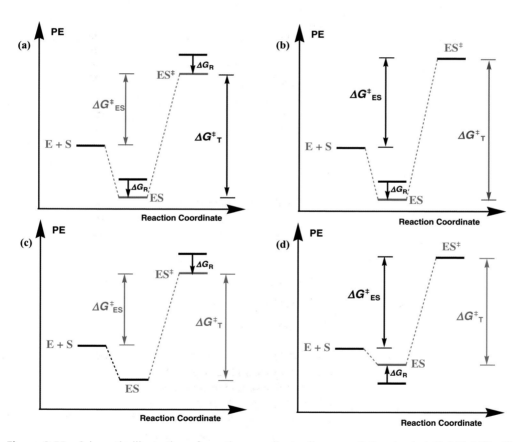

Figure 8.55 Schematic illustration of reaction coordinate diagrams of the simplest **Uni Uni Kinetic Scheme** (**Scheme 8.1**) for bio-catalysis. (**a**) Illustrates the neutral effect of **uniform stabilisation** of **ES** and **ES‡** by $\triangle G_R$. (**b**) The deleterious effect of **differential stabilisation** of **ES** by $\triangle G_R$. (**c**) The optimally beneficial effect of **differential stabilisation** of **ES‡** by $\triangle G_R$. (**d**) The partially beneficial effect of **differential destabilisation** of **ES** by $\triangle G_R$.

an extent ΔG_R more effectively than $ES^{\ddagger}$ then K_m is reduced but there is a fall in k_{cat} too since $\Delta G^{\ddagger}_T$ must increase (Figure 8.55). That is to say that there is an actual reduction in catalytic enhancement! In fact an increase in catalytic enhancement can only occur if $ES^{\ddagger}$ is bound to an extent ΔG_R more effectively than ES, or if ES is bound to an extent ΔG_R less effectively than $ES^{\ddagger}$ (Figure 8.55). In the former case, K_m remains unchanged but k_{cat} is increased while in the latter case K_m increases but k_{cat} is simultaneously increased. In both of these scenarios where differential binding interactions between substrate and transition state are able to bring about catalytic enhancement, then this is known as **catalysis of an elementary step**.

By contrast, conditions where $K_m \gg [S]$ are often known as the 'k_{cat}/K_m **conditions**' of catalysis. When $K_m \gg [S]$ then the binding equilibrium is very much less in favour of ES formation (i.e., ES formation is much less energetically favoured) and free biocatalyst E will be generated. Hence the first equilibrium reappears and the measured rate constant of reaction, k_P in Equation (8.108) becomes identified directly with the second order Michaelis–Menten term k_{cat}/K_m according to Equation (8.11). Furthermore, $\Delta G_0^{\ddagger}$ in Equation (8.108) now becomes identified with $\Delta G_{ES}^{\ddagger}$. The relevant reaction coordinate diagram is illustrated in Figure 8.56. When both ES and $ES^{\ddagger}$ are bound equally more effectively by a uniform value ΔG_R, then K_S and by implication K_m decrease but k_{cat}/K_m increases since $\Delta G^{\ddagger}_{ES}$ is reduced, implying catalytic enhancement (Figure 8.57). When ES is bound to an extent ΔG_R more effectively than $ES^{\ddagger}$, K_m decreases but k_{cat}/K_m remains unchanged (Figure 8.57). If we scrutinise the other two alternatives, then when $ES^{\ddagger}$ is bound to an extent ΔG_R more effectively than ES,

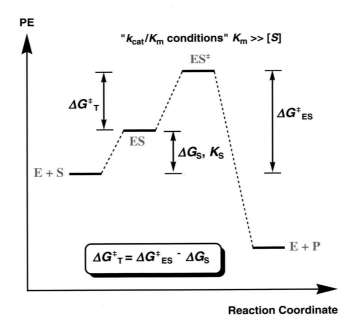

Figure 8.56 Schematic illustration of reaction coordinate diagram for the simplest **Uni Uni Kinetic Scheme** (**Scheme 8.1**) for bio-catalysis. The reaction coordinate profile is drawn under the assumption that substrate is limited so that k_{cat}/K_m **conditions** prevail.

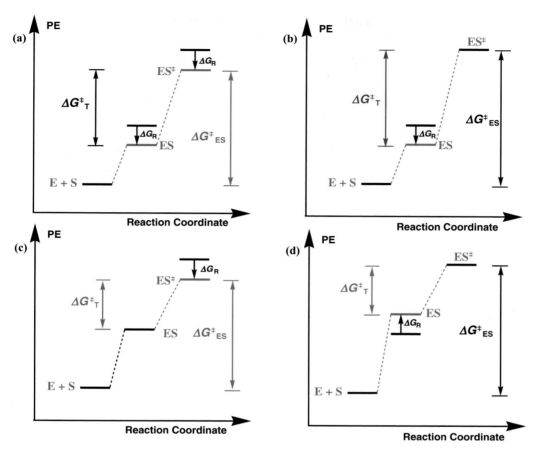

Figure 8.57 Schematic illustration of reaction coordinate diagrams of the simplest **Uni Uni Kinetic Scheme (Scheme 8.1)** for bio-catalysis. (**a**) Illustrates the partially beneficial effect of **uniform stabilisation** of **ES** and **ES‡** by $\triangle G_R$. (**b**) The neutral effect of **differential stabilisation** of **ES** by $\triangle G_R$. (**c**) The optimally beneficial effect of **differential stabilisation** of **ES‡** by $\triangle G_R$. (**d**) The neutral effect of **differential destabilisation** of **ES** by $\triangle G_R$.

K_m remains unchanged but k_{cat}/K_m is increased again. Finally, if ES is bound to an extent $\triangle G_R$ less effectively than ES‡, then K_m increases but k_{cat}/K_m remains constant. A quick comparison between the reaction coordinate analyses for k_{cat} and k_{cat}/K_m conditions (Figures 8.55 and 8.57) shows that only differential binding of the transition state is sufficient to render catalytic enhancement under both conditions of catalysis. Hence, binding energy released through the binding of a substrate or transition state to a biocatalyst can be used in a variety of ways to bring about catalytic enhancement, but the only consistent way to achieve catalytic enhancement under all operating conditions of a biocatalyst is through differential binding of the transition state in preference to binding of the substrate. This is then the purest condition for catalysis of an elementary step, and represents the primary means by which any biocatalyst may bring about reaction catalysis according to transition state theory.

8.4.8 'Perfect biocatalyst' theory

A single biocatalyst is said to reach perfection when k_{cat}/K_m reaches a value of 10^8–10^9 M^{-1} s^{-1}. At this value, the biocatalyst must be catalysing multi-step reactions at the diffusion limit when catalytic rate becomes a matter purely of encounter efficiency between substrate and biocatalyst, or else controlled release of product. At the same time, flux through the chemical inter-conversion pathways must be optimal and cannot be increased. In order to achieve all this, free energy barriers between different chemical species in a biocatalysis pathway must be equivalent in magnitude to each other as well as to the physical free energy barriers associated with either substrate binding or product release. Accordingly, internal equilibrium constants governing the concentrations of different biocatalyst species (comprising bound substrate/product) must also be almost identical in order to avoid accumulation of any one intermediate over another.

In practical terms, taking a simple kinetic scheme (Scheme 8.19), the relative proportions of biocatalyst species ES and EP are critical in order to establish catalytic perfection. According to **Brønsted-type rate–equilibrium relationships** (Section 8.4.4), the relative ratio of ES to EP will have a direct effect upon barrier heights to the transition state ES‡ in both directions and hence the catalysis of an elementary step. Therefore, when a biocatalyst is operating in the presence of equilibrium concentrations of substrate S and product P, the optimal internal equilibrium constant K_{int} should be unity (i.e., ES and EP are iso-energetic) to ensure that the conversion between S and P is diffusion limited. When operating far from equilibrium, K_{int} is adjusted so that the rate of chemical transformation matches the rate of release of product P, ensuring that only the rate of release of product P determines the rate of catalysis and not the chemical transformation step. The protein biocatalyst or enzyme triose phosphate isomerase (TIM) is notable for having catalytic characteristics close to perfection. The appearance of a rate determining product release step and a value of $K_{int} \approx 1$ are illustrated by the known TIM reaction coordinate diagram linking free substrate with released product (Figure 8.58). Most other biocatalysts are not perfect, but are usually adequate biocatalysts for the biological niche in which they are required to operate.

8.4.9 Linear free energy relationships

Linear free energy relationships derive from so-called Brønsted-type rate–equilibrium relationships and represent a potentially useful tool for unlocking the topography of the reaction

$$\text{E} + \text{S} \rightleftharpoons \text{ES} \rightleftharpoons \text{EP} \rightleftharpoons \text{E} + \text{P}$$

Scheme 8.19

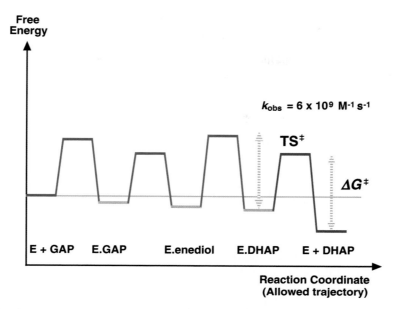

Figure 8.58 Schematic illustration of **reaction coordinate diagram** of Triose Phosphate Isomerase (TIM) enzyme illustrating near perfect energy landscape pathway allowing for near perfect 1:1:1 stoichiometric equilibrium between all enzyme-bound species optimal for flux through from one enzyme-bound species to another. Enzyme turnover rate **k_{obs}** is at the diffusion limit, the rate determining step is the association of **dihydroxy acetone phosphate** (**DHAP**) with the TIM catalytic site, see **Fig. 8.1**, hence chemistry is not rate limiting. Therefore, TIM is considered a perfect enzyme! For TIM enzyme assay see **Fig. 8.17**; for TIM enzyme mechanism see **Fig. 8.49** (illustration adapted from Knowles, 1991, Fig. 2).

coordinate or '**energy landscape**' linking a sequence of equilibrated biocatalyst species of the type described above (Section 8.4.8). The critical idea is encapsulated in the following equation:

$$k_n = A K_{eq,n}^{\beta} \tag{8.110}$$

where k_n is the rate constant for a given conversion step of interest between adjacent biocatalyst species in a catalytic pathway while $K_{eq,n}$ represents the related equilibrium constant defining the concentration relationship between either two ground state species or a ground state and a transition state species (see Section 8.4.7). The power term β is known as a **Brønsted coefficient** or '**beta value**'. In the event that k_n varies according to substrate/product structure or even according to variations in biocatalyst structure (such as changes in amino-acid sequence in an enzyme), there is always the possibility that the linked variations of k_n and $K_{eq,n}$ values will obey the following linear relationship:

$$\log(k_n) = \text{const} + \beta \log(K_{eq,n}) \tag{8.111}$$

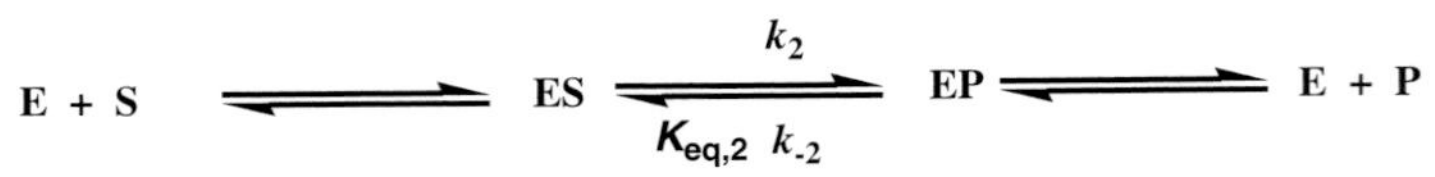

$$E + S \rightleftharpoons ES \underset{K_{eq,2} \; k_{-2}}{\overset{k_2}{\rightleftharpoons}} EP \rightleftharpoons E + P$$

Scheme 8.20

The implications of linearity can be explained quite simply. Consider the catalytic pathway in Scheme 8.20, in which E corresponds to an enzyme. Assume that values of $K_{eq,2}$ and k_2 have been measured by pre-steady-state kinetic analyses for the wild-type enzyme E together with the values for a variety of point mutant enzymes wherein the amino-acid residue change takes place at one residue position and most changes influence catalytic rate k_2 at least to some extent. Provided that a plot of values of $K_{eq,2}$ and k_2 is linear, then the gradient β may be determined for the conversion of ES to EP (Figure 8.59). Taking into account the standard relationship between a rate constant such as k_2 and the standard free energy of activation, see Equation (8.108), then we could say that β represents the fractional change in binding energy for the conversion of ES to EP. For instance, if β is $+0.8$, then 80% of the binding energy is realised in the transition state, $ES^{\ddagger}$, for the conversion of ES to EP, and as a result EP also closely resembles $ES^{\ddagger}$ in energy and structure. More specifically, we could say that 80% of the binding energy generated by interactions between the specific amino-acid residue position and substrate is realised in binding the transition state. Clearly, the maximum possible value for β is $+1.0$. Under these circumstances, 100% of the binding energy generated by interactions between the specific amino-acid residue position and substrate is realised in binding the transition state only and hence interactions between the specific amino-acid residue position and the substrate ground state are negligible! This is almost the perfect situation for catalysis of an elementary step!

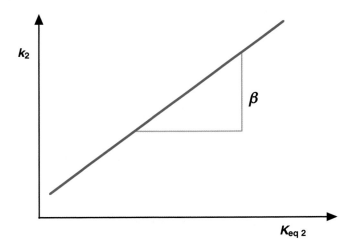

Figure 8.59 Schematic illustration of a **linear free energy relationship**.

8.5 Electron transfer

Traditionally in electron transfer reactions, there is an electron donor species D and an electron acceptor species A. D and A are usually brought together by diffusion with the assistance of long range electrostatic forces (see Chapter 7). Thereafter, short range forces ensure molecular recognition and binding in order to optimise electron transfer rates through the formation of a **specific encounter complex** (DA). Electron transfer then takes place prior to separation.

8.5.1 Electron transfer kinetics

The corresponding kinetic scheme is as illustrated in Scheme 8.21. This kinetic scheme bears some similarity to the simplest kinetic scheme and hence the simplest Briggs–Haldane steady state kinetics treatment can usefully apply on the assumption that the donor species D is in excess (i.e., $[D] \gg [A]$) and so is constant during the progress of the reaction. In this case, we can make the assumption that acceptor species A behaves in an equivalent manner to a biocatalyst substrate and donor species D to the biocatalyst itself at a fixed total concentration of $[D]_0$. Hence, Equation (8.6) neatly transforms into

$$\frac{v}{[D]_0} = \frac{k_{ET}[A]}{\left(k_{ET} + {k_{-1}}/{k_1}\right) + [A]} \tag{8.112}$$

where the term k_2 in Equation (8.6) is replaced by the equivalent term k_{ET} in Equation (8.112) that is the rate constant for the actual electron transfer step, about which more later! Term $v/[D]_0$ represents the rate of the total electron transfer process described by the kinetic scheme above. Equation (8.112) neatly rearranges to

$$\frac{v}{[D]_0} = \frac{k_1 k_{ET}[A]}{k_{ET} + k_{-1} + k_1[A]} \tag{8.113}$$

At the extreme where $k_{ET} \gg k_{-1} + k_1[A]$, Equation (8.113) reduces to

$$\frac{v}{[D]_0} = k_1[A] \tag{8.114}$$

$$D + A \underset{k_{-1}}{\overset{k_1}{\rightleftharpoons}} (DA) \xrightarrow{k_{ET}} (\overset{\oplus}{D}\overset{\ominus}{A}) \longrightarrow \overset{\oplus}{D} + \overset{\ominus}{A}$$

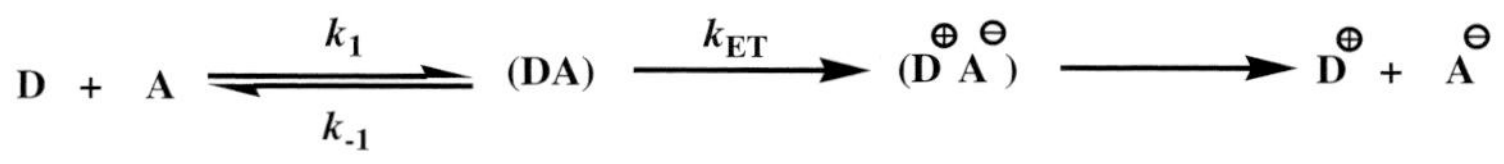

Scheme 8.21

This equation corresponds to the situation when the rate of the total electron transfer process is said to be at the diffusion limit, and so is as perfect as possible! At another extreme where $k_{-1} \gg k_{ET} + k_1[A]$ Equation (8.113) reduces to

$$\frac{\nu}{[D]_0} = \frac{k_1 k_{ET}[A]}{k_{-1}} = K_{a,DA} k_{ET}[A] \tag{8.115}$$

where $K_{a,DA}$ is the **equilibrium association constant** (k_1/k_{-1}) that **governs the association binding equilibrium between acceptor species A and donor species D**. At this extreme, the rate of the total electron transfer process is said to be activation controlled with a reaction pre-equilibrium. That is, the reaction rate depends partly upon the rate of the actual electron transfer step that is associated with a free energy of activation, and the equilibrium association between acceptor species A and donor species D.

8.5.2 Electron transfer step

The actual electron transfer step is enormously complex since such a process goes right to the heart of the quantum mechanical description of atoms and molecules. Therefore, we are going to keep the discussion as simple as possible here! For instance, in chemical biology we only need be concerned by electron transfer processes involving transfers within or between proteins in which the actual electron transfer processes take place between redox-active prosthetic groups and/or redox-active amino-acid residues (usually tyrosine). Redox-active prosthetic groups are many and various, varying from the haem system of cytochrome c (see Chapter 1) through to varieties of iron–sulphur clusters, blue copper complexes and flavins (see Chapter 4). Multiple assemblies of redox-active prosthetic groups are also found embedded in the enormous protein assemblies that make up the photosynthesis photosystems in many plants.

The great paradox of electron transfer processes involving redox-active prosthetic groups embedded in proteins is that these electron transfer processes are able to take place without any one redox-active prosthetic group/amino-acid residue making direct contact one with another. In fact, the central theme of biological electron transfer is that the redox-active centres are 'insulated' one from another by 'polypeptide walls' that are usually several Å thick. Electron transfer takes place without the formation of intermediate protein excited states so that there is no sense in which polypeptide walls facilitate electron transfer by acting as electronic conductors. Instead, these electron transfer processes involve primarily long range electron tunnelling (see Chapter 6) between localised donor and acceptor redox-active centres. Under these circumstances, the rate constant k_{ET} for the actual electron transfer step is then defined by the following equation, known as the **Fermi equation**:

$$k_{ET} = \frac{2\pi}{\hbar} |T_{DA}|^2 (FC) \tag{8.116}$$

where the modulus squared $|T_{DA}|^2$ is the **equivalent of the square of an electronic wave-function** and is a measure of frontier orbital overlap between linked redox-active donor and

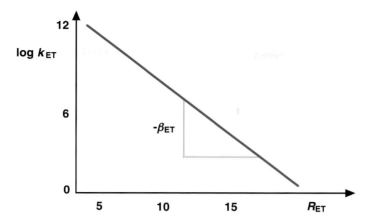

Figure 8.60 Schematic illustration of the inverse linear relationship between **electron transfer rates** and **edge-to-edge distances** R_{ET} between redox-active donor and acceptor groups.

acceptor centres, while (FC) is known as the **Franck–Condon term** and is a measure of overlap between the nuclear wavefunctions of linked donor and acceptor centres. Note how the equation separates the dependency of the electron transport rate constant into electronic and nuclear overlap terms. This apparently complex equation may be simplified by the following proportionality:

$$|T_{DA}|^2 \propto \exp\left(-\beta_{ET} R_{ET}\right) \tag{8.117}$$

that converts into the following equation by amalgamation with Equation (8.116):

$$\log k_{ET} = C - \beta_{ET} R_{ET} \tag{8.118}$$

where R_{ET} is the **edge-to-edge distance between redox-active donor and acceptor groups** while β_{ET} is known as the '**beta value**' for electron transfer. When $\log k_{ET}$ values measured for electron transfers between redox-active donor and acceptor groups embedded in proteins are plotted as a function of the R_{ET} distance between them, then the result is a straight line function over a separation range of 20 Å, encompassing values of k_{ET} distributed over 12 orders of magnitude (Figure 8.60). The resulting beta value is 1.4 Å^{-1}, a little more than the value of 1.2 Å^{-1} found for electron transfers through glassy solvents. In other words, all polypeptide walls of whatever thickness, whether comprised of one or more polypeptide backbones, behave in a similar way to a glassy solvent. Undeniably a beautifully simple approximation!

9
Mass Spectrometry and Proteomics

9.1 Mass spectrometry in chemical biology

Mass spectrometry is a technique with origins in the physical sciences that has fast become one of the most powerful techniques available for probing biological systems. Advances in mass spectrometry made possible by the advent of **soft ionisation techniques** have made possible detailed investigations into the primary structures of biological macromolecules and amphiphilic lipids. Indeed, mass spectrometry could be seen as the pre-eminent technique for determining the primary structures of polypeptides, nucleic acids, and complex carbohydrates owing to the possibility of obtaining molecular mass and sequence information using minute quantities of material (femtomole–picomole, even attomole levels). Such information can be obtained without even the need for recombinant technologies (see Chapter 3). Hence, although three-dimensional information is not directly available by mass spectrometry, impressive amounts of primary structural information are nevertheless available that can be integrated with other pieces of information to try and provide useful insights into biological macromolecular structure without the need for analyses of the type presented in Chapters 5 and 6. However, nowadays, mass spectrometry is also known to be essentially indispensable to the field of **proteomics**, defined as the study of all the interactions and implied functions of all the proteins expressed from a genome. Chemical biology and multidisciplinary thinking have very much driven the development of proteomics – from the development of suitable mass spectrometric methods for large scale protein identification, to the development of suitable chromatographic systems to map out protein networks (Figure 9.1). In other words, mass spectrometry not only gives us primary structures but also has the capacity to define complex, functional, three-dimensional networks of interacting proteins and polypeptides within cells. Mass spectrometry quite simply lifts us from the opportunity to make detailed investigations into the structures and functions of certain biological macromolecules of interest

Essentials of Chemical Biology   Andrew Miller and Julian Tanner
© 2008 John Wiley & Sons, Ltd

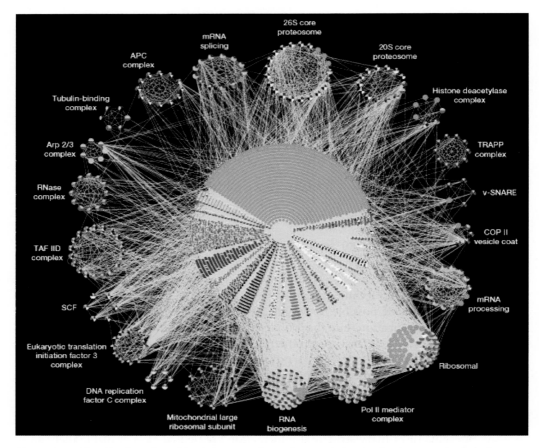

Figure 9.1 Visualisation of combined datasets of protein-protein interaction in yeast. A total of 14,000 physical interactions obtained from the **GRID database** were represented with the **Osprey network visualization** system (see http://biodata.mshri.on.ca/grid). Each edge in the graph represents an interaction between nodes, which are coloured according to **Gene Ontology** (**GO**) functional annotation. Highly connected complexes within the data set, shown at the perimeter of the central mass, are built from nodes that share at least three interactions within other complex members. The complete graph contains 4,543 nodes of 6,000 proteins encoded by the yeast genome, 12,843 interactions and an average connectivity of 2.82 per node. The 20 highly connected complexes contain 340 genes, 1,835 connections and an average connectivity of 5.39 (Reproduced from Tyers and Mann, 2003, Fig. 2).

to the opportunity to study interactions in multi-protein complexes and beyond to networks of protein–protein interactions, which determine not just molecular function but also cellular function. Hence, there should be no doubt that any discussion on mass spectrometry should follow those Chapters 7 and 8 that deal with individualised functions for biological macromolecules of interest. In this chapter we present mass spectrometry to enable the move from individual to collective molecular structure and function analyses that must surely be an ultimate goal for chemical biology research.

9.2 Key principles in mass spectrometry

Mass spectrometry involves the ionisation of individual molecules in the gas/vapour phase followed by their differentiation and detection according to mass/charge (m/z) ratio. Typically, z is unity so the ratio is equivalent to mass. Accordingly, mass spectrometry was used primarily to determine molecular weight precisely from the identification of the **molecular ion** ($[M]^+$). Fortuitously, ions in gas phase are able to undergo decomposition reactions (spontaneous) leading to **fragment ions** ($[M - x]^+$) that could be used to identify elements of structure. In instrumental terms, a mass spectrometer consists of three basic components: an ionisation source, a mass analyser and the detector (Figure 9.2). The molecules must first be passed into the gas phase as ionic species by the **ionisation source** so that their flight may be manipulated. The flight takes place under high vacuum so that the ions are able to avoid colliding or interacting with other species. A **mass analyser** separates the ions for detection according to their m/z ratio. The **detector** measures both the abundance (a function of the signal) and m/z (a function of physical property and/or time) of detected ions.

Mass spectrometry has a long history in chemistry, using classic methods of ionisation such as electron bombardment or chemical ionisation to analyse the molecular weights of small molecules, although neither technique was actually applicable for the mass analysis of biological macromolecules or lipid amphiphiles. However, the development of **fast atom bombardment (FAB) mass spectrometry** in the early 1980s brought the mass analysis of oligo- and polypeptides into the sphere of mass spectrometry. Thereafter, the development of **matrix-assisted laser desorption ionisation (MALDI)** and e**lectrospray ionisation (ESI) mass spectrometry** set up extensive possibilities for the mass analysis of nearly all biological macromolecules and lipid amphiphiles. Hence, the focus of the chemical biology reader is naturally drawn to these three main soft ionisation techniques and how these are then linked with appropriate mass analyser and detector units to derive mass spectrometers appropriate for biological macromolecule and amphiphilic lipid characterisation.

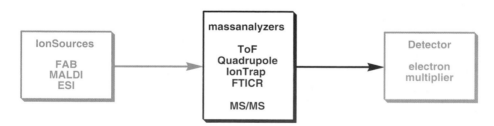

Figure 9.2 The basic components of a mass spectrometer. All mass spectrometers consist of an **ion source** linked to a **mass analyser** then to a detector. The important ion sources and mass analysers for biological mass spectrometry are listed. There are many other potential ion sources and mass analysers used generally in mass spectrometry, but only the indicated are of use in the analysis of biological macromolecules and amphiphilic lipids, and also in proteomics; **FAB: fast atom bombardment; MALDI: matrix-assisted laser desorption and ionization; ESI: electrospray ionization; ToF: time of flight; FTICR: fourier transform ion cyclotron resonance; MS/MS: tandem mass spectrometry.**

9.2.1 Ionisation sources

9.2.1.1 Traditional techniques of ionisation

Electron ionisation (EI) is the most widespread technique of ionisation used for mass spectrometry in synthetic chemistry. EI consists of two steps: first, the sample of a molecule of interest is passed into the **vapour phase** before being bombarded, second with with a stream of electrons. Should the energy of the colliding electron exceed the ionisation energy of the molecule then an electron will be displaced, resulting in a positively charged molecule ion $[M]^+$ (radical cation). Since the mass of an electron is negligible, then the observed mass of $[M]^+$ must correlate with the molecular mass. Excess collisional energy encourages spontaneous fragmentation and fragment ion $[M - x]^+$ formation, from which information the structure of the molecule of interest (analyte) may be deduced at least in part. EI remains a useful technique for the analysis of small molecules (<1000 Da) but has some significant drawbacks. First, fragmentation is often so widespread that the molecular ion cannot be observed. Second, neither thermally labile compounds nor non-volatile compounds can be analysed by this ionisation technique, which is too high energy (i.e. **hard**) for mass analysis of either biological macromolecules or lipid amphiphiles.

Chemical ionisation (CI) was developed as a technique to complement EI wherein the ionisation method was not quite so hard. In this technique a reagent gas at a partial pressure significantly greater than that of a sample analyte molecule of interest in the vapour phase is ionised with a beam of electrons (Figure 9.3). The ionised reagent gas then combines with the analyte molecule of interest to form **stable molecule–ion adducts**: the *m/z* ratio may be measured and the adduct mass accounted for during analysis. A number of different reagent gases may be used for this purpose, such as hydrogen, methane, water, methanol, ethanol or ammonia – the extent of fragmentation can be controlled by the choice of reagent gas to an extent. Although CI has some advantages over EI to the extent that the fragmentation is more controlled (although EI would hold the advantage of being able to provide more detailed structural information), this ionisation technique remains a hard technique that has similar drawbacks to EI regarding non-volatile compounds, so is only suitable for the analysis of compounds of <1000 Da.

9.2.1.2 Desorption ionisation techniques – FAB and MALDI

Virtually all desorption ionisation methods share the same approach to ionisation: the analyte molecule of interest is combined with/dissolved in a matrix before being bombarded with high energy particles or light, resulting in the production of a high concentration of solvated gas phase neutral or ionic species just above the point of impact. After the impact of the beam, vaporisation occurs before thermal decomposition so that ions are able to 'escape' the impact region before fragmentation begins. The original desorption ionisation techniques included **field desorption** (**FD**) and **plasma desorption**. In FD, ions were desorbed directly into the vapour phase by means of an extremely strong electric field – the field lowers the barrier to removal of an electron from the molecule by **quantum mechanical tunnelling**,

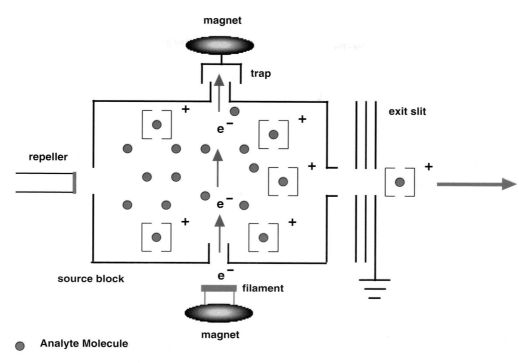

Figure 9.3 Schematic of **chemical ionization**. A reagent gas is present in the source block and is initially ionized by a beam of electrons, which then interacts with sample **analyte molecules** also in the vapour phase to form **stable molecular ion adducts** that are repelled into the mass analyzer. The mass of the reagent gas adduct must be corrected for during the analysis.

leaving a radical cation molecular ion $[M]^+$. Although FD spectrometry was successful for the mass analysis of non-volatile compounds, the technique was not particularly popular due to difficulties experienced in making reproducible emitter electrodes to enable ionisation. The need for softer, more versatile ionisation techniques was obvious.

The first of these versatile soft ionisation techniques to be developed was the technique of FAB, which is also a desorption technique. FAB makes use of a fast stream of argon or xenon atoms to strike the analyte molecule of interest dissolved in a liquid matrix (typically glycerol) (Figure 9.4). This fast stream of inert gas atoms is created by electron bombardment of inert gas atoms to generate ions that are accelerated through a potential difference. The fast moving ions are then converted to atoms by a cloud of excess neutral gas atoms that neutralise these ions by an electron transfer process (residual ions are deflected by a potential field before they are able to strike the matrix). Impact of the fast moving large atoms with the matrix causes a number of ions to be sputtered from the sample including the molecular ions $[M + H]^+$ or $[M - H]^-$. If FAB is run in the **positive ion mode**, then the protonated molecular ion and cationic fragment ions are picked up and mass analysed. If the **negative ion mode** is used, then only the deprotonated molecular ion and anionic fragment ions will be mass analysed.

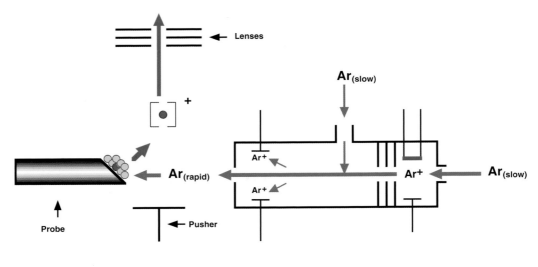

Figure 9.4 Schematic of **Fast Atom Bombardment**. A stream of inert atoms (argon or xenon) strike a probe target on which **analyte molecules** of interest are dissolved in a liquid matrix (frequently **glycerol**). The fast stream of inert atoms is created by electron bombardment of inert atoms to create ions that are accelerated by a potential difference. Kinetic energy is transferred from ions to more inert atoms leading to the stream of fast atoms that act to sputter molecular and fragment ion species into the vapour phase for mass analysis.

In the positive ion mode, Na^+ and K^+ molecular ion adducts (i.e., $[M + Na]^+$ or $[M + K]^+$) are also seen frequently.

Irrespective of mode, fragmentation is also observed that is usually well balanced with respect to molecular ion intensity, so FAB mass spectrometry can also be used to gain insight into the structure of the analyte molecule of interest. One of the main reasons for this is that FAB mass spectra can be acquired over timescales of minutes, during which time molecular ion and fragment ion intensities can be sustained and even increase. The reason for this is the nature of the matrix. The matrix plays an important role in FAB mass spectrometry, absorbing the excess energy of the atomic bombardment and replenishing the matrix surface with analyte molecules of interest during the collision process. Viscous, non-volatile liquids such as glycerol are favoured FAB mass spectral matrices, but occasionally other matrices are useful. FAB mass spectrometry has proved very useful for the mass analysis of amphiphilic lipids and smaller biological macromolecules (or fragments thereof) of <4000 Da, comprising short polysaccharides, short polypeptides, and oligodeoxy- or oligonucleotides.

MALDI represents an important technical development on FAB. In MALDI, the analyte molecule of interest is dispersed in a crystalline, not liquid, matrix and the beam of fast atoms is replaced by laser irradiation. The analyte is pre-mixed with a matrix material and crystals are then placed on a solid surface (Figure 9.5). Nanosecond laser pulses sublime the matrix

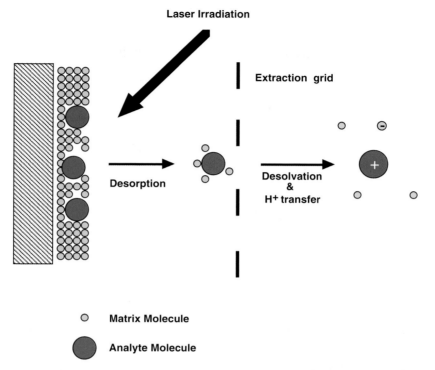

Figure 9.5 Schematic of **Matrix Assisted Laser Desorption Ionisation (MALDI).** The laser is fired at the sample analyte of interest admixed with a **crystalline matrix** that readily absorbs laser energy and allows the sputtering of analyte into the vapour phase in association with matrix molecules of solvation. Desolvation and proton transfer leads to naked **molecular ion species**, ready for mass analysis.

together with the analyte molecule of interest. Thereafter, the matrix absorbs most of the laser energy, preventing excessive breakdown of the analyte during sublimation and subsequent ionisation, so ensuring a significant molecular ion population in the vapour phase. The crystalline matrix plays two other important supporting roles in MALDI. First, the matrix actually solvates the analyte, hence reducing aggregation of the analyte molecule and thereby promoting molecular ion formation in the vapour phase. Second, matrices have been identified with specific characteristics for specific applications (Figure 9.6). The most commonly used matrix used for the mass analysis of oligo-/polypeptides and for peptide fingerprinting is α-**cyano-4-hydroxycinnamic acid** (**CHCA**). **Sinapinic acid** (**SA**) is often used as the matrix of choice for the mass analysis of proteins, **hydroxypicolinic acid** (**HPA**) for oligonucleotides and oligodeoxynucleotides, **di-2,5-hydroxybenzoic acid** (**DHB**) for oligosaccharides and **5-hydroxy-2-methoxybenzoic acid** (**HMB**) for lipids. MALDI is sufficiently soft and versatile as an ionisation technique to allow for the observation of the molecular ions of even very large biological macromolecules, approaching 10^6 Da, when using an appropriate version of MALDI mass spectrometry.

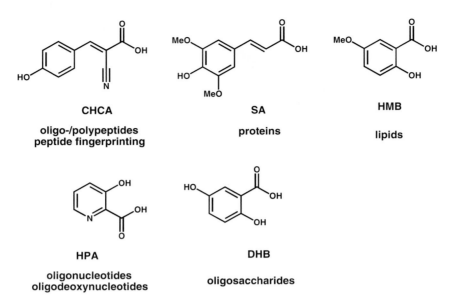

Figure 9.6 Summary of main MALDI **matrices** matched with the analytes most widely mass analyzed with the assistance of each of these different matrix materials.

9.2.1.3 Spray ionisation techniques – thermospray and electrospray

Spray ionisation techniques solve many of the problems of how to pass liquid solutions into the gas phase. As these techniques all take samples from the liquid phase, these are the ones most easily coupled to a liquid chromatography system. Unlike desorption techniques described above, these techniques take place at ambient pressure rather than in a vacuum. One of the first spray ionisation techniques to be reported was **thermospray ionisation** (**TI**). This technique is best suited to volatile compounds of < 1000 Da, so has no role for biological macromolecule of amphiphilic lipid mass analysis, but the technique is illustrative. TI involves passing a solution containing the analyte molecule of interest through a heated capillary; the rapid expansion and cooling of the liquid results in the ejection, from the end of a capillary, of a superheated mist containing a mixture of tiny droplets together with analyte molecules in the vapour phase. Sprayed droplets have a tendency to become charged, allowing molecular ions to develop for onward mass analysis. Thermospray is a useful ionisation technique for the analysis of small oligopeptides, dinucleotides and dideoxynucleotides, small oligosaccharides and other small organic molecules.

ESI is the large molecule upgrade of TI. ESI was developed as an elaboration of the **atmospheric pressure chemical ionisation** (**APCI**) technique. In the case of ESI, a solution containing the analyte molecule of interest is passed through a capillary to which is applied a potential difference of 3–16 kV, producing a significant electrostatic field around the tip of the capillary that aids in molecular ion generation (Figure 9.7). As the solution leaves the end of the capillary, the electrostatic field enables the generation of a 'spray' of droplets.

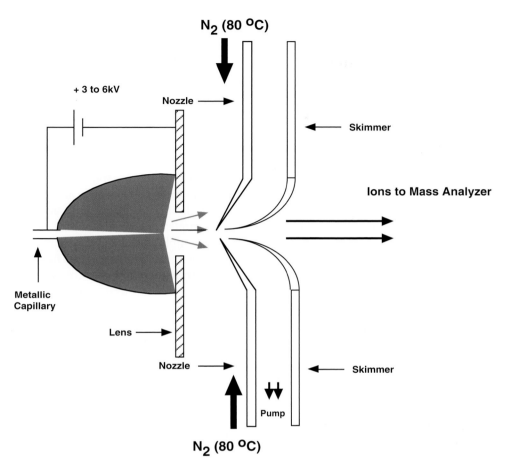

Figure 9.7 Schematic of **Electrospray ionization.** A "spray" of droplets is formed that evaporate until the destabilizing electrostatic forces cause the droplets to "explode" releasing **multi-charged molecular ion** species for mass analysis.

Two forces then determine the stability of the droplet. First, droplet surface tension acts to maintain droplet integrity. Second, electrostatic forces in the analyte act to disintegrate the droplet. Hence, as droplets evaporate, destructive electrostatic forces increase until droplets 'explode', releasing molecular ions and fragments ions for mass analysis. Unusually in the case of the ESI technique, analyte ions may be multiply charged. For instance, biological macromolecules such as proteins frequently produce molecular ion series of the form $[M + zH]^{z+}$ or $[M - zH]^{z-}$. As with FAB, so with ESI both positive and negative ion modes are available using this technique, hence the cationic molecular ion series can be observed in the positive ion mode and the anionic molecular ion series in the negative ion mode. A main advantage of multiple ion series is that, while actual values of m/z are within range of the mass analysis, true molecular ion weights can be orders of magnitude greater. Hence, ESI opens up the possibility for mass analysis of very large biological macromolecules, indeed of at least 10^6 Da in molecular weight.

9.2.2 Mass analysers in mass spectrometry

Soft ionisation devices for FAB, MALDI and ESI are the front end of the modern mass spectrometer used by the chemical biology researcher. Clearly, these devices need to be associated with mass analysers for the resolution and subsequent detection of molecular and fragment ions. The traditional EI mass spectrometer relied upon the use of different combinations of electric and magnetic sectors to perturb ion motion *in vacuo* through arc trajectories that were a function of ion mass, velocity and net charge. Such mass analysers were large and unwieldy, making mass analysis instrumentation highly specialised. Nowadays, the provision of soft ionisation devices has opened the door for much less complex mass analysers that considerably reduce instrument specialisation in favour of more complex experiments. There are four major types of mass analyser of most importance to the chemical biology reader. These are the **time of flight (TOF)**, **quadrupole**, **ion trap** and **Fourier transform ion cyclotron resonance (FTICR)** analysers. These mass analyser devices are linked to a soft ionisation device either singly or in tandem in certain optimal combinations as described below.

9.2.2.1　*Time of flight (TOF) mass analysers*

TOF mass analysis is based on the simple principle that molecular and fragment ions are separated as a function of ion velocities. Ions are all accelerated with the same electrostatic potential and hence acquire the same total kinetic energy. Accordingly, after acceleration to a constant kinetic energy (equivalent to zV_z, where V_z is the **accelerating electrostatic potential**), **ions travel at a velocity**, v_z, that is related to m/z according to

$$v_z = \sqrt{\frac{2zV_z}{m}} \qquad (9.1)$$

Therefore, ions are accelerated to velocities proportional to the inverse square roots of their m/z values. Post acceleration, ions are allowed to travel in a **field free flight tube** of length L_z (typically over a 1 m length), before striking the detector (Figure 9.8). Of course, lighter ions have a greater velocity and reach the detector in less time than heavier ions. The **time to detector**, t_z, is quantified according to

$$t_z = \frac{L_z}{v_z} = L_z\sqrt{\frac{m}{2zV_z}} \qquad (9.2)$$

illustrating that the t_z value of a given ion is proportional to the square root of the corresponding m/z value. Obviously, optimal resolution in ion detection requires that all accelerated ions are coordinated to enter the field-free flight tube at the same time. For this reason TOF mass analysers are best matched with MALDI ionisation devices, although it is possible to couple

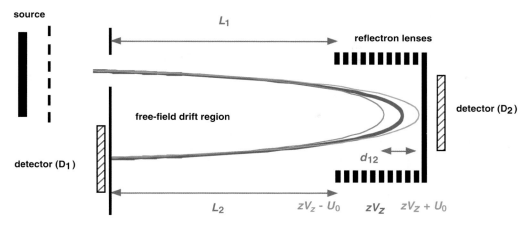

source

L_1

reflectron lenses

detector (D$_2$)

free-field drift region

detector (D$_1$)

d_{12}

L_2 $zV_z - U_0$ zV_z $zV_z + U_0$

Figure 9.8 Schematic of a **reflectron time of flight mass analyser.** Reflectron lenses act as an electrostatic mirror to both increase the effective length of the flight path, but also to compensate for ion kinetic energy variations (U_0), resulting in higher mass accuracy relative to purely linear time of flight mass analyzers. Consequently, linear time of flight analyzers are nowadays largely obsolete.

continuous ionisation techniques such as ESI to TOF if care is taken in the design of the way ions are delivered into the flight tube.

Many of the first TOF mass analysers consisted of linear flight tubes, but space can now be saved with a **reflectron** device that uses multiple ion reflection to increase the effective value of L_z and hence the resolution of mass analysis. A reflectron is in effect an electrostatic mirror consisting of a series of electrical lenses, which not only improves upon resolution by increasing the effective value of L_z, but also does so by equalising out small variations in ion kinetic energy, should they exist, due to coupling between laser energy and ion kinetic energies (Figure 9.8). Where a reflectron device is used, then Equation (9.2) should be modified to

$$t_z = (L_1 + L_2 + d_{12})\sqrt{\frac{m}{2zV_z}} \qquad (9.3)$$

where the terms L_1, L_2 and d_{12} correspond to the illustrated distance elements in the reflectron device (Figure 9.8). Please note that another method for improving MALDI-TOF resolution is by using **delayed extraction**, where the electrical charge for acceleration is applied shortly after the laser shot onto the solid surface for MALDI.

9.2.2.2 Quadrupole mass analysers

Quadrupole mass analysers are said to work on a filtration principle. They consist of four cylindrical rods organised in an orthogonal array (Figure 9.9). A quadrupole field is created by applying an oscillating current at a set frequency to one opposing pair of rods, and repeating the same to the other opposing pair of rods, ensuring that the current oscillation is 180° (π)

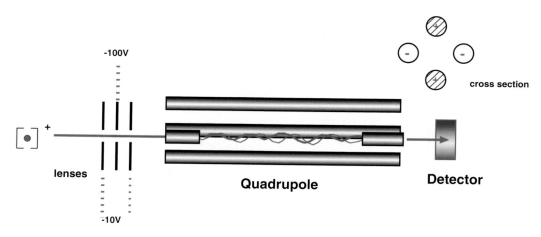

Figure 9.9 Schematic of a **quadrupole mass analyzer.** Four cylindrical rods form an **orthogonal array.** One of the rods has been cut-away in the diagram to illustrate the complex trajectories of analyte ions trapped between the electrodes. For a given potential cycling between opposing rods, a molecular ion with a certain weight **m/z** will be enabled to follow a zero-field trajectory to the detector. Changes in potential, change the **m/z** values of detectable analyte ions.

out of phase with respect to the current experienced by the first opposing pair of rods. In so doing, an oscillating electric field is generated between the rods. By convention, the field z-axis is parallel to the rods and located equidistant from each rod of the orthogonal array, such that the **field potential** $\phi_{x,y}$ at any point between the rods in any arbitrary (x, y)-plane perpendicular to the rods is described according to

$$\phi_{x,y} = \phi_0 \frac{x^2 - y^2}{r_0^2} \tag{9.4}$$

where x and y are distances from the z-axis along the x- and y- axes, and r_0 is the **field radius** between the rods (i.e. the perpendicular distance from the z-axis to the centre-line of each rod of the orthogonal array). The term ϕ_0 corresponds to the **maximum possible field potential.** Equation (9.4) indicates that the field potential will decline to zero if x and y are either zero or otherwise equivalent in magnitude. Hence, if an ion were able to travel from the ionisation device and follow a trajectory of zero-field potential along or parallel to the z-axis of the orthogonal array in the mass analyser, then the ion would be able to reach a detector at the other end. Hence, the link between Equation (9.4) and m/z can be described in the following terms. For each ion type with a given value of m/z there is a corresponding value of ϕ_0 when interactions between ion type and external quadrupole field are such as to enable this ion type to follow a zero-field potential trajectory to the detector. Increasing values of ϕ_0 are obtained using increasing current amplitudes. Therefore, a full mass spectrum may be obtained by sweeping the current amplitude (frequency is kept constant) of the oscillating applied current that creates the quadrupolar field between the rods. In so doing, different values of ϕ_0 are generated, enabling ions of different m/z to traverse the quadrupole on a

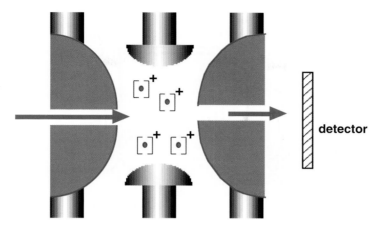

Figure 9.10 Schematic of an **Ion Trap Mass Analyser.** Ion traps work on a similar principle to quadrupole analysers, but here the trap acts as a three-dimensional capture box that releases ions when the potential and *m/z* are such that the analyte ion has a field-free path to the detector.

stable trajectory in order to reach the detector at the other end. The filtration principle is now clear. Only ions with a value of *m/z* appropriate for the given value of Φ_0 are able to reach the detector; all other ions are otherwise 'filtered out'.

9.2.2.3   Ion trap mass analysers

Ion trap analysers use a similar principle to quadrupole mass analysers but employ a system of entrance, exit and end-cap electrodes together with a ring electrode that surrounds the **trap cavity** (Figure 9.10). As with quadrupole so with ion trap, for each ion type with a given value of *m/z* there is a corresponding value of ϕ_0 when interactions between ion type and external quadrupole field are such as to enable the trapping of ion within the analyser prior to release for detection. Ion traps are relatively inexpensive, quite sensitive and robust, so are fairly widespread, despite being less accurate than TOF and quadrupole mass analysers.

9.2.2.4   Fourier transform ion cyclotron resonance (FTICR) mass analysers

Fourier transform ion cyclotron resonance represents an alternative type of trap mass analyser that requires superconducting magnets and high vacuum (Figure 9.11). Ions are constrained spacially by both electric and magnetic fields, and move in **circular orbits**. The technique uses a three-step process. First, following release from the ionisation device, ions are trapped within a small potential in a 3D cell. Second, an excitation pulse is applied so that ions with a precessional frequency matching the excitation pulse absorb the excitation pulse's energy. Third, ions are detected by measuring the image current induced when ions move in close proximity to receiving plates. The method displays excellent sensitivity and mass accuracy but these mass analysers are expensive, and are better suited to molecular rather than fragment

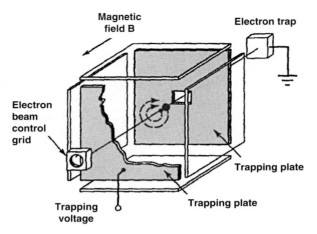

Figure 9.11 Schematic of a **Fourier Transform Ion Cyclotron Resonance (FTICR) Mass Analyser.** Ions are constrained in circular orbits by electric and magnet fields generated by superconducting magnet before selective detection. These analysers have the highest sensitivity and accuracy of any mass analysers presently available (Reproduced from Daas, 2001 [Wiley]).

ion analysis. It is likely however that this class of mass analyser will grow in popularity in coming years due its unsurpassed accuracy.

9.2.2.5 *Tandem mass analysers (MS/MS)*

Tandem mass analysis, also known as **mass spectrometry/mass spectrometry (MS/MS)**, results from the coupling together of two consecutive mass analysers in a mass spectrometer so as to obtain further information regarding the sample. Typically, there are three stages to tandem mass analysis:

(a) **mass selection** of a user-defined precursor parent ion

(b) **fragmentation** of the parent ion to form product daughter ions, followed by

(c) **mass analysis** of the product ions.

Fragmentation is typically achieved through the impact of neutral gas atoms such as by using a stream of argon or helium for **collision-induced dissociation (CID)**. The **triple-sector quadrupole (TSQ)** is one of the most popular tandem mass analysers. In this instance, the mass analyser consists of three sectors. The first and last sectors are normal quadrupole mass analysers, but the central sector constitutes a collision cell where CID can take place. The first sector is normally chosen to transmit a particular **parent ion** (or **precursor ion**) (such as a molecular or fragment ion of interest), which then enters the collision cell and undergoes controlled fragmentation into **daughter fragment ions** (or **product ions**) that are subsequently scanned or mass analysed in the third sector (a **product ion scan**). Alternatively, a specific daughter fragment ion (or product ion) of interest can be targeted in the third sector, and the first sector used to scan the parent ions (or precursor ions) for that parent ion responsible for the selected daughter ion targeted in the third sector (a **precursor ion scan**).

Post-source decay (**PSD**) is another mass analyser technique that is incorporated into some reflectron TOF instruments. **Metastable dissociation** refers to the dissociation of ions during flight in a TOF mass analyser. In a linear TOF mass analyser, metastable dissociation would make no difference to the time of arrival of the molecular or fragment ions at the detector. However, with PSD mass analysis, a parent ion can be selected by monitoring the linear detector, then the reflectron is switched off just as the parent ion is passing through. A second detector then records the daughter fragment ions from metastable dissociation of the selected parent ion. Typically, the reflectron voltage is stepped so that a wide range of daughter fragment ions may be observed from as many parent ions as possible. As the chemical biology reader might expect in this ever growing world of mass spectrometry, more exotic tandem mass analyser combinations are now becoming more and more widespread as well, including hybrid **quadrupole-TOF** (**Q-TOF**) instruments. Using this device combination, parent ions are easily selected using the quadrupole filter, fragmented in a collision cell, after which a TOF mass analyser may be used for accurate resolution of the daughter fragment ions prior to detection. The configurations of the major use combinations of ion sources, mass analysers and detectors are illustrated in Figure 9.12.

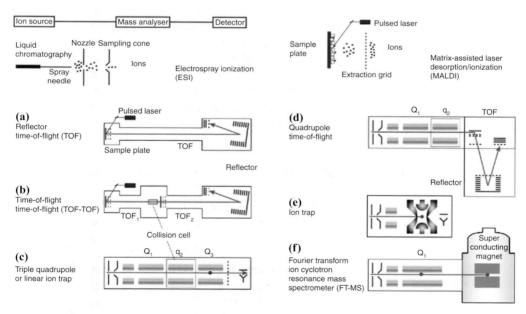

Figure 9.12 Summary of the major use combinations of ion sources and mass analyzers in use in biological mass spectrometry today. (**a**) **MALDI-ToF**; (**b**) **MALDI-ToF-ToF**; (**c**) **ESI-triple Q**; (**d**) **ESI-double Q-ToF**; (**e**) **ESI-ion trip**; (**f**) **ESI-Q-FTICR**. The combination between MALDI ion source and ToF is becoming standard, so is the combination of ESI ion source and Q mass analyzer. The combinations above also split into MS systems (**a** and **e**), and MS/MS systems (**b**, **c**, **d**, **f**). MS/MS systems are themselves becoming more popular due to product ion scanning (illustration after Aebersold and Mann, 2003, Fig. 2).

9.3 Structural analysis of biological macromolecules and lipids by mass spectrometry

The mass analysis of biological macromolecules and amphiphilic lipids can be very sophisticated given the range of possible mass spectrometers available, including the range of ionisation techniques. Clearly, the data from the mass analyser depends heavily on the ionisation method used. ESI can give a matrix of multiply charged ions, particularly when molecular ions are very heavy, whereas MALDI will typically result in single molecular ions. Fragment ions should be seen in both cases, but tandem MS/MS mass analysis will be more helpful if fragment ion analysis is required.

9.3.1 Analysis of individual peptides by mass spectrometry

With respect to oligo-/polypeptides, the parent molecular ion may be identified by most FAB, MALDI and ESI mass spectrometry. Besides detection of the molecular ion, a great deal of primary structure information can be gained from studying the mass spectra of an individual oligo-/polypeptide. Oligo-/polypeptides have standard fragmentation patterns in the positive ion mode based upon charge separation in individual peptide links and amino-acid residues. These fragmentations give rise to a_n, b_n, c_n series fragments, corresponding to the situation where fragmentation in the nth amino-acid residue creates defined N-terminal fragment ions; then there is the x_n, y_n, z_n series of fragments, where fragmentation in the nth amino-acid residue creates defined C-terminal fragment ions (Figure 9.13). These fragment ions are readily seen in sequence in FAB mass spectra of oligo-/polypeptides (particularly b_n and y_n fragment ions, which straddle the peptide bond between nth and $(n + 1)$th amino-acid residues), allowing the oligo-/polypeptide amino-acid residue sequences to be determined from the mass differences between consecutive, sequential fragment ion peaks. Typically, the molecular ion $[M + H]^+$ is most abundant, followed by fragment ions adequate to identify five to six amino-acid residues in sequence, moving in either the C- or N-terminal direction from the point of fragmentation according to the fragmentation series followed, hence identifying a sequence length of 10–12 amino-acid residues. This approach has proved excellent for sequence mapping small signal peptides found in minute quantities in mammalian brains or oligopeptide toxins excreted in similarly small quantities from sources such as *Xenopus* (frog) skin.

Polypeptide sequencing becomes possible using fragment ions and the technique of **peptide ladder sequencing**. According to this technique, a parent molecular ion is identified and then the N- or C-terminal amino-acid residue is removed before the new parent molecular ion is found. The mass difference between original and new parent molecular ion identifies the original N- or C-terminal amino-acid residue. This process can be continued for as long as desired to build up a polypeptide sequence. N-terminal residues are removed sequentially either by **aminopeptidase** enzymes, specific for peptide link hydrolysis at the N-terminus of polypeptides, or vapour phase acid hydrolysis. C-terminal residues are removed by carboxypeptidase

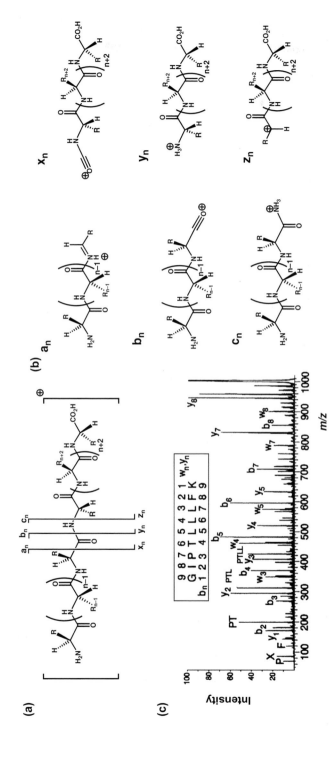

Figure 9.13 Mass spectrometry of oligo-/polypeptides. (**a**) origin of main fragmentation ions as illustrated (**b**); (**c**) Example of FAB MS/MS mass spectrum of indicated oligopeptide. The main fragment ions visible are the **b**$_n$ series (*N*-terminal fragment ions), and the **y**$_n$ series (*C*-terminal fragment ions). Mass differences between consecutive **b**$_n$ series fragment ions define oligopeptide primary structure (*N* to *C* direction); mass differences between consecutive **y**$_n$ series fragment ions define oligopeptide primary structure (*C* to *N* direction) (illustration c) from Biemann, 1988 [Wiley]).

enzymes such as **carboxypeptidase Y**, which is specific for peptide link hydrolysis at the *C*-terminus of polypeptides. Such peptide ladder sequencing is laborious and has been largely superseded by mass spectrometry with a tandem MS/MS mass analyser system making use of product ion scanning. In this instance, a single tandem MS/MS mass analysis of a pure polypeptide of interest can be sufficient to reveal the entire b_n and y_n fragment ion series. In addition, tandem mass spectrometers are often coupled with software to ease the time-consuming procedure of assigning observed peaks to expected b_n and y_n daughter fragment ions.

9.3.2 Analysis of proteins by mass spectrometry

Proteins may be analysed using two main approaches by mass spectrometry – the molecular mass may be measured for the whole protein and/or the protein may be broken into smaller peptides, which may be individually analysed, providing insight into the structure of the parent protein.

9.3.2.1   Protein molecular weight determination

Using either ESI or MALDI mass spectrometry the molecular weight determination of the protein may be determined to an accuracy of ± 0.01 per cent (Figure 9.14). This information can provide initial clues as to any deviation from the expected sequence, or potential types of modification to the protein post translation. Furthermore, the softness of MALDI or ESI ionisation ensures that even non-covalent complexes between a protein and cognate ligand or substrate can be observed. Post-translational modifications frequently include glycosylation (covalent addition of heteroglycan oligo-/polysaccharides to amino or hydroxyl functional groups) and phosphorylation of serine, threonine and/or tyrosine amino-acid residues.

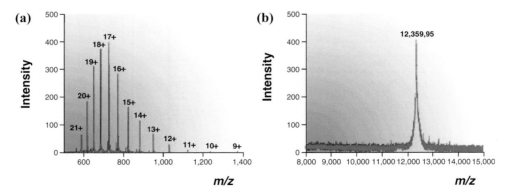

Figure 9.14   Comparison of protein mass analysis data from ESI and MALDI mass spectrometry. (**a**) ESI produces a family of multi-charged molecular ions, whereas (**b**) MALDI typically generates single molecular ion species (Reproduced from Glish and Vachet, 2003, Fig. 2).

9.3.2.2 Gel-based isolation and digestion of a protein for mass spectrometry

The real power in using mass spectrometry is analysis of minute amounts (picomoles) of proteins isolated from biological sources. In this case the stage is to digest the protein 'in gel' with an **endopeptidase**, such as **trypsin**, into oligo-/polypeptide fragments that can be individually isolated and sequenced by ESI or MALDI tandem mass spectrometry. Sequence mapping of all of these oligo-/polypeptide fragments allows for at least partial reconstruction of the protein amino-acid residue sequence. Complete sequences may then be determined by repeating the process again with another endopeptidase such as chymotrypsin to derive another endopeptidase sequence map. By comparing the two endopeptidase sequence maps all the oligo-/polypeptide fragments should then interlock together in order to define a unique protein amino-acid residue sequence.

Gel-based isolation of a protein followed by digestion with trypsin and identification of the protein from tryptic fragment analysis is now a standard approach in proteomics (Figure 9.15). Gel-separated proteins (1D and 2D gel electrophoresis) are initially stained by modified silver staining methods that omit glutaraldehyde, and employ a rapid destaining that makes use of iron ferricyanide together with sodium thiosulphate. After staining, intact protein bands are cut from the gel and destained (an optional step involves cysteine blocking with iodoacetamide), then treated with a peptidase/proteinase solution to fragment the protein into resolvable oligo-/polypeptides with distinct m/z values that can be mass analysed. The range of proteinases is as follows. First and foremost there is trypsin, which catalyses peptide link hydrolysis on the C-terminal side of arginine and lysine residues. Then there is chymotrypsin, which catalyses peptide link hydrolysis on the C-terminal side of tyrosine, phenylalanine and tryptophan residues, with occasional cleavage at lysine residues. Alternatives include **V8 protease** (also known as **glutamyl endoproteinase I** or **Glu-C**), which cleaves peptide links on the C-terminal side of glutamic and aspartic acid residues, **endopeptidase Lys-C**, which cleaves on the C-terminal side of lysine residues, **endopeptidase Arg-C** (also known as clostripain), which cleaves on the C-terminal side of arginine residues, and **endopeptidase Asp-N**, which cleaves on the N-terminal side of aspartic acid residues. Chemicals such as **cyanogen bromide** may also be used to chemically cleave on the carboxylic side of methionine residues, converting the methionine to a homoserine, which can cyclise to a lactone.

9.3.2.3 Peptide mass fingerprinting for protein identification

MALDI-TOF mass spectrometry is frequently used alone to identify proteins by a technique called **peptide mass fingerprinting** (also known as peptide mapping or peptide-mass mapping), although similar approaches can be taken using ESI-mass spectrometry. A protein digest (prepared as in Section 9.3.2.2) is spotted or combined with the matrix (usually α-cyano-4-hydroxycinnamic acid, CHCA) onto the MALDI probe. The experimentally observed peptide masses are then compared with a calculated list of proteolytic masses generated from gene databases. Peptide mass fingerprinting is most useful when working with proteins from sequenced species to enable this matching to be carried out. Typically, only 20 per cent of a protein sequence needs to be observed in order to unequivocally identify a protein.

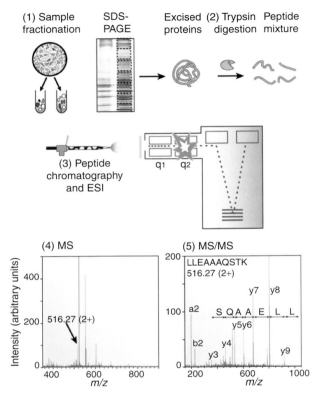

Figure 9.15 Typical mass spectrometry based experiment for protein identification/characterization. (**1**) Proteins are fractionated by chromatography, separated by **sodium dodeyl sulphate** (**SDS**) **polyacrylamide gel electrophoresis** (**PAGE**), then excised from gel; (**2**) the protein of interest is digested into peptide fragments, that are then (**3**) identified by ESI MS/MS; (**4**) the first dimension involves molecular ion analysis for **peptide mass finger-printing** (q1, MS only). (**5**) Tandem MS/MS is used when protein identification is not unambiguous, in which case parent molecular ions are activated by CID (q2) and daughter (product) ions are characterized (ToF) according to the technique of **product ion scanning** (illustration from Aebersold and Mann, 2003, Fig. 1).

In fact, rarely more than 60 per cent of any protein amino-acid sequence is fitted to the databases, therefore peptide mass fingerprinting is remarkably efficient. Should peptide mass fingerprinting prove inadequate to identify a protein unambiguously, then tandem mass spectrometry may be required to further narrow the list of candidate proteins.

9.3.2.4   Tandem mass spectrometry for protein identification

Tandem mass spectrometry provides a most definitive approach to protein identification. For tandem mass spectrometry, the work-up of proteins – typically by gel-based isolation and digestion – is exactly the same as for peptide mass fingerprinting. Also, the 'first dimension' of mass spectrometry gives information practically identical to fingerprinting. However, the real power of tandem mass spectrometry is in product ion scanning. The molecular ions of each individual oligo-/polypeptide in a proteinase digest can be individually selected as a parent ion in the first sector of tandem MS/MS mass analyser, allowing the corresponding b_n and y_n daughter fragment ions to be generated, resolved and assigned in the second and third sectors of the mass analyser (Figure 9.15). Fragment ion determination like this represents the 'second dimension' of mass spectrometry. The combination of peptide mass fingerprinting and specific sequence analysis (product ion scanning) should be sufficient to identify the protein unambiguously, provided that the protein derives from a well sequenced organism. If this is not possible, then complete sequencing becomes necessary, using more protein and different endopeptidase enzymes.

9.3.3 Analysis of nucleic acids by mass spectrometry

With respect to oligonucleotides-/oligodeoxynucleotides, the parent molecular ion may be identified by most MALDI and ESI mass spectrometry. In addition, besides detection of the molecular ion, primary structure information can be gained from studying the mass spectra of an individual oligonucleotide-/oligodeoxynucleotide as with oligo-/polypeptides. With re-gard to ESI mass spectrometry, negative ion mode tends to give better results than positive ion mode, yielding a sequence of multiply charged molecular ions $[M - zH]^{z-}$. Metal cation must be excluded from oligonucleotide-/oligodeoxynucleotide samples, since metal cation adducts suppress signal to noise and complicate spectra. By contrast, MALDI mass spectrom-etry has proved more useful for primary structure analysis. Once again, it is important to take steps to avoid metal cation adduct formation. The recommended matrix when working with oligonucleotides-/oligodeoxynucleotides is hydroxypinolic acid (HPA). In a comparable way to oligo-/polypeptides, oligonucleotides-/oligoydeoxynucleotides have standard frag-mentation patterns in the negative ion mode based upon charge separation in individual phosphodiester links. These fragmentations give rise to *simple* fragments corresponding to the situation where fragmentation in the phosphodiester link between the nth and $(n + 1)$th nucleotide/deoxynucleotide residues creates defined 5'-fragment ions or 3'-fragment ions (Figure 9.16). These fragment ions are readily seen in sequence in MALDI mass spectrome-try, allowing the oligonucleotide-/oligodeoxynucleotide residue sequences to be determined from the mass differences between consecutive, sequential fragment ion peaks. Typically, the molecular ion $[M - H]^-$ is most abundant, followed by fragment ions. Of course, sequence analysis is potentially much enhanced by MALDI tandem mass spectrometry again, in the same way that polypeptide and protein sequencing is also much enhanced using product ion scanning. Alternatively, **ladder sequencing** can be done in an equivalent manner to pep-tide ladder sequencing (see Section 9.3.1) using exonuclease enzymes to selectively hydrolyse the phosphodiester link nearest the 5'- or 3'-terminus. However, this is laborious. In the event, neither product ion scanning nor ladder sequencing compete very well with gel- or capillary-electrophoresis-based ddNTP approaches to sequencing (see Chapter 3).

Although the sensitivity and efficacy of MALDI mass spectrometry is not as high as that of gel-based approaches, mass spectrometry does allow identification of nucleic acid changes more specifically. Indeed, the main application of mass spectrometry of nucleic acids is in the identification of **single-nucleotide polymorphisms** (**SNPs**), using mass spectrometry as a platform for genomic studies. Single-nucleotide polymorphisms are single-base variations in

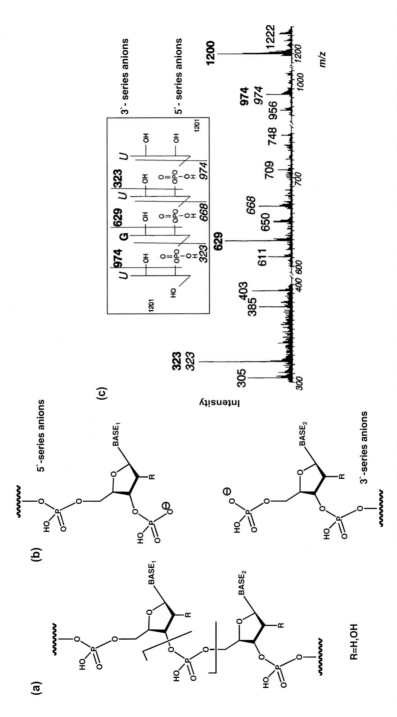

Figure 9.16 Mass spectrometry of oligonucleotides/oligodeoxynucleotides. (**a**) origin of main fragmentation ions as illustrated (**b**); (**c**) Example of negative FAB mass spectrum of indicated oligonucleotide. The main fragment ions visible are the 5′-series (5′-terminus fragment anions), and the 3′-series (3′-terminus fragment anions). Mass differences between consecutive 5′-series fragment anions define oligonucleotide primary structure (5′ to 3′ direction); mass differences between consecutive 3′-series fragment ions define oligonucleotide primary structure (3′ to 5′ direction) (illustration 5c) reproduced from Grotjahn 1986 [Wiley]).

the genome that occur at a significant frequency (greater than one per cent) in the human population, typically appearing once on average every 1000 bases in the human genome. Typically, biotin-tagged ddNTPs are used for extension together with primers that anneal immediately next to the polymorphic sites. The terminated products are captured by streptavidin protein binding, and MALDI-TOF mass spectrometry can be used to identify polymorphic variation by the combined mass of the product.

9.3.4 Analysis of carbohydrates and glycoproteins by mass spectrometry

In contrast with nucleic acids, MALDI and ESI mass spectrometry come into their own with oligo-/polysaccharide sequencing, particularly where heteroglycans are involved. Oligo-/polysaccharides have standard fragmentation patterns in the positive ion mode based upon charge separation in individual glycosidic links and within monosaccharide residues. These fragmentations give rise to A_n, B_n and C_n series fragments corresponding to the situation where fragmentation in the nth and monosaccharide residue $(n + 1)$th creates defined *non-reducing end* fragment ions; then there is the X_n, Y_n, Z_n series of fragments, where fragmentation in the nth and monosaccharide residue $(n + 1)$th creates defined *reducing end* fragment ions (Figure 9.17). As with the oligo-/polypeptide sequencing, B_n and Y_n fragment ions that involve the glycosidic link between the nth and $(n + 1)$th monosaccharide residues of a given oligo-/polysaccharide chain are important. So too are the A_n and X_n fragment ions that characterise actual fragmentations within the nth and $(n +1)$th monosaccharide residues. These are critical to demonstrate the presence and location of multiple oligo-/polysaccharide-chain branching from a single monosaccharide residue. Consequently, careful analysis of fragment ion series by MALDI or ESI mass spectrometry and tandem mass spectrometry become very powerful tools for the primary structure characterisation of complex oligo-/polysaccharides, isolated in very small quantities (picomoles) from biological sources such as glycoproteins.

The oligo-/polysaccharides associated with glycoproteins can generally be characterised in a series of steps. First, the molecular weight of the entire glycoprotein can be measured, typically by ESI mass spectrometry. Peptide maps of the glycoprotein can then be compared before and after treatment with an endoglycosidase enzyme, for instance **peptide-N4-acetyl-β-glucosaminyl-asparagine amidase** (**PNGase**), which cleaves the bond between asparagine amino-acid residues and 2-amino-2-deoxyglucopyranose residues. Otherwise, $NaBH_4$/NaOH is sufficient to release oligo-/polysaccharides by reductive cleavage. Comparative peptide maps allow for the identification of glycopeptides, and their precise site of glycosylation within the amino acid residue chain can be determined by tandem mass spectrometry. Otherwise, the oligo-/polysaccharides can be resolved by chromatography from the glycoprotein and separately sequence characterised as indicated above.

9.3.5 Analysis of lipids by mass spectrometry

FAB, MALDI and ESI mass spectrometry are both suitable to observe molecular ions of amphiphilic lipids. This molecular ion is normally more than enough to determine structure

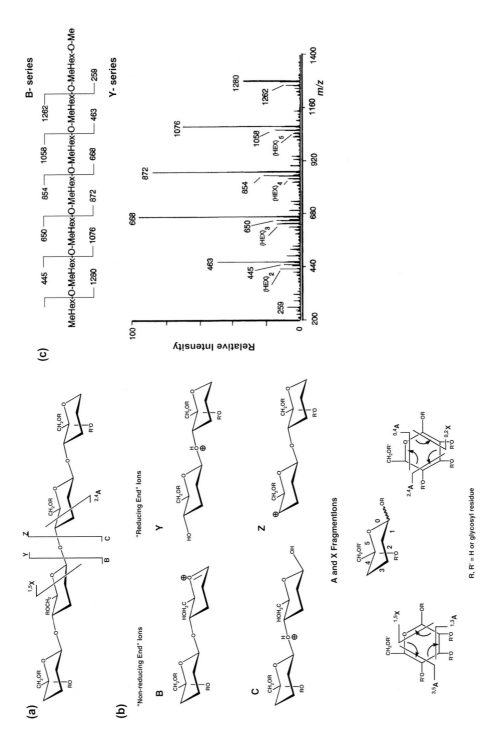

Figure 9.17 Mass spectrometry of oligosaccharides. (**a**) origin of main fragmentation ions as illustrated (**b**); (**c**) Example of ESI MS/MS CID mass spectrum of indicated methylated oligosaccharide. The main fragment ions visible are the **B-series** (non-reducing terminus fragment ions), and the **Y-series** (reducing terminus fragment ions). Mass differences between consecutive B-series fragment anions define oligosaccharide primary structure (non-reducing to reducing end direction); mass differences between consecutive Y-series fragment ions define oligosaccharide primary structure (reducing to non-reducing end direction) (Reproduced c) from Reinhold et al., 1995, Fig. 7).

since molecular ions are unique between biologically important acylglycerols, phospholipids and cholesterol. Should more information be required, lipids are able to fragment about ester bonds, yielding fragment ions that are best visualised in negative ion mode. These include fatty acid fragment ions that may further fragment by carboxyl group dehydration to by ω-decomposition to reveal fatty acid alkyl chain length and homologation (Figure 9.18).

9.4 The challenge of proteomics

Studies on individual biological macromolecules and macromolecular lipid assemblies have done much to explain the inner workings of cells and organisms. This will almost certainly continue to be the case. Much can be gained by removing cellular components then seeking to characterise their structures and functions without complication from the 'background noise' of other cellular components. Having said this, the 'background noise' must be every bit as much associated with the function, and even structure, of the cellular components of interest. Therefore, chemical biology research must seek to follow not only the reductionist philosophy of chemistry but also the inclusionist philosophies of biology and medicine. In this respect, mass spectrometry through the study and practise of proteomics has an enormously powerful role 'to enable the move from individual to collective molecular structure and function analyses', as stated previously. This is especially true of studies involving cellular proteins, since there is a growing appreciation that proteins do not always function in isolation but are also frequent participants in larger multi-protein complexes. In other words, quaternary association of catalytic and functional units is far more widespread than previously assumed. The implications of this realisation remain to be established.

9.4.1 Early developments in proteomics

Attempts to describe systems of proteins on a large scale were initially outlined during the 1970s with the development of 2D polyacrylamide gel electrophoresis (PAGE) as a method to visualise sets of proteins (Figure 9.19). This method involved separation of protein mixtures by pI in the first dimension and then by molecular mass in the second dimension, resulting in a 2D gel that may then be stained and visualised as a complex pattern. Experiments were typically conducted comparatively, for example two tissues were compared, one diseased and one normal. Patterns were then probed to check for changes in protein spot pattern. The problem with this original approach was that it was very difficult to identify the protein from the spot. Chemical degradation could be attempted to sequence the protein, but still the protein could only be identified if the protein was already known and sequenced. These difficulties really held 2D electrophoresis back during the 1980s, and there has only been resurgent popularity in recent years given access to large gene databases together with soft-ionisation mass spectrometry techniques to identify peptides from proteins digested 'in gel'.

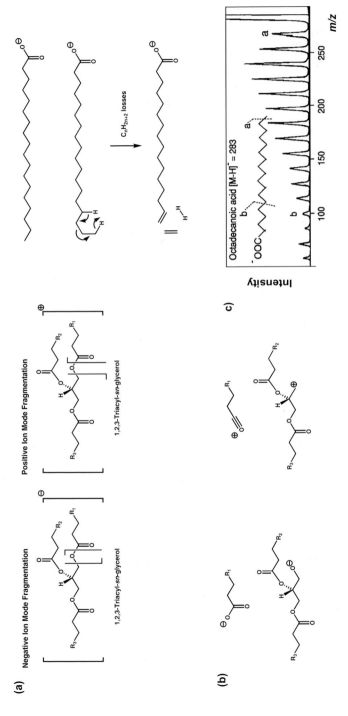

Figure 9.18 Mass spectrometry of glycerides, phospholipids and fatty acids. (**a**) origin of main fragmentation ions as illustrated (**b**); (**c**) Example of negative ion FAB MS/MS CID mass spectrum of indicated fatty acid. The main fragment ions visible are homologation fragment anions. Mass differences between consecutive fragment anions define fatty acid CH_2-length (ω to α carboxyl group direction) (illustration c) adapted from Jensen et al., 1985, Fig. 1).

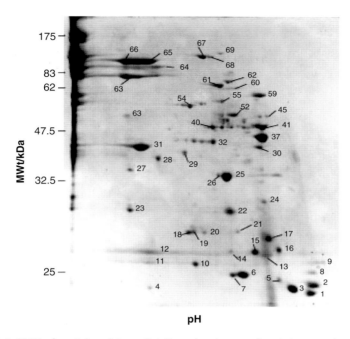

Figure 9.19 2-D PAGE of protein mixture. Relative abundances of proteins may be visualised by gel staining and each individual spot can be excised and identified by mass spectrometry. (Reproduced from Pandey and Mann, 2000, Fig. 6A).

9.4.2 Using 2D gel electrophoresis with mass spectrometry

The combination of 2D gel electrophoresis and mass spectrometry is a traditional approach towards proteomics. 2D gel electrophoresis separates proteins according to orthogonal properties; gels are stained, then spots cut from the gel and identified by mass spectrometry using sequence information from gene databases coupled with peptide mass fingerprinting (Figure 9.20). The use of these techniques alone has allowed types of 'cataloguing' experiments to be performed wherein patterns on 2D gels can be examined and spots on gel identified. These approaches have had most impact when examining systems somewhat simpler than the whole cell situation, for instance the compositions of subcellular organelles or multi-protein complexes. Alternatively, comparative experiments may be performed using pattern-matching algorithms to compare 2D gel electrophoresis results in an attempt to make out the differences, for example in protein profiles between diseased and normal tissues thereby uncovering disease biomarkers.

However, there are significant problems with using the combination of 2D electrophoresis and mass spectrometry. First, only the high abundance proteins are identified on 2D gels – it has been estimated that the number of genes expressed at any one time in a human cell type could exceed 10 000. If post-translational modification were also considered then the numbers of distinct polypeptides even within a single cell could run into the millions. On

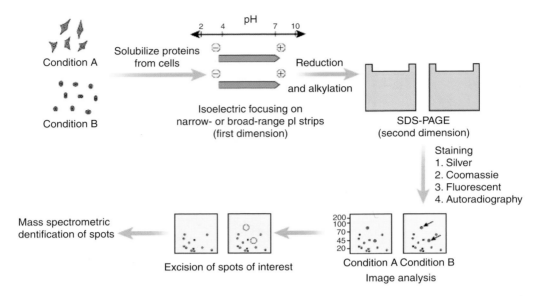

Figure 9.20   Comparative 2-D Electrophoresis / MS approach to Proteomics. Proteins in two separate gels can be compared, differentially expressed spots identified, and identities confirmed by mass spectrometry (Reproduced from Pandey and Mann, 2000, Fig. 3).

a 2D gel several hundred spots may be separately analysed, perhaps increasing a few-fold with specialised techniques of subcellular fractionation or zoom gels that cover narrower pH ranges. In addition, many membrane and basic proteins may not be separated on 2D gels at all. As a result, when one examines the databases that catalogue proteins in certain tissues, the bulk of proteins are the abundant proteins such as cytoskeletal proteins, chaperones and matrix-associated proteins. Many low-abundance proteins, such as signalling proteins, transmembrane receptors and the like, are very under-represented. Hence the push for a more quantitative proteomics becomes imperative.

9.4.3 Isotope-coded affinity tags

One of the main problems to overcome in order to realise quantitative proteomics is that mass spectrometry is not strictly a quantitative technique with respect to molecular abundance. One approach to overcome this problem is to perform comparative experiments in parallel where one sample is labelled with an isotope (such as ^{18}O or ^{2}H) and the other is unlabelled. Mass differences between labelled and unlabelled samples may be observed in a mass spectrometer and the relative ratios quantified (Figure 9.21). Obviously this method of quantification relies on equivalent mass 'expression' by both samples in spite of the isotopic labelling of the one and not the other. In other words, in spite of the labelling, both samples should behave identically chemically. The simplest way to effect labelling is to use **isotope-coded affinity tags** (**ICATs**). According to this technique, two identical populations of proteins

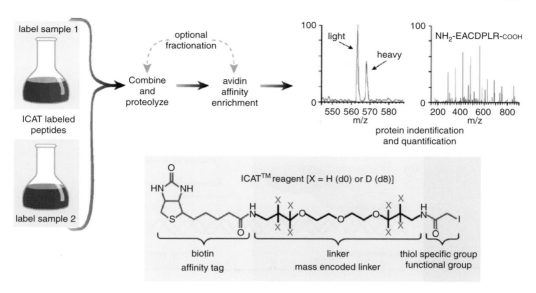

Figure 9.21   Isotope Coded Affinity Tagging as an approach for comparative proteomics. Two pools of peptides can be differentially labelled with tags of different masses, then the pools combined, enriched by avidin affinity column purification (avidin has a very high affinity for biotin) and relative abundance of particular peptides can be directly compared by mass spectrometry (Reproduced from Patterson and Aebersold, 2003, Fig. 5).

are maintained under different conditions (e.g. temperature, pH, ionic strength) but tagged differently on conclusion with isotope-coded affinity tags (ICATs). Tagging is site specific (e.g. on sulphydryl, amine groups or phosphate esters) and the ICAT tagging agent also possesses an affinity tag. Typically, the heavier ICAT has a mass difference of 8 relative to the lighter ICAT, owing to the substitution of eight ^{1}H hydrogen atoms for eight ^{2}H deuterium atoms. Both protein populations are then pooled post-tagging and digested into oligo-/polypeptides prior to affinity purification of the affinity-tagged oligo-/polypeptides of the combined digest. Tagged oligo-/polypeptides are then compared directly by tandem mass spectrometry, looking for quantitative differences in molecular ion abundance that can be linked back to differences in the conditions under which the two identical populations of proteins were maintained. This remains one of the best approaches to quantitative and comparative proteomics.

9.4.4 Deciphering protein networks by tandem affinity purification

One of the most notable early successes of proteomics has been in providing a protein–protein interaction map for yeast cells. A major approach to building such maps has been to use the genetic approach of **yeast two-hybrid mapping**. Yeast two-hybrid experiments are based on the idea that some transcriptional activators require the activities of two proteins – one involved in DNA binding, and the other involved in transcriptional activation (Figure 9.22).

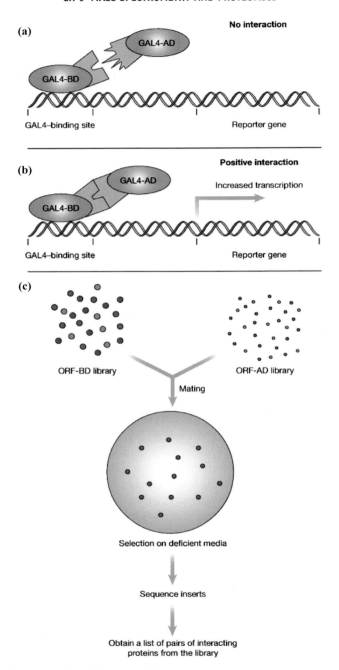

Figure 9.22 The **Yeast Two-Hybrid System.** Different open reading frames are fused to a **Gal4 DNA-binding domain (BD)** or an **activation domain (AD).** If the encoded proteins interact then a reported gene is transcribed and translated, allowing for identification of protein-protein interactions. (illustration from Pandey and Mann, 2000, Fig. 7).

Transcriptional activation only takes place when the two proteins are tethered to one another. Typically, the yeast protein **GAL4** is used as the transcriptional activator together with the DNA binding domain of *E. coli* **LexA** as the other component. Two proteins can be probed for binding interactions with each other by fusing the activation domain to one protein and a complementary DNA binding domain to the second protein; if the two proteins interact then a reporter gene will be transcribed by default.

There are two approaches to performing these experiments on a large scale – either using an array approach or a library approach. In an array approach, a living array of haploid yeast transformants (the **prey**) is designed, each expressing a different open reading frame (ORF) fused to a transcriptional activation domain. Another yeast transformant (the **bait**) is prepared, expressing a single protein of interest fused with the corresponding DNA-binding domain. When the bait transformant is mated with all the transformants on the array, diploid yeast strains are produced, but only those expressing proper molecular partners to the single protein of interest from the ORFs will show transcriptional activation. Since the identities of ORFs in the array are known together with their array addresses, molecular partners to our single protein of interest should be identified with ease. In a library approach, all the prey transformants are pooled and fused to the bait transformant. According to this method, transcriptional activation is associated with a survival trait (e.g. antibiotic resistance) so that the only surviving diploid yeast strains are those expressing proper molecular partners to the single protein of interest from the ORFs. Following this, molecular partners of the protein of interest are identified separately by gene sequencing of the 'survival' ORFs.

Tandem affinity purification (**TAP**) is another method for probing protein–protein interactions that is able to characterise multi-protein complexes rather than just the binary partners as illustrated with the yeast two-hybrid method. **Tandem affinity purification** (**TAP**) is an extension of protein tagging – two tags are used so as to enable specific purification of molecular partners interacting with the specific bait protein of interest. Two different protease sites are also included, one between the two tags (**Tag 1** and **Tag 2**) and one between the two tags and the specific bait protein of interest. Initially, an extract (which includes the TAP-tagged bait protein of interest) is passed over an affinity column for Tag 1, allowing Tag 1 to bind. The column is then washed and Tag 1 is protease cleaved from Tag 2, allowing the protein of interest and interacting protein partners to elute from the affinity column in association with each other. This enriched protein mixture is passed subsequently over a second affinity column for Tag 2, allowing Tag 2 to bind. This time, the bait protein of interest is protease cleaved from the Tag 2, allowing protein of interest and molecular partners to elute together free of non-specific binding interactions. The bait protein of interest and partners can then be identified by 2D gel electrophoresis and mass spectrometry.

9.4.5 The challenge of membrane proteins in proteomics

It has been estimated that 20–30 per cent of proteins encoded by the human genome are membrane proteins. Clearly, this makes membrane proteins a vital class to understand, and furthermore more than 70 per cent of drug targets are membrane proteins. A significant problem in mass spectrometry is that a far smaller number of membrane proteins are identified than are known by other methods to be present in any particular sample. The observation of membrane proteins by standard 2D gels is hindered by solubility. First, these proteins are not solubilised in the buffer (for the first dimension). Second, solubilised membrane proteins will all too easily precipitate again at their isoelectric point pI. One approach to solving the initial problem is solubilising membrane proteins in either organic solvents or non-ionic/zwitterionic detergents. The pI problem may be avoided by just using 1D gels. However, even if membrane proteins are clearly resolved within a gel, further problems are encountered during the digestion steps because oligo-/polypeptides in digests tend to be particularly hydrophobic (Figure 9.23).

An alternative to using gels is **shotgun proteomics** (i.e., *in situ* digestion of complex mixtures of proteins followed by 2D liquid chromatography mass spectrometry (2D LC-MS) to identify proteins in particular samples (Figure 9.24). Again, initial solubilisation is an

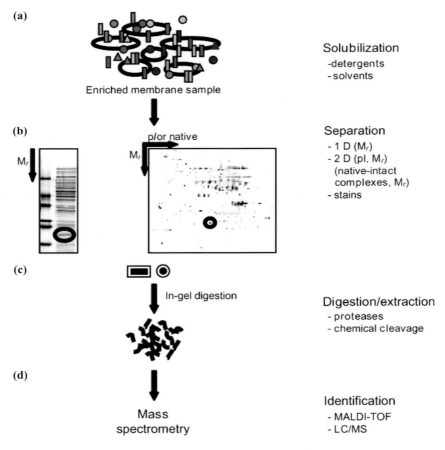

Figure 9.23 Gel-based **Membrane Proteomics.** Membrane proteins can be analysed by a four-step process of solubilization, separation, digestion/extraction, and finally MS identification (illustration from Wu and Yates, 2003, Fig. 1).

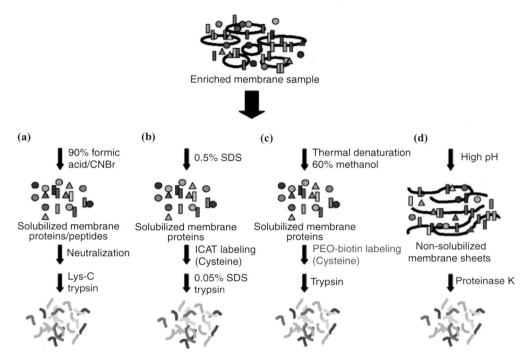

Figure 9.24 Comparison of four methods to prepare membrane proteins for analysis. Analysis can be by shotgun proteomics or by conventional mass spectrometry (Reproduced from Wu and Yates, 2003, Fig.2).

important factor – organic acids and solvents, as well as various detergents, may be used. Proteolysis may be carried out with enzymes (e.g. trypsin; trypsin is even functional in 60 per cent methanol) or chemically (e.g. cyanogen bromide). An alternative approach is to cleave the exposed soluble domains using a non-specific protease such as **proteinase K**, then use LC-MS to sequence the resultant peptides and employ protein mass fingerprinting to identify proteins. To summarise, membrane protein proteomics remains a challenge, but these approaches will undoubtedly become more widespread, especially considering the pharmaceutical interest in membrane proteins.

9.4.6 Proteomics and post-translational modifications

Post-translational modifications (**PTMs**) are vitally important in modifying protein structure and function, especially in eukaryotes. On a large scale, researchers are faced with a separate challenge. Normally in proteomics experiments, proteins can be isolated identified by protein mass fingerprinting combined with product ion scanning if necessary. Unfortunately, **PTM analysis** requires a much more thorough analysis of the entire amino-acid sequence. This is further complicated by the fact that modifications are not typically homogeneous, and a wide range of modifications can be found on a single type of protein of interest. The role of PTMs in cells remains a huge area of research and remains widely open to the chemical biology reader to explore since not even biologists understand structural and functional consequences.

9.4.6.1   *Comprehensive PTM analysis of a single protein*

The first stage in a comprehensive PTM analysis of a protein of interest is purification. Depending on the initial level of purification, this can be most conveniently achieved by gel electrophoresis, either a 1D or a 2D gel. Often electrophoresis may give clues to the nature of modification; for example, **phosphorylation** of a protein can result in spots separated horizontally on a 2D gel due to differential pI values between phosphorylated and non-phosphorylated states of the protein of interest. A useful first stage in the process is to accurately identify the molecular ion; comparisons between the expected and measured mass can give initial information about which modifications may be present. After gaining information on the intact protein, detailed information regarding site(s) of modification may be obtained by analysing peptides obtained after enzymatic or chemical degradation. A typical combination would be to use trypsin in one experiment and then to use endoproteinase Asp-N or Glu-C in a second experiment. Modified oligo-/polypeptides in digests can be identified by unexpected molecular ions and then analysed by product ion scanning to determine the amino-acid residues at which PTMs have taken place. **Acetylation** (often on arginine amino-acid residues) is easiest to identify. Phosphorylation can be either stable or labile (phosphotyrosine tends to be stable, phosphothreonine less so, whilst phosphoserine tends to be labile), but can usually be seen. Unfortunately, **sulphation** and **glycosylation** modification sites can be much more labile and less easy to identify by tandem mass spectrometry.

9.4.6.2   *PTM analysis of protein populations*

The PTM mapping of protein populations requires a different approach to the single-protein approach. For instance, once a protein sample mixture has been resolved by 2D-gel electrophoresis, then phosphorylated proteins can be identified by western blot using **anti-phospho-amino-acid antibodies**. Individual anti-phosphoserine, anti-phosphothreonine or anti-phosphotyrosine antibodies may also be used. Another approach is to specifically target and purify a subset of proteins from a complex mixture by affinity column purification. For instance, anti-phospho-amino-acid antibodies coupled to a resin (e.g. agarose beads) may be used to affinity purify phospho-proteins from a complex protein mixtures. The enriched population of proteins may then be eluted from the column and resolved by 2D electrophoresis and individual proteins identified with phosphorylation sites defined by tandem mass spectrometry.

   Gels may be eliminated by shotgun proteomics, but specific protein modifications of interest need to reviewed and resolved by some form of chromatography prior to mass spectrometry. For example, phosphopeptides may be specifically purified pre mass spectrometry using immobilised-metal affinity chromatography (IMAC) (see Chapter 2). Both iron (as Fe^{3+}) and gallium (as Ga^{3+}) have proved useful in metal ion affinity column purification of phosphorylated peptides prior to mass spectrometry. Their sequences and site(s) of phosphorylation can then be identified with ease by tandem mass spectrometry, and subsequently related back to the identities of the parent proteins from which these daughter digest peptides derived. The use of mass spectrometry in PTM analysis is an important growth area for the future.

9.5 Genomics – assigning function to genes and proteins

Gene sequences deriving from the ORFs for many organisms are already available; therefore, the bottleneck in biology has moved from gene sequencing to gene function and protein structure/function. Protein network studies by yeast two-hybrid and proteomics screens are useful steps forward (all described above in this chapter), but these need to be complemented and supplemented by other approaches to obtain information on proteins and other biological macromolecules of interest.

9.5.1 Protein microarrays

Protein microarray technology has emerged from the more established technique of DNA microarray technology. Microarrays are simply a technique where individual molecules such as oligonucleotides-/oligodeoxynucleotides, proteins, antibodies and small molecules can be separately spotted onto a surface such as a glass slide and then the surface is analysed for specific functions or activities (Figure 9.25). **DNA microarrays** can now be used at densities of tens of thousands of different oligonucleotide probes per square centimetre and can be used for genetic analysis as well as expression analysis at the mRNA level. As previously discussed, mRNA levels do not strictly correlate with protein levels, and therefore protein microarrays have also been developed to probe proteomes in a microarray format. One significant problem with protein arrays relative to oligonucleotide arrays is stability – it is important to array the proteins without denaturing but maintaining a reasonable density for facile detection of activity. The surfaces are therefore modified and engineered to prevent evaporation and drying by the use of sophisticated pads, films, nano-wells and micro-fluidic channels. Arrays used in proteomics take two forms – analytical arrays and functional arrays:

9.5.1.1 Analytical arrays

Analytical arrays typically use molecules that are able to capture and bind to proteins from a complex protein mixture. For instance, antibodies, antigens, carbohydrates or small molecules are spotted onto a derivatised surface. The typical approach used is that two protein populations from different biological states are compared – one set is labelled with a red fluorescent dye, the other labelled with a green fluorescent dye; they are mixed, and then incubated with the chips. Each spot in the array is then analysed for the relative quantities of the two dyes. This information can lead to insights regarding structural and functional differences between

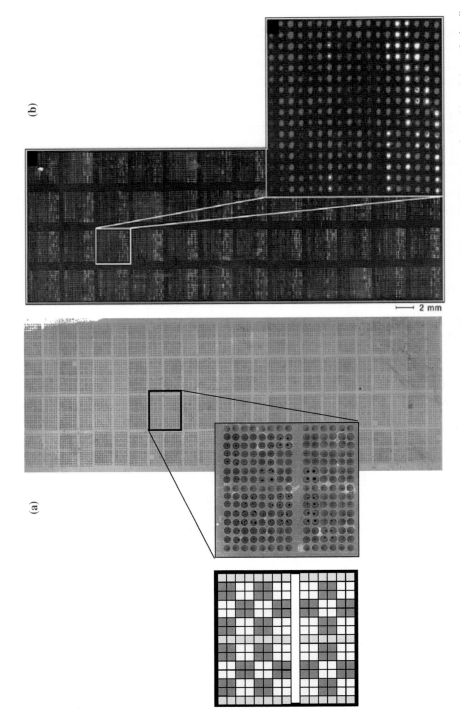

Figure 9.25   DNA and **Protein Microarrays. (a)** DNA microarray comprising 10080 features and 1959 plasmid DNA clones for probing. Schematic detail indicates layout arrangment for each clone analyzed as a clusters of $n = 4$ between guide tracks of GFP expressing pDNA (illustration adapted from Palmer et al., 2006, Fig. 1); **(b)** Protein microarray comprising 6566 Proteins are arrayed on a microscope slide, such arrays have a diverse number of applications in globally understanding proteome function (Reproduced from MacBeath, 2002, Fig. 5).

protein populations maintained in two different biological states prior to experiment. Nevertheless, there remain significant problems with the general stability of protein microarrays.

9.5.1.2 Functional arrays

Functional arrays use individually purified or synthesised proteins or peptides that are arrayed onto a suitable surface. The microarray can then be probed for binding partners of many different types. For instance, proteins, nucleic acids, drugs or other small molecules could be passed over the surface to identify macromolecular binding interactions. This technique has growing importance in drug discovery and drug validation research programs. In fact functional arrays for many organisms are close to completion now. For instance, the near complete proteome of yeast has now been assembled into microarray formats. The method used was to His-tag all ORFs (see Chapter 2) so that all expressed yeast proteins may be spotted onto Ni-coated slides.

9.5.2 Biochemical genomics

Another approach is to assign not just binding interactions but catalytic function to proteins in a large scale manner too. Once again, work in yeast has demonstrated the proof of principle. The principle of the approach is as follows.

(a) Construction of several thousand yeast strains by standard genetic recombination methods recombination, each bearing a plasmid expressing a different GST-ORF fusion under the control of an inducible promoter.

(b) Pooling of extracts from a convenient number of yeast strains (e.g. 100) so that each of the pools may be assayed side by side for a specific activity.

(c) Purification of the GST-ORFs from the pooled strains so that each pool contains approximately 100 GST-tagged proteins.

(d) Each pool is assayed for an enzymatic activity; if a specific pool is found to have activity then it is possible to create smaller and smaller sub-pools within the pool, eventually narrowing down the search until the ORF encoding the activity is pinpointed.

As biochemical genomics uses catalytic activity rather than solely binding activity, the sensitivity of the technique can be controlled by the time of incubation of the enzyme reaction, thereby dramatically increasing sensitivity compared with most binding assays. As proteins are tested within pools initially rather than individually it can also provide information about catalytic activities that might be dependent on complexes of proteins that would be missed when working with the protein in isolation. The drawbacks of the method are that the libraries bias against larger proteins, and any overexpressed GST-ORF fusions that retard growth during propagation of the yeast strain will also be underrepresented in the pool.

9.5.3 Chemical genomics

In recent times, libraries of chemical compounds have been instituted due to the advent of combinatorial chemistry. The quality of libraries is highly variable and often of doubtful utility, but the approach is here to stay. Such libraries can be built in a more controlled way by diversity-orientated synthesis that seeks to create chemical diversity in a less randomised manner underpinned by greater synthetic robustness. The benefits of libraries prepared with better chemical control is then the opportunity to screen the library against cells, looking either for any reproducible phenotypic change or looking for one phenotypic characteristic in particular. Once a reproducible phenotype is found, synthesis of a pure compound can then definitively match a novel small molecule with a novel biological function. This **chemical genomics** approach clearly opens the possibility of identifying novel leads for pharmaceutical investigation against cancer, virus infection etc. In addition, chemical genomics should certainly contribute in the discovery of the next generation of chemical tools for the investigation of structure and function in chemistry and biology.

9.5.4 Structural genomics

Structural genomics aims to take large scale approaches at the protein structural level – to compile a dictionary of protein structure from the level of the fold to the domain, to the protein and to its quaternary interactions. Although it shares a philosophy with that of the hugely successful sequencing projects of the 1990s, it will be a far more challenging task to solve protein structure on a large scale due to great variation in protein structure compared to the conservative properties of nucleic acids. Rapid developments are taking place in both X-ray crystallography and NMR spectroscopy to facilitate high throughput structure analysis by partial automation of various stages of each process.

9.5.5 Perspectives on the future of proteomics with genomics

Proteomics has been very much driven by technology, and the discipline remains fragmented by competing approaches and interests. These approaches and interests must be harmonised and data sets integrated for comparison with genomic expression data. Proteomics should make essential contributions in mapping protein interaction pathways in cells in the same way that genomic expression data is making possible today. Proteomics also opens up the whole issue of PTMs and epigenetic (i.e. non-genome-based) control of structure and function in cells and organisms. Again, this is still in the early stages. Proteomics should also play a role in diagnostic medicine though the identification of robust biomarkers of disease, and the links between this and mass spectrometry.

10

Molecular Selection and Evolution

10.1 Chemical biology and the origins of life

The origins of life and existence are uniquely interesting. There can be no more significant scientific or philosophical question than what is/was the origin of life and existence. Leaving aside all but scientific approaches to this question, this chapter aims to introduce the chemical biology reader to a rudimentary theory for the origins of life as seen from the perspective of chemical biology and chemistry. Seeing as biological macromolecules and assemblies, as well as cofactors and prosthetic groups, are the primary building blocks of living organisms, then there can be no more logical a starting point. Once our rudimentary theory is in place, a number of useful processes will be described that have drawn inspiration from these ideas and principles.

10.1.1 Order from complexity

The simplest description of a living organism is that *the organism consists of a system of chemicals that has the capacity to catalyse its own reproduction.* Given this view, the root property of life is the achievement of autocatalytic closure among a collection of molecular species. Alone, each molecular species is 'dead'; jointly, the collective system of molecules is 'alive'. This concept is very compelling for the chemical biologist, since biocatalysis no longer just sustains life but is also a key requirement for the origins of life. However, catalysis alone cannot be enough to originate life. All living systems 'eat'; they take in matter and energy in order to sustain and reproduce themselves. Therefore, living systems must be the equivalent of closed autocatalytic but open (non-equilibrium) thermodynamic systems. However, even supposing that life can originate from autocatalytic closure among a collection of molecular species, how does this view of life account for the astonishing order that characterises living systems and seems so much at variance with the second law of thermodynamics? In Kauffman's view, this order

Essentials of Chemical Biology   Andrew Miller and Julian Tanner
© 2008 John Wiley & Sons, Ltd

arises directly from molecular diversity and complexity in an open thermodynamic system. That is to say, *self-organisation arises naturally as a direct consequence of molecular diversity and complexity in an open thermodynamic system* (i.e., 'order for free').

10.1.2 Evolution from the molecular level

Amongst biologists, discussions about the origins of life have been focussed by arguments of natural selection. There has been an apparent tendency to ignore self-organisation. Most likely this is because there is a fundamental difficulty in recognising how living systems may be governed simultaneously by two sources of order, self-organisation born of molecular diversity and complexity, and the 'forces' of natural selection. However, if we are to understand properly the origin of life, a final theory of biology must allow for the commingling of self-organisation and selection processes as an expression of an even deeper order. Surely, as Kauffman argues, self-organisation precedes natural selection. For natural selection to be able to operate there should be two main criteria satisfied:

(a) the existence of compartmentalisation or the means of compartmentalisation;

(b) the existence of low energy, self-organised molecule states ('robust systems') that provide a foundation upon which to exercise the forces of natural selection to create and mould living organisms.

Compartmentalisation is a key part of the self-organisation process, if for nothing else than to sustain spatial integrity and prevent dilution of the reacting molecules that comprise each living system. The ability of lipids to self-assemble into lipid bilayers and more complex mesophases is well established, and has long been accepted to form a key part of compartmentalisation in biology (see Chapter 1). **Stable, low energy, self-organised states** ('robust systems') such as DNA, RNA and even folded proteins (including their prosthetic groups and cofactors) intuitively provide a sound foundation upon which to exercise the forces of natural selection to create and mould living organisms (see Chapter 1). For the forces of natural selection to have an effect, random structural variations (**mutations**) must exist in the primary structure of all such robust systems (namely base variations in nucleic acids and amino-acid residue sequence variations in proteins) that represent a molecular pool of diversity upon which selection pressures can act. Natural selection pressures should then select for that mutation or group of mutations belonging to a given robust system that are most beneficial for the existence of the self-assembled living system. For instance, if enhanced catalytic efficiency is required, then the forces of 'natural selection' acting under the influence of a given set of metabolic selection pressures should select for that amino-acid residue mutation or group of mutations that promote the necessary enhancements in catalytic efficiency of a key enzyme or group of enzymes. This is a form of **molecular evolution**.

Molecular evolution is the putative engine of macro-evolution and is thought to involve primarily successions of single (point) mutations leading to ever more enhanced robust systems that in turn promote the well being and competitiveness of the self-assembled living system. Such molecular evolution by a succession of single point mutations seems to be a satisfying way to define the molecular basis of natural selection. Hence, if we combine this with the idea that natural selection is preceded by self-organisation, then we have an integrated, holistic **molecular hypothesis for the origin of life**. In other words, the origin of life should be explained as follows. First, self-organisation exists as a direct consequence of molecular complexity and diversity in order to provide the means to compartmentalise a 'living' system of reacting molecules. Second, self-organisation results in stable, low energy, 'robust' systems such as DNA, RNA and folded proteins that can be moulded under pressure of natural selection by a succession of single point mutations so as to promote catalysis or other functions necessary to originate and promulgate living organisms. Reproduction should then be the final stage, resting upon a process of autocatalytic replication of robust systems once the enclosed chemical environment allows such reactivity to take place, converting closed autocatalytic 'living' systems of reacting molecules into sustainable living organisms.

10.1.3 Chemical self-organisation from complexity

If self-organisation exists as a direct consequence of molecular complexity and diversity, then such a hypothesis must be tested experimentally as well as by theoretical mathematical treatments. In other words, chemical biology should be able to provide clear evidence for molecular diversity and complexity leading to life-like 'order for free', through well designed **pre-biotic chemistry** experiments. The main objective of pre-biotic chemistry is to try to generate by experimental means chemical structures that accurately presage the biological macromolecules of life including their cofactors and prosthetic groups, by reaction from pre-biotic 'starting materials'. In so doing, credible molecular links can be established from these pre-biotic 'starting materials' to recognisable robust systems, and hence 'living' organisms. There are three key early experiments that provide the foundations for pre-biotic chemistry, namely the **Miller**, **Oro** and **Fischer** experiments (Figure 10.1). In the Miller experiment, proteinogenic amino acids were generated spontaneously by electrical discharge through anaerobic mixtures containing methane, ammonia, hydrogen and water vapour. In the Oro experiment, adenine was generated through the heating of aqueous ammonium cyanide. Finally, in the Fischer experiment, formaldehyde and water generated sugars in the presence of calcium hydroxide (**formose reaction**).

Although all three types of experiment are important, they have now been superseded by studies involving 'starting mixtures' of compounds known to be resident in interstellar gas clouds, or else 'starting mixtures' of compounds identified from amongst gas phase products generated in methane/nitrogen mixtures post electrical discharge (Figure 10.2). Molecular compositions are impressively similar in both cases. Clearly water/oxygen is not present, but this could be introduced at a later, more appropriate stage. Significantly, there are many triple-bond-containing 'starting materials' that are chemical-energy-storage molecules (in an anaerobic environment) and that certainly could have the chemical potential for substantial forward reactions (Figure 10.3). In some cases, these forward reactions have actually been studied now and certain key structures have been identified that form routinely from the pool of anaerobic, interstellar/electrical discharge 'starting materials'. These are known as

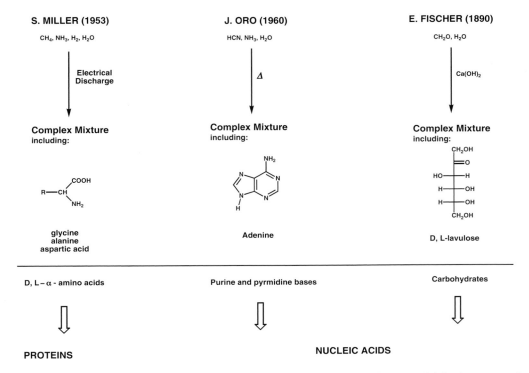

S. MILLER (1953)

CH$_4$, NH$_3$, H$_2$, H$_2$O

Electrical Discharge

Complex Mixture
including:

glycine
alanine
aspartic acid

J. ORO (1960)

HCN, NH$_3$, H$_2$O

Δ

Complex Mixture
including:

Adenine

E. FISCHER (1890)

CH$_2$O, H$_2$O

Ca(OH)$_2$

Complex Mixture
including:

D, L-lavulose

D, L–α - amino acids

Purine and pyrimidine bases

Carbohydrates

PROTEINS

NUCLEIC ACIDS

Figure 10.1 The foundations of pre-biotic chemistry showing the "starting materials", the means of provoking reaction and a summary of main elemental compounds produced.

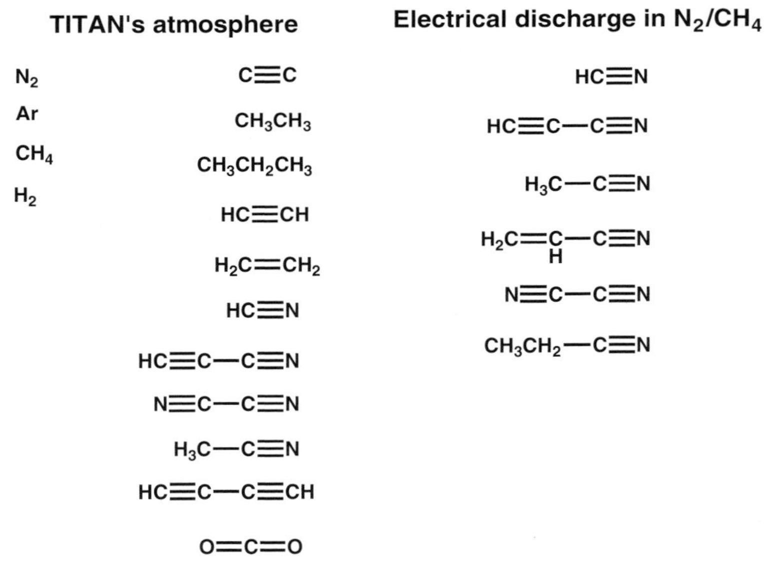

TITAN's atmosphere

N$_2$

Ar

CH$_4$

H$_2$

C≡C

CH$_3$CH$_3$

CH$_3$CH$_2$CH$_3$

HC≡CH

H$_2$C=CH$_2$

HC≡N

HC≡C—C≡N

N≡C—C≡N

H$_3$C—C≡N

HC≡C—C≡CH

O=C=O

Electrical discharge in N$_2$/CH$_4$

HC≡N

HC≡C—C≡N

H$_3$C—C≡N

H$_2$C=C—C≡N
　　　H

N≡C—C≡N

CH$_3$CH$_2$—C≡N

Figure 10.2 Interstellar gas cloud (TITAN's atmosphere) "starting materials" for pre-biotic chemistry, compared with the compounds that result from electrical discharge in an atmosphere of N$_2$ and CH$_4$. Note the extraordinary compatibility between these lists!

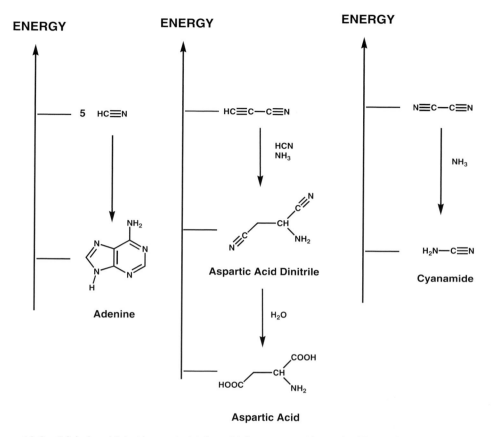

Figure 10.3 Triple bond "starting materials" are high energy and have significant chemical potential for onward conversion into elemental compounds that form basic building blocks for biological macromolecule formation.

elementary structures (from a chemical point of view). A molecular theory of the origins of life demands that anaerobic equivalents of amino acids, bases, prosthetic groups and cofactors should all be elementary structures able to form from lists of triple-bond compounds, by any one of a number of energetically acceptable pathways. A growing body of evidence appears to suggest that this is indeed the case.

10.1.4 Origins of biological macromolecules of life

There is a reasonable argument to suggest that protein prosthetic groups and cofactors should arise in advance of proteins and enzymes, since these are often directly responsible for the chemical reactivity of a given protein, supported by the surrounding polypeptide infrastructure. For this reason prosthetic groups and cofactors are sometimes referred to as 'molecular fossils'. A good example of a molecular fossil is **uroporphyrinogen III**, which is the main precursor to **protoporphyrin IX** found in **myoglobin**, **haemoglobin** and **cytochrome c** proteins (see Chapter 1). The anaerobic version of uroporphyrinogen III is **cyano-uroporphyrinogen III**, which can originate from cyano-aspartate and cyano-glycine (α-amino nitriles) via a number of steps involving heat or acid catalysis (Figure 10.4). Cyano-uroporphyrinogen III is therefore a classic elementary structure! There are four main isomers of cyano-uroporphyrinogen, but even with this relatively crude level of pre-biotic chemistry the type III isomer still dominates the other three and readily yields protoporphyrin IX after oxidation and hydrolysis. The main DNA/RNA purine and pyrimidine bases are also elementary structures. The formation of anaerobic versions of each of these from such simple chemical starting points is even more impressive, as shown in Figure 10.5. Please note that putative intermediates formed along the way even suggest pre-biotic routes to anaerobic forms of the redox active cofactors/prosthetic groups as well. Therefore, these may also be regarded as elementary structures.

Mapping putative pathway(s) from such anaerobic precursors to fully functional proteins or nucleic acids is not straightforward. In particular, routes to DNA need some careful consideration. The formose reaction gives complex product mixtures and low levels of racemic 5-carbon ribose, which may conflict with the Gilbert concept of a pre-biotic '**RNA world**' in spite of the appearance of catalytic RNA (ribozymes, see Chapter 8). One of the conundrums yet to be resolved in pre-biotic chemistry is the apparent preference for hexose over pentose sugars. Given this preference, why are DNA and RNA constructed from a pentose sugar and not hexose sugars? The answer may lie with the discovery that hexose DNA (**homo-DNA**) (Figure 10.6) is able to form antiparallel helices without rigorous application of the Watson–Crick base pair rules to such an extent that this critical basis of helical cohesion does not apply. Consequently, autocatalytic molecular replication of homo-DNA could not lead to the propagation of base-sequence-encoded genetic information. By contrast, pentose DNA does obey Watson–Crick base pair rules rigorously and therefore offers the best means for the transmission of base-sequence-encoded genetic information, coincident with autocatalytic molecular replication. From this discovery now flows a **chemical aetiology** of nucleic acid structure (Figure 10.6). In effect, the molecular evolution of nucleic acids requires a convergence upon pentose DNA and RNA via hexose nucleic acid 'evolutionary intermediates' (Figure 10.6).

10.2 Molecular breeding; natural selection acting on self-organisation

Breeding is essentially a man made process of natural selection. Mankind has used breeding to select for desired traits in other species for millennia. Crops have been bred to improve the yield and quality of their produce, yeasts for baking and fermentation, livestock for their increased nutritional value and increased docility, horses for their speed and strength and cats and dogs for their companionship. For these many thousands of years, all that was understood was that cross-breeding of individual organisms showing the desired characteristics often led to

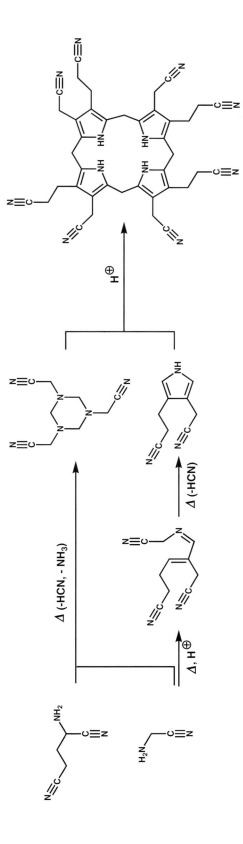

Cyano-uroporphyrinogen III

Figure 10.4 Putative pre-biotic chemistry route of conversion of **cyano-aspartic** and **cyano-glycine** (α-amino nitriles) into **cyano-uroporphyrinogen III**, the anaerobic equivalent to the key biosynthetic intermediate **uroporphyrinogen III** that is required for the subsequent formation of cofactor **protoporphyrin IX** found in **myoglobin**, **hemoglobin** and **cytochrome c** (see Chapter 1). Uroporphyrinogen III also gives rise to many other porphyrin-related pigments employed in respiration and photosynthesis.

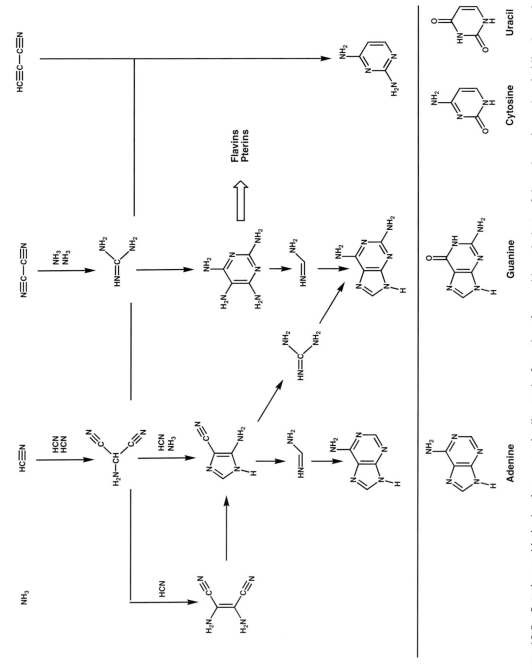

Figure 10.5 Putative pre-biotic chemistry routes leading to the formation of anaerobic equivalents of the main **purine** and **pyrimidine bases found in DNA and RNA**. Intermediates formed also suggest pathways to anaerobic equivalents of **redox active cofactors** (see Chapter 4).

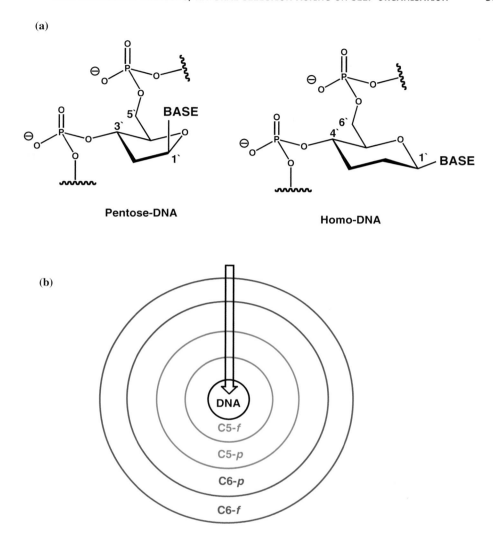

Figure 10.6   (a) Structural comparison between **DNA** (pentose-DNA) and **Homo-DNA**. Homo-DNA forms double helices in which Watson-Crick base pair rules are not rigorously retained; **(b)** diagram to illustrate the aetiology of nucleic acid polymer formation. The **formose reaction** generates very little and few pentose (**C5**) sugars hence pre-biotic nucleic acids are presumed to be made initially from hexose (**C6**) sugars first in furanose (*f*) and then pyranose (*p*) cyclic conformations, prior to selection of **C5-*p*** and then **C5-*f*** rings that confer nucleic acid double helices which both require and enable Watson-Crick base pairing.

the accumulation of desired characteristics in their progeny and subsequent generations. This approach was and is entirely empirical – function and utility were improved without any real understanding of the underlying principles behind the improvements. Since the pioneering work of Mendel, we are nowadays aware of the genes that 'code for traits', and how breeding seeks to modify or mutate genes. Furthermore, we are more aware of how these genes are controlled and/or regulated, in order to code for alternative traits that are considered desirable (or which may offer some selective advantage) in the biological niche required by the breeder.

As yet, the entire process of breeding cannot be replicated *de novo* in the laboratory at the molecular level, but those aspects concerning the modification or mutation of genes leading to protein mutations certainly can be. This might be thought of as the basis of **molecular breeding** in its simplest form. One theory of natural selection acting at the molecular level is that protein structure is the most open class of biological macromolecule to moulding and adaptation of function by successive mutations. Therefore, protein mutations are central to the process of organismal adaptation under selection pressure. The provision of a pool of protein mutations is then a mainstay requirement for the evolutionary process at the molecular level. However, there is some divergence of opinion between those who maintain that routes to improvements or new functions always involve a sequential evolutionary series of protein species each differing from its neighbouring species, before and after, by a single point mutation and those who allow for multiple mutations in each evolutionary series of protein species as well. In either event, the road to molecular breeding of improved or new protein functions becomes clear. Provided that a form of artificial selection pressure can be applied to an appropriately created pool of single or multiple mutations, then mutant proteins can be identified and isolated in principle with improved or new functions according to the desires of the molecular breeder.

The usual approach in chemistry is to firstly gain an understanding of structure and mechanism to provide insights that enable a reasoned approach to improved or altered binding or reactivities. Most of synthetic organic chemistry has used this approach to build an impressive corpus of knowledge that couples structure and reaction mechanism. This philosophy has also been extended to rational protein design – knowledge of structure and mechanism followed by reasoned site-directed mutagenesis can, for example, improve the catalytic efficiency of an enzyme. The **molecular breeding approach** is the obverse. In principle, molecular breeding allows for the discovery of improvements or alterations in biocatalytic activities (or binding activities) of proteins and RNA (and even now DNA) without much pre-knowledge of structure and mechanism. Hence, the problems involved in molecular breeding are quite different to the usual problems encountered in chemistry – how do we generate **molecular diversity** and then select for specific desired traits in an iterative process? Although not yet orthodoxy, this molecular breeding approach is having some practical and academic success. Practically, evolved proteins such as improved lipases and evolved modified green fluorescent protein are already in the marketplace. Academically, *in vitro* evolution is providing insight into the evolutionary process itself, and in studies of evolution of self-replicating systems may even be providing further insights into the molecular origins of life.

10.3 Directed evolution of protein function

One of the simplest approaches to molecular breeding is to begin with a gene for an enzyme that performs a certain activity, then introduce **variation** or molecular diversity at the genetic level into the gene by a number of methods including chemical mutagenesis, error-prone PCR,

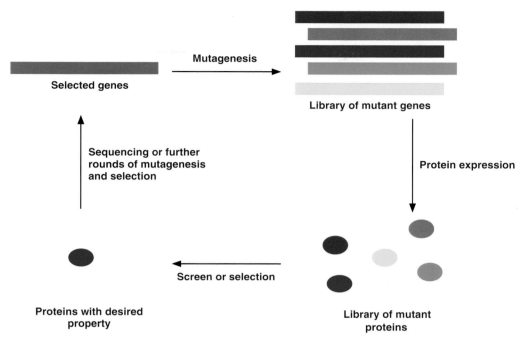

Figure 10.7 General strategy for **directed evolution** of protein activity. The gene of interested is mutated by different methods and the resultant **mutant gene library** is translated in to a library of protein mutants or variants. A **selection screen** is then used to identify protein mutants or **variants** with improved or novel characteristics. The corresponding mutant genes coding for the most improved or novel protein variants are then reselected for further rounds (iterations) of mutation and selection screening to allow for the identification of further improved protein variants. This iterative procedure of directed evolution continues as long as is required.

gene shuffling or incremental truncation. Virtually all basic molecular breeding approaches start with a protein that has a desired trait (at least to a small extent) – then the aim of the experiment *in vitro* is to improve or evolve that trait. Such a molecular breeding experiment may be called **directed evolution** of protein function. Mutant genes are generated and then protein variants are expressed and selected for by a specific assay designed to provide the artificial selection pressure. The most improved mutant protein variant is then identified and then the whole process is repeated again starting from the gene for the improved mutant protein variant (Figure 10.7).

10.3.1 Random mutagenesis and PCR

A useful method for the generation of molecular diversity starting from a given gene is to use a method of random mutagenesis by **error-prone polymerase chain reaction (error-prone PCR)** (Figure 10.8). Using error-prone PCR, the mutation rate must be carefully tuned – beneficial mutations are rare but deleterious mutations are common. If the mutation

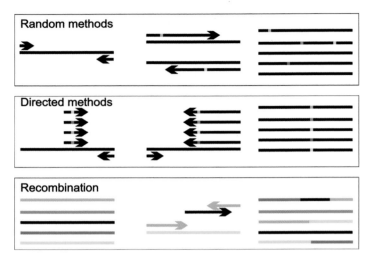

Figure 10.8 Methods for the randomization of DNA sequences using PCR. Each line in left column represents DNA duplex and each arrow a primer; the 5′-sense primer initiates strand copying using the complementary strand as a template, and the 5′-complementary primer initiates strand copying of the complementary strand using the sense strand as a template. **Random methods** such as **error-prone PCR** introduce random changes at positions throughout the gene sequence. **Directed methods** will introduce changes at a specific position(s) defined by lesions in the primers themselves. **Recombination methods** such as **family shuffling** start from a library of homologous genes from related species that can be artificially fragmented by DNAse I treatment and recombined by PCR (without added primers) leading to chimeric genes that code for chimeric proteins. These methods confer high levels of molecular diversity upon which to exercise selection screening for novel or improved characteristics.

rate is too high, then all beneficial mutations might be inactivated by secondary deleterious mutations. Conversely, if the mutation rate is too low then too few beneficial mutations will be observed. However, this method has significant drawbacks in that usually only one advantageous mutation will take place per selection event. Even by using sequential random mutagenesis, it is a relatively slow process to evolve a protein, and many useful mutations may be discarded (whose usefulness might only be uncovered through the presence of a second mutation), and other negative mutations are likely to linger. There are many ways of experimentally performing error-prone PCR. The standard PCR enzyme Taq polymerase is remarkably accurate, so different approaches are required to increase the error rate such as using Mn^{2+} in place of Mg^{2+} and varying the levels of dNTPs away from equimolar amounts. However, it is very difficult to eliminate **bias** from an error-prone PCR experiment. For instance, the characteristics of the polymerase mean that some mutations are more likely to occur than others (**error bias**). There are also problems in the nature of the genetic code, as some amino acids are coded for by single codons, whereas others are coded by many different codons; this means the likelihood of substituting for a particular amino acid within a particular codon varies from amino acid to amino acid (**codon bias**). A further source of bias is in the iterative nature of PCR itself – any mutation that occurs early in PCR is likely to occur in a significant percentage of the final DNA sequences (**amplification bias**). An alternative approach to error-prone PCR is to use **chemical mutagenesis**, where chemical mutagens are used to introduce less biased variations into the gene coding the original protein of interest. Another approach is to use **mutator strains.** These are bacterial strains that have defects in the DNA repair pathways, resulting in a far higher mutation rate than usual in the DNA carried in these strains. A significant problem with both these approaches is that there is little control over the extent of mutation – mutations will be found in the chromosome as well as in the construct harbouring the intended target gene. Also when using mutator strains, there is no simple control of the rate of mutation. Accordingly, error-prone PCR has generally superseded both of these methods as the preferred method to bring about random mutagenesis due to the greater control of mutagenesis rate and position on which this technique is able to deliver.

10.3.2 Mutagenesis and DNA shuffling

A great step forward was made with the development of DNA shuffling as a combinatorial approach for searching 'sequence space'. DNA shuffling consists of mixing together similar sequences harbouring mutations (Figure 10.8). **DNA shuffling**, or **sexual PCR**, solves the problem concerning the loss of potentially useful mutations in using error-prone PCR, mentioned above. Performing DNA shuffling involves a number of steps. First, random mutations are introduced into a sequence using error-prone PCR. These random mutations are initially screened to evaluate those that are apparently beneficial. Second, these beneficial mutants are then mixed together and gene sequences are randomly fragmented using the enzyme DNAse I, then recombined by performing a PCR reaction in the absence of added primer. Consequently, each beneficial mutant is embedded in a mixture of recombined genes at different locations in the gene sequence. Furthermore, new mutations might also be generated during this stage. Finally, primers are added before a final cycle of PCR to obtain a full-length PCR product. An extension of DNA shuffling approach is to start from a library of homologous genes that were originally from related species. This approach has been termed **family shuffling**, and it is possible to generate interesting chimeric genes and proteins that incorporate features of many of the parent genes into a single gene coding for a single polypeptide. In many ways, DNA shuffling is much closer than error-prone PCR to the events that give rise in nature to the pool of random mutations upon which the forces of natural selection operate for the evolution of improved protein activities or new functions.

10.3.3 Oligodeoxynucleotide cassette mutagenesis

Where more limited randomness is either desired or required, then selected sequences of the gene coding for the protein of interest may be targeted by oligonucleotide cassette mutagenesis. Typically, a short region of the gene 10–30 bases in length is selected for mutagenesis and primers may be chosen for focused error-prone PCR within this short region, after which the amplified region is recombined back into the wild-type gene replacing the original short region PCR. Alternatively, multiple 'site directed mutagenesis' experiments can be performed (see Chapter 3), using oligodeoxynucleotide mutagenesis primers ('dirty oligos') that are 'spiked' at each position of the primer with a small percentage of the three alternative nucleotides to the correct, complementary Watson–Crick base pair nucleotide at each position. 'Spiking' is designed to ensure that each mutant gene generated at the conclusion of the mutagenesis experiment will possess only one or possibly two base mutations per mutant gene. Accordingly, the 'spiking' should ensure that as close as possible to every possible single-point amino-acid residue mutation may be sampled in a mutant library across the entire range of the chosen short region within the original protein of interest. This process represents **random** or **saturation mutagenesis** in the purest sense (Figure 10.9). One the other hand, mutagenesis primers may instead be designed to promote only single point mutations of single amino-acid residues of a similar type, class or identity. There is in fact a huge range of possibilities using cassette mutagenesis for the creation of molecular diversity within a limited region of structure within a given protein of interest.

10.3.4 Screening strategies

The number of protein variants that can be screened in a molecular breeding experiment is often limited by the speed and convenience of the assay for the activity that is desired. Therefore, the screen should be well designed so that there is an easy way of identifying improved proteins when they arise. For instance, if improved fluorescent properties are required in a molecular breeding experiment then the screen only needs to measure gains in protein fluorescence above a set threshold. Other objectives of a molecular breeding experiment may be to change the conditions under which biocatalysis take place, for example in non-aqueous solvents, under different conditions of pH or at increased temperatures. In these cases, simple screens can also be devised to identify improved proteins. Where altered enzyme specificity is required, the design of effective screens becomes more challenging and especially so if *de novo* biocatalytic activity is required. The following worked example should serve to demonstrate how a screening process integrates with the mutagenesis steps in a molecular breeding experiment to lead to the identification of improved proteins with the desired functions.

Asymmetric catalysis is the ability of a chiral catalyst to catalyse an achiral substrate to a chiral product with a bias for the formation of one of the enantiomers. There is a huge demand for chiral products throughout the chemical industry, in particular for pharmaceuticals, where it is often the case that for chiral drugs only one of the enantiomers is pharmaceutically active, and in the most infamous example of thalidomide the other enantiomer can actually be harmful. Despite the demand, asymmetric catalysis remains a significant challenge using conventional organic chemistry. One approach to meeting the challenge is in the use of directed evolution of a carefully selected enzyme to evolve the requisite, desired enantioselectivity. There are two main challenges in realising such a molecule breeding experiment.

(a) Designing methods to introduce molecular diversity that is likely to be beneficial.

(b) Designing a simple high-throughput screen to identifying improved proteins.

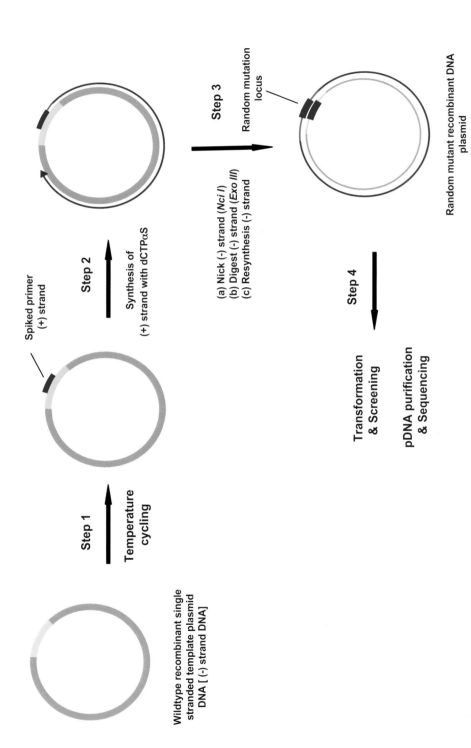

Figure 10.9 Non-PCR random mutagenesis. Overview of a random site-directed mutagenesis method. Obtain template DNA [ssDNA (−) strand]; Step 1: anneal spiked oligodeoxy nucleotide mutagenic primer (blue) with desired mutation range; Step 2: extend and incorporate mutagenic primer into new (+) strand containing dCTPαS; Step 3: digest the template DNA (−) strand with *Nci I* and *Exo III*, then reynthesize (−) strand to include mutations into (−) strand as well; Step 4: transform *E. coli* with random mutant recombinant DNA plasmid ready for selection, DNA purification and sequence identification of mutant recombinant DNAs.

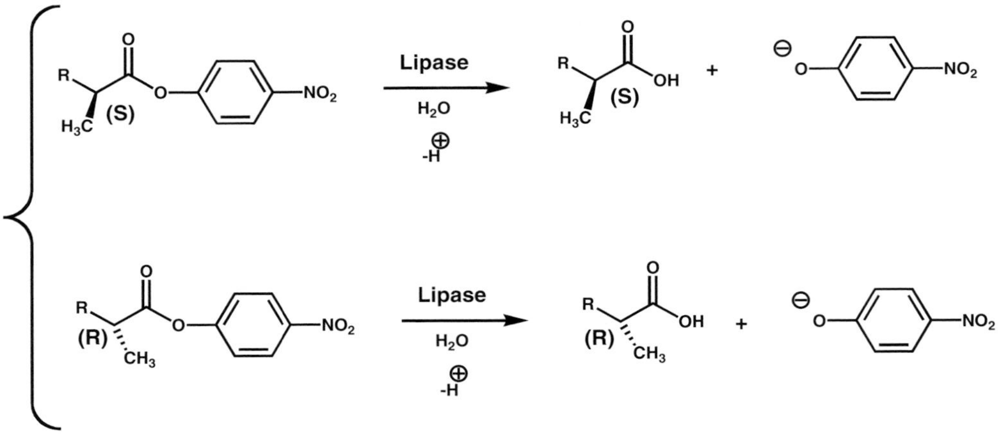

Figure 10.10　Reaction catalysed by a **lipase** from *Pseudomonas aeruginosa* chosen for **directed evolution of enantioselectivity**.

In the following case, we shall look at the molecular breeding of the lipase from the bacterium *Pseudomonas aeruginosa*. This particular molecular breeding experiment was the first example of the directed evolution of an enantioselective enzyme. The wild-type enzyme catalyses the hydrolysis of esters to carboxylic acid (Figure 10.10), and shows very little enantioselectivity – only two per cent enantiomeric excess biased towards the (S) configuration.

In the original experiment, molecular diversity was introduced by error-prone PCR, used under conditions designed to ensure that only one or possibly two base mutations were introduced per mutant gene in an attempt to ensure that every possible single point amino-acid residue mutation could be sampled at least across the entire primary structure of the original protein of interest (Figure 10.11). The numbers start to speak for themselves. The lipase of interest consists of 285 amino acids. Each amino acid could be mutated to any one of the 19 other natural amino acids, so there can be 5415 possible single point amino-acid residue mutants produced. This figure rises where double point mutants are concerned to 15 million possible unique variations, onwards to 52 billion possible variations when unique triple point mutants are envisaged. Such numbers are normal for protein mutant libraries and reflect the size of the challenge for efficient and effective screening. **High throughput screening** is indispensable given such molecular diversity. In the case of this lipase example, the assay used was a simple UV–visible spectroscopy assay monitoring effective enzymatic hydrolysis in terms of the appearance of the *p*-nitrophenolate anion (detected by absorbance A_{405}). Each mutant protein was tested in a pairwise assay, testing hydrolysis of both the (S)- and the (R)-substrates. The relative rates of hydrolysis gave a measure of the enantiomeric selectivity (the **enantiomeric excess**, ee, as a percentage) as given by

$$ee = \left(\frac{[R] - [S]}{[R] + [S]} \right) \times 100 \tag{10.1}$$

where [R] and [S] are the molar concentrations of the (R)- and (S)-products respectively.

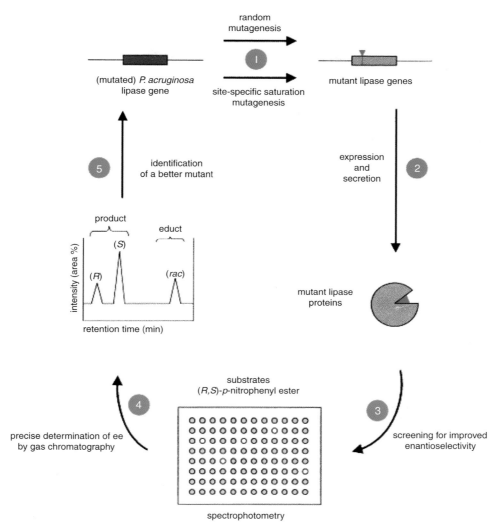

Figure 10.11 Strategy for evolving an enantioselective lipase. Molecular diversity is introduced by random mutagenesis of the lipase gene and site-specific random or saturation mutagenesis. Mutant genes resulting are segregated and separately expressed in individual bacterial clones. Protein product is secreted into the extracellular medium and a **spectrophotometric assay used to assay for nitrophenolate production** from **(R)** and **(S)** **substrates** by action of active lipase enzymes (see Fig 10.10). Relative quantities of **(R)** and **(S)** product are quantified by gas chromatography and where enantioselectivity is also discovered then the corresponding gene is harvested for another round of mutagenesis and selection (Reproduced from Liebeton et al., 2000, Fig. 5).

In the initial screening around 1000 mutant enzymes were generated from the first (and subsequent) rounds of mutation, and of these approximately one per cent showed an increased enantioselectivity, up to 31 per cent ee, a significant improvement over the wild type enzyme. These mutant enzymes were then subject to three further rounds of mutation and selection, after which a mutant was identified, able to deliver on an enantioselectivity of up to 81 per cent ee (corresponding to an E value of 11.3). Saturation mutagenesis was then performed at local 'hot spots', designated in the primary sequence where amino-acid residue changes were thought most likely to be beneficial, leading to a mutant enzyme competent to produce an E value of 25. Further improvements to this efficacy were obtained by a new error-prone PCR step modified to introduce around three mutations per gene per generation, followed by DNA shuffling, resulting in a mutant protein with an E value of 32 post selection. Finally, a modified form of DNA shuffling named **combinatorial multiple-cassette mutagenesis** resulted in the identification of a much improved mutant with the ability to deliver on an E value of over >52.

10.4 Directed evolution of nucleic acids

The evolution of nucleic acids is a more direct process when compared with the evolution of proteins. For directed protein evolution, the full cycle of transcription and translation is required to take place, and this generally means that stages of the process have to be performed using a living system to translate the protein. Selection and evolution of nucleic acids can, however, be routinely carried out using an entirely chemical *in vitro* process – *in vitro* **molecular breeding.** The binding strengths of nucleic acids can approach those of proteins, though the catalytic repertoire of nucleic acids is significantly reduced. In this section, we shall describe approaches for the selection and evolution of both RNA and DNA for both binding and catalysis.

10.4.1 Aptamers

Nucleic acids can play roles far beyond merely harbouring the coding information for proteins. Single-stranded nucleic acids can fold into intricate structures capable of molecular recognition and even catalysis. Three-dimensional structures are specified by the primary structure, namely the deoxynucleotide (or nucleotide, for RNA) sequence ($5' \rightarrow 3'$, by analogy to the situation in which the amino-acid residue sequence determines the three-dimensional structures of polypeptides. In nature, transfer RNAs (tRNAs) use their three-dimensional shape for molecular recognition, while some ribosomal RNAs (rRNAs) are able to catalyse crucial steps even within the protein synthetic pathways themselves.

From a technology perspective, a massive pool of nucleic acids (RNA, DNA or modified nucleotides) (that provides for the required molecular diversity) represents a huge library from which to select, amplify and identify novel binding partners (**aptamers**) or even novel biocatalysts (**aptazymes**). This type of molecular breeding is known as the systematic evolution of ligands by exponential enrichment (**SELEX**) **process** (Figure 10.12). Using the SELEX

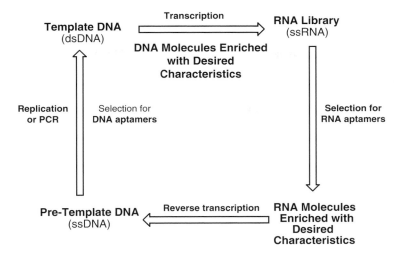

Figure 10.12 A general scheme for the *in vitro* selection and evolution of **DNA** and/or **RNA aptamers**, otherwise known as **SELEX** (selective evolution of ligands by exponential enrichment).

process, it is possible to evolve naïve nucleic acids until they are capable of binding specifically to proteins, peptides, cells, nucleic acids and even other small molecules. Nucleic acids capable of catalysing chemical reactions may also be evolved. SELEX may be used to select from both RNA and DNA libraries. RNA has greater potential structural diversity than DNA, hence affinities for a potential target should be generally higher overall. DNA has less structural diversity than RNA, hence affinities for a potential target should be generally lower overall, albeit with a higher degree of overall intrinsic stability. SELEX steps are outlined below.

10.4.1.1 Design and construction of a polydeoxynucleotide/polynucleotide library

A polydeoxynucleotide library is synthesised for molecular breeding by standard solid phase methodologies except that randomised single-stranded DNA (**pre-template DNA**) is synthesised with a 3'-flanking region of known sequence that can be recognised by a primer in a PCR reaction. Randomisation is achieved by using an approximately equal mix of the four phosphoramidite building blocks during solid phase synthesis (see Chapter 2) weighted according to differences in coupling efficiencies in order to ensure lack of deoxynucleotide bias in the final library. When a fully randomised polydeoxynucleotide is prepared from the four main deoxynucleotide building blocks (dA, dG, dC, dT), then the molecular diversity is equivalent to 4^n, where n is the number of randomised base positions (25 in this case, giving a total number of 10^{15} library sequences). If n is increased to 30, then the molecular diversity increases to a library of 10^{18}. Beyond this, molecular diversity becomes unmanageable. For instance, if a stretch of 100 random positions were to be studied, then the molecular diversity would approach the number of elementary particles in the universe! Therefore, 25–30 randomised positions are typically used in preference. After the pre-template DNA is synthesised, a primer is annealed to the known sequence region and complementary strands are synthesised using the **Klenow fragment** of DNA polymerase I, yielding randomised double-stranded DNA (**template DNA**).

In nature, natural RNA–protein recognition sites comprise 15–25 nucleotide residues, suggesting that a high affinity binding polynucleotide should also be 25–30 nucleotide residues in length. Therefore, an appropriate **RNA library** may be generated by direct transcription from template DNA by means of T7 RNA polymerase operating from a T7 promoter element inserted during synthesis of the template DNA. Often modified nucleotides are used in place of the natural ones to confer extra stability on RNA molecules produced – this is especially important in the design of aptamers for therapeutic purposes. The most common approach is to modify β-D-ribofuranose rings attached to pyrimidine bases with $2'$-F or $2'$-NH$_2$, modifications that confer resistance to most RNAases. The 5-position of the uracil base may also be modified. Fortuitously, the T7 RNA polymerase is able to tolerate the insertion of modified bases and β-D-ribofuranose rings at the $2'$-position reasonably well.

10.4.1.2   Partition, amplification and iteration

The next stage in the molecular breeding of functional DNA molecules from template DNA should be simple screening in order to distinguish those DNA molecules that are able to perform the required task from those that are not. For instance, if DNA aptamers are desired then the target ligand could be immobilised on a column and **affinity chromatography** used: nucleic acids that do bind to the column would bind to the target ligand, whilst those that do not would pass through. An alternative that is often used in SELEX experiments is to immobilise the target on a **nitrocellulose filter**. Partition is the most critical variable of a SELEX experiment: it is important to be able to efficiently cut down the initial complexity of 10^{15}–10^{18} sequences in a template DNA library to a manageable number of sequences in as few rounds of screening as possible. Part of this process is also to prevent or minimise the possibility of non-specific binding of nucleic acids to column or filter media giving rise to false positives. Several rounds of screening may be carried out to refine the pool of high affinity DNA binders to the target ligand of choice before proceeding to sequence characterisation.

In the case of RNA library screening for RNA aptamers, the process involves first the isolation of functional mRNA that survives the selection procedure, and then this selected pool of mRNA is converted first into next-generation pre-template DNA by reverse transcription and then into next generation template DNA by means of PCR (this is equivalent to the cDNA synthesis described previously; see Chapter 3). Transcription by means of T7 RNA polymerase is subsequently performed so that RNA selection may then begin again starting from this reduced, next generation mRNA library of 'positive hits'. Selection then proceeds through further complete rounds of target ligand binding and release until high affinity RNA binders to the target ligand of choice are found. If required, the template DNA can be introduced into a cloning vector and individual clones may be sequenced (see Chapter 3).

Where the identification of either DNA or RNA aptamers is required, alignment of either set of sequences post several rounds of screening should lead to the identification of critical consensus sequences, required for the desired aptameric activity. Often this results in **families of aptamers** – competition experiments may then be performed to see whether these families compete for the same target. The aptamer families selected can then be refined in a number of ways. First, **truncation** may be used to determine the minimum length aptamer capable of binding to the target with high affinity. Sometimes possible truncations may be clear from the alignments of the various sequences; truncations can be easily designed and tested using standard molecular biology techniques. Alternatively, digestions from either end may be attempted then separated against the target to define the exact length required for high affinity binding. Several structures of aptamers in complex with their targets have been solved (Figures 10.13 and 10.14).

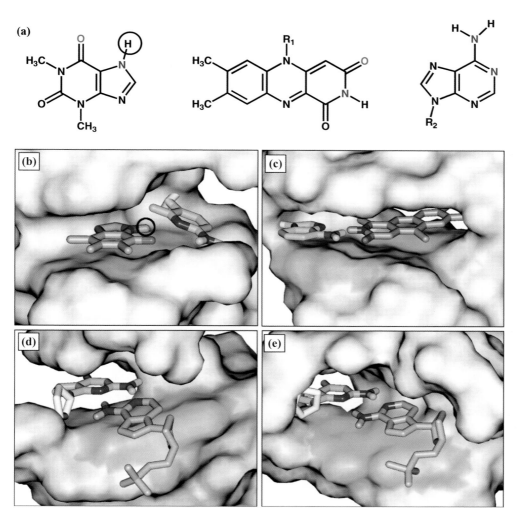

Figure 10.13 Examples of structures for **RNA aptamers** (b-e) selected against small molecules (panel A). Small molecules are rendered in **stick format** and aptamers in **Van der Waals surface representations** (Reproduced from Hermann and Patel, 2000, Fig. 1).

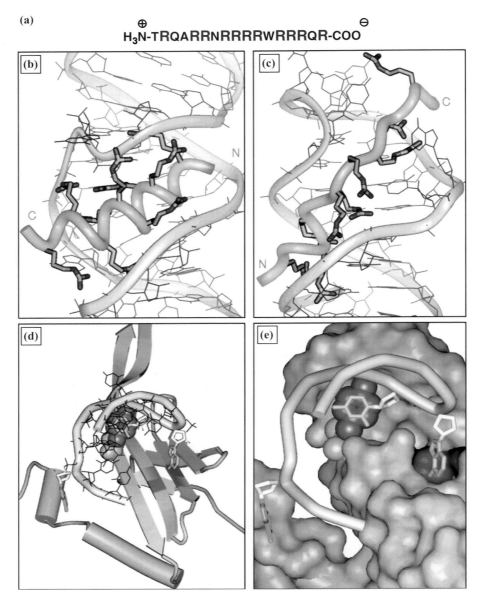

Figure 10.14 **Molecular recognition** of peptide (panel **a**) by nucleic acid aptamers (**b & c**) and of proteins by nucleic acid aptamers (**d & e**). Aptamers are rendered throughout in **ribbon representation** (grey); peptide (yellow-brown) as α-**carbon backbone trace** with **amino acid side chains in a stick representation**; protein (yellow brown) in **cartoon representation** (**d**) and **Van der Waals surface representation** (**e**). Protein binding pockets are illustrated in red (Reproduced from Hermann and Patel, 2000, Fig. 4).

10.4.1.3   *Applications of aptamers*

Many parallels may be seen between **therapeutic aptamers** and **therapeutic antibodies**. Although therapeutic antibodies have perhaps a more established reputation, aptamers compete well with antibodies in the following respects.

(a) Aptamers are selected in an entirely *in vitro* process that allows for specificity and affinity to be tightly controlled, and allows selection against toxic or non-immunogenic targets.

(b) Aptamers generally bind more strongly to a target than an antibody, and are able to disrupt protein-protein interactions.

(c) Aptamers show little immunogenicity and no toxicity, and can be delivered subcutaneously.

(d) Aptamers are easily synthesised, readily producible in bulk and easily stored as lyophilised powders.

Similarly to antibodies, aptamers are able to bind to virtually any target with an affinity in the nanomolar to micromolar range. In order to play a therapeutic role, they must bind tightly and inhibit a specific biomolecule function by binding tightly whilst showing no harmful side-effects. One such aptamer tested in a therapeutic context was a DNA aptamer against thrombin that is able to prolong blood clot time *in vitro*. Aptamers are also playing increasingly important roles in molecular diagnostics: for example, they can be linked to fluorescence tags and be converted into beacons to signify the presence of a key disease marker at very low levels of detection.

10.4.2 Selection of catalytic RNA

There are two general steps to evolving a catalytic RNA. First, from a pool of sequence variants there must be a screening protocol that separates active RNA with the desired trait from others without it. Second, the genome of the survivors must be copied and amplified via DNA intermediates prior to the next round of selection. The process is iterative, and heavily reliant on the ease of nucleic acid copying by PCR amplification. Thereafter, there are two methods of selection, direct or indirect. In a **direct selection**, there is chemical transformation of the catalytic RNA during the selection step. In an **indirect selection**, an RNA aptamer approach is taken but RNA aptamers are identified and evolved to bind to a transition state in the reaction that is desired to be catalysed (this indirect method is similar to the strategy used to develop catalytic antibodies – see Section 10.5).

In **direct selection**, one needs a method to separate catalytic from non-catalytic RNA. There are three general approaches:

(a) **differential migration** by polyacrylamide gel electrophoresis

(b) **primer-binding site tagging** technique

(c) **affinity probe tagging** technique.

In differential migration, the catalytic RNA itself is the product of the reaction, and therefore may be selected. For example, the target may be self-cleavage of RNA or the ligation of RNA that is already covalently linked to the catalytic region elsewhere. Clearly, if a reaction takes place then the result should have a different electrophoretic mobility to the situation where no reaction takes places. Hence PAGE may be used to separate cleanly reacting from non-reacting scenarios. Alternatively, the primer-binding site tagging technique is useful where, for example, a ligation reaction is being analysed. In this case, successful ligation introduces a stretch of RNA sequence onto the catalytic RNA itself that could double as a PCR primer site. Consequently, successful PCR amplification will only be possible if the ligation reaction has succeeded in the first place. Therefore only RNA that is properly catalytic can and will be amplified by PCR amplification. Finally, affinity probe tagging is useful for the identification of catalytic RNA that is able to catalyse other chemical reactions. The chemical reaction of interest should be designed to result in the RNA self-tagging with an affinity probe such as biotin. Hence correctly catalytic RNA may then be simply separated from non-catalytic RNA by streptavidin protein affinity chromatography.

A number of attempts have been made to evolve catalytic RNAs or ribozymes from **natural ribozymes** and also from pools of random sequence RNA. Natural ribozymes have the advantage that a natural active site already exists so can be evolved – such approaches have had some success in improving or altering catalytic properties. Otherwise, ribozymes that have been evolved so far include catalytic RNA nucleases, ligases and polynucleotide kinases. Similar approaches have also been employed to evolve ribozymes that catalyse reactions at carbon bonds, such as functional group transfers, including N-alkylation (e.g. using the 2-amino functional group of guanosine to displace iodide from iodoacetamide) and S-alkylation (e.g. using 5′-phosphorothioate to displace bromide from an N-bromacetyl peptide). In general, the structure of catalytic RNAs that catalyse reactions at carbon bonds tends to be more complex than those that catalyse reactions at phosphodiester bonds, reflecting the more complex conformations required to bind non-nucleotide substrates. Overall, natural ribozymes turn out to be much more efficient catalysts than evolved ribozymes so there is much room for further research in this area.

10.4.3 DNA aptamers and catalytic DNAs

Catalytic DNA is made possible because single-stranded DNA can adopt complex tertiary structures in a similar way to RNA, although unlike RNA no DNA-based catalysts have yet been found in nature. Both DNA aptamers and **DNA catalysts** (**deoxyribozymes**) can be evolved by molecular breeding experiments equivalent to those used to evolve RNA aptamers and ribozymes. However, DNA polydeoxynucleotide sequences are less flexible and accommodating than corresponding RNA polynucleotide sequences owing to the absence of a 2'-hydroxyl group in the sugar ring of each deoxynucleotide residue. Nevertheless, DNA aptamers and deoxyribozymes are significantly more stable to most nucleases than unmodified RNA aptamers and ribozymes, and the possibility of deoxyribozyme catalysts has reignited the debate about the molecular origins of life and reopened the RNA world concept to further scrutiny!

Single-stranded DNA aptamers identified were found to bind thrombin with a K_d value of 25–200 nM. The central core (15–17 residues in length) was found to assume a **G-quartet structure**, a very common structural motif in both DNA and RNA aptamers (Figure 10.15). DNA aptamers that bind other proteins have since been found to have several

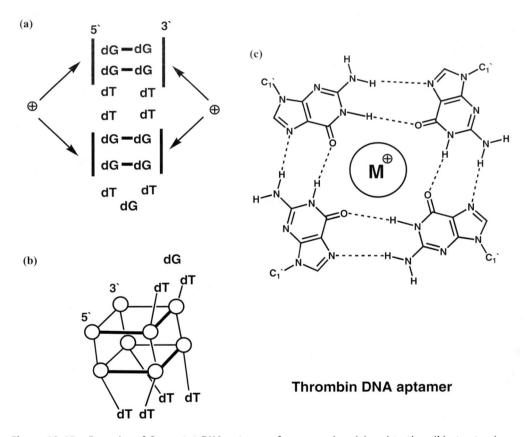

Thrombin DNA aptamer

Figure 10.15 Examples of **G-quartet DNA aptamers** from secondary (**a**) and tertiary (**b**) structural perspectives. The planar G quartet found in many DNA aptamers is also illustrated in detail (**c**). Solid bars (**a**) indicate regions of G quartet motifs. The **M**$^+$ ion in (**c**) is typically Na$^+$ or K$^+$. G-quartets produce stacks wherein backbones can be parallel or anti-parallel with respect to each other. Stacked G-quartets are also identified in special regions of eukaryotic chromosomes called **telomeres**.

other defining structural features, including bulges, stem-loops and pseudoknots. DNA aptamers have also been enriched against small molecules. For instance, a DNA aptamer has been evolved to selectively bind ATP with a 6 μM affinity. DNA aptamers have also been enriched that bind to a variety of porphyrin rings. Curiously, where RNA aptamers have been evolved to bind the same target ligands, they show no sequence homology with DNA aptamers at all. In other words, DNA and RNA aptamers are in fact structurally diverse although functionally equivalent.

Going beyond DNA aptamers, catalytic DNA, or **deoxyribozymes**, have been evolved to cleave RNA or DNA, metalate porphyrins, cleave *N*-glycosidic bonds and ligate DNA. The majority of deoxyribozymes isolated catalyse RNA cleavage by phosphoester transfer, usually in the presence of a metal cofactor. The general approach for discovery of a cleaving deoxyribozyme is follows. An initial population of single-stranded DNA is synthesised that incorporates a primer target site, a target sequence, a randomised sequence with a second 3′-primer target site, and a 5′-end biotin label for simple immobilisation. This multifunctional polydeoxynucleotide is first immobilised on a **streptavidin protein** matrix, then non-binding DNA molecules are washed away. Those immobilised DNA molecules are then incubated under suitable reaction conditions, importantly incorporating potential deoxyribozyme metal cofactors. Thereafter, successful catalytic DNA molecules that self-cleave from the column are washed clear and then amplified using PCR and a biotin-labelled primer. Double-stranded DNA from PCR amplification is then rebound to the streptavidin matrix. The process is repeated until the catalytic activity of the deoxyribozyme reaches a plateau. At this stage the evolved deoxyribozyme may then be eluted, sequenced and the different species aligned to define the catalytic motif. In order to evolve deoxyribozymes against other fissile bonds or links, the screening procedure is actually the same, although the appropriate target cleavage site should be included in the initial multifunctional polydeoxynucleotide.

The process of discovering a deoxyribozyme capable of ligation of RNA is an excellent example of catalytic DNA development. The process was begun with an initial multifunctional polydeoxynucleotide designed to possess two regions complementary to two arbitrary RNA substrates (Figure 10.16). Between these two arms was positioned a randomised sequence wherein ligase activity was to be evolved and enriched. Otherwise, a few bases of the RNA were left unpaired to minimise steric hindrance with respect to DNA. In the first step of selection, right-hand side RNA was annealed to the DNA, and ligated using T4 RNA ligase enzyme. PAGE was then used to separate out and purify any DNA/RNA duplex formed. In the second step, the left-hand side RNA incorporating a 2′, 3′-cyclic phosphate was added. This second RNA was expected to anneal by Watson–Crick base pairing to the available DNA binding site to set up the opportunity for ligation. Any such potential ligation reactions were also enabled through the incorporation of potential deoxyribozyme metal cofactors again. Successful ligation was diagnosed by a change in electrophoretic mobility on polyacrylamide gels of the ligated product as compared to the mobility of the non-ligated, uncatalysed situation. In this way, catalytic DNA was gradually separated from non-catalytic DNA. This whole process was actually repeated in an iterative manner with multiple cycles until most of the pool of DNA remaining was observed to have some ligase activity.

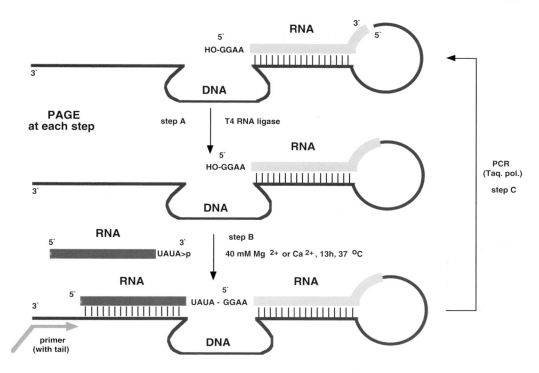

Figure 10.16 Deoxyribozymes. An approach to selection of deoxyribozymes that **ligate RNA**. DNA template is represented by dark grey line. The DNA loop contains random sequence variations to allow for the possibility of catalysis. **Step A:** complementary RNA (**yellow**) is ligated to a DNA template with a 5'-terminal overhang; **Step B:** a second RNA (**red**) is Watson-Crick base pair associated with the same DNA template but with a 3'-terminal overhang. Ligation reaction is then promoted. Where ligation is possible, the PAGE electrophoretic mobility of the product will differ from the un-ligated situation; **Step C:** PCR is then used to determine the DNA sequence(s) responsible for RNA ligation catalysis. Further rounds of maturation are also possible [illustration adapted from Flynn-Charlebois *et al.*, 2003, Fig. 1B).

10.5 Catalytic antibodies

Many parallels can be drawn between the use of aptamers and the use of antibodies. Of course, the critical structural difference is that aptamers are based on polynucleotide or polydeoxynucleotide chains whilst antibodies are based on polypeptide chains and in particular the immunoglobulin fold. A vertebrate immune system typically has the capacity to biosynthesise, in immune cells known as B-cells, at least 10^{10} structurally distinct antibodies, each with a specific affinity to foreign materials known as antigens (see Chapter 7). Antibody production comprises part of the **humoral immune response** mounted against invading pathogens or other foreign agents. If a chemical ligand (**hapten**) is coupled to a carrier protein such as **keyhole limpet haemocyanin (KLH)** or **bovine serum albumin (BSA)** then the bioconjugation product can be very immunogenic with respect to the humoral immune response. Injection of such a product into a mouse or rabbit creates a substantial blood-borne response that is reflected by huge B-cell production in their spleens. Hence, these animals are sacrificed and their spleens extracted for B-cell populations that are fused to cancer cell lines such as myeloma cells, resulting in immortalised B-cell lines (**hybridomas**). Hybridomas are intended to act as antibody cell factories, and each hybridoma should be able to produce a unique antibody specific to a different antigen. Where hybridomas are responsible for the production of anti-hapten antibodies, they are identified by cell population screening, isolated and cloned by cell culturing. Each hybridoma so cloned should be responsible for the production of one single type of antibody (**monoclonal antibody**). Typically, monoclonal antibodies must be subject to final screening to identify that population of monoclonal antibodies optimal for hapten binding.

According to the most advanced theories of enzyme catalysis, differential stabilisation of reaction transition states relative to ground states is the most effective way to effect catalysis irrespective of whether there is an excess or lack of substrate available for biocatalysis (see Chapter 8; Figure 10.17). Therefore, in order for an antibody to act as an enzyme, the antibody

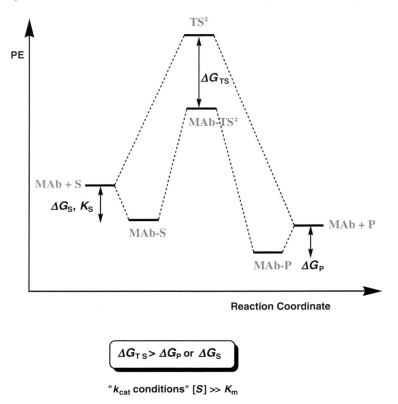

Figure 10.17 Illustration of **catalytic monoclonal antibody (MAb)** catalyzed conversion of substrate **S** to product **P** versus the uncatalyzed situation. Catalysis by antibody is made possible by **differential stabilization of the rate determining step transition state** for the reaction relative to **S** and/or **P**. This is also a fundamental for enzyme-based reaction catalysis as well (see Chapter 8).

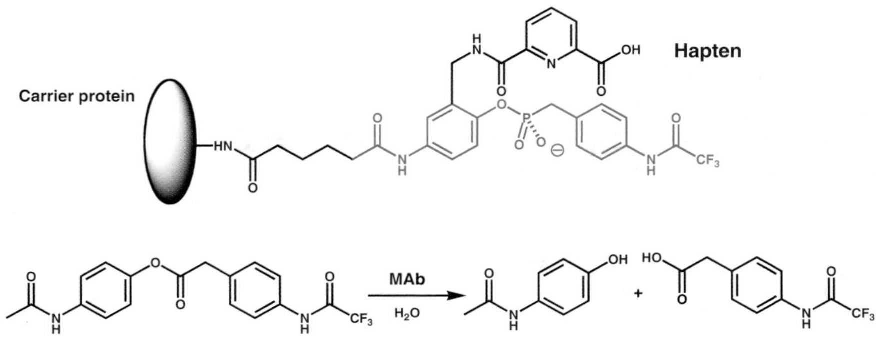

Figure 10.18 Catalytic monoclonal antibody (MAb) mediated **ester hydrolysis**. The MAb was generated through immunoreaction with the illustrated **hapten** linked to an appropriate carrier protein. The part of the hapten related to the substrate structure is shown in red. The **phosphonate link** is used as a **transition state analogue** of the rate determining step transition state leading to the key tetrahedral intermediate of ester hydrolysis. The MAb should optimally bind the rate determining step transition state relative to substrate or products in order to effect maximum catalytic effect.

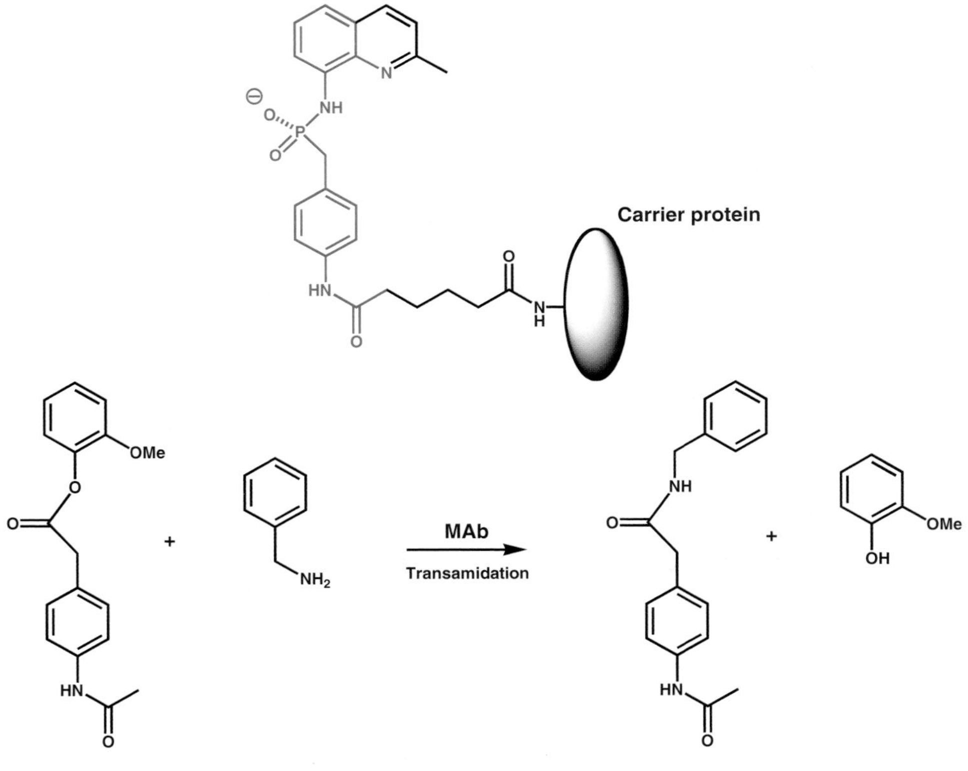

Figure 10.19 Catalytic monoclonal antibody (MAb) mediated **transamidation**. The MAb was generated through immunoreaction with the illustrated hapten linked to an appropriate carrier protein. The part of the hapten related to the substrate structure is shown in red. The **phosphoamidate** link is used as a transition state analogue of the rate determining step transition state leading to the key tetrahedral intermediate. The MAb should optimally bind the rate determining step transition state relative to the substrates or products in order to effect maximum catalytic effect.

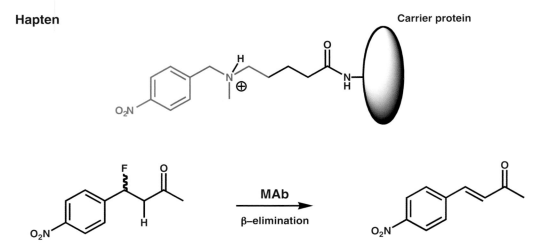

Figure 10.20 Catalytic monoclonal antibody (MAb) mediated β-**elimination** of HF. The MAb was generated through immunoreaction with the illustrated hapten linked to an appropriate carrier protein. The part of the hapten related to the substrate structure is shown in red. The **tertiary amine functional group** is introduced to encourage the generation of catalytic antibodies with complementary base/nucleophiles in the vicinity of the substrate α-proton when substrate binds to MAb in order to facilitate catalysis of **E2 elimination** by a combination of general base catalysis as well as the more usual differential stabilization of the rate determining step transition state through binding. Enzymes usually employ more than just differential stabilization of rate determining step transition states in order to effect catalysis but also employ several other physical "tricks" as well (see Chapter 8).

should possess an optimal affinity in binding no longer to a ground state molecule such as an antigen but to a reaction transition state. In principle then, any monoclonal antibody raised against a transition state analogue should be able to act as a biocatalyst for the corresponding reaction (Figure 10.17). The design of a transition state analogue requires an element of chemical surrogacy and imagination. For instance, phosphonate appears to be a useful surrogate for the rate determining tetrahedral transition state formed by the addition of water to an ester, prior to the second alcohol elimination step. Indeed, not only is the phosphonate group mono-charged but the P–O bond (1.521 Å) is intermediate in length between the C–O bond found in the actual tetrahedral intermediate and the presumed C–O bond length projected in the transition state. Other examples of transition state analogues and catalytic antibody catalysis are shown in Figure 10.18. Catalytic antibodies may also affect biocatalysis of biomolecular reactions such as transamidation (Figure 10.19). A word of caution though: as with natural ribozymes so with natural enzymes, on the whole catalytic antibodies do not affect biocatalysis with the same efficiency as natural enzymes. Indeed, they usually fall a long way short. Hence, in order to improve catalytic-antibody-mediated biocatalysis, alternative, additional theories of catalysis have been employed including general acid–base, nucleophilic and/or electrophilic catalysis (see Chapter 8; Figure 10.20). Advances in the area of catalytic antibodies continue to be made.

References

Chapter 1

General reading

D. Voet, J. G. Voet and C. W. Pratt, *Fundamentals of Biochemistry*, 1999, Wiley, New York.

A. R. Fersht, *Structure and Mechanism in Protein Science, a Guide to Enzyme Catalysis and Protein Folding*, 1999, Freeman, New York.

A. M. Lesk, *Protein Architecture a Practical Approach*, 1991, IRL Press at Oxford University Press, Oxford.

M. J. E. Sternberg (Ed.), *Protein Structure Prediction a Practical Approach*, 1996, IRL Press at Oxford University Press, Oxford.

C. Branden and J. Tooze, *Introduction to Protein Structure*, 2nd Edition, 1999, Garland, New York.

T. E. Creighton, *Proteins*, 2nd Edition, 1993, Freeman, New York.

D. A. Rees, *Outline Studies in Biology Polysaccharide Shapes*, 1977, Chapman and Hall, London.

J. F. Kennedy and C. A. White, *Bioactive Carbohydrates in Chemistry, Biochemistry and Biology*, 1983, Ellis Horwood, Chichester.

G. O. Aspinall (Ed.) *The Polysaccharides* Vol. 1, 1982, Academic, New York.

G. O. Aspinall (Ed.) *The Polysaccharides* Vol. 2, 1983, Academic, New York.

G. M. Blackburn and M. J. Gait (Eds.), *Nucleic Acids in Chemistry and Biology*, 1990, IRL Press at Oxford University Press, Oxford.

R. R. Sinden, *DNA Structure and Function*, 1994, Academic, San Diego.

D. M. Small, *Handbook of Lipid Research 4 The Physical Chemistry of Lipids*, 1986, Plenum, New York.

G. Cevc (Ed.) *Phospholipids Handbook*, 1993, Dekker, New York.

P. W. Atkins, *Physical Chemistry*, 5th Edition, 1995, Oxford University Press, Oxford.

Extra reading

D. W. Banner, A. Bloomer, G. A. Petsko, D. C. Phillips and I. A. Wilson, Atomic coordinates for triose phosphate isomerase from chicken muscle, *Biochem. Biophys. Res. Commun.*, 1976, **72**, 146–155 (pdb: **1tim**).

K. K. Kannan, M. Ramanadham and T. A. Jones, Structure, refinement, and function of carbonic anhydrase isozymes: refinement of human carbonic anhydrase I, *Ann. N.Y. Acad. Sci.*, 1984, **429**, 49–60 (pdb: **2cab**).

R. Diamond, Real-space refinement of the structure of hen egg-white lysozyme, *J. Mol. Biol.*, 1974, **82**, 371–391 (pdb: **6lyz**).

G. W. Bushnell, G. V. Louie and G. D. Brayer, High-resolution three-dimensional structure of horse heart cytochrome c, *J. Mol. Biol.* 1990, **214**, 585–595 (pdb: **1hrc**).

C. Lionetti, M. G. Guanziroli, F. Frigerio, P. Ascenzi and M. Bolognesi, X-ray crystal structure of the ferric sperm whale myoglobin: imidazole complex at 2.0 A resolution, *J. Mol. Biol.*, 1991, **217**, 409–412 (pdb: **1mbi**).

R. Z. Kramer, J. Bella, P. Mayville, B. Brodsky and H. M. Berman, Sequence dependent conformational variations of collagen triple-helical structure, *Nat. Struct. Biol.*, 1999, **6**, 454–457 (pdb: **1bkv**).

J. A. Frier and M. F. Perutz, Structure of human foetal deoxyhaemoglobin. *J. Mol. Biol.*, 1977, **112**, 97–112 (pdb:**1fdh**).

J. R. Tame and B. Vallone, The structures of deoxy human haemoglobin and the mutant Hb Tyrα42His at 120 K, *Acta Crystallogr., Sect. D*, 2000, **56**, 805–811 (pdb: **1a3n**).

S. Arnott, W. E. Scott, D. A. Rees and C. G. McNab, Iota-carrageenan: molecular structure and packing of polysaccharide double helices in oriented fibres of divalent cation salts, *J. Mol. Biol.*, 1974, **90**, 253–267 (pdb: **1car**).

S. Arnott, A. Fulmer, W. E. Scott, I. C. Dea, R. Moorhouse and D. A. Rees, The agarose double helix and its function in agarose gel structure, *J. Mol. Biol.*, 1974, **90**, 269–284 (pdb: **1aga**).

D. A. Rees and P. J. C. Smith, Polysaccharide conformation. Part IX. Monte-Carlo calculation of conformational energies for disaccharides and comparison with experiment, *J. Chem. Soc.-Perkin Trans. 2*, 1975, 836–840.

H. R. Drew, R. M. Wing, T. Takano, C. Broka, S. Tanaka, K. Itakura and R. E. Dickerson, Structure of a B-DNA dodecamer: conformation and dynamics. *Proc. Natl. Acad. Sci. USA*, 1981, **78**, 2179–2183 (pdb: **1bna**).

G. Govil, Conformational structure of polynucleotides around O–P bonds; refined parameters for CPF calculations, *Biopolymers*, 1976, **15**, 2303–2307.

M. Egli, G. Minasov, V. Tereshko, P. S. Pallan, M. Teplova, G. B. Inamati, E. A. Lesnik, S. R. Owens, B. S Ross, T. P. Prakash and M. Manoharan, Probing the influence of stereoelectronic effects on the biophysical properties of oligonucleotides: comprehensive analysis of the RNA affinity, nuclease resistance, and crystal structure of ten 2'-O-ribonucleic acid modifications, *Biochemistry*, 2005, **44**, 9045–9057 (pdb: **1wv5**).

N. Verdaguer, J. Aymani, D. Fendandez-Forner, I. Fita, M. Coll, T. Huynh-Dinh, J. Igolen and J. A. Subirana, Molecular structure of a complete turn of A-DNA, *J. Mol. Biol.*, 1991, **221**, 623–635 (pdb: **2d47**).

B. Pan, C. Ban, M. C. Wahl and M. Sundaralingam, Crystal structure of d(GCGCGCG) with 5'-overhang G residues, *Biophys. J.*, 1997, **73**, 1553–1561 (pdb: **331d**).

R. S. Brown, J. C. Dewan and A. Klug, Crystallographic and biochemical investigation of the lead (II)-catalyzed hydrolysis of yeast phenylalanine tRNA, *Biochemistry* 1985, **24**, 4785–4801 (pdb: **1tn2**).

J. M. Seddon, Structure of the inverted hexagonal (H$_{II}$) phase and non-lamellar transitions of lipids, *Biochim. Biophys. Acta*, 1990, **1031**, 1–69.

Chapter 2

General reading

W. C. Chan and F. D. White (Eds.), *FMOC Solid Phase Peptide Synthesis: a Practical Approach*, 2000, Oxford University Press, Oxford.

P. Herdewijn (Ed.), *Oligonucleotide Synthesis – Methods and Applications*, 2005, Humana, Totowa.

S. M. Hecht (Ed.), *Bioorganic Chemistry: Carbohydrates*, 1999, Oxford University Press, Oxford.

P. H. Seeberger (Ed.), *Solid Support Oligosaccharide Synthesis and Combinatorial Carbohydrate Libraries*, 2001, Wiley–Interscience, New York.

J. F. Robyt, *Essentials of Carbohydrate Chemistry*, 1998, Springer, New York.

F. Gunstone, *Fatty Acid and Lipid Chemistry*, 1996, Blackie, Glasgow.

D. Voet and J. G. Voet, *Biochemistry*, 3rd Edition, 2004, Wiley, New York.

The Busy Researcher's Guide to Biomolecule Chromatography, 1996, Perseptive Biosystems, Framingham.

Extra reading

M. Fedurco, A. Romieu, S. Williams, I. Lawrence and G. Turcatti, BTA, a novel reagent for DNA attachment on glass and efficient generation of solid-phase amplified DNA colonies, *Nucleic Acids Res.*, 2006, **34**, e22.

P. M. Takahara, C. A. Frederick and S. J. Lippard, Crystal structure of the anticancer drug cisplatin bound to duplex DNA, *J. Am. Chem. Soc.*, 1996, **118**, 12 309–12 321.

B. A. Chabner and D. L. Longo (Eds.), *Cancer Chemotherapy and Biotherapy: Principles and Practice*, 4th Edition, 2005, Lippincott Williams and Wilkins, Philadelphia, PA.

P. E. Nielsen, J. B. Hansen and O. Buchardt, Photochemical cross-linking of protein and DNA in chromatin.1. Synthesis and application of a photosensitive cleavable derivative of 9-aminoacridine with 2 photoprobes connected through a disulfide-containing linker, *Biochem. J.*, 1984, **223**, 519–526.

P. H. Seeberger and W.-C. Haase, Solid-phase oligosaccharide synthesis and combinatorial carbohydrate libraries, *Chem. Rev.*, 2000, **100**, 4349–4393.

K. M. Koeller and C.-H. Wong, Synthesis of complex carbohydrates and glycoconjugates: enzyme-based and programmable one-pot strategies, *Chem. Rev.*, 2000, **100**, 4485–4493.

S. Fletcher, A. Ahmad, E. Perouzel, A. Heron, A. D. Miller and M. R. Jorgensen, In vivo studies of dialkynoyl analogues of DOTAP demonstrate improved gene transfer efficiency of cationic liposomes in mouse lung, *J. Med. Chem.*, 2006, **49**, 349–357.

S. Fletcher, A. Ahmad, E. Perouzel, M. R. Jorgensen and A. D. Miller, A dialkynoyl analogue of DOPE improves gene transfer efficiency of lower-charged, cationic lipoplexes, *Org. Biomol. Chem.*, 2006, **4**, 196–199.

S. Fletcher, A. Ahmad, W. S. Price, M. R. Jorgensen and A. D. Miller, Biophysical properties of CDAN/DOPE-analogue lipoplexes account for enhanced gene delivery, *ChemBioChem*, 2008, **9**, 455–463.

M. R. Jorgensen, T. Røst, Y. A. H. Bhurruth-Alcor, P. Bohoy, C. Guisado, K. Kostarelos, E. Dyrøy, R. K. Berge, A. D. Miller and J. Skorve, Development of novel lipids for the treatment of the metabolic syndrome and diabetes Type II, *J. Med. Chem.*, 2008, in press.

J. Farkaš, M. Ledvina, J. Brokeš, J. Ježek J. Zajíček and M. Zaoral, The synthesis of O-(2-acetamido-2-deoxy-β-D-glucopyranosyl)-(1→4)-N-acetylnormuramoyl-L-α-aminobutanoyl-D-isoglutamine, *Carbohydr. Res.*, 1987, **163**, 63–72.

M. Ledvina, J. Ježek, D. Šaman, T. Vaisar and V. Hříbalová, Synthesis of O-[2-acetamido-2-deoxy-6-O-stearoyl- and -6-O-(2-tetradecylhexadecanoyl)-β-D-glucopyranosyl]-(1→4)-N-acetylnormuramoyl-L-α-aminobutanoyl-D-isoglutamine, lipophilic disaccharide analogs of MDP, *Carbohydr. Res.*, 1994, **251**, 269–284.

Chapter 3

General reading

D. Voet and J. G. Voet, *Biochemistry*, 3rd Edition, 2004, Wiley, New York.

A. R. Fersht, *Structure and Mechanism in Protein Science, a Guide to Enzyme Catalysis and Protein Folding*, 1999, Freeman, New York.

B. Alberts, A. Johnson, J. Lewis and M. Raff, *Molecular Biology of the Cell*, 2002, Garland, New York.

J. D. Watson, T. A. Baker, S. P. Bell, and A. Gann, *Molecular Biology of the Gene*, 5th Edition, 2003, Benjamin–Cummings, San Francisco.

J. Sambrook and D. W. Russell, *Molecular Cloning: a Laboratory Manual*, 2001, Cold Spring Harbor Laboratory Press, New York.

R. R. Sinden, *DNA Structure and Function*, 1994, Academic, San Diego.

Extra reading

J. J. Perona and A. M. Martin, Conformational transitions and structural deformability of EcoRV endonuclease revealed by crystallographic analysis, *J. Mol. Biol.*, 1997, **273**, 207–225 (pdb: **1az0**).

J. M. Pascal, P. J. O'Brien, A. E. Tomkinson and T. Ellenberger, Human DNA ligase I completely encircles and partially unwinds nicked DNA, *Nature*, 2004, **432**, 473–478 (pdb: **1 x 9n**).

M. S. Lah, M. M. Dixon, K. A. Pattridge, W. C. Stallings, J. A. Fee and M. L. Ludwig, Structure–function in *Escherichia coli* iron superoxide dismutase: comparisons with the manganese enzyme from *Thermus thermophilus*, *Biochemistry* 1995, **34**, 1646–1660 (pdb: **1isa**).

Chapter 4

General reading

C. R. Cantor and P. R. Schimmel, *Biophysical Chemistry Part II*, 1980, Freeman, San Francisco.

C. R. Cantor and P. R. Schimmel, *Biophysical Chemistry Part III*, 1980, Freeman, San Francisco.

W. Kaim and B. Schwederski, *Bioinorganic Chemistry: Inorganic Elements in the Chemistry of Life*, 1994, Wiley, Chichester.

D. H. Williams and I. Fleming, *Spectroscopic Methods in Organic Chemistry*, 1995, McGraw-Hill, New York.

J. Walker (Ed.), *The Protein Protocols Handbook*, 2002, Humana, Totowa.

R. P. Haugland, *Handbook of Fluorescent Probes and Research Products*, 9th Edition, 2002, Molecular Probes, Eugene.

I. N. Serdyuk, N. R. Zaccai and J. Zaccai, *Methods in Molecular Biophysics, Structure Dynamics and Function*, 2007, Cambridge University Press, Cambridge.

Extra reading

T. S. H. El-Thaher, A. F. Drake, S. Yokota, A. Nakai, K. Nagata and A. D. Miller, The pH-dependent, ATP-independent interaction of collagen specific serpin/stress protein HSP47, *Prot. Pept. Lett.*, 1996, **3**, 1–8.

M. Preuss, M. Tecle, I. Shah, D. A. Matthews and A. D. Miller, Comparison between the interactions of adenovirus-derived peptides with plasmid DNA and their role in gene delivery mediated by liposome-peptide-DNA virus-like nanoparticles, *Org. Biomol. Chem.*, 2003, **1**, 2430–2438.

T. Homma, D. Olerenshaw, M. Wright, T. R. Dafforn and A. D. Miller, Investigations into the mechanism of heat shock protein 47 (HSP47), 2008, in preparation.

B. E. Cohen, T. B. McAnaney, E. S. Park, Y. N. Jan, S. G. Boxer and L. Y. Jan, Probing protein electrostatics with a synthetic fluorescent amino acid, *Science*, 2002, **296**, 1700–1703.

K. Brejc, T. K. Sixma, P. A. Kitts, S. R. Kain, R. Y. Tsien, M. Ormo and S. J. Remington, Structural basis for dual excitation and photoisomerization of the *Aequorea victoria* green fluorescent protein, *Proc. Natl. Acad. Sci. USA*, 1997, **94**, 2306–2311 (pdb: **1emb**).

B. A. Griffin, S. R. Adams and R. Y. Tsien, Specific covalent labeling of recombinant protein molecules inside live cells, *Science*, 1998, **281**, 269–272.

M. Keller, R. P. Harbottle, E. Perouzel, M. Colin, I. Shah, A. Rahim, L. Vaysse, A. Bergau, S. Moritz, C. Brahimi-Horn, C. Coutelle and A. D. Miller, Nuclear localisation sequence templated nonviral gene delivery vectors: investigation of intracellular trafficking events, of LMD and LD vector systems, *ChemBioChem*, 2003, **4**, 286–298.

D. M. J. Lilley and T. J. Wilson, Fluorescence resonance energy transfer as a structural tool for nucleic acids, *Curr. Opin. Chem. Biol.*, 2000, **4**, 507–517.

J. A. Tanner, M. Wright, E. M. Christie, M. K. Preuss and A. D. Miller, Investigation into the interactions between diadenosine $5',5'''-P^{-1},P^{-4}$-tetraphosphate and two proteins: molecular chaperone GroEL and cAMP receptor protein, *Biochemistry*, 2006, **45**, 3095–3106.

M. Wright and A. D. Miller, Novel fluorescent labelled affinity probes for diadenosine $5',5'''-P^{1},P^{4}$-tetraphosphate (Ap$_4$A)-binding studies, *Bioorg. Med. Chem. Lett.*, 2006, **16**, 943–948.

M. Tecle, M. Preuss, and A. D. Miller, Kinetic study of DNA condensation by cationic peptides used in nonviral gene therapy: analogy of DNA condensation to protein folding, *Biochemistry*, 2003, **42**, 10 343–10 347.

E. Palmer, and T. Freeman, Investigation into the use of C- and N-terminal GFP fusion proteins for sub-cellular localization studies using reverse transfection microarrays, *Compar. Funct. Genom.*, 2004, **5**(4), 342–353.

S. Weiss, Fluorescence spectroscopy of single biomolecules, *Science*, 1999, **283**(5408), 1676–1683.

Chapter 5

General reading

J. N. S. Evans, *Biomolecular NMR Spectroscopy*, 1995, Oxford University Press, Oxford.

P. W. Atkins, *Physical Chemistry*, 5th Edition, 1995, Oxford University Press, Oxford.

K. Wuthrich, *NMR of Proteins and Nucleic Acids*, 1986, Wiley, New York.

I. N. Serdyuk, N. R. Zaccai, and J. Zaccai, *Methods in Molecular Biophysics, Structure Dynamics and Function*, 2007, Cambridge University Press, Cambridge.

A. R. Leach, *Molecular Modelling, Principles and Applications*, 2nd Edition, 2001, Prentice-Hall, Harlow.

Extra reading

B. C. Finzel, L. L. Clancy, D. R. Holland, S. W. Muchmore, K. D. Watenpaugh and H. M. Einspahr, Crystal structure of recombinant human interleukin-1β at 2.0 Å resolution, *J. Mol. Biol.*, 1989, **209**, 779–791 (pdb: **1i1b**).

G. M. Clore, P. T. Wingfield and A. M. Gronenborn, High-resolution three-dimensional structure of interleukin 1β in solution by three- and four-dimensional nuclear magnetic resonance spectroscopy, *Biochemistry*, 1991, **30**, 2315–2323 (pdb: **7i1b**).

L. E. Kay, M. Ikura and A. Bax, The design and optimization of complex NMR experiments: application to a triple-resonance pulse scheme correlating Hα, NH, and ^{15}N chemical-shifts in ^{15}N-^{13}C-labeled proteins, *J. Magn. Reson.*, 1991, **91**, 84–92.

G. M. Clore, A. Bax, P. C. Driscoll, P. T. Wingfield and A. M. Gronenborn, Assignment of the side-chain ^1H and ^{13}C resonances of interleukin-1β using double-resonance and triple-resonance heteronuclear 3-dimensional NMR-spectroscopy, *Biochemistry*, 1990, **29**, 8172–8184.

M. Ikura, A. Bax, G. M. Clore and A. M. Gronenborn, Detection of nuclear Overhauser effects between degenerate amide proton resonances by heteronuclear 3-dimensional nuclear-magnetic-resonance spectroscopy, *J. Am. Chem. Soc.*, 1990, **112**, 9020–9022.

B. R. Reid, Sequence-specific assignments and their use in NMR-studies of DNA-structure, *Quart. Rev. Biophys.*, 1987, **20**, 1–34.

D. J. Patel, L. Shapiro and D. Hare, DNA and RNA – NMR-studies of conformations and dynamics in solution, *Quart. Rev. Biophys.*, 1987, **20**, 35–112.

S. S. Wijmenga and B. N. M. van Buuren, The use of NMR methods for conformational studies of nucleic acids, *Prog. NMR Spec.*, 1998, **32**, 287–387.

H. van Halbeck and L. Poppe, Conformation and dynamics of glycoprotein oligosaccharides as studied by ^1H-NMR spectroscopy, *Magn. Reson. Chem.*, Special issue, 1992, **30**, S74–S86.

S. W. Homans, Oligosaccharide conformations – application of NMR and energy calculations, *Prog. NMR Spec.*, 1990, **22**, 55–81.

J. Seelig and P. M. MacDonald, Phospholipids and proteins in biological-membranes – ^2H-NMR as a method to study structure, dynamics, and interactions, *Acc. Chem. Res.*, 1987, **20**, 211–228.

R. E. Jacobs and E. Oldfield, NMR of membranes, *Prog. NMR Spec.*, 1980, **14**, 113–136.

Chapter 6

General reading

J. Drenth, *Principles of Protein X-Ray Crystallography*, 1994, Springer, New York.

D. E. McRee, *Practical Protein Crystallography*, 2nd Edition, 1999, Academic, San Diego.

R. Egerton, *Physical Principles of Electron Microscopy: An Introduction to TEM, SEM, and AEM*, 2005, Springer, New York.

R. Wiesendanger, *Scanning Probe Microscopy and Spectroscopy*, 1994, Cambridge University Press, Cambridge.

S. J. Lippard and J. M. Berg, *Principles of Bioinorganic Chemistry*, 1994, University Science, Mill Valley, CA.

Extra reading

S. Onesti, A. D. Miller and P. Brick, The crystal structure of the lysyl-tRNA synthetase (LysU) from *Escherichia coli*, *Structure*, 1995, **3**, 163–176 (pdb: **1lyl**).

G. Desogus, F. Todone, P. Brick and S. Onesti, Active site of lysyl-tRNA synthetase: structural studies of the adenylation reaction, *Biochemistry*, 2000, **39**, 8418–8425 (pdbs: **1e1t**, **1e22** & **1e24**).

Z. Xu, A. L. Horwich, and P. B Sigler, The crystal structure of the asymmetric GroEL–GroES–(ADP)$_7$ chaperonin complex, *Nature* 1997, **388**, 741–750 (pdb: **1aon**).

J. Wang and D. C. Boisvert, Structural basis for GroEL-assisted protein folding from the crystal structure of (GroEL-KMgATP)$_{14}$ at 2.0 A resolution, *J. Mol. Biol.*, 2003, **327**, 843–855.

J. Wang and L. Chen, Domain motions in GroEL upon binding of an oligopeptide, *J. Mol. Biol.*, 2003, **334**, 489–499.

N. A. Ranson, D. K. Clare, G. W. Farr, D. Houldershaw, A. L. Horwich and H. R. Saibil, Allosteric signaling of ATP hydrolysis in GroEL–GroES complexes. *Nat. Struct. Mol. Biol.*, 2006, **13**, 147–152 (fitted coordinates, Cryo-EM) (pdbs: **2c7c** & **2c7d**).

N. A. Ranson, G. W. Farr, A. M. Roseman, B. Gowen, W. A. Fenton, A. L. Horwich and H. R. Saibil, ATP-bound states of GroEL captured by cryo-electron microscopy, *Cell*, 2001, **107**, 869–879 (pdbs: **1gr5** & **1gru**).

A. M. Roseman, S. Chen, H. White, K. Braig and H. R. Saibil, The chaperonin ATPase cycle: mechanism of allosteric switching and movements of substrate-binding domains in GroEL, *Cell*, 1996, **87**, 241–251.

N. A. Ranson, H. E White and H. R. Saibil, Chaperonins, *Biochem. J.*, 1998, **333**, 233–242.

H. Jones, M. Preuss, M. Wright and A. D. Miller, The mechanism of GroEL/GroES folding/refolding of protein substrates revisited, *Org. Biomol. Chem.*, 2006, **4**, 1223–1235.

H. Jones, J. Dalmaris, M. Wright, J. H. G. Steinke and A. D. Miller, Hydrogel polymer appears to mimic the performance of the GroEL/GroES molecular chaperone machine, *Org. Biomol. Chem.*, 2006, **4**, 2568–2574.

C. M. Smith, R. J. Kohler, E. Barho, T. S. H. El-Thaher, M. Preuss and A. D. Miller, Characterisation of Cpn60 (groEL) bound cytochrome c: the passive role of molecular chaperones in assisting folding/refolding of proteins, *J. Chem. Soc., Perkin Trans. 2*, 1999, 1537–1546.

N. Boonyalai, S. Thipayang, M. Wright, I. R. Gould and A. D. Miller, Investigating the binding of GTP to lysyl-tRNA synthetase enzyme (LysU) *in vitro* and *in silico*, 2008, in preparation.

S. J. Hughes, J. A. Tanner, A. D. Hindley, A. D. Miller and I. R. Gould, Functional asymmetry in the lysyl-tRNA synthetase explored by molecular dynamics, free energy calculations and experiment, *BMC Structural Biology*, 2003, **3**, 5.

S. J. Hughes, J. A. Tanner, A. D. Miller and I. R. Gould, Molecular dynamics simulations of LysRS: an asymmetric state, *Proteins*, 2006, **62**, 649–662.

J. F. Conway, B. L. Trus, F. P. Body, W. W. Newcomb, J. C. Brown and A. C. Steven, Visualization of three-dimensional density maps reconstructed from cryoelectron micrographs of viral capsids, *J. Struct. Biol.*, 1996, **116**, 200–208.

W. R. Wikoff, C. J. Tsai, G. J. Wang, T. S. Baker, and J. E. Johnson, The structure of cucumber mosaic virus: cryoelectron microscopy, X-ray crystallography, and sequence analysis, *Virology*, 1997, **232**, 91–97.

M. Agbandje, C. R. Parrish and M. G. Rossmann, The structure of parvoviruses, *Semin. Virol.*, 1995, **6**, 299–309.

C. H. Chen, D. O. Clegg, and H. G. Hansma, Structures and dynamic motion of laminin-1 as observed by atomic force microscopy, *Biochemistry*, 1998, **37**, 8262–8267.

R. Guckenberger, M. Heim, G. Cevc, H. F. Knapp, W. Wiegrabe and A. Hillebrand, Scanning-tunneling-microscopy of insulators and biological specimens based on lateral conductivity of ultrathin water films, *Science*, 1994, **266**, 1538–1540.

D. J. Muller, H. Janovjak, T. Lehto, L. Kuerschner and K. Anderson, Observing structure, function and assembly of single proteins by AFM, *Prog. Biophys. Mol. Biol.*, 2002, **79**, 1–43.

Chapter 7

General reading

R. H. Pain (Ed.), *Mechanisms of Protein Folding*, 1994, IRL Press–Oxford University Press, Oxford.

C. R. Cantor and P. R. Schimmel, *Biophysical Chemistry Part II*, 1980, Freeman, San Francisco.

M. D. Houslay and K. K. Stanley, *Dynamics of Biological Membranes*, 1982, Wiley, Chichester.

A. R. Leach, *Molecular Modelling: Principles and Applications*, 2nd edition, 1996, Pearson, Harlow.

J. E. Ladbury and B. Z. Chowdury (Eds.), *Biocalorimetry: Applications of Calorimetry in the Biological Sciences*, 1998, Wiley, Chichester.

D. S. Bendall (Ed.), *Protein Electron Transfer*, 1996, BIOS, Oxford

T. E. Creighton (Ed.), *Protein Function: a Practical Approach*, 1989, IRL Press, Oxford.

D. Voet and J. G. Voet, *Biochemistry*, 2nd Edition, 1995, Wiley, New York.

D. Voet, J. G. Voet and C. W. Pratt, *Fundamentals of Biochemistry*, 1999, Wiley, New York.

Extra reading

M. Harel, D. M. Quinn, H. K. Nair, I. Silman and J. L. Sussman, The X-ray structure of a transition state analog complex reveals the molecular origins of the catalytic power and substrate specificity of acetylcholinesterase, *J. Am. Chem. Soc.*, 1996, **118**, 2340–2346 (pdb: **1amn**).

J. Kleinjung, M. C. Petit, P. Orlewski, A. Mamalaki, S. J. Tzartos, V. Tsikaris, M. Sakarellos-Daitsiotis, C. Sakarellos, M. Marraud and M. T. Cung, The third-dimensional structure of the complex between an Fv antibody fragment and an analogue of the main immunogenic region of the acetylcholine receptor: a combined two-dimensional NMR, homology, and molecular modeling approach, *Biopolymers*, 2000, **53**, 113–128 (pdb: **1f3r**).

G. P. Vigers, L. J. Anderson, P. Caffes and B. J. Brandhuber, Crystal structure of the type-I interleukin-1 receptor complexed with interleukin-1β. *Nature*, 1997, **386**, 190–194 (pdb: **1itb**).

T. E. Ellenberger, C. J. Brandl, K. Struhl and S. C. Harrison, The GCN4 basic region leucine zipper binds DNA as a dimer of uninterrupted alpha helices: crystal structure of the protein–DNA complex, *Cell*, 1992, **71**, 1223–1237 (pdb: **1ysa**).

S. Onesti, A. D. Miller and P. Brick, The crystal structure of the lysyl-tRNA synthetase (LysU) from *Escherichia coli*, *Structure*, 1995, **3**, 163–176 (pdb: **1lyl**).

G. Desogus, F. Todone, P. Brick and S. Onesti, Active site of lysyl-tRNA synthetase: structural studies of the adenylation reaction, *Biochemistry*, 2000, **39**, 8418–8425 (pdbs: **1e1t, 1e22 & 1e24**).

B. C. Finzel, L. L. Clancy, D. R. Holland, S. W. Muchmore, K. D. Watenpaugh and H. M. Einspahr, Crystal structure of recombinant human interleukin-1β at 2.0 A resolution, *J. Mol. Biol.*, 1989, **209**, 779–791 (pdb: **1i1b**).

G. P. Vigers, P. Caffes, R. J. Evans, R. C. Thompson, S. P. Eisenberg and B. J. Brandhuber, X-ray structure of interleukin-1 receptor antagonist at 2.0-A resolution, *J. Biol. Chem.*, 1994, **269**, 12 874–12 879 (pdb: **1ilt**).

M. Keller, T. Tagawa, M. Preuss and A. D. Miller, Biophysical characterization of the DNA binding and condensing properties of adenoviral core peptide μ (mu), *Biochemistry*, 2002, **41**, 652–659.

M. Preuss, J. P. Hutchinson, and A. D. Miller, Secondary structure forming propensity coupled with amphiphilicity is an optimal motif in a peptide or protein for association with Chaperonin 60 (GroEL), *Biochemistry*, 1999, **38**, 10 272–10 286.

M. Preuss and A. D. Miller, Interaction with GroEL destabilises non-amphiphilic secondary structure in a peptide, *FEBS Lett.*, 1999, **461**, 131–135.

T. R. Dafforn, M. Della and A. D. Miller, The molecular interactions of heat shock protein 47 (Hsp47) and their implications for collagen biosynthesis, *J. Biol. Chem.*, 2001, **276**, 49 310–49 319.

T. Homma, D. Olerenshaw, M. Wright, T. R. Dafforn and A. D. Miller, Investigations into the mechanism of heat shock protein 47 (HSP47), 2008, in preparation.

N. Boonyalai, S. Thipayang, M. Wright, I. R. Gould and A. D. Miller, Investigating the binding of GTP to lysyl-tRNA synthetase enzyme (LysU) *in vitro* and *in silico*, 2008, in preparation.

S. J. Hughes, J. A. Tanner, A. D. Hindley, A. D. Miller and I. R. Gould, Functional asymmetry in the lysyl-tRNA synthetase explored by molecular dynamics, free energy calculations and experiment, *BMC Structural Biology*, 2003, **3**, 5.

S. J. Hughes, J. A. Tanner, A. D. Miller and I. R. Gould, Molecular dynamics simulations of LysRS: an asymmetric state, *Proteins*, 2006, **62**, 649–662.

J. R. Heal, S. Bino, K. P. Ray, G. Christie, A. D. Miller and J. G. Raynes, A search within the IL-1 type 1 receptor reveals a peptide with hydropathic complementarity to the IL-1β trigger loop which binds to IL-1 and inhibits in vitro responses, *Mol. Immunol.*, 1999, **36**, 1141–1148.

J. R. Heal, S. Bino, G. W. Roberts, J. G. Raynes and A. D. Miller, Mechanistic investigation into complementary (antisense) peptide mini-receptor inhibitors of cytokine interleukin-1, *ChemBioChem*, 2002, **3**, 76–85.

Chapter 8

General reading

J. M. GoodFellow and D. S. Moss (Eds.), *Computer Modelling of Biomolecular Processes*, 1992, Ellis Horwood, Chichester.

I. H. Segel, *Enzyme Kinetics*, 1975, Wiley, New York.

A. R. Fersht, *Enzyme Structure and Mechanism*, 2nd Edition, 1985, Freeman, New York.

A. R. Fersht, *Structure and Mechanism in Protein Science, A Guide to Enzyme Catalysis and Protein Folding*, 1999, Freeman, New York.

S. Gul, S. K. Sreedharan and K. Brocklehurst, *Enzyme Assays, Essential Data*, 1998, Wiley, Chichester.

R. Eisenthal and M. J. Danson (Eds.), *Enzyme Assays, a Practical Approach*, 1992, IRL Press at Oxford University Press, Oxford.

P. W. Atkins, *Physical Chemistry*, 5th Edition, 1995, Oxford University Press, Oxford.

Extra reading

D. W. Banner, A. Bloomer, G. A. Petsko, D. C. Phillips and I. A. Wilson, Atomic coordinates for triose phosphate isomerase from chicken muscle, *Biochem. Biophys. Res. Commun.*, 1976, **72**, 146–155 (pdb: **1tim**).

J. J. Birktoft, G. Rhodes and L. J. Banaszak, Refined crystal structure of cytoplasmic malate dehydrogenase at 2.5-Å resolution, *Biochemistry*, 1989, **28**, 6065–6081 (pdb: **4mdh**).

H. Tsukada and D. M. Blow, Structure of α-chymotrypsin refined at 1.68 Å resolution, *J. Mol. Biol.*, 1985, **184**, 703–711 (pdb: **4cha**).

A. Wlodawer, L. A. Svensson, L. Sjolin and G. L. Gilliland, Structure of phosphate-free ribonuclease A refined at 1.26 Å, *Biochemistry*, 1988, **27**, 2705–2717 (pdb: **7rsa**).

A. A. Morollo, G. A. Petsko and D. Ringe, Structure of a Michaelis complex analogue: propionate binds in the substrate carboxylate site of alanine racemase, *Biochemistry*, 1999, **38**, 3293–3301 (pdb: **2sfp**).

G. Capitani, D. De Biase, C. Aurizi, H. Gut, F. Bossa and M. G. Grutter, Crystal structure and functional analysis of *Escherichia coli* glutamate decarboxylase, *EMBO J.*, 2003, **22**, 4027–4037 (pdb: **1pmo** & **1pmm**).

D. L. Smith, S. C. Almo, M. D. Toney and D. Ringe, 2.8-Å-resolution crystal structure of an active-site mutant of aspartate aminotransferase from *Escherichia coli*, *Biochemistry*, 1989, **28**, 8161–8167 (pdb: **2aat**).

R. Diamond, Real-space refinement of the structure of hen egg-white lysozyme, *J. Mol. Biol.*, 1974, **82**, 371–391 (pdb: **6lyz**).

A. Lewendon, I. A. Murray, W. V. Shaw, M. R. Gibbs and A. G. Leslie, Evidence for transition-state stabilization by serine-148 in the catalytic mechanism of chloramphenicol acetyltransferase, *Biochemistry*, 1990, **29**, 2075–2080 (pdb: **1cla**).

G. E. Borgstahl, H. E Parge, M. J. Hickey, W. F. Beyer Jr., R. A. Hallewell and J. A. Tainer, The structure of human mitochondrial Mn^{3+} superoxide dismutase reveals a novel tetrameric interface of two 4-helix bundles, *Cell*, 1992, **71**, 107–118 (pdb: **1n0j**).

K. K. Kannan, M. Ramanadham and T. A. Jones, Structure, refinement, and function of carbonic anhydrase isozymes: refinement of human carbonic anhydrase I, *Ann. N. Y. Acad. Sci.*, 1984, **429**, 49–60 (pdb: **2cab**).

H. Harel, D. M. Quinn, H. K. Nair, I. Silman and J. L. Sussman, The X-ray structure of a transition state analog complex reveals the molecular origins of the catalytic power and substrate specificity of acetylcholinesterase, *J. Am. Chem. Soc.*, 1996, **118**, 2340–2346 (pdb: **1amn**).

S. Onesti, A. D. Miller and P. Brick, The crystal structure of the lysyl-tRNA synthetase (LysU) from *Escherichia coli*, *Structure*, 1995, **3**, 163–176 (pdb: **1lyl**).

G. Desogus, F. Todone, P. Brick and S. Onesti, Active site of lysyl-tRNA synthetase: structural studies of the adenylation reaction, *Biochemistry*, 2000, **39**, 8418–8425 (pdb: **1e1t, 1e22 & 1e24**).

P. A. Fields, E. L. Rudomin and G. N. Somero, Temperature sensitivities of cytosolic malate dehydrogenases from native and invasive species of marine mussels (genus *Mytilus*): sequence–function linkages and correlations with biogeographic distribution, *J. Exp. Biol.*, 2006, **209**, 656–667.

K. Masaki, T. Aizawa, N. Koganesawa, T. Nimori, H. Bando, K. Kawano, and K. Nitta, Thermal stability and enzymatic activity of a smaller lysozyme from silk moth (*Bombyx mori*), *J. Prot. Chem.*, 2001, **20**, 107–113.

P. J. Day and W. V. Shaw, Acetyl coenzyme A binding by chloramphenicol acetyltransferase, *J. Biol. Chem.*, 1992, **267**, 5122–5127.

M. Wright, N. Boonyalai, J. A. Tanner, A. D. Hindley and A. D. Miller, The duality of LysU, a catalyst for both Ap$_4$A and Ap$_3$A formation, *FEBS J.*, 2006, **273**, 3534–3544.

M. E. Stroupe, M. DiDonato and J. A. Tainer, Manganese superoxide dismutase, in *Handbook of Metalloproteins*, A. Messerschmidt, R. Huber, T. Poulos and K. Wieghardt (Eds.), 2001, Wiley, Chichester.

F. Abbate, A. Casini, T. Owa, A. Scozzafava and C. T. Supuran, Carbonic anhydrase inhibitors: E7070, a sulfonamide anticancer agent, potently inhibits cytosolic isozymes I and II, and transmembrane, tumor-associated isozyme IX, *Bioorg. Med. Chem.*, 2004, **14**, 217–223.

M.-E. Theoclitou, E. P. L. Wittung, A. D. Hindley, T. S. H. El-Thaher and A. D. Miller, Characterisation of stress protein LysU. Enzymic synthesis of diadenosine $5',5'''$-P^1,P^4-tetraphosphate (Ap$_4$A) analogues by LysU, *J. Chem. Soc., Perkin Trans. 1*, 1996, 2009–2019.

M. Wright, J. A. Tanner and A. D. Miller, Quantitative single-step purification of dinucleoside polyphosphates, *Anal. Biochem.*, 2003, **316**, 135–138.

M. Wright and A. D. Miller, Synthesis of novel fluorescent-labelled dinucleoside polyphosphates, *Bioorg. Med. Chem. Lett.*, 2004, **14**, 2813–2816.

M. Wright and A. D. Miller, Novel fluorescent labelled affinity probes for diadenosine $5',5'''$-P^1,P^4-tetraphosphate (Ap$_4$A)-binding studies, *Bioorg. Med. Chem. Lett.*, 2006, **16**, 943–948.

S. R. Kirk, N. W. Luedtke and Y. Tor, 2-aminopurine as a real time probe of enzymatic cleavage and inhibition of hammerhead ribozymes, *Bioorg. Med. Chem.*, 2001, **9**, 2295–2301.

J. J. Burbaum, R. T. Raines, W. J. Albery and J. R. Knowles, Evolutionary optimization of the catalytic effectiveness of an enzyme, *Biochemistry*, 1989, **28**, 9293–9305.

J. R. Knowles, Enzyme catalysis – not different, just better, *Nature*, 1991, **350**, 121–124.

Chapter 9

General reading

C. Dass, *Principles and Practice of Biological Mass Spectrometry*, 2001, Wiley–Interscience, New York.

E. De Hoffmann, J. Charette and V. Stroobant, *Mass Spectrometry Principles and Applications*, 1996, Wiley, Chichester; Masson, Paris.

J. Laskin and C. Lifshitz (Eds.), *Principles of Mass Spectrometry Applied to Biomolecules*, 2006, Wiley, Hoboken, NJ.

S. R. Pennington and M. J. Dunn, *Proteomics from Protein Sequence to Function*, 2001, Springer-Verlag Telos, New York.

R. M. Twyman, *Principles of Proteomics*, 2004, BIOS Scientific, Oxford.

M. Kinter and N. E. Sherman, *Protein Sequencing and Identification using Tandem Mass Spectrometry*, 2000, Wiley–Interscience, New York.

M. H. Hamdan and P. G. Righetti, *Proteomics Today: Protein Assessment and Biomarkers Using Mass Spectrometry, 2D Electrophoresis and Microarray Technology*, 2005, Wiley–Interscience, New York.

Nature Insight Proteomics, *Nature*, 2003, **422**, 193–237.

Extra reading

K. Biemann, Contributions of mass-spectrometry to peptide and protein-structure, *Biomed. Environ. Mass Spectrom.*, 1988, **16**, 99–111.

L. Grotjahn, in *Mass Spectrometry in Biomedical Research*, S. J. Gaskell (Ed.), 1986, Wiley, New York, pp. 215–234.

V. N. Reinhold, B. B. Reinhold and C. E Costello, Carbohydrate molecular-weight profiling, sequence, linkage, and branching data – ES-MS and CID, *Anal. Chem.*, 1995, **67**, 1772–1784.

N. J. Jensen, K. B. Tomer and M. L. Gross, Gas-phase ion decompositions occurring remote to a charge site, *J. Am. Chem. Soc.*, 1985, **107**, 1863–1868.

N. J. Jensen, K. B. Tomer and M. L. Gross, FAB MS/MS for phosphatidylinositol, -glycerol, phosphatidylethanolamine and other complex phospholipids, *Lipids*, 1987, **22**, 480–489.

M. Tyers and M. Mann, From genomics to proteomics, *Nature*, 2003, **422**, 193–197.

R. Aebersold and M. Mann, Mass spectrometry-based proteomics, *Nature*, 2003, **422**, 198–207.

G. L. Glish and R. W. Vachet, The basics of mass spectrometry in the twenty-first century, *Nat. Rev. Drug Discov.*, 2003, **2**, 140–150.

A. Pandey and M. Mann, Proteomics to study genes and genomes, *Nature*, 2000, **405**, 837–846.

S. D. Patterson and R. H Aebersold, Proteomics: the first decade and beyond, *Nat. Genet.*, 2003, **33**, 311–323.

C. C. Wu and J. R. Yates, The application of mass spectrometry to membrane proteomics, *Nat. Biotechnol.*, 2003, **21**, 262–267.

G. MacBeath, Protein microarrays and proteomics, *Nat. Genet.*, 2002, **32**, 526–532.

E. L. Palmer, A. D. Miller and T. C. Freeman, Identification and characterization of human apoptosis inducing proteins using cell-based transfection microarrays and expression analysis, *BMC Genomics*, 2006, **7**, 145.

Chapter 10

General reading

S. Kauffman, *At Home in the Universe*, 1995, Viking, London.

D. M. Small, *Handbook of Lipid Research 4: The Physical Chemistry of Lipids* (D. J. Hanahan, Ed.), 1986, Plenum, New York.

G. Cevc (Ed.), *Phospholipids Handbook*, 1993, Dekker, New York.

K. D. Janda, C. G. Shevlin and C. H. L. Lo, *Catalytic Antibodies Chemical and Biological Approaches: Comprehensive Supramolecular Chemistry* (Y. Murakami, Ed.), 1996, Pergamon, London, pp. 43–72.

Extra reading

A. Eschenmoser and M. V. Kisakurek, Chemistry and the origin of life, *Helv. Chimica Acta*, 1996, **79**, 1249–1259.

Y.-B. Xiang, S. Drenkard, K. Baumann, D. Hickey and A. Eschenmoser, Chemistry of α-amino-nitriles. 12. Exploratory experiments on thermal-reactions of α-amino-nitriles, *Helv. Chimica Acta*, 1994, **77**, 2209–2250.

A. Eschenmoser and E. Loewenthal, Chemistry of potentially prebiological natural products, *Chem. Soc. Rev.*, 1992, **21**, 1–16.

A. Eschenmoser, Chemical etiology of nucleic acid structure, *Science*, 1999, **284**, 2118–2124.

A. Eschenmoser and R. Krishnamurthy, Chemical etiology of nucleic acid structure, *Pure Appl. Chem.*, 2000, **72**, 343–345.

K. Liebeton, A. Zonta, K, Schimossek, M. Nardini, D. Lang, B. W. Dijkstra, M. T. Reetz and K. E. Jaeger, Directed evolution of an enantioselective lipase, *Chem. Biol.*, 2000, **7**, 709–718.

T. Hermann and D. J. Patel, Biochemistry – adaptive recognition by nucleic acid aptamers, *Science*, 2000, **287**, 820–825.

A. Flynn-Charlebois, Y. M. Wang, T. K. Prior, I. Rashid, K. A. Hoadley, R. L. Coppins, A. C. Wolf, and S. K. Silverman, Deoxyribozymes with 2′–5′ RNA ligase activity, *J. Am. Chem. Soc.*, 2003, **125**, 2444–2454.

R. R. Breaker, DNA aptamers and DNA enzymes, *Curr. Opin. Chem. Biol.*, 1997, **1**, 26–31.

J. R. Williamson, G-Quartet structures in telomeric DNA, *Annu. Rev. Biophys. Biomol. Struct.*, 1994, **23**, 703–730.

Index

Note: *italic numbers* indicate Figures and Tables